BIG IDEAS
MATH®
Modeling Real Life

Grade K

TEACHING EDITION

Volume 1

Ron Larson
Laurie Boswell

BIG IDEAS
LEARNING®

Erie, Pennsylvania
BigIdeasLearning.com

Big Ideas Learning, LLC
1762 Norcross Road
Erie, PA 16510-3838
USA

For product information and customer support, contact Big Ideas Learning
at 1-877-552-7766 or visit us at BigIdeasLearning.com.

Cover Image
Paul Lampard /123RF.com, enmyo/Shutterstock.com

Printed in the U.S.A.

ISBN 13: 978-1-63598-873-4

3 4 5 6 7 8 9 10—22 21 20 19

Dr. Ron Larson and Dr. Laurie Boswell are a hands-on authorship team that began writing together in 1992. Since that time, they have authored over four dozen textbooks. This successful collaboration allows for one voice from Kindergarten through Algebra 2.

Ron Larson

Ron Larson, Ph.D., is well known as the lead author of a comprehensive program for mathematics that spans school mathematics and college courses. He holds the distinction of Professor Emeritus from Penn State Erie, The Behrend College, where he taught for nearly 40 years. He received his Ph.D. in mathematics from the University of Colorado. Dr. Larson's numerous professional activities keep him actively involved in the mathematics education community and allow him to fully understand the needs of students, teachers, supervisors, and administrators.

Laurie Boswell

Laurie Boswell, Ed.D., is the former Head of School at Riverside School in Lyndonville, Vermont. In addition to textbook authoring, she provides mathematics consulting and embedded coaching sessions. Dr. Boswell received her Ed.D. from the University of Vermont in 2010. She is a recipient of the Presidential Award for Excellence in Mathematics Teaching and is a Tandy Technology Scholar. Laurie has taught math to students at all levels, elementary through college. In addition, Laurie has served on the NCTM Board of Directors and as a Regional Director for NCSM. Along with Ron, Laurie has co-authored numerous math programs and has become a popular national speaker.

Contributors, Reviewers, and Research

Big Ideas Learning would like to express our gratitude to the mathematics education and instruction experts who served as our advisory panel, contributing specialists, and reviewers during the writing of *Big Ideas Math: Modeling Real Life*. Their input was an invaluable asset during the development of this program.

Contributing Specialists and Reviewers

- **Sophie Murphy**, Ph.D. Candidate, Melbourne School of Education, Melbourne, Australia
  Learning Targets and Success Criteria Specialist and Visible Learning Reviewer

- **Linda Hall**, Mathematics Educational Consultant, Edmond, OK
  Advisory Panel

- **Michael McDowell**, Ed.D., Superintendent, Ross, CA
  Project-Based Learning Specialist

- **Kelly Byrne**, Math Supervisor and Coordinator of Data Analysis, Downingtown, PA
  Advisory Panel

- **Jean Carwin**, Math Specialist/TOSA, Snohomish, WA
  Advisory Panel

- **Nancy Siddens**, Independent Language Teaching Consultant, Las Cruces, NM
  English Language Learner Specialist

- **Kristen Karbon**, Curriculum and Assessment Coordinator, Troy, MI
  Advisory Panel

- **Kery Obradovich**, K–8 Math/Science Coordinator, Northbrook, IL
  Advisory Panel

- **Jennifer Rollins**, Math Curriculum Content Specialist, Golden, CO
  Advisory Panel

- **Becky Walker**, Ph.D., School Improvement Services Director, Green Bay, WI
  Advisory Panel and Content Reviewer

- **Deborah Donovan**, Mathematics Consultant, Lexington, SC
  Content Reviewer

- **Tom Muchlinski**, Ph.D., Mathematics Consultant, Plymouth, MN
  Content Reviewer and Teaching Edition Contributor

- **Mary Goetz**, Elementary School Teacher, Troy, MI
  Content Reviewer

- **Nanci N. Smith**, Ph.D., International Curriculum and Instruction Consultant, Peoria, AZ
  Teaching Edition Contributor

- **Robyn Seifert-Decker**, Mathematics Consultant, Grand Haven, MI
  Teaching Edition Contributor

- **Bonnie Spence**, Mathematics Education Specialist, Missoula, MT
  Teaching Edition Contributor

- **Suzy Gagnon**, Adjunct Instructor, University of New Hampshire, Portsmouth, NH
  Teaching Edition Contributor

- **Art Johnson**, Ed.D., Professor of Mathematics Education, Warwick, RI
  Teaching Edition Contributor

- **Anthony Smith**, Ph.D., Associate Professor, Associate Dean, University of Washington Bothell, Seattle, WA
  Reading and Writing Reviewer

- **Brianna Raygor**, Music Teacher, Fridley, MN
  Music Reviewer

- **Nicole Dimich Vagle**, Educator, Author, and Consultant, Hopkins, MN
  Assessment Reviewer

- **Janet Graham**, District Math Specialist, Manassas, VA
  Response to Intervention and Differentiated Instruction Reviewer

- **Sharon Huber**, Director of Elementary Mathematics, Chesapeake, VA
  Universal Design for Learning Reviewer

Student Reviewers

- T.J. Morin
- Alayna Morin
- Ethan Bauer
- Emery Bauer
- Emma Gaeta
- Ryan Gaeta
- Benjamin SanFrotello
- Bailey SanFrotello
- Samantha Grygier
- Robert Grygier IV
- Jacob Grygier
- Jessica Urso
- Ike Patton
- Jake Lobaugh
- Adam Fried
- Caroline Naser
- Charlotte Naser

Research

Ron Larson and Laurie Boswell used the latest in educational research, along with the body of knowledge collected from expert mathematics instructors, to develop the *Modeling Real Life* series. By implementing the work of renowned researchers from across the world, *Big Ideas Math* offers at least a full year's growth within a full year's learning while also encouraging a growth mindset in students and teachers. Students take their learning from surface-level to deep-level, then transfer that learning by modeling real-life situations. For more information on how this program uses learning targets and success criteria to enhance teacher clarity, see pages xxix–xxxi.

The pedagogical approach used in this program follows the best practices outlined in the most prominent and widely accepted educational research, including:

- *Visible Learning*, John Hattie © 2009
- *Visible Learning for Teachers*
  John Hattie © 2012
- *Visible Learning for Mathematics*
  John Hattie © 2017
- *Principles to Actions: Ensuring Mathematical Success for All*
  NCTM © 2014
- *Adding It Up: Helping Children Learn Mathematics*
  National Research Council © 2001
- *Mathematical Mindsets: Unleashing Students' Potential through Creative Math, Inspiring Messages and Innovative Teaching*
  Jo Boaler © 2015
- *What Works in Schools: Translating Research into Action*
  Robert Marzano © 2003
- *Classroom Instruction That Works: Research-Based Strategies for Increasing Student Achievement*
  Marzano, Pickering, and Pollock © 2001
- *Principles and Standards for School Mathematics*
  NCTM © 2000
- *Rigorous PBL by Design: Three Shifts for Developing Confident and Competent Learners*
  Michael McDowell © 2017

- *Universal Design for Learning Guidelines*
  CAST © 2011
- *Rigor/Relevance Framework®*
  International Center for Leadership in Education
- *Understanding by Design*
  Grant Wiggins and Jay McTighe © 2005
- Achieve, ACT, and The College Board
- *Elementary and Middle School Mathematics: Teaching Developmentally*
  John A. Van de Walle and Karen S. Karp © 2015
- *Evaluating the Quality of Learning: The SOLO Taxonomy*
  John B. Biggs & Kevin F. Collis © 1982
- *Unlocking Formative Assessment: Practical Strategies for Enhancing Students' Learning in the Primary and Intermediate Classroom*
  Shirley Clarke, Helen Timperley, and John Hattie © 2004
- *Formative Assessment in the Secondary Classroom*
  Shirley Clarke © 2005
- *Improving Student Achievement: A Practical Guide to Assessment for Learning*
  Toni Glasson © 2009

Mathematical Processes and Proficiencies

Big Ideas Math: Modeling Real Life reinforces the Process Standards from NCTM and the Five Strands of Mathematical Proficiency endorsed by the National Research Council. With *Big Ideas Math*, students get the practice they need to become well-rounded, mathematically proficient learners.

Problem Solving/Strategic Competence

- *Think & Grow: Modeling Real Life* examples use problem-solving strategies, such as drawing a picture, circling knowns, and underlining unknowns.
- Real-life problems are provided to help students learn to apply the mathematics that they are learning to everyday life.
- Real-life problems help students use the structure of mathematics to break down and solve more difficult problems.

Reasoning and Proof/Adaptive Reasoning

- *Explore & Grows* allow students to investigate math and make conjectures.
- Questions ask students to explain their reasoning.

Communication

- Cooperative learning opportunities support precise communication.
- *Apply and Grow: Practice* exercises allow students to demonstrate their understanding of the lesson up to that point.
- *ELL Support* notes provide insights into how to support English learners.

Connections

- Prior knowledge is continually brought back and tied in with current learning.
- Performance Tasks tie the topics of a chapter together into one extended task.
- Real-life problems incorporate other disciplines to help students see that math is used across content areas.

Representations/Productive Disposition

- Real-life problems are translated into pictures, diagrams, tables, equations, or graphs to help students analyze relations and to draw conclusions.
- Visual problem-solving models help students create a coherent representation of the problem.
- Multiple representations are presented to help students move from concrete to representative and into abstract thinking.
- *Learning Targets* and *Success Criteria* at the start of each chapter and lesson help students understand what they are going to learn.
- Real-life problems incorporate other disciplines to help students see that math is used across content areas.

Conceptual Understanding

- *Explore & Grows* allow students to investigate math to understand the reasoning behind the rules.

Procedural Fluency

- Skill exercises are provided to continually practice fundamental skills.
- Prior knowledge is continually brought back and tied in with current learning.

Meeting Proficiency and Major Topics

Meeting Proficiency

As standards shift to prepare students for college and careers, the importance of focus, coherence, and rigor continues to grow.

FOCUS *Big Ideas Math: Modeling Real Life* emphasizes a narrower and deeper curriculum, ensuring students spend their time on the major topics of each grade.

COHERENCE The program was developed around coherent progressions from Kindergarten through eighth grade, guaranteeing students develop and progress their foundational skills through the grades while maintaining a strong focus on the major topics.

RIGOR *Big Ideas Math: Modeling Real Life* uses a balance of procedural fluency, conceptual understanding, and real-life applications. Students develop conceptual understanding in every *Explore and Grow*, continue that development through the lesson while gaining procedural fluency during the *Think and Grow*, and then tie it all together with *Think and Grow: Modeling Real Life*. Every set of practice problems reflects this balance, giving students the rigorous practice they need to be college- and career-ready.

Major Topics in Kindergarten

Counting and Cardinality
- Know number names and the count sequence.
- Count to tell the number of objects.
- Compare numbers.

Operations and Algebraic Thinking
- Understand addition as putting together and adding to, and understand subtraction as taking apart and taking from.

Number and Operations in Base Ten
- Work with numbers 11–19 to gain foundations for place value.

Use the color-coded Table of Contents to determine where the major topics, supporting topics, and additional topics occur throughout the curriculum.

- ■ Major Topic
- ■ Supporting Topic
- ■ Additional Topic

1 Count and Write Numbers 0 to 5

2 Compare Numbers 0 to 5

■ Major Topic
■ Supporting Topic
■ Additional Topic

3

Count and Write Numbers 6 to 10

Think and Grow: Modeling Real Life

Weather Chart

Monday	Tuesday	Wednesday	Thursday	Friday

Compare Numbers to 10

Compose and Decompose Numbers to 10

■ Major Topic
■ Supporting Topic
■ Additional Topic

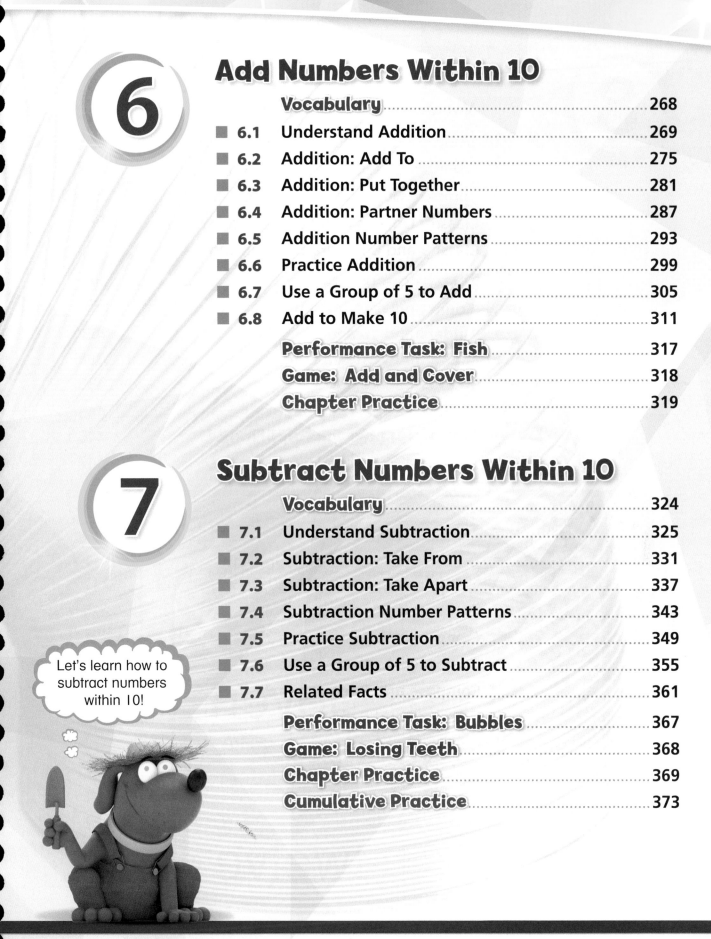

Add Numbers Within 10

6

Subtract Numbers Within 10

7

Let's learn how to subtract numbers within 10!

8 Represent Numbers 11 to 19

Think and Grow

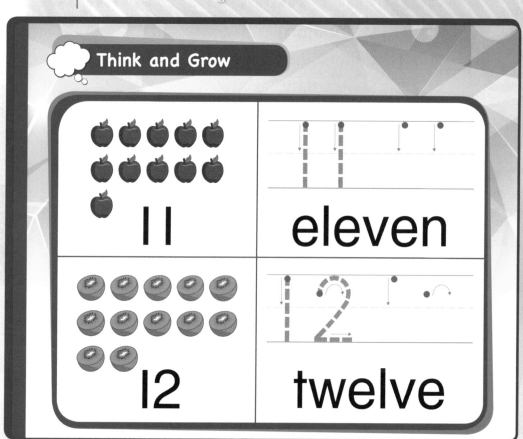

11   eleven

12   twelve

9 Count and Compare Numbers to 20

10 Count to 100

Identify Two-Dimensional Shapes

Identify Three-Dimensional Shapes and Positions

■ Major Topic
■ Supporting Topic
■ Additional Topic

13 Measure and Compare Objects

Think and Grow

Meeting the Needs of All Learners

Print Resources

Student Edition Volumes 1 and 2

Teaching Edition Volumes 1 and 2

Resources by Chapter
- ○ Family Letter
- ○ Warm-Ups
- ○ Extra Practice
- ○ Reteach
- ○ Enrichment and Extension

Assessment Book
- ○ Prerequisite Skills Practice
- ○ Pre- and Post-Course Tests
- ○ Course Benchmark Tests
- ○ Chapter Tests

Instructional Resources
- ○ Vocabulary Cards
- ○ Activities
- ○ Counting Stories
- ○ Blackline Masters

Differentiated Rich Math Tasks

Skills Review Handbook

Additional Resources

Manipulative Kits

Literature Kits

Math Musicals

Newton and Descartes Puppet Set

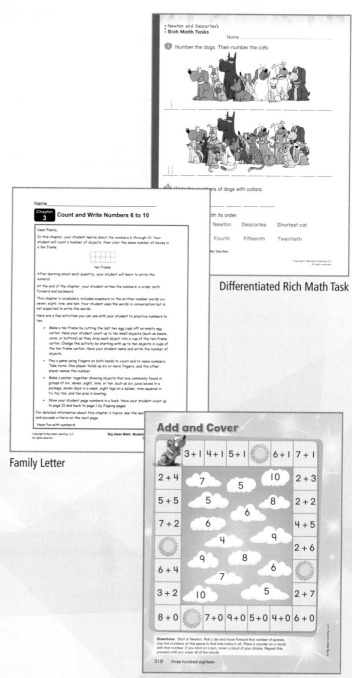

Differentiated Rich Math Task

Family Letter

Game (in the Student Edition)

Through Program Resources

Technology Resources

Dynamic Student Edition
- Virtual Manipulatives
- Interactive Explorations
- Digital Examples

Dynamic Classroom
- Laurie's Notes
- Virtual Manipulatives
- Interactive Explorations
- Digital Examples
- Formative Check
- Flip-To

Dynamic Teaching Tools
- Skills Trainer
- Digital Flashcards
- Game Library
- Multi-Language Glossary
- Additional Online Resources
  - Lesson Plans
  - Differentiating the Lesson
  - Graphic Organizers
  - Pacing Guides
  - Math Tool Paper

Dynamic Assessment System
- Customized Practice and Assessments
- Detailed Reports

Video Support for Teachers
- Professional Development Videos
- Concepts and Tools Videos

Instructional Design with Embedded

The *Big Ideas Math: Modeling Real Life* program uses a Universal Design for Learning to create a fun and innovative program that uses hands-on activities and scaffolded instruction. This allows for balanced lessons with built-in Response to Intervention that appeal to students and teachers alike. Learning targets and success criteria help to focus student learning and make learning visible to teachers and students. Explorations help students develop a growth mindset by engaging them in productive struggle, leading to conceptual understanding. With a strong emphasis on problem solving in the classroom, students can transfer their mathematical knowledge to new concepts and apply their understanding to real-life situations. Through practice and problem solving, students become more comfortable with the problem-solving process to become strategic mathematical thinkers.

Big Ideas Math: Modeling Real Life comes with a unique Teaching Edition, written by co-author Laurie Boswell, that provides professional development and instructional support at your fingertips. *Laurie's Notes* are provided at point-of-use and include step-by-step support, guiding questions, common errors and misconceptions, extensions, and much more!

Starting the Lesson

Laurie's Overview

About the Math

Students developed their number sense by counting and comparing numbers to 10. In this chapter, students deepen their number sense by identifying pairs of numbers that are embedded or "hidden" within a number. Understanding how numbers can be put together and taken apart is the beginning of thinking about addition and subtraction. These operations are *not* the focus of this chapter, and hence the vocabulary we use needs to be precise. We want the learning in this chapter to help students think of putting together two groups of objects (composing) and taking apart a group of objects (decomposing).

Arrangements of 3:

The concept of embedded or hidden numbers is introduced in the ~~first~~ along with partner numbers and the part-part-whole relationship.

Laurie's Overviews offer chapter-level support to help teachers build the math background they need to teach with confidence.

Laurie's ***Dig Ins*** engage students' natural curiosity and help students discover concepts in a fun and hands-on way.

Learning Targets and ***Success Criteria*** show students what they will be learning and encourage them to self-assess and evaluate their learning.

Learning Target

Use counting to compare the numbers of objects in two groups.

Success Criteria

- Compare the numbers of objects in two groups using *greater than*, *less than*, or *equal to*.
- Explain how to compare two groups by counting.

Dig In (Circle Time)

- Show students a tower of five linking cubes and one single cube.
- ? "If I put together these *parts*, what is the *whole*?" 6 "If I take apart the whole, what numbers could be the parts?" *Sample answers:* 2 and 4, 3 and 3, 6 and 0
- Model with Mathematics: Give each pair of students six linking cubes. Have one student show a set of partner numbers for six, while the other student names the partner numbers.
- "Hold up your partner numbers if you had 5 and 1." Pause. "Are there other partner numbers for 6?" Repeat until all pairs are mentioned.
- Now it is time to record student thinking about partner numbers for six on an anchor chart. See page T-211C for anchor chart ideas.
- ◉ You have now spent time on the first success criterion. Have students use their fingers to show a set of partner numbers for 6.
- Call on several students to describe the parts and whole they are modeling with their fingers. Expect students to use the vocabulary, parts and whole.

Professional Development

Rigorous by Design

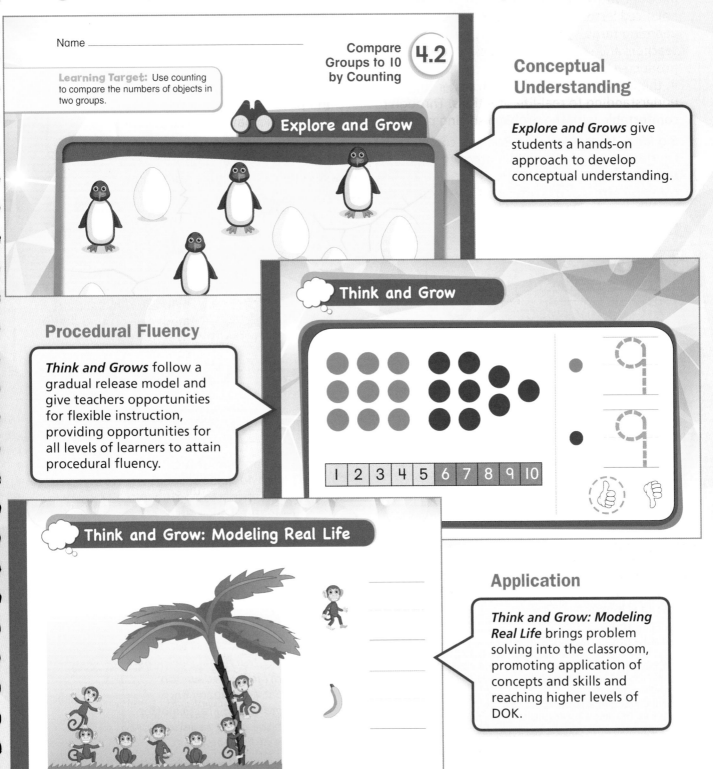

Conceptual Understanding

Explore and Grows give students a hands-on approach to develop conceptual understanding.

Procedural Fluency

Think and Grows follow a gradual release model and give teachers opportunities for flexible instruction, providing opportunities for all levels of learners to attain procedural fluency.

Application

Think and Grow: Modeling Real Life brings problem solving into the classroom, promoting application of concepts and skills and reaching higher levels of DOK.

In-Class Practice

✓ **Apply and Grow: Practice**

4 legs	not 4 legs	beak	no beak

> The exercises after the *Think and Grows* give teachers the opportunity for continual formative assessment and allow students to take ownership of their learning and communicate mathematically in a group setting.

Directions: ① Circle the scooters that are red. Cross out the scooters that are *not* red. ② Circle the toys that are balls. Cross out the toys that are *not* balls.

> ***Apply and Grow: Practices*** provide independent practice to help students monitor their own understanding.

Apply and Grow: Practice
MAKING INSTRUCTIONAL DECISIONS

In this lesson, students used matching to decide which group has more. The arrangement of the objects affects the students' ability to subitize and visually identify which group has more. Matching the objects one-to-one is necessary for many students.

EMERGING students may have difficulty identifying the number of objects in a group. They may also compare attributes such as size versus counting the quantity of the objects in each group. If students are not secure with the counting sequence, then it may be more difficult to identify a group of four objects as being more than a group of three objects.

PROFICIENT students can identify the number of objects in a group and use a strategy for deciding which group has more. These students may be using the counting sequence to say that a group of four objects is more than a group of three objects because four is greater than three.

Supporting Learners
- Provide two types of markers, such as fine-line and thick. Have one student select a random amount of fine-line markers to hold. The other student should select more thick markers than the thin-line markers. Each student counts their markers and states the amount.
- Read the directions to students, allowing time between sentences. This time will allow students to complete each step, one at a time.

Extension: Adding Rigor
- Roll two dice. Students tell which die has more dots on its face.

> ***Making Instructional Decisions*** and ***Scaffolding Instruction*** notes that accompany each *Apply and Grow: Practice* offer point-of-use differentiation for all levels of learners.

Embedded Teaching Support

> Ready to use *Center* activities include print and digital opportunities for enhancement and differentiation.

> *Cross-Curricular Connections* allow teachers to integrate mathematics across multiple subjects.

Centers

Center 1: Number Flip and Find
Materials: Student Edition page 446, Number Flip and Find Cards*
Have students complete the activity. See page T-446 for the directions.

Center 2: Skills Trainer
Materials: computers or devices with Internet access
Have students go to *BigIdeasMath.com* to access the Skills Trainer.

Center 3: Counting Objects
Materials per pair: craft sticks, counters
Students will draw a craft stick with a number between 11-19 written on it. Students will use the counting objects provided to count out that number of items represented on the craft stick.

Center 4: Roll Twenty Frames
Materials: 3 dice, whiteboard, dry erase marker
Students roll all three dice and count the number of dots represented together. Students use a whiteboard and a dry erase marker to draw double ten frames and fill them in with the number represented on the dice. Students can work together in partners.

Cross-Curricular Connections
Language Arts
- *Pete the Cat and His Four Groovy Buttons* by Eric Litwin; Have students retell the story using a five frame to organize and sequence the events. Give each student a five frame. Cut out and decorate construction paper buttons to glue on the five frame each time Pete loses one.
- Show and say three or four letter words such as *and, the, can, this,* and *come.* Have students identify the number of letters in the word. Then have students repeat the word.
- Have the class clap and count the syllables in students' names.

Science
- Have students name and count the four seasons. Have them think of three or four things that relate to each season.

> Teaching support notes are embedded throughout the Teaching Edition.
>
> **?** Guiding questions and teaching prompts are marked with this symbol.
>
> **⊙** Content marked with this symbol relates to the learning target for that section.

? Gather students to the circle in groups of 3 or 4. "As I tap your shoulder, move to the circle." Count aloud to 3 or 4 as you tap each shoulder. Pause between each group of students. "How many students moved to the circle?" 3, 4

⊙ Introduce the learning target and success criteria. Students will model the numbers 3 and 4 in a variety of ways.

- Have students chorally count with you to 3. Count multiple times as you engage their different senses; clap, hold up fingers, tilt their heads, hop on one foot. Gradually lower your own voice so that the students' voices are heard.

Dynamic Technology

Big Ideas Math: Modeling Real Life comes with an innovative and dependable technology package that supports and enhances the curriculum for teachers and students.

Dynamic Classroom

The *Dynamic Classroom* mimics the students' *Dynamic Student Edition*, with additional resources and support for teachers. Point-of-use *Laurie's Notes* guide instruction, providing dig ins, motivation suggestions, teaching tips, questions to ask the students, closure strategies, and more! Interactive explorations and digital examples from the textbook create a 21st-century classroom atmosphere that engages students. The *Formative Check* provides teachers with immediate feedback on student progress, making it easy to differentiate and provide support where it is needed the most.

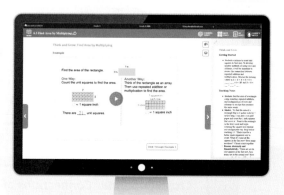

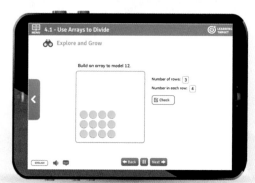

Dynamic Student Edition

The *Dynamic Student Edition* is a complete, interactive version of the Student Edition. Students have access to interactive explorations, digital examples, virtual manipulatives, and digital exercises from the textbook.

Game Library

The online *Game Library* includes interactive versions of the activities from the Student Edition. Students can practice concepts from each chapter in fun and engaging ways using one- and two-player games. These can be used for center activities, review, or to help students get extra practice with concepts. Students have access to the *Game Library* at *BigIdeasMath.com*, so they can play in school or at home!

Dynamic Assessment System

With the *Dynamic Assessment System*, teachers can create customizable homework and assessments with *Big Ideas Math* question banks or items they create! Students complete the assignments online and can receive immediate feedback on their progress. Items include a variety of question types, all of which are automatically scored except for the newly released *Essay* question type. The reports in this system provide the feedback teachers need to drive instruction.

Skills Trainer

The *Skills Trainer* is an online interactive tool for skill practice that comes with detailed reports for teachers to gain insight into each student's proficiency. Students have access to every skill found within the *Modeling Real Life* series. The *Skills Trainer* can be used to engage students in remediation or as the daily warm-up for the lessons!

Video Support

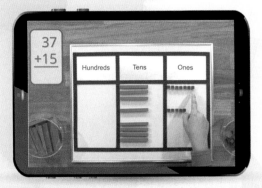

Laurie Boswell's *Professional Development Videos* and *Concepts and Tools Videos* offer teachers support. From first-year teachers to veteran teachers, everyone can benefit from her insight and years of teaching experience. *Professional Development Videos* cover topics such as, teacher efficacy, formative assessment, developing learning targets and success criteria, and much more. *Concepts and Tools Videos* show examples of ways to use different manipulatives in the classroom.

Fun with Newton and Descartes

Newton and Descartes are helpful math assistants that accompany students through their math book. They help guide students to think deeper and remember helpful information.

Math Musicals

Math Musicals are a fun way of bringing music and literature into your math classroom. *Big Ideas Math's* own Newton and Descartes team up in educational stories, songs, and animations that enhance student learning. Storybooks and animations featuring Newton and Descartes help students see the mathematics that surrounds them in everyday life.

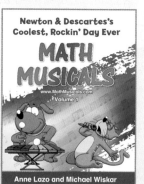

Differentiated Rich Math Tasks

Differentiated Rich Math Tasks combine music and literature with math to create interdisciplinary activities and discussions that are directly tied to *Math Musicals*. Newton and Descartes are featured throughout these rich and engaging tasks that ask students to make sense of and extend the ideas presented in each of the stories and songs. Each task has three different levels, giving every student the opportunity to work on the same task, but at their own, individual level. *Differentiated Rich Math Tasks* bring the fun of *Math Musicals* and the rigor of *Big Ideas Math* together to give every student the opportunity to succeed!

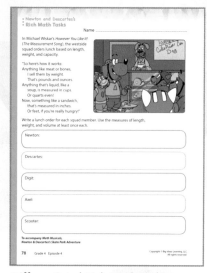

Differentiated Rich Math Task

Math Musicals story and animation

Meeting the Needs of All Learners

Through print and digital resources, the *Big Ideas Math* program completely supports the 3-Tier **Response to Intervention (RTI)** model. Using research-based strategies, teachers can reach, challenge, and motivate each student with high-quality **differentiated instruction**, targeted to individual needs. Teachers can diagnose student proficiencies or weaknesses throughout each lesson, allowing them to remediate and differentiate as necessary.

Diagnose student needs every step of the way.

Before Instruction:

The online Progression Benchmark Test measures a student's understanding of learning objectives across grade levels through multiple domains. Teachers can use this data to prescribe learning paths with tailored instruction at the appropriate tier. The Prerequisite Skills Test evaluates student understanding to determine the appropriate level of intervention prior to teaching new content.

Customized Learning Intervention

3 Tier

2 Tier — Strategic Intervention

1 Tier — Daily Intervention

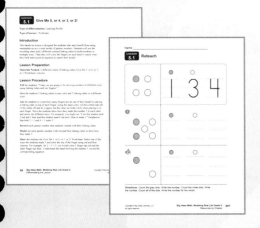

Throughout Instruction:

The Show and Grow serves as a formative assessment as students move into independent practice and application. The Formative Check provides teachers with immediate feedback on student progress. In the Progressions Through the Chapter, the standards are called out for each lesson so teachers can monitor progress of each standard. Laurie's Notes include opportunities to track progress of learning targets in each lesson.

After Instruction:

Summative assessment data from Chapter Tests, Performance Tasks, Assessments or Assignments built using the Dynamic Assessment System, and Course Benchmark Tests guide teachers' remediation plans for each student. Rubrics and reports aid in analyzing student performance to drive effective instructional decisions.

Tier 1

Daily Intervention is embedded throughout the instructional design.

Tier 2

Strategic Intervention is offered through parallel support resources.

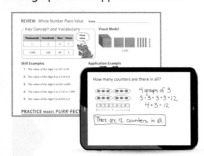

Tier 3

Customized Learning Intervention is provided through access to cohesive content at all grade levels.

Strategic Scaffolding

Big Ideas Math supports English Language Learners with a mix of print and digital resources. When teaching English learners, it is essential to create an environment that minimizes stress and is conducive to learning. Notes throughout the Teaching Edition cue possibilities to support students' cultural knowledge as they develop language.

Three notes are systematically placed within each lesson to help students access its content:

1. Support Language, Connect to Prior Knowledge, and Increase Comprehension

- Clarify language that may be difficult or confusing for English learners
- Connect new learning to something students already know
- Increase comprehension by using multiple modes of representation

2. Practice Language as Well as Content

- Practice math while improving language skills
- Use students' language as a resource to develop fluency and procedural skills
- Expectations are outlined for Beginner, Intermediate, and Advanced English Language Learners

3. Assess Understanding

- Check for development of mathematical reasoning and understanding
- Informal ongoing assessment of student understanding
- Detailed suggestions for comprehension checks that assess a large group

ELL Support

Have students continue to practice verbal language. One student asks the other, "Are the numbers equal?" Then have them switch roles for the other exercise.

Beginner students may only answer "yes" or "no."

Intermediate students may answer with a simple sentence, such as, "They are not equal."

Advanced students may answer with a sentence, such as, "No, 10 is greater than 7."

for English Learners

Embedded resources such as the Multi-Language Glossary, Family Letters, Spanish audio in the Dynamic Student Edition and eBook, Spanish translations of the Vocabulary Flash Cards, and Games in the online Game Library ensure that every student is successful.

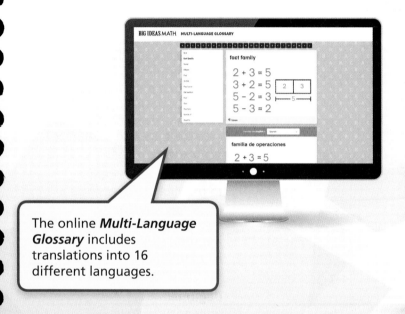

The *Dynamic Student eBook* and online *Dynamic Student Edition* include Spanish audio.

The online *Multi-Language Glossary* includes translations into 16 different languages.

Games are available in print in Spanish and with Spanish audio online.

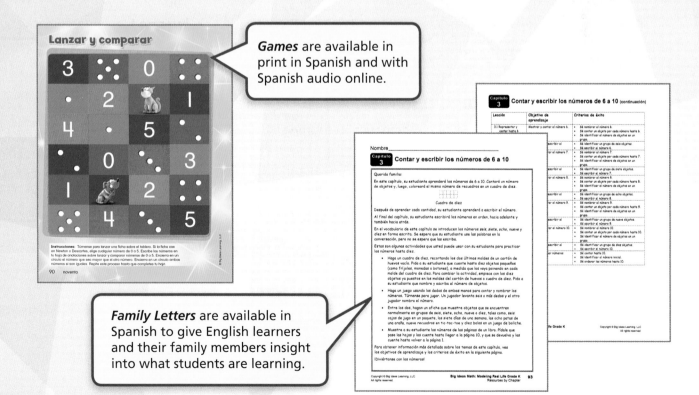

Family Letters are available in Spanish to give English learners and their family members insight into what students are learning.

Assessments

Big Ideas Math: Modeling Real Life offers a variety of opportunities for both formative and summative assessment. Student ownership and accountability for learning is a vital component of fluency. The program offers a variety of print and digital assessment options.

Formative Assessment

Formative assessment is built in with the Show and Grow and Apply and Grow, making it easy to differentiate and provide support where it is needed the most. The Formative Check in the online Dynamic Classroom provides teachers with immediate feedback on student progress.

Summative Assessment

The Assessment Book contains a variety of summative assessments including Prerequisite Skills Practice, a Pre-Course Test, Chapter Tests, Course Benchmark Tests, and a Post-Course Test to assess progress throughout the year. The online assessments in the Dynamic Assessment System offer the flexibility teachers need to customize digital summative assessments.

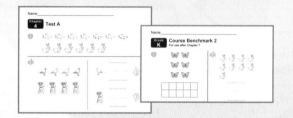

Print Assessment

Print assessments can be found throughout the program in the Assessment Book and Performance Tasks. The assessments in the Assessment Book are available as blackline masters and online as PDFs and editable Word documents.

Digital Assessment

With the Dynamic Assessment System, teachers can build customizable assessments with *Big Ideas Math* question banks aligned to standards and varying DOK levels. They can also create and edit their own unique items.

Includes technology enhanced items

Standards Tracking

Teachers can track individual student progress of standards with detailed Standards Reports. Teachers can also test students on content domains across grade levels with the adaptive Progression Benchmark Test.

Teacher Clarity

Ron Larson and Laurie Boswell used the latest in educational research to develop the *Modeling Real Life* series, along with the body of knowledge collected from expert mathematics educators. The pedagogical approach used in this program follows the best practices outlined in the most prominent and widely accepted educational research, including:

- *Visible Learning, John Hattie* © 2009
- *Visible Learning for Teachers, John Hattie* © 2012
- *Visible Learning for Mathematics, John Hattie* © 2017
- *Principles to Actions: Ensuring Mathematical Success for All, NCTM* © 2014

John Hattie developed a way of ranking various influences related to learning and achievement according to their effect sizes. He found that the average effect size of all the interventions he studied was 0.40. In three of his meta-analyses, *Visible Learning, Visible Learning for Teachers*, and *The Applicability of Visible Learning to Higher Education* (Hattie, J. (2015). *Scholarship of Teaching and Learning in Psychology*, 1(1), 79–91), Teacher Clarity consistently had a 0.75 effect size on student learning. Hattie's studies support the finding that the influence of Teacher Clarity amounts to almost 2 years' worth of learning. Therefore, it can be concluded that this teacher practice has a positive effect on student learning and achievement outcomes.

> ## " *Effective Teaching Practices:*
> ## *Establish mathematics goals to focus learning.*
>
> *Effective teaching of mathematics establishes clear goals for the mathematics that students are learning, situates goals within learning progressions, and uses the goals to guide instructional decisions.*
>
> — *NCTM's Principles to Actions: Ensuring Mathematical Success for All*

John Hattie's Visible Learning work outlines the effect size and growth that can be achieved when using learning targets and success criteria to provide clarity and understanding. When students and teachers know the learning intention of a chapter and lesson sequence, it helps them to focus on the purpose of the activity, rather than simply completing the activities in isolation.

Big Ideas Math: Modeling Real Life supports Teacher Clarity through the consistent use of learning targets and success criteria. This ensures positive outcomes for student learning and achievement in mathematics.

Making Learning Visible with

Sophie Murphy, M.Ed, wrote the chapter-level learning targets and success criteria for this program. Sophie is currently completing her Ph.D. at the University of Melbourne in Australia with Professor John Hattie as her leading supervisor. Sophie completed her Masters thesis with Professor John Hattie in 2015 and specifically investigated the nature and extensiveness of teacher voice in their classrooms. Sophie brings 20 years of experience as a teacher and school leader from ELC-Year 12 in private and public school settings in Australia.

What are Learning Targets and Success Criteria?

- **Learning targets** are descriptions of what learners should know, understand, and be able to do by the end of a learning period. The learning target outlines what the learner should be able to understand as a result of the learning throughout each lesson and chapter.

- **Success criteria** are the measures used to determine whether, and how well, learners have met and understood the learning targets. They can provide the milestones that assist learners and teachers in tracking and assessing learner progress and help teachers understand the impact of their teaching.

Using Learning Targets and Success Criteria

A learning target and corresponding success criteria are provided for each chapter and lesson. The success criteria are the guideposts that enable students to self-assess by asking, "Am I succeeding in my learning?" There are four success criteria in each chapter. The first two are yellow while the last two are green. Yellow indicates surface level, while green indicates deeper levels that lead to transfer of learning from one chapter to another. Students know exactly what the learning looks like and how they will move from surface to deep levels of learning to transfer their understandings from one chapter to another. John Hattie's Visible Learning work outlines the effect size and growth that can be achieved when using learning targets and success criteria to provide clarity and understanding.

At the chapter level

Chapter Learning Target: Understand partner numbers.

Chapter Success Criteria:
- ◻ I can identify the parts and the whole.
- ◻ I can name partner numbers.
- ◼ I can compare parts of numbers.
- ◼ I can model taking apart numbers.

At the lesson level

Learning Target: Use partner numbers to show numbers to 5.

Learning Targets and Success Criteria

How will I know when and how to talk about the Learning Target and Success Criteria?

Laurie's Notes give specific language, questions, or suggestions for making an explicit connection between what students have experienced and one or more success criteria. The more teachers integrate this language into their instructional routine, the more natural it will become.

> **Learning Target**
> Use partner numbers to show numbers to 5.
>
> **Success Criteria**
> • Name each part.
> • Name the whole.
> • Name the partner numbers for a whole.

⊙ As students are working on the exercises, continue to refer to the success criteria. "There are three cats. The *whole* is 3. There is one yellow cat and there are two black cats. The *parts* are 1 and 2, and 1 and 2 are partner numbers for 3."

⊙ Choose several students to share their partner numbers. Refer to the anchor chart to review the different sets of partner numbers for 4. Also have students use their thumb signals to show how confident they are in knowing what parts, whole, and partner numbers are.

Using the learning targets, success criteria, and *Laurie's Notes*, the teacher should be able to explain the following.

• What is to be learned
• The specific surface- to deep-level understandings that should occur throughout each chapter and lesson
• How the success criteria relate to the learning target in a logical, sequential way that provides transfer of understanding
• How this new learning will impact future learning in future lessons and beyond the textbook, into real-life situations and other learning

During each lesson, learners should be able to answer the following questions.

• What are you learning?
• How are you learning this?

• Why are you learning this?
• How will you know when you have learned it?

Welcome to a new year! We sincerely hope that the research-based approach and supports of the student and teaching editions result in at least one year's growth for all learners.

Ron Larson   *Laurie Boswell*   *Sophie*

Depth of Knowledge

Big Ideas Math uses Norman Webb's Depth of Knowledge to help teachers meet all levels of complexity while using the program. From explorations and examples to practice and performance tasks, students encounter varying Depth of Knowledge levels, reaching higher cognitive demand and promoting student discourse.

Explorations

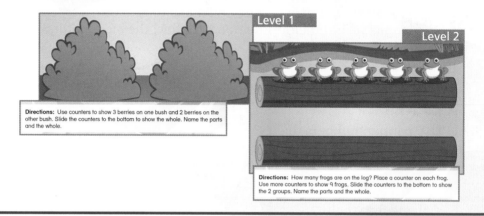

Directions: Use counters to show 3 berries on one bush and 2 berries on the other bush. Slide the counters to the bottom to show the whole. Name the parts and the whole.

Directions: How many frogs are on the log? Place a counter on each frog. Use more counters to show 9 frogs. Slide the counters to the bottom to show the 2 groups. Name the parts and the whole.

Examples

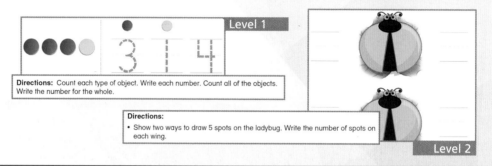

Directions: Count each type of object. Write each number. Count all of the objects. Write the number for the whole.

Directions:
- Show two ways to draw 5 spots on the ladybug. Write the number of spots on each wing.

Practice

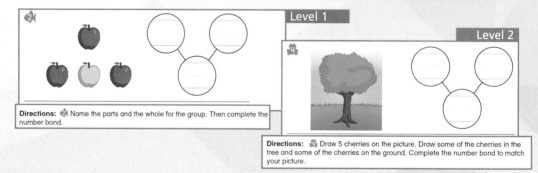

Directions: Name the parts and the whole for the group. Then complete the number bond.

Directions: Draw 5 cherries on the picture. Draw some of the cherries in the tree and some of the cherries on the ground. Complete the number bond to match your picture.

Performance Tasks

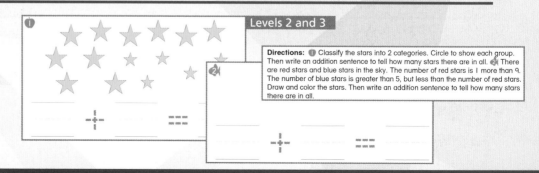

Directions: ① Classify the stars into 2 categories. Circle to show each group. Then write an addition sentence to tell how many stars there are in all. ② There are red stars and blue stars in the sky. The number of red stars is 1 more than 9. The number of blue stars is greater than 5, but less than the number of red stars. Draw and color the stars. Then write an addition sentence to tell how many stars there are in all.

Home Connection

The Big Ideas Math: Modeling Real Life program comes with built-in parent support. Parents have access to lesson pages and online interactive supports.

QR codes

Each *Practice* page has a QR Code® to link students and parents to lesson pages for at-home practice.

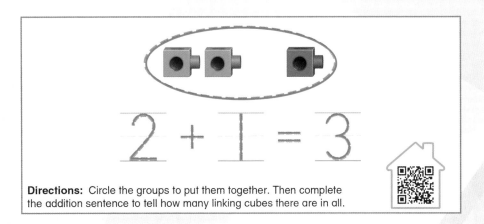

Directions: Circle the groups to put them together. Then complete the addition sentence to tell how many linking cubes there are in all.

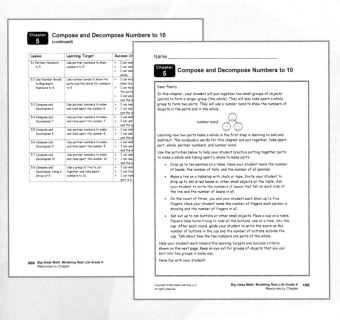

Family Letters

Family Letters keep the home-school connection strong by involving parents in their student's learning. Parents can stay up-to-date on their child's education, giving them the ability to understand concepts in a whole new way and better assist their child with practice and review for assessments.

Online Support

Parents can access a multitude of online resources such as:
- *Game Library*
- flash cards
- interactive explorations
- digital examples
- *Dynamic Student Edition*
- Skills Trainer

Cohesive Progressions

	Counting and Cardinality	Operations and Algebraic Thinking	Number and Operations in Base Ten
K	Know number names and the count sequence. Count to tell the number of objects. Compare numbers. *Chapters 1–4, 6, 8–10*	Understand addition as putting together and adding to, and understand subtraction as taking apart and taking from. *Chapters 5–7*	Work with numbers 11–19 to gain foundations for place value. *Chapter 8*
1		Solve problems involving addition and subtraction within 20. Apply properties of operations. Work with addition and subtraction equations. *Chapters 1–5, 10, 11*	Extend the counting sequence. Use place value and properties of operations to add and subtract. *Chapters 6–9*
2		Solve problems involving addition and subtraction within 20. Work with equal groups of objects. *Chapters 1–6, 15*	Use place value and properties of operations to add and subtract. *Chapters 2–10, 14*
3		Solve problems involving multiplication and division within 100. Apply properties of multiplication. Solve problems involving the four operations, and identify and explain patterns in arithmetic. *Chapters 1–5, 8, 9, 14*	Use place value and properties of operations to perform multi-digit arithmetic. *Chapters 7–9, 12*
4		Use the four operations with whole numbers to solve problems. Understand factors and multiples. Generate and analyze patterns. *Chapters 2–6, 12*	Generalize place value understanding for multi-digit whole numbers. Use place value and properties of operations to perform multi-digit arithmetic. *Chapters 1–5*
5		Write and interpret numerical expressions. Analyze patterns and relationships. *Chapters 2, 12*	Understand the place value system. Perform operations with multi-digit whole numbers and with decimals to hundredths. *Chapters 1, 3–7*

Through the Grades

	Number and Operations — Fractions	Measurement and Data	Geometry
K		Describe and compare measurable attributes. Classify objects and count the number of objects in each category. *Chapters 4, 11, 13*	Identify and describe shapes. Analyze, compare, create, and compose shapes. *Chapters 11, 12*
1		Measure lengths indirectly and by iterating length units. Tell and write time. Represent and interpret data. *Chapters 10–12*	Reason with shapes and their attributes. *Chapters 13, 14*
2		Measure and estimate lengths in standard units. Relate addition and subtraction to length. Work with time and money. Represent and interpret data. *Chapters 11–14*	Reason with shapes and their attributes. *Chapter 15*
3	Understand fractions as numbers. *Chapters 10, 11, 14*	Solve problems involving measurement and estimation of intervals of time, liquid volumes, and masses of objects. Represent and interpret data. Understand the concepts of area and perimeter. *Chapters 6, 12, 14, 15*	Reason with shapes and their attributes. *Chapters 10, 13*
4	Extend understanding of fraction equivalence and ordering. Build fractions from unit fractions. Understand decimal notation for fractions, and compare decimal fractions. *Chapters 7–11*	Solve problems involving measurement and conversion of measurements from a larger unit to a smaller unit. Represent and interpret data. Understand angles and measure angles. *Chapters 10–13*	Draw and identify lines and angles, and classify shapes by properties of their lines and angles. *Chapters 13, 14*
5	Add, subtract, multiply, and divide fractions. *Chapters 6, 8–11*	Convert measurement units within a given measurement system. Represent and interpret data. Understand volume. *Chapters 11, 13*	Graph points on the coordinate plane. Classify two-dimensional figures into categories based on their properties. *Chapters 12, 14*

Suggested Pacing Guide

Chapters 1–13   147 Days

Chapter 1   (12 Days)

Chapter Opener	1 Day
Lesson 1.1	1 Day
Lesson 1.2	1 Day
Lesson 1.3	1 Day
Lesson 1.4	1 Day
Lesson 1.5	1 Day
Lesson 1.6	1 Day
Lesson 1.7	1 Day
Lesson 1.8	1 Day
Connect and Grow	2 Days
Chapter Assessment	1 Day
Year-To-Date	**12 Days**

Chapter 2   (9 Days)

Chapter Opener	1 Day
Lesson 2.1	1 Day
Lesson 2.2	1 Day
Lesson 2.3	1 Day
Lesson 2.4	1 Day
Lesson 2.5	1 Day
Connect and Grow	2 Days
Chapter Assessment	1 Day
Year-To-Date	**21 Days**

Chapter 3   (15 Days)

Chapter Opener	1 Day
Lesson 3.1	1 Day
Lesson 3.2	1 Day
Lesson 3.3	1 Day
Lesson 3.4	1 Day
Lesson 3.5	1 Day
Lesson 3.6	1 Day
Lesson 3.7	1 Day
Lesson 3.8	1 Day
Lesson 3.9	1 Day
Lesson 3.10	1 Day
Lesson 3.11	1 Day
Connect and Grow	2 Days
Chapter Assessment	1 Day
Year-To-Date	**36 Days**

Chapter 4   (9 Days)

Chapter Opener	1 Day
Lesson 4.1	1 Day
Lesson 4.2	1 Day
Lesson 4.3	1 Day
Lesson 4.4	1 Day
Lesson 4.5	1 Day
Connect and Grow	2 Days
Chapter Assessment	1 Day
Year-To-Date	**45 Days**

Chapter 5   (12 Days)

Chapter Opener	1 Day
Lesson 5.1	1 Day
Lesson 5.2	1 Day
Lesson 5.3	1 Day
Lesson 5.4	1 Day
Lesson 5.5	1 Day
Lesson 5.6	1 Day
Lesson 5.7	1 Day
Lesson 5.8	1 Day
Connect and Grow	2 Days
Chapter Assessment	1 Day
Year-To-Date	**57 Days**

Chapter 6   (12 Days)

Chapter Opener	1 Day
Lesson 6.1	1 Day
Lesson 6.2	1 Day
Lesson 6.3	1 Day
Lesson 6.4	1 Day
Lesson 6.5	1 Day
Lesson 6.6	1 Day
Lesson 6.7	1 Day
Lesson 6.8	1 Day
Connect and Grow	2 Days
Chapter Assessment	1 Day
Year-To-Date	**69 Days**

Chapter 7 (11 Days)

Chapter Opener	1 Day
Lesson 7.1	1 Day
Lesson 7.2	1 Day
Lesson 7.3	1 Day
Lesson 7.4	1 Day
Lesson 7.5	1 Day
Lesson 7.6	1 Day
Lesson 7.7	1 Day
Connect and Grow	2 Days
Chapter Assessment	1 Day
Year-To-Date	**80 Days**

Chapter 8 (15 Days)

Chapter Opener	1 Day
Lesson 8.1	1 Day
Lesson 8.2	1 Day
Lesson 8.3	1 Day
Lesson 8.4	1 Day
Lesson 8.5	1 Day
Lesson 8.6	1 Day
Lesson 8.7	1 Day
Lesson 8.8	1 Day
Lesson 8.9	1 Day
Lesson 8.10	1 Day
Lesson 8.11	1 Day
Connect and Grow	2 Days
Chapter Assessment	1 Day
Year-To-Date	**95 Days**

Chapter 9 (10 Days)

Chapter Opener	1 Day
Lesson 9.1	1 Day
Lesson 9.2	1 Day
Lesson 9.3	1 Day
Lesson 9.4	1 Day
Lesson 9.5	1 Day
Lesson 9.6	1 Day
Connect and Grow	2 Days
Chapter Assessment	1 Day
Year-To-Date	**105 Days**

Chapter 10 (10 Days)

Chapter Opener	1 Day
Lesson 10.1	1 Day
Lesson 10.2	1 Day
Lesson 10.3	1 Day
Lesson 10.4	1 Day
Lesson 10.5	1 Day
Lesson 10.6	1 Day
Connect and Grow	2 Days
Chapter Assessment	1 Day
Year-To-Date	**115 Days**

Chapter 11 (11 Days)

Chapter Opener	1 Day
Lesson 11.1	1 Day
Lesson 11.2	1 Day
Lesson 11.3	1 Day
Lesson 11.4	1 Day
Lesson 11.5	1 Day
Lesson 11.6	1 Day
Lesson 11.7	1 Day
Connect and Grow	2 Days
Chapter Assessment	1 Day
Year-To-Date	**126 Days**

Chapter 12 (10 Days)

Chapter Opener	1 Day
Lesson 12.1	1 Day
Lesson 12.2	1 Day
Lesson 12.3	1 Day
Lesson 12.4	1 Day
Lesson 12.5	1 Day
Lesson 12.6	1 Day
Connect and Grow	2 Days
Chapter Assessment	1 Day
Year-To-Date	**136 Days**

Chapter 13 (11 Days)

Chapter Opener	1 Day
Lesson 13.1	1 Day
Lesson 13.2	1 Day
Lesson 13.3	1 Day
Lesson 13.4	1 Day
Lesson 13.5	1 Day
Lesson 13.6	1 Day
Lesson 13.7	1 Day
Connect and Grow	2 Days
Chapter Assessment	1 Day
Year-To-Date	**147 Days**

1 Count and Write Numbers 0 to 5

Chapter Overview

Lesson	Learning Target	Success Criteria
1.1 Model and Count 1 and 2	Show and count the numbers 1 and 2.	• Name the numbers 1 and 2. • Count one or two objects. • Tell the number of objects in a group.
1.2 Understand and Write 1 and 2	Understand and write the numbers 1 and 2.	• Identify groups of one and two objects. • Write the numbers 1 and 2.
1.3 Model and Count 3 and 4	Show and count the numbers 3 and 4.	• Name the numbers 3 and 4. • Count one object for each number to 4. • Tell the number of objects in a group.
1.4 Understand and Write 3 and 4	Understand and write the numbers 3 and 4.	• Identify groups of three and four objects. • Write the numbers 3 and 4.
1.5 Model and Count 5	Show and count the number 5.	• Name the number 5. • Count one object for each number to 5. • Tell the number of objects in a group.
1.6 Understand and Write 5	Understand and write the number 5.	• Identify a group of five objects. • Write the number 5.
1.7 The Concept of Zero	Understand, name, and write the number 0.	• Name the number 0. • Explain that 0 means having no objects. • Identify a group of zero objects. • Write the number 0.
1.8 Count and Order Numbers to 5	Count and order numbers to 5.	• Count from 1 to 5. • Identify the starting number. • Order numbers up to 5.

Chapter Learning Target:
Understand counting.

Chapter Success Criteria:
▦ Identify numbers.
▦ Name numbers.
▦ Order numbers.
▦ Write numbers.

Progressions

Through the Grades	
Kindergarten	**Grade 1**
• Name, count, and write numbers within 5. • Pair each number name with an object. • Determine that the last number stated names the total. • Count objects in different arrangements. • Order numbers within 5 both forward and backward. • Understand that the next number stated is one number greater.	• Represent, write, and solve "Add To" and "Put Together" problems with unknowns. • Write and solve addition number sentences. • Solve addition word problems. • Represent, write, and solve "Take From" and "Take Apart" problems with unknowns. • Write and solve subtraction number sentences. • Solve subtraction word problems. • Solve addition and subtraction comparison problems.

Standard	Through the Chapter							
	1.1	**1.2**	**1.3**	**1.4**	**1.5**	**1.6**	**1.7**	**1.8**
When counting objects, say the number names in the standard order, pairing each object with one and only one number name and each number name with one and only one object.	●		●		●			
Understand that the last number name said tells the number of objects counted. The number of objects is the same regardless of their arrangement or the order in which they were counted.	●		●		●			
Count to answer "how many?" questions about as many as 20 things arranged in a line, a rectangular array, or a circle, or as many as 10 things in a scattered configuration; given a number from 1–20, count out that many objects.	●	●	●	●	●	●	●	●
Write numbers from 0 to 20. Represent a number of objects with a written numeral 0–20.		●		●		●	●	●
Understand that each successive number name refers to a quantity that is one larger.								●

Key: ▲ = Preparing   ● = Learning   ★ = Complete

Laurie's Overview

Note from Laurie

The students in your class are feeling a range of emotions for a variety of reasons. This is an exciting time for all of them. Sharing what the classroom climate and culture will be, along with some thoughts about the first chapter, will help students form a positive mindset as they begin the year.

From the very first day, you want to establish a norm in your classroom that each student will discuss mathematical problems with a partner or group. Math time will begin in a circle where the skill or concept for the lesson will be explored. This part of the lesson is interactive, exploratory, and provides an opportunity for students to start thinking about the new skill or concept. I hope you find the suggestions in Laurie's Notes to be helpful in supporting and enhancing your teaching, and in promoting student discourse.

About the Math

Young children learn how to count aloud before they ever attach meaning to each number word. They may even match the words to objects. Counting means you can tell how many objects are in a group, and that the last counting word stated tells the total number of objects. Children who make this connection are said to understand cardinality.

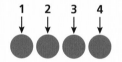

Learning to count is a developmental process in which children build their knowledge and understanding of number names and quantities. They first learn to orally count numbers and do not associate numbers with quantities of objects. Children then realize numbers relate to quantity, but may still have difficulty counting a group. Children then recognize one-to-one correspondence and can then associate one number word for each object being counted.

Cardinality is developed as students understand that the last number they say when counting is the total number of objects. Cardinality is understood perceptually when students can physically move or point to objects. Next, they track physical objects with their eyes to count. Students become figurative counters when they visualize a group of objects and can count the amount they picture. Students who demonstrate cardinality may say things such as, "I used three crayons to color my picture" or "There are four people in my family."

"I see 2 dots."

"I see 4 dots and 2 dots."

We want students to fluently add and subtract within five, and a key step in doing this is to see a grouping of objects and knowing its amount without counting. This is called *subitizing*. Give students numerous opportunities to practice subitizing, as it is a skill that cannot be explicitly taught. One way to assess the ability to subitize is to roll a die and ask how many dots are shown. If students can immediately name the quantity, they are able to subitize. Each lesson is intentionally designed so that students focus on perceptually subitizing numbers as they count groups of objects arranged in different formations. Some students may also develop conceptual subitizing when they can see a number as the sum of two parts.

There are different number formations that students should experience when they are asked to count objects. Linear formations are easiest for students to track. Array formations, set up in rows and columns, help build strong connections to addition. When objects are arranged in a circular formation, students must decide where to start counting and know when to stop. Scattered formations are the most difficult for students, as it is easy to lose track of which objects have been counted.

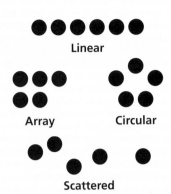

Linear

Array   Circular

Scattered

Students first learn to model and count each number before they associate the symbol to the number name and quantity. In this chapter, students learn to write the numbers 0 through 5 using verbal pathways. These are the short action statements about how to form the numbers 0 to 5, which are listed below.

0 - pull back and around
1 - pull down
2 - pull around, slant down, across
3 - pull around and in, around and stop
4 - pull down a little, across and stop, pull down
5 - pull down a little, around and stop, pull across

When we count, we start with the number 1. The set of numbers 1, 2, 3, 4, ... are called the *counting numbers.* The numbers 1 to 5 are learned before the number 0. Zero is a difficult concept for students to grasp, as they cannot point to or count objects. Students learn that 0 stands for having none of something. After students learn the numbers 0 to 5, they show the numbers in sequential order. Counting forward, backward, and from a given number helps students understand the number sequence and prepares them for comparing numbers in the next chapter.

Models
- Children are often familiar with counting or showing their age with their fingers. They use their fingers to count and show quantities.

- The five frame is a rectangular array used to organize counters when modeling numbers.

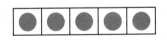

- Linking cubes are used to help show one-to-one correspondence when counting and can be used to model and compare numbers. Linking cubes are easy to manipulate and the range of colors can be used to teach various number concepts.

- Number and subitizing cards can be used in a variety of ways to help students associate a symbol and quantity.

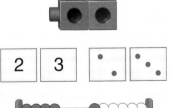

- A rekenrek is a tool used to model and count each number. Students practice counting as they slide the beads over one at a time.

Chapter Materials and Resources

The primary materials and resources needed for this chapter are listed below. Other materials may be needed for the additional support ideas provided throughout the chapter.

Check out the virtual manipulatives.
BigIdeasMath.com

Classroom Materials	Chapter Opener	1.1	1.2	1.3	1.4	1.5	1.6	1.7	1.8	Connect and Grow
scissors	•									•
two-color counters		•	•	•	•	•	•	•		
linking cubes		•		•		•		•	•	
rekenrek		+		+		+				
collections of objects to count and model 1–5		+	+		+					
manipulatives for game pieces										•
crayons										•
construction paper										•
glue or tape										•
stamps or stickers										•

Instructional Resources	Chapter Opener	1.1	1.2	1.3	1.4	1.5	1.6	1.7	1.8	Connect and Grow
Vocabulary Cards	•	+		+		+		+	+	
My Pets			•							
Subitizing Cards 0–5			+		+		+			•
Number Cards 0–5			+		+		+		*	•
We Go Camping					•					
At the Pond							•			
Dot Cards 0-5 Sets 1–3							+	+		
Five Frame Cards 0–5							+			
My Toys								•		
Color by Numbers 0–5										•
Five Frames										*

• class set   + teacher only   * per pair/group

Suggested Pacing

Day				Vocabulary			
Day 1	Chapter Opener	Performance Task Preview					
Day 2	Lesson 1.1	Warm-Up	Dig In	Explore	Think	Apply: Practice	Think: Modeling Real Life
Day 3	Lesson 1.2	Warm-Up	Dig In	Explore	Think	Apply: Practice	Think: Modeling Real Life
Day 4	Lesson 1.3	Warm-Up	Dig In	Explore	Think	Apply: Practice	Think: Modeling Real Life
Day 5	Lesson 1.4	Warm-Up	Dig In	Explore	Think	Apply: Practice	Think: Modeling Real Life
Day 6	Lesson 1.5	Warm-Up	Dig In	Explore	Think	Apply: Practice	Think: Modeling Real Life
Day 7	Lesson 1.6	Warm-Up	Dig In	Explore	Think	Apply: Practice	Think: Modeling Real Life
Day 8	Lesson 1.7	Warm-Up	Dig In	Explore	Think	Apply: Practice	Think: Modeling Real Life
Day 9	Lesson 1.8	Warm-Up	Dig In	Explore	Think	Apply: Practice	Think: Modeling Real Life
Day 10	Connect and Grow	Performance Task		Activity		Chapter Practice	
Day 11		Centers					
Day 12	Chapter Assessment	Chapter Assessment					

Year-to-Date: 12 Days

Laurie's Notes

Performance Task Preview

? Assess students' prior knowledge of numbers and counting as you preview the page. Ask, "What kinds of animals live on a farm? How many legs does each animal have?"

- Get students ready and excited about the chapter by relating the picture to animals they may have seen in stories, sung about in songs, or seen on an actual farm.
- In the Performance Task at the end of the chapter students will count and tell the number of farm animals in a picture.

Count and Write Numbers 0 to 5

1

Chapter Learning Target:
Understand counting.

Chapter Success Criteria:
- I can identify numbers.
- I can name numbers.
- I can order numbers.
- I can write numbers.

- What kinds of animals live on a farm?
- How many legs does each animal have?

© Big Ideas Learning, LLC

one   1

Laurie's Notes

Vocabulary Review

? **Preview:** "What do you see on the page? What do you notice about the ducks?" They are white; they are not colored in; there are two ducks. "What do you think of when I say the word *color*?" Students will likely give an example such as the blue water, or color a picture. Discuss the review word color.

• Have students trace and color the ducks. Observe fine motor skills as students trace the ducks and listen for them to identify the color they use to color the ducks.

• **Extension:** Provide crayons for students to draw two more objects in the pond. Model how to draw simple objects such as a circle for a lily pad or a thick line for a log.

Chapter 1 Vocabulary

• Prepare students to cut out the vocabulary cards. Discuss how to handle the scissors and model how to cut the cards on the dotted lines. Depending on students' familiarity with scissors, you may decide to cut these vocabulary cards out before the lesson. Have both right and left-handed scissors available.

• Prepare two sets of laminated vocabulary cards. Display both the words and their definitions on the wall.

• **Teaching Tip:** Offer envelopes or small bags for students to store their vocabulary cards. Students can reference these cards as needed throughout the chapter.

Activity

• **Ready, Set, Action!:** Have the students repeat as you say and show a vocabulary word and model the action provided below. To demonstrate the *count* card, hold up one hand and act like you are counting on your fingers to five. The *number* card can be acted out by pointing to a sign in the room that has a number on it. Stomp or clap to act out the numbers 1 through 5. Use a closed hand for 0. For the *five frame* card, draw and then point to a five frame on the board. Have students get in line to act out the *order* card.

MATH MUSICALS

Math Musicals can be used with current topics, to review previous topics, or to preview upcoming topics. There are many *Math Musicals* to choose from!

Use your hand puppets to act out new stories and have students sing the songs several times to take full advantage of the power of music to learn math!

Vocabulary

© Big Ideas Learning, LLC

Directions: Trace and color the ducks.

2   two

Chapter 1 Vocabulary Cards

count

five

five frame

four

number

one

order

three

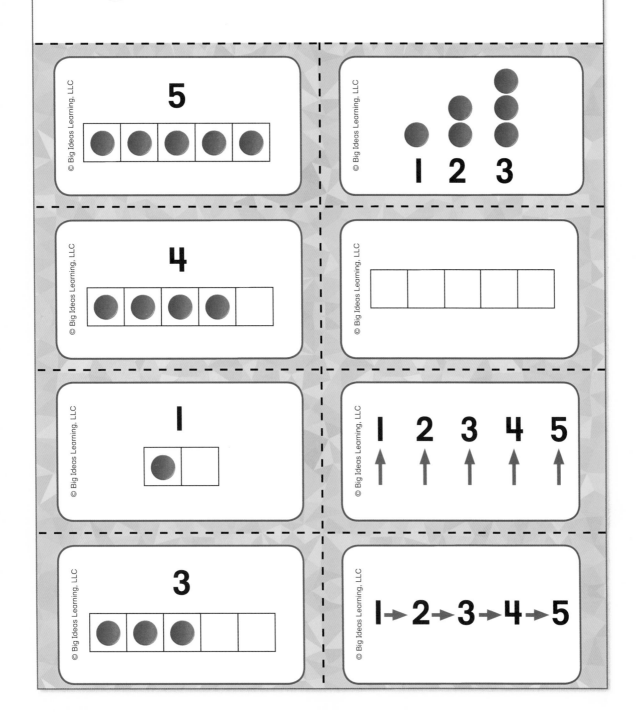

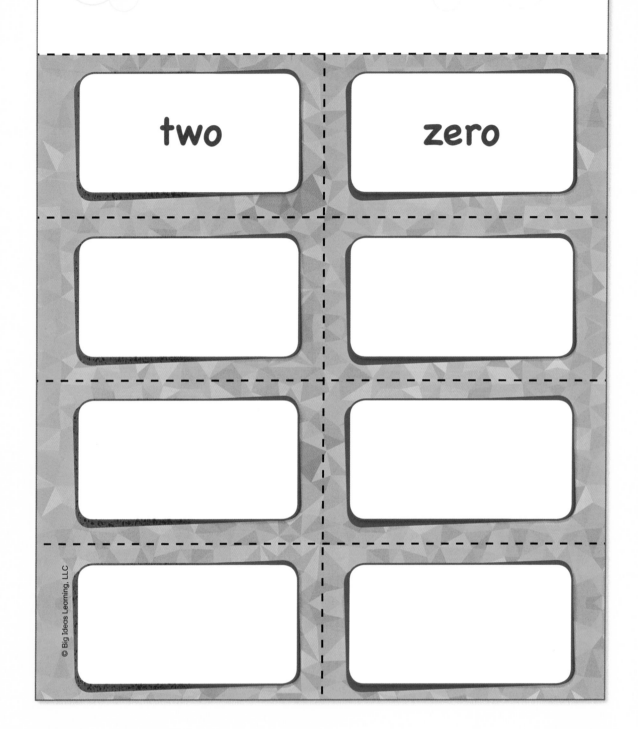

two

zero

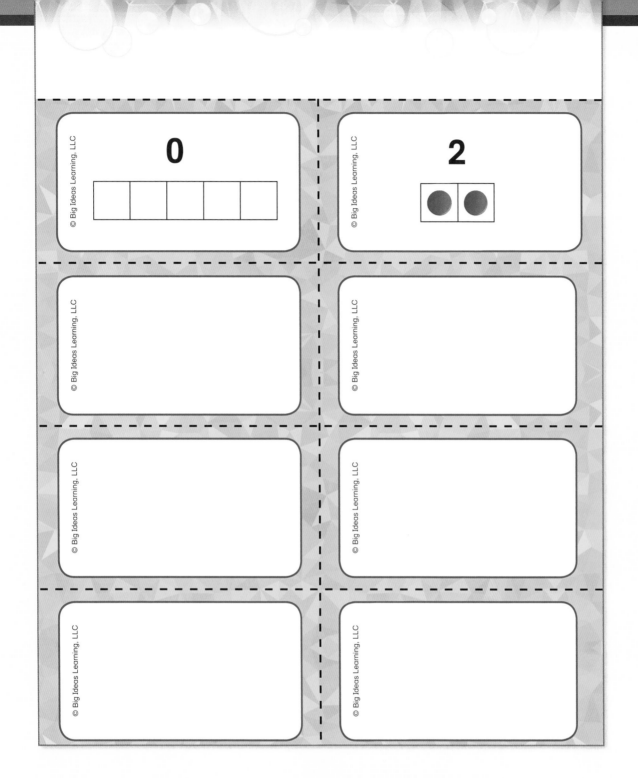

0

2

Laurie's Notes

Preparing to Teach

Many students are able to orally count numbers, meaning they can recite the sequence one, two, three, and so on. A second and different skill is connecting the sequence of the words *one, two, three,* and so on in a one-to-one correspondence with objects being counted. In this first lesson, students use one-to-one correspondence to count one or two objects and tell how many objects are in a group. They should understand that the last number they count is the total number of objects.

All of the "Model and Count" lessons in this chapter have the same design but a different theme. The theme of this lesson is related to trees.

Materials

- collections of objects to count one and two
- two-color counters
- linking cubes
- rekenrek

Dig In (Circle Time)

Share your routine for circle time and your expectations for student engagement, listening, and partner discussion. This will be the time each day to introduce the learning target and success criteria.

- Use the small collections of objects to count. Example: Place a bean bag in the center of the circle and have students whisper to a partner or share aloud how many bean bags there are.
- Point to your nose and say, "I have one nose. What else do you see one of in the room?" Allow students to share. Ask a student to take one object out of your collection and place it in the middle of the circle.
- Each time an example of **one** object is given, have students clap once. You could alternate with one jump, one tap on the belly, or by holding up one finger.
- Place two bean bags in the center of the circle and ask how many. Probe how students know there are two. Listen for a student to say, "I counted them."
- Spend time counting "1, 2" as students identify collections of two objects in the classroom. Each time, have students clap twice, jump twice, tap twice, or show two fingers.

Learning Target

Show and count the numbers 1 and 2.

Success Criteria

- Name the numbers 1 and 2.
- Count one or two objects.
- Tell the number of objects in a group.

ELL Support

Homophones are words that sound alike and have different meanings. These words are particularly challenging for ELLs. The word *one* has one homophone, *won.* The word *two* has two homophones, *to* and *too.* Explain to students that they need to listen to everything being said to be sure they understand which word is being used.

❓ Teaching Prompt   ◉ Learning Target

Learning Target: Show and
count the numbers 1 and 2.

Explore and Grow

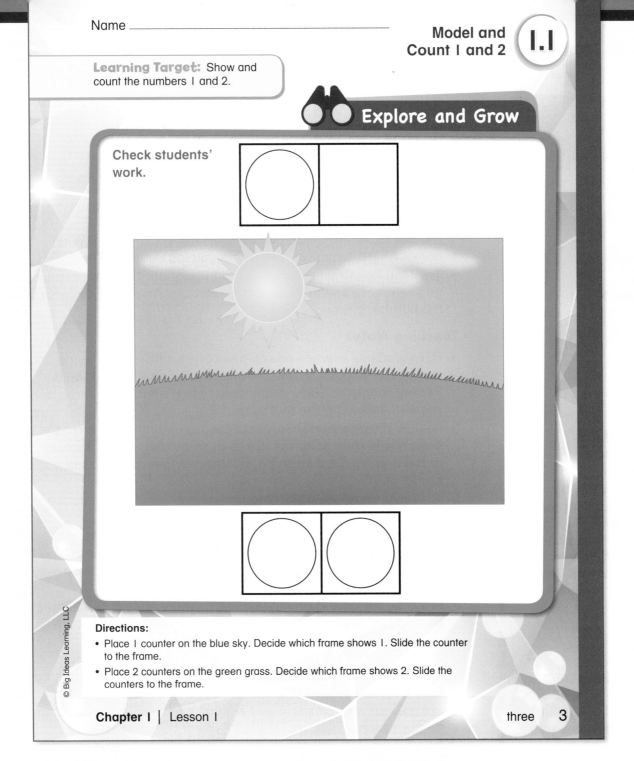

Check students'
work.

Directions:
- Place 1 counter on the blue sky. Decide which frame shows 1. Slide the counter to the frame.
- Place 2 counters on the green grass. Decide which frame shows 2. Slide the counters to the frame.

© Big Ideas Learning, LLC

Chapter 1 | Lesson 1   three 3

Explore and Grow

- The Explore and Grow is for students to show and count 1 and 2. You also have the opportunity to observe students' knowledge of colors, positions (above, up, below, and down) and directions.
- Distribute counters. "I was outside when I saw a bird flying high in the sky. Use a counter to show the bird in the sky." Have students point to the frame that shows one and slide their counter from the sky to the frame.
- "Then I saw two bunnies hopping on the grass. Use counters to show the bunnies on the grass." Have students point to the frame that shows two and slide their counters from the grass to the frame.

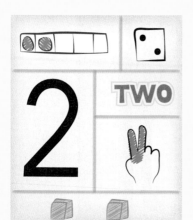

Laurie's Notes

Think and Grow

Getting Started

- Introduce the vocabulary cards for **count, number, one,** and **two.** Model the meaning of each.
- **? Turn and Talk:** "What does each word make you think about?" one lost tooth; two pets; numbers on a phone.
- **? Sample Questions:** "Can you show 1 finger? 2 fingers? What comes after 1 when counting? Can you tap your two knees?"
- **Teaching Tip:** Create anchor charts throughout the year to use as a reference and to assist visual learners. An anchor chart for the number 2 is shown.

Teaching Notes

- Have students practice one-to-one correspondence by using their finger to point to the tree and by placing a counter on it as they count, "1." Have students note that one of the boxes is shaded. Repeat for the two trees.
- ◉ Review the directions. Students can use counters to cover the objects and then color the boxes to show their understanding of the third success criterion, tell the number of objects in a group.
- ◉ A discussion of using learning targets and success criteria is located in the Front Matter of the book.
- ◉ Review the three success criteria with students. Students have had time to explore and demonstrate their proficiency with naming and counting the numbers 1 and 2, and telling how many.
- **Note:** Counting and understanding quantity are different. In the next lesson, the focus is on understanding the quantities, which some students may already exhibit.
- **? Extension:** "If I am counting the acorns, then does it matter which acorn I point to first? Tell your partner what you think." Students may believe that you need to count left-to-right just like they do when reading and writing.
- **Supporting Learners:** Review the counting sequence with students often. Build students' figurative counting skills by having them imagine two apples on the tree. Have students draw what they pictured.
- **Supporting Learners:** Students may benefit from using a rekenrek to show each number. Start with all the beads to the right and slide one bead at a time into play. Students practice one-to-one correspondence as they slide one bead for each count.

Directions: Count the objects. Color the boxes to show how many.

4   four

Laurie's Notes

Meeting the needs of all learners.

Apply and Grow: Practice

MAKING INSTRUCTIONAL DECISIONS

Children develop an understanding of numbers by working with models. In this lesson students practice modeling and counting one and two by working with counters and coloring boxes. They do not write the number that represents the quantity.

Keep in mind that to count, a student needs to find out "how many." Counting is not just repeating a number sequence. Not all students will be aware that they should demonstrate one-to-one correspondence as they count. They may point to the objects as they say the sequence but not fully understand the association with the quantity stated. Once students realize this, they will begin to touch each object as they count. They are then at the beginning stage of learning to count.

EMERGING students may have difficulty associating one number word with one object when counting. They may not know the correct number sequence.

- Provide counters for students to place on the objects. Encourage them to point to each counter as they count aloud.

PROFICIENT students can demonstrate one-to-one correspondence while counting. They know "how many" after counting.

- Help students fill in the following sentences based on the counters they use for each exercise. "I have _____ counters. I counted _____."

Extensions: Adding Rigor

- Have students make different-colored finger models representing one and two. Color each model.
- Use opportunities that come up throughout the day to reinforce the students' understanding of showing and counting 1 and 2. An example of this might be, "I see one apple on her plate," as you help students through the lunch line.

Name _____

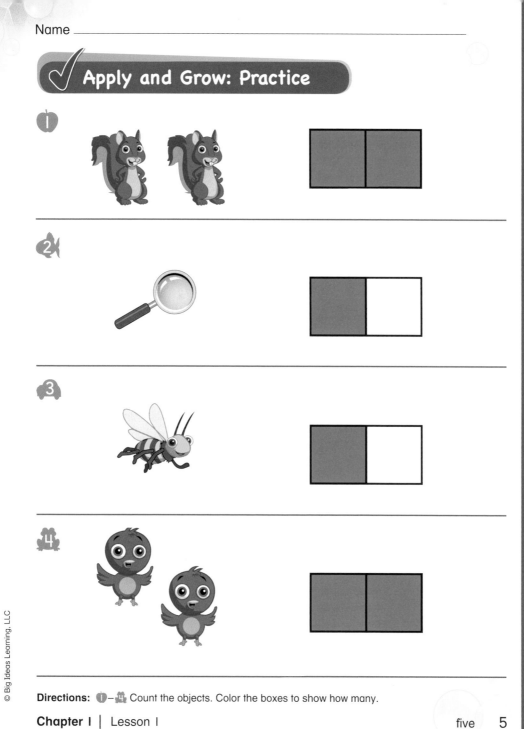

1

2

3

4

Directions: ❶–❹ Count the objects. Color the boxes to show how many.

© Big Ideas Learning, LLC

Laurie's Notes

Think and Grow: Modeling Real Life

⊙ You should have a sense of students' progress with the learning target, and more importantly, the students should understand how their own learning is progressing.

> "Today our learning target was to show and count the numbers 1 and 2. In the circle, we counted 1 or 2 objects. Do you remember showing and counting 1? showing and counting 2? How did we show how many?" clap, jump, fingers, counters, and coloring boxes "I want to know how comfortable you are showing the number 2." Model this by placing two counters on the table. "If you think you can do it, show me a thumbs up. (Demonstrate a thumbs up.) If you think you can do it with help, show me a sideways thumb. (Demonstrate a sideways thumb.) If you don't think you can do it yet, use your thumb like this." (Demonstrate a thumbs down.)
>
> Explain that each day they will talk about the learning target and they will decide how they are doing with their learning.
>
> "Let's practice again. This time I want to know how comfortable you are counting the number 2." Model this by touching the two counters as you say, "one, two." "If you are pretty good use your thumb. (Demonstrate a thumbs up.)" Continue with a sideways thumb and thumbs down.

? **Preview:** "What do you think is happening in the picture? What do you see on the leaf? Have you ever looked at something through a magnifying glass?"

? "Think to yourself. How can you find the number of ants and the number of caterpillars on the leaf? How can you show the number?" Make a connection between these questions and the learning target.

? "Are there any other objects in the picture in which you can only count one?" leaf, magnifying glass

• **Supporting Learners:** Allow students to manipulate counters or linking cubes to practice counting one or two objects.

Closure

• Prompt students to use objects, drawings, fingers, or actions to show the number one or two to a partner. Have the partner say the number.

 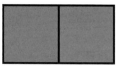

 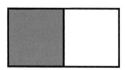

Directions: Count the objects in the picture. Color the boxes to show how many.

6   six

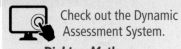
Connect and Extend Learning

Practice Notes

You will need to decide daily whether students will complete the Practice exercises as homework or as in-class practice. The decision may vary for different groups of students. Use your classroom observations and the learning needs of students to inform your decision.

The exercises presented on the Practice pages modle examples completed earlier in the lesson. The exercises are purposely not extensions of the day's lesson. Students practice the skills and concepts they have acquired. The number of exercises on the Practice pages is quite small which is developmentally appropriate. In later grades, the number of exercises will increase. We will begin to include *spaced practice* that brings back skills and concepts previously learned. Reference to earlier content can also be accomplished during the lesson.

- **Exercises 1–5:** Preview the direction lines to clarify any questions.
- **Exercise 5:** Make sure students do not count the objects next to the boxes.

Cross-Curricular Connections

Language Arts

- *Brown Bear, Brown Bear, What Do You See?* by Bill Martin Jr. and Eric Carle; Count characters or objects throughout the story. Be sure that the quantities one and two are shown.
- Show one or two letter words such as *I, a, in,* or *at.* Have students identify the number of letters in each word and repeat them after you.
- Model how to clap syllables in one or two syllable words. Say each word and have students repeat. They can clap as they say the word.

Science

- Take your students for a walk outside. Have them find and count two things that are the same or different.

Name _____

Learning Target: Show and count the numbers 1 and 2.

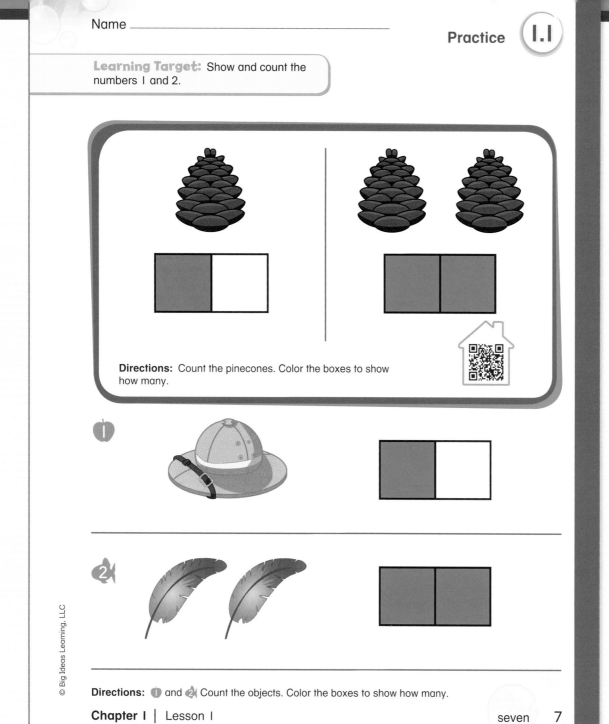

Directions: Count the pinecones. Color the boxes to show how many.

1

2

Directions: **1** and **2** Count the objects. Color the boxes to show how many.

© Big Ideas Learning, LLC

Chapter 1 | Lesson 1

seven   7

Connect and Extend Learning

Extend Student Learning

Visual-Spatial

- Extend the lesson by having students find objects around the school that are found in groups of one or two such as one office, one drinking fountain, one fire extinguisher, two windows, two staplers, and two restrooms.

Lesson Resources	
Surface Level	**Deep Level**
Resources by Chapter • Extra Practice • Reteach Differentiating the Lesson Skills Review Handbook Skills Trainer	Resources by Chapter • Enrichment and Extension Graphic Organizers Dynamic Assessment System • Lesson Practice

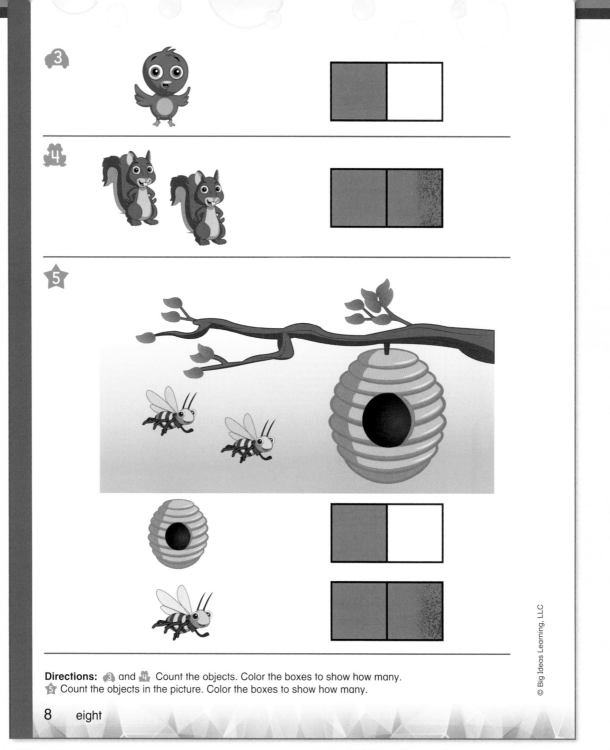

Directions: 3 and 4 Count the objects. Color the boxes to show how many.
5 Count the objects in the picture. Color the boxes to show how many.

8   eight

Laurie's Notes

Learning Target
Understand and write the numbers 1 and 2.

Success Criteria
- Identify groups of one and two objects.
- Write the numbers 1 and 2.

Warm-Up
Practice opportunities for the following are available in the Resources by Chapter or at *BigIdeasMath.com.*
- Daily skills
- Vocabulary
- Prerequisite skills

ELL Support
Explain to students that, as you read, they should listen carefully for the words *one* and *two,* and which pets are named after each number. Remind them that both *one* and *two* have words that sound just like them. Tell students to listen carefully to everything being said in order to understand which word is being used.

Preparing to Teach

In kindergarten, students learn to write the numerals 0 to 9 and letters from A to Z. Learning to write numerals or letters is not the same as learning to count or spell. In this lesson, students develop an understanding of the numbers 1 and 2, learn to trace numeral outlines, and write the numbers by using verbal pathways. This is their first exposure to perceptual subitizing, the ability to instantly recognize a small group of objects as a number. Students begin to see that they are not *counting* to know there are two. They *recognize* and *understand* there is a collection of two objects and that the arrangement of objects does not change the amount.

All "Understand and Write" lessons in this chapter have the same design but a different theme. This lesson's theme is pets.

Materials
- collections of objects to model one and two
- *My Pets**
- two-color counters
- Subitizing Cards 0–5*
- Number Cards 0–5*

**Found in the Instructional Resources*

Dig In (Circle Time)

Place groups of one and two objects in the center of the circle leaving space between the groups. For example, place two blocks next to each other, and one bear over to the side.

- ? "How many blocks are there? How many bears are there? Can someone name a group that has just one object in it? What group has two objects in it?"
- ? Now focus only on one group of two objects. Place objects in different orientations, such as beside, apart, and on top of each other. Each time ask, "How many objects are there?" Stress that arrangement does not change the number of objects.
- ? Distribute *My Pets* booklets. "Who has one or two pets?" Have students share. Identify and count the pets as you read.
- ? "How many dogs are in the story?" Model how to write the number 1 using the verbal pathway, "pull down." Have students finger trace 1 in the booklet and air write 1 several times as they repeat the verbal pathway. Repeat for two fish using the verbal pathway, "pull around, slant down, across."
- Note: Remember you are facing students as you write 2 in the air. You do not want the orientation to be backwards.
- Students should then return to their seats with their booklets.

? Teaching's Prompt   ⊙ Learning Target

Name _____

Learning Target: Understand and write the numbers 1 and 2.

Explore and Grow

Directions: Use counters to show how many dogs and how many fish are in the story *My Pets*. Write how many dogs and how many fish are in the story.

© Big Ideas Learning, LLC

Chapter 1 | Lesson 2   nine   9

Explore and Grow

? Use the story *My Pets.* Ask, "How many dogs does the child have? Use your counters to show the dog in the doghouse." Have students explore how to write the number 1 in the other doghouse.

• Repeat this process for the fish in the story, and have students explore how to write the number 2.

• Note: Writing lines are not shown until students formally learn how to write the numbers in the Think and Grow. Students should attempt to make the numbers based on the verbal pathway.

Laurie's Notes

ELL Support

Explain that each animal pictured can be described with two words: *bunny* or *rabbit,* and *kitten* or *cat.* Have students practice language as they did in the previous lesson. One student asks the other, "How many bunnies are there?" Then have them switch roles for the second example.

Beginner students may only answer "one" or "two."

Intermediate students may answer "one" or "two" and name the type of animal being counted.

Advanced students may answer using a complete sentence, such as, "There is one bunny."

Think and Grow

Getting Started

- Show students the subitizing and number cards for 1 and 2. Hold or display the cards where all students can see them. These cards will be used as students complete the page.
- Notice that there is a group, a dot model, and a traceable numeral for each number.

Teaching Notes

- **Teaching Strategy:** Have students practice writing the number with their index finger in the air, in the palm of their other hand, or across the table or desk without a pencil. They can also trace the numbers on the page. Remind students to start at the dot and follow the arrows. As they trace they should say the verbal pathway.
- ? "Does it matter which kitten you point to first when you count them?" No, the number is the same both ways.
- **Common Error:** Students may reverse the number 2. This is especially common with left-handed students. If a student continues to rewrite the number and the reversal continues, use hand-over-hand assistance, or use a highlighter to write the number and have them trace it.
- ⊙ You have had time to observe students' proficiency with identifying groups of one or two objects, and writing the numbers. In each lesson, remind students of the learning target and how they know they have been successful in learning it.

> "Today our learning target was to understand and write the numbers 1 and 2. In the circle, we identified one or two objects. Do you remember when I asked you which groups had one object? two objects? Can you look and know how many? Did you know how many kittens were on the page without pointing and counting? I want to know how you feel about knowing when there are two objects. If you think you can do it, use your thumb. (Demonstrate a thumbs up.) If you think you can do it with help, use your thumb like this. (Demonstrate a sideways thumb.) If you don't think you can do it yet, use your thumb like this. (Demonstrate a thumbs down.)"
>
> "Let's practice again. This time I want to know how you feel about writing the number 2." Model how to write the number 2 while saying the verbal pathway. "If you think you are pretty good, use your thumb. (Demonstrate a thumbs up.)" Continue with a sideways thumb and a thumbs down.

- **Supporting Learners:** Have students point to objects in the classroom that have one or two in the group such as one nose on Laurie, one flag pole, one door, one sink handle, two eyes, two windows, and two books.

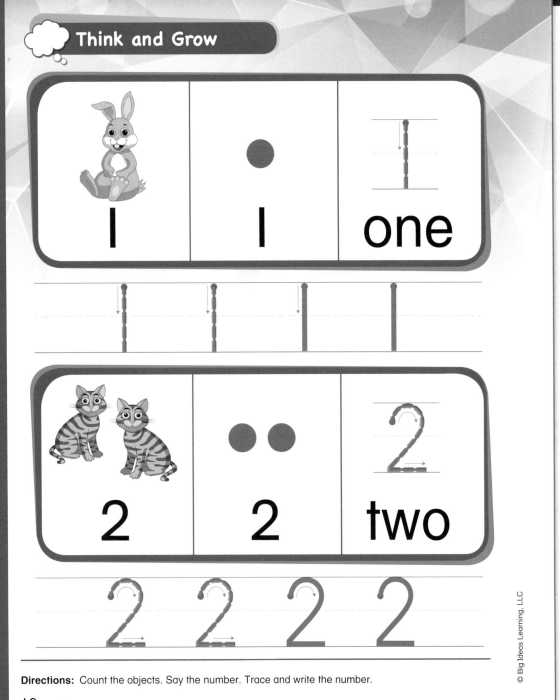

Directions: Count the objects. Say the number. Trace and write the number.

10   ten

Meeting the needs of
all learners.

Apply and Grow: Practice
MAKING INSTRUCTIONAL DECISIONS

Through exploration and practice, students make sense of
numbers and quantities. Students should now associate the
number word to the number symbol. The size of the quantity is
small so it is easy for students to distinguish between a group
of one and a group of two. As the quantity increases, this will
become more difficult.

Students are not thinking about sequencing at this stage,
meaning that the order of the numbers 1 and 2 is not part of their
understanding. What students do understand is that the numbers
1 and 2 name two different quantities and that two is more than
one. This is a result of answering questions posed to them such
as, "How many do you want?" or "How many do you have?"
Understanding a quantity of one or a quantity of two involves
subitizing, which means students can then recognize that a group
has one object or two objects without counting.

EMERGING students may have to use their fingers or count aloud
to know how many are in a group or collection. They may need
to use counters. When writing the numerals 1 or 2 they may need
guidance with their pencil to trace the numeral.

- Provide students with counters to cover and track each object as
  they count. Emphasize that the final word said when covering
  the last object is the written number.

PROFICIENT students can identify a group of one or two objects.
They are able to follow the verbal pathways in tracing the
numbers 1 and 2.

- Have students walk around the classroom, and identify objects
  to draw that have the numbers 1 and 2 on them. They could
  draw a clock, blocks, the calendar, a die, puzzles, books, or a
  hundred chart. Make sure students write the number.

Extensions: Adding Rigor

- Have students use two manipulatives to tell and act out a story
  that includes the words *one* and *two*. Have them share the story
  with a partner or the class.
- Make several copies of the subitizing cards and number cards
  for 1 and 2. Put them in a stack. Students draw a card, say the
  number and verbal pathway as they trace the number in the air,
  and find a group of one or two in the room.

Name _____

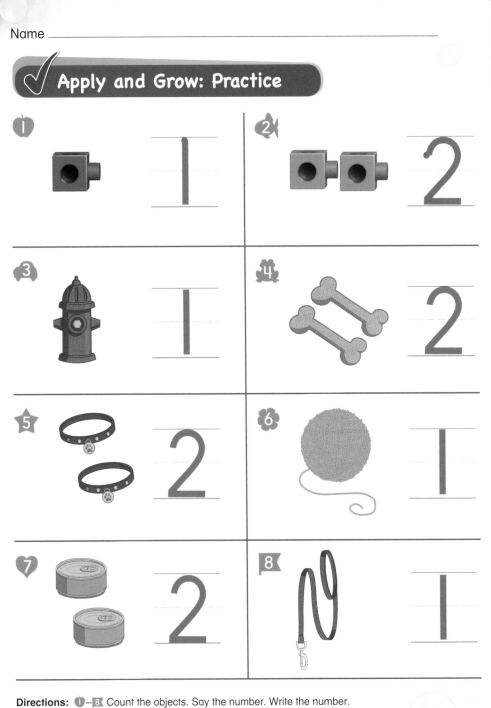

1 | 1

2 | 2

3 | 1

4 | 2

5 | 2

6 | 1

7 | 2

8 | 1

Directions: **1**–**8** Count the objects. Say the number. Write the number.

Chapter 1 | Lesson 2

eleven 11

Think and Grow: Modeling Real Life

⊙ You should have referenced the two success criteria at the beginning of the lesson, and during the lesson. Students should now be able to say what they have learned today. Their language may not be precise but their understanding of the concept should be clear.

> **Sample Student Language:** "I can tell when there are one or two things in the group. I can write 1 and 2."

? Show students the numbers 1 and 2 and ask, "What are these?" These are the numbers 1 and 2. Students are learning to write letters, so it is important for them to know that 1 and 2 are numbers.

- **Preview:** "What do you see on the page? Do you know what kind of store this is? Have you ever been to a store like this?" Students like to tell stories about their personal experiences.

- Students need to identify how many of each type of pet is shown. Observe students' progress. Who is counting aloud? Who can track with their eyes? Who is pointing with their finger?

- **Note:** If students are not yet ready to work through the exercises independently, complete the page as a class.

? "Look in the Pet Shop. Do you see any pets where there is only one of them? If so, talk about it with your neighbor." Say, "I see one lizard. Now find that pet below the Pet Shop and write the number 1." Ask if there are other groups of only one.

- Repeat for the pets in which there are groups of two. You may need to review and assist some students with writing the number 2.

? **Extension:** "Does the pet store have the same number of each animal?" No, there is 1 lizard and 2 each of the other animals.

- **Supporting Learners:** Students may have trouble focusing on one animal at a time. Have students cover the animal they are counting with counters. Students can then focus on just counting the counters.

Closure

- Prompt students to think about places other than school where they might see the numbers 1 or 2. You could suggest a billboard or a telephone as an example.

 1 2

 2  2

Directions: Count the objects in the picture. Say the number. Write the number.

12   twelve

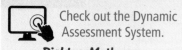
Connect and Extend Learning

Practice Notes

See page T-7 for general information about the Practice.

- Have students count the group of objects in each problem and say how many.
- **Exercises 1–9:** Prompt students to use the verbal pathways and to locate or draw the dot before writing any numbers.
- **Exercises 1–9:** Consider offering supports such as paper-made counters, pencil grips, or cover sheets.
- **Exercise 9:** Remind students not to count the snail and crab next to the writing lines and to look for those animals in the picture.

Cross-Curricular Connections

Language Arts

- *My Five Senses* by Aliki; Identify the number of body parts used during the introduction of each sense.
- Have students write the numbers along with their word form each time new numbers are introduced. This practice can be repeated throughout the year.
- Clap high frequency words having one and two syllables.

Science

- Have students count and write the numbers for living and non-living things.

Learning Target: Understand and write the numbers 1 and 2.

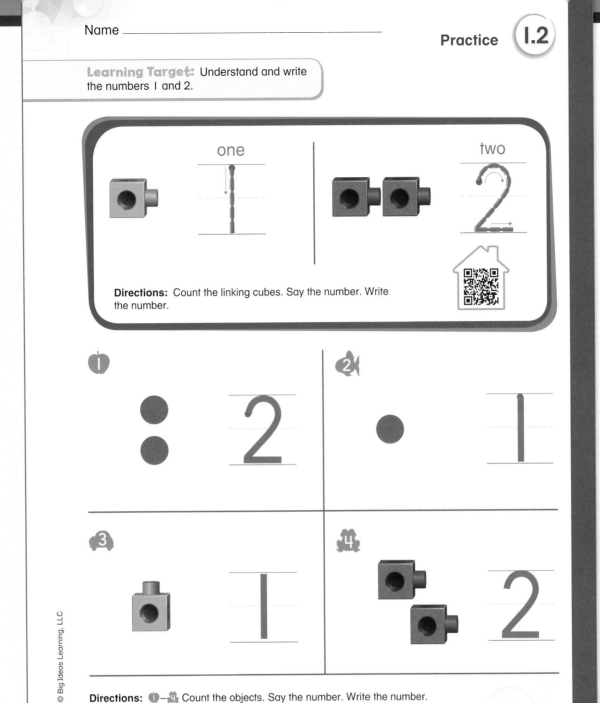

one

two

Directions: Count the linking cubes. Say the number. Write the number.

1 apple

2

2 fish

1

3 car

1

4 frog

2

Directions: **1**–**4** Count the objects. Say the number. Write the number.

Connect and Extend Learning

Extend Student Learning

Linguistic

- Create a classroom book called *Our Number Walk: 1 and 2.* Take a walk with students and have them look for objects that are found in groups of one or two. Have students draw the object or objects on a page with the corresponding numeral. Create a cover for the book. To assemble the book, gather the cover and the students' pages, punch holes at the spine, and tie them together with yarn. Read the book to the class and put the book in the reading center for students to read independently or with a partner.

Bodily-Kinesthetic

- Have students identify objects that are found in groups of one or two and have them air write the numbers. Whisper the verbal pathways as students write. Students may say things such as one office, one girls' and one boys' bathroom, one drinking fountain, one fire extinguisher, one flag, one clock, two doors, and two shelves.

Lesson Resources	
Surface Level	**Deep Level**
Resources by Chapter • Extra Practice • Reteach Differentiating the Lesson Skills Review Handbook Skills Trainer	Resources by Chapter • Enrichment and Extension Graphic Organizers Dynamic Assessment System • Lesson Practice

5 1

6 2

7 2

8 1

9

1   2

Directions: **5** – **8** Count the objects. Say the number. Write the number.
9 Count the objects in the picture. Say the number. Write the number.

14   fourteen

© Big Ideas Learning, LLC

1.3

Learning Target

Show and count the numbers 3 and 4.

Success Criteria

- Name the numbers 3 and 4.
- Count one object for each number to 4.
- Tell the number of objects in a group.

Warm-Up

Practice opportunities for the following are available in the Resources by Chapter or at *BigIdeasMath.com*.

- Daily skills
- Vocabulary
- Prerequisite skills

ELL Support

Explain that the word *for* sounds like *four*. Provide an example of each in a phrase or sentence. Remind students to listen carefully to everything being said in order to understand which word is being used.

Laurie's Notes

Preparing to Teach

Students continue to develop one-to-one correspondence and cardinality as they count groups of three and four objects. A five frame is introduced in this lesson to model 3 and 4. Draw attention to how the counters are placed in the frame using only one counter in each box. Given three counters, students may initially leave spaces between counters, though with repeated practice they will recognize that it is easier to see a quantity of three when they fill in the frame left to right with no gaps. Provide five frames for each student and when possible, use a large version for whole class instruction. The lesson is similar in design to the previous "Model and Count" lesson and the theme is children's toys.

Materials

- linking cubes
- rekenrek
- two-color counters

Dig In (Circle Time)

? Gather students to the circle in groups of 3 or 4. "As I tap your shoulder, move to the circle." Count aloud to 3 or 4 as you tap each shoulder. Pause between each group of students. "How many students moved to the circle?" 3, 4

◉ Introduce the learning target and success criteria. Students will model the numbers 3 and 4 in a variety of ways.

- Have students chorally count with you to 3. Count multiple times as you engage their different senses; clap, hold up fingers, tilt their heads, hop on one foot. Gradually lower your own voice so that the students' voices are heard.

- Play "One More Please." One partner has three linking cubes. He hands one cube to his partner and counts, "1." His partner says, "One more please." He hands a second cube to his partner and counts, "2." His partner says, "One more please." He hands a third cube to his partner and counts, "3." Have students reverse roles.

- Repeat choral counting (claps, fingers, tilting head, hopping) and the game for the number 4.

- Introduce the five frame, and model and count the numbers 3 and 4. You could also use a rekenrek.

? Teaching Prompt   ◉ Learning Target

Learning Target: Show and count the numbers 3 and 4.

Explore and Grow

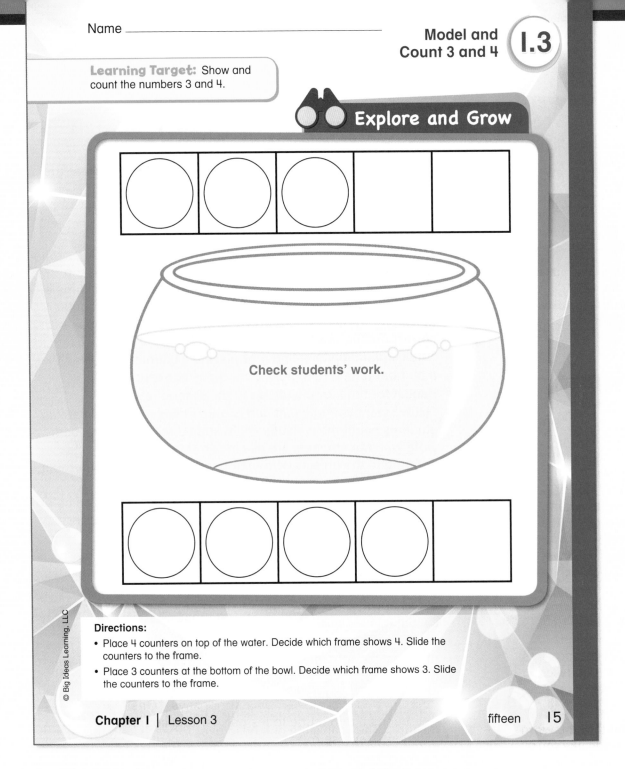

Check students' work.

Directions:
- Place 4 counters on top of the water. Decide which frame shows 4. Slide the counters to the frame.
- Place 3 counters at the bottom of the bowl. Decide which frame shows 3. Slide the counters to the frame.

© Big Ideas Learning, LLC

Explore and Grow

- Discuss with students things they think might sink or float in water. Make connections to playing in a bathtub or pool.
- ? Distribute the counters. "Pretend a yellow counter is one toy boat. Use your counters to show me four toy boats. Where will you put the boats?" float
- ? "Which frame shows 4? Slide your counters to that five frame."
- ? "Pretend a red counter is one rock. Use counters to show three rocks. Where will you put the rocks?" sink "Slide your counters to the five frame."
- **Turn and Talk:** "Use counters to tell your partner a story about three or four objects that float or sink."

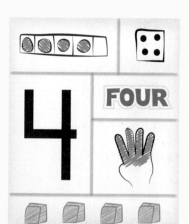

Laurie's Notes

Think and Grow

Getting Started

- Introduce the vocabulary cards for **three** and **four**. Discuss the anchor chart for each number.
- **?** Show the vocabulary card for **five frame**. "What did we call this model?" frame or five frame

Teaching Notes

- **Model:** Together as a class, count each pinwheel in the top row. Have students place a counter on a pinwheel each time a number is said in the counting sequence. Slide each counter to the five frame to count how many. Have students color each corresponding box.
- **Note:** Pointing with a finger or placing a counter each time that a number is said reinforces one-to-one correspondence.
- Repeat for the four pinwheels in the second row.
- "Now I want you to count each group of whistles." Circulate as students count the whistles and restate directions as needed. Note whether students are placing counters on the objects, pointing to the objects with their fingers, or saying the number word aloud as they track with their eyes.
- ⊙ Students can use counters to cover the objects and then color the boxes to show their understanding of the third success criterion, tell the number of objects in a group.
- **Big Idea:** Students see two different arrangements for the quantities 3 and 4. The pinwheels are in a line and the whistles are in an array. Students need to see quantities organized in different ways. Both are important arrangements to help build spatial relationships.
- **Common Error:** Students may recount objects or miss an object that they thought they counted because they lose track of where they started. Have students lay counters or cross out each object as they count.
- **Supporting Learners:** Students may benefit from using a rekenrek. They can slide one bead over for each item they count to reinforce the concept of one-to-one correspondence. Each time they slide a bead, they say another number.

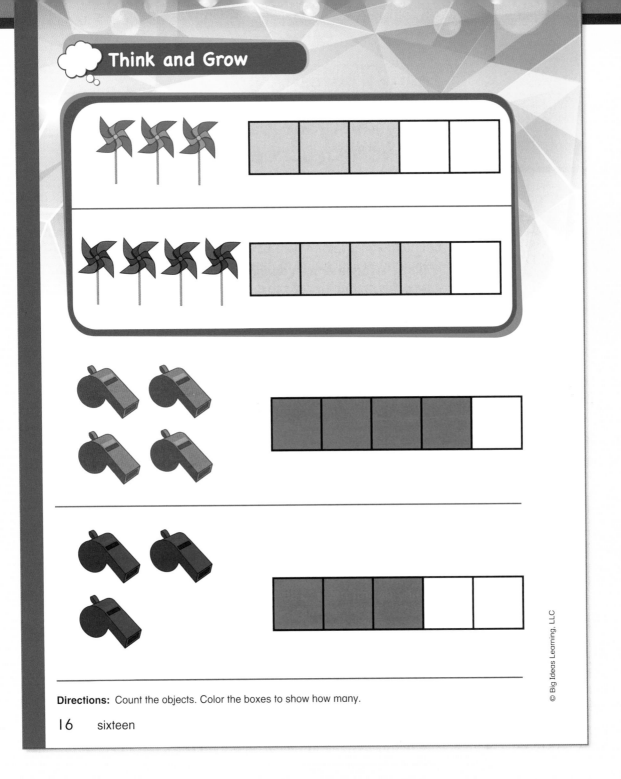

Directions: Count the objects. Color the boxes to show how many.

16   sixteen

Laurie's Notes

Apply and Grow: Practice

MAKING INSTRUCTIONAL DECISIONS

Cardinality is understanding that the last number word said when counting tells how many objects have been counted. Show students four counters and ask, "How many counters are there?" Observe and listen closely to their responses. Use the information below to assess what type of counter they are at this time. Use the descriptions as a guide to make instructional decisions.

EMERGING students not yet demonstrating cardinality may recount, hesitate, or not yet emphasize the last object counted. They will need more interaction and support with counting.

- **Emergent Counters** may have difficulty associating one number word with one object when counting. They may not use the correct number sequence.
- **Perceptual Counters** can count a collection of objects only when they are visible. They count the objects starting at 1.

PROFICIENT students can explain how they count and emphasize the last spoken number word. They realize that the number of objects in a group is not affected by their arrangement.

- **Figurative Counters** can count and visualize a collection of objects even when some objects are blocked from their view. They count the objects starting at 1 and imagine or visualize some objects.
- **Counting-on Counters** start from a given number other than 1. They do not need to see the objects to count.
- **Non-Count-by-Ones Counters** partition and combine the numbers that make up the quantity. For example, they may see four by recognizing that two and two combined is four.

Supporting Learners

❓ To assist students in moving on from a perceptual counter to a figurative counter, play a game in which you show three large cups on a table. Ask, "How many cups are there?" Show the students another large cup and then place the cup behind your back. Tell students to count all the cups you showed and see whether they include the one behind your back.

Extension: Adding Rigor

- Show students different amounts of dots (1 to 4) or other objects on paper. Have them count the objects. Take the paper away and have students close their eyes. Ask students, "How many objects were on the paper? Can you imagine the dots?" Go deeper by having them visualize three or four specific objects without showing the amount on paper. Use familiar objects such as crayons or balls.

Meeting the needs of all learners.

✓ Apply and Grow: Practice

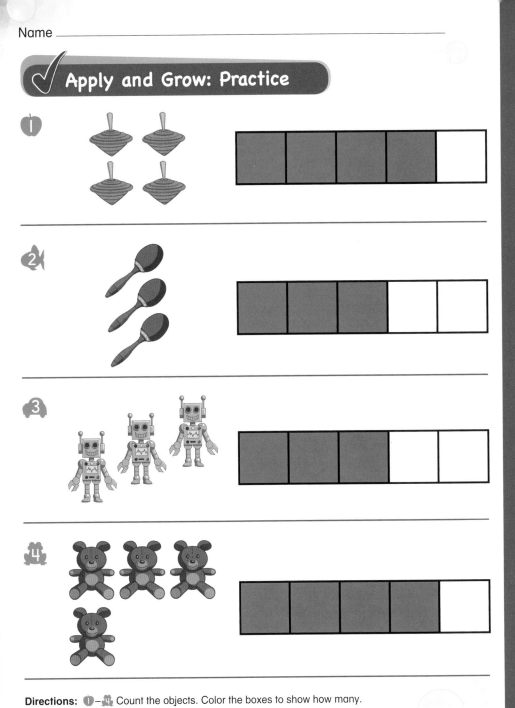

Directions: ❶–❹ Count the objects. Color the boxes to show how many.

Chapter 1 | Lesson 3   seventeen   17

Think and Grow: Modeling Real Life

This application helps students count to answer "how many" with the numbers 3 and 4.

⊙ Students heard the three success criteria at the beginning of the lesson and you have referenced the criteria throughout the lesson. Ask students to think about what they learned today and tell their neighbors. Again, their language may not be precise but their understanding of the concept should be clear.

Sample Student Language: "I can count to 3 (or 4). I can tell when there are three (or four) objects. I can make a group of three (or four)."

⊙ Have students use a thumbs up, sideways thumb, or thumbs down to signal their understanding of each success criterion. Explain again that you know they can be good counters and you will ask them often how they are doing with their learning. They can use their thumb signals to tell you.

• **Preview:** "What do you see on the shelves? Where have you seen toys on a shelf? What do you think is happening in the picture?"

? **Model with Mathematics:** "Think to yourself. How can you tell the number of balls and airplanes on the shelves?" Count to know how many. "How can you show the number?" counters, linking cubes, fingers, claps Make the connection to the learning target.

• **Common Error:** Students may count all of the toys and not sort their counting between the balls and airplanes. Remind students to only count the balls. Then count the airplanes.

? **Extension:** "How many toys are on the top shelf? on the bottom shelf?"

• **Supporting Learners:** Some students may have developed their conceptual subitizing skills. When answering the Extension question, students may see two balls and two airplanes and automatically know that there are four toys without counting. Continue to probe their understanding as students begin to develop an awareness of partner numbers.

Closure

• Prompt students to use objects, drawings, fingers, or actions to show the number 3 or 4 to a partner. Have the partner say the number.

Directions: Count the objects in the picture. Color the boxes to show how many.

18   eighteen

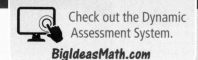

Connect and Extend Learning

Practice Notes

See page T-7 for general information about the Practice.

- To support students' understanding, find three or four objects in your classroom that are the same, and arrange them like the exercise. Count the objects together and then rearrange them. Have students count the objects again to emphasize that the count is the same.
- **Exercise 5:** Remind students not to count the train and maraca next to the five frames.

Cross-Curricular Connections

Language Arts

- *Pete the Cat and His Four Groovy Buttons* by Eric Litwin; Have students retell the story using a five frame to organize and sequence the events. Give each student a five frame. Cut out and decorate construction paper buttons to glue on the five frame each time Pete loses one.
- Show and say three or four letter words such as *and, the, can, this,* and *come.* Have students identify the number of letters in the word. Then have students repeat the word.
- Have the class clap and count the syllables in students' names.

Science

- Have students name and count the four seasons. Have them think of three or four things that relate to each season.

Learning Target: Show and count the numbers 3 and 4.

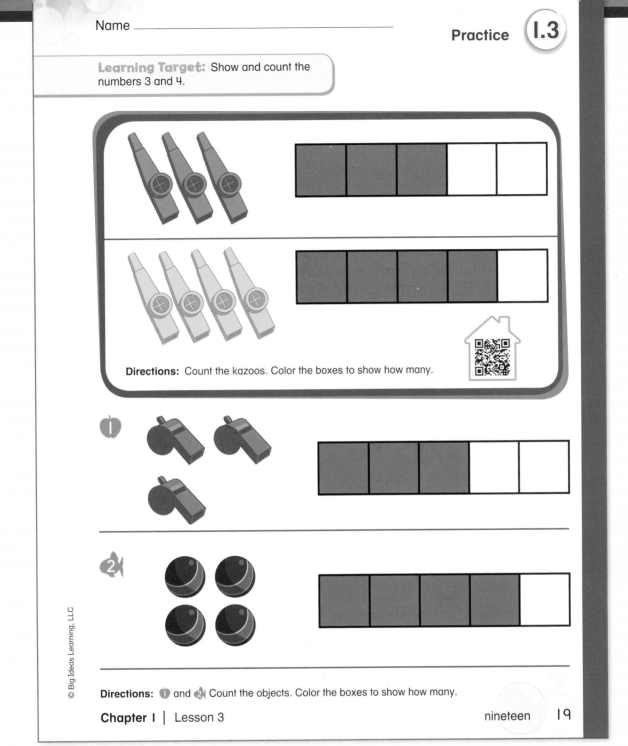

Directions: Count the kazoos. Color the boxes to show how many.

Directions: ① and ② Count the objects. Color the boxes to show how many.

Connect and Extend Learning

Extend Student Learning

Interpersonal

- Extend the lesson by having the class play a game in which students form groups of three or four depending on how many fingers you hold up.

  Reason Abstractly and Quantitatively: If there is a leftover group of students, ask, "How can you make this group have three or four students?" Put the teacher into that group; put students from another class into that group. This type of thinking is expanded upon in later lessons when students learn to add.

Lesson Resources	
Surface Level	**Deep Level**
Resources by Chapter • Extra Practice • Reteach Differentiating the Lesson Skills Review Handbook Skills Trainer	Resources by Chapter • Enrichment and Extension Graphic Organizers Dynamic Assessment System • Lesson Practice

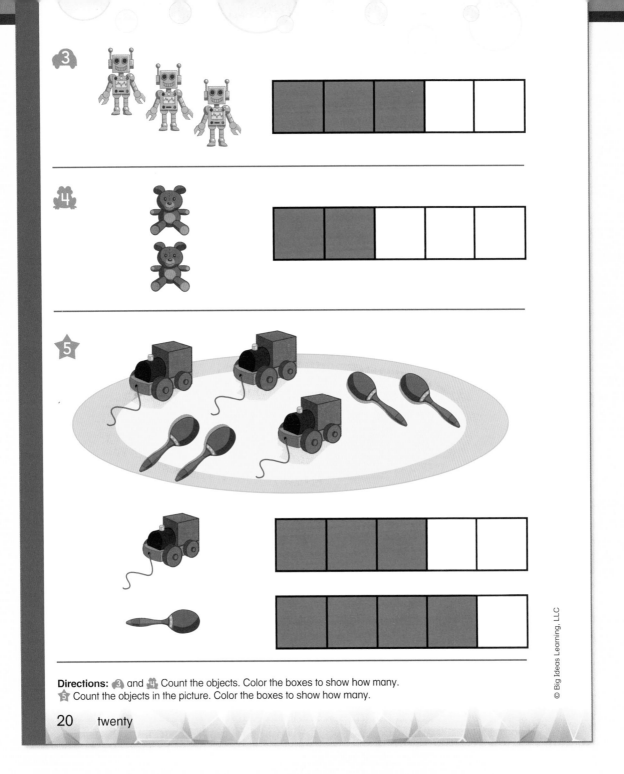

Directions: 3️⃣ and 4️⃣ Count the objects. Color the boxes to show how many.
5️⃣ Count the objects in the picture. Color the boxes to show how many.

© Big Ideas Learning, LLC

1.4

Laurie's Notes

Learning Target

Understand and write the numbers 3 and 4.

Success Criteria

- Identify groups of three and four objects.
- Write the numbers 3 and 4.

ELL Support

Preview the words *tree* and *bird* by pointing to each and stating its name. Explain to students that, as you read, they should listen carefully for the words *three* and *four,* and which things are named after each number. Say the words *three* and *tree* and have them repeat, enunciating the differences. Tell them to listen carefully, because these words sound similar.

Preparing to Teach

Students learn to write the numbers 3 and 4 by using the verbal pathways as they trace the numbers. When you show groups of three or four objects, be sure to think about how they are arranged. You want students to be familiar with objects arranged in a line and in an array. You will notice that some students still need to count to know a group has three or four objects. They do not yet recognize a collection of three or four. Throughout the lesson, look for opportunities to show sets of 3 and 4 patterned dots (counters or linking cubes).

The lesson is similar in design to the previous "Understand and Write" lesson, and the theme is camping.

Materials

- collections of objects to model three and four
- two-color counters
- *We Go Camping**
- Subitizing Cards 0–5*
- Number Cards 0–5*

**Found in the Instructional Resources*

Dig In (Circle Time)

Place groups of three (or four) objects in the center of the circle. Leave space between the groups.

- **?** Hold up a subitizing card for 3 (or 4) for students to see. "Look at my card. Count the dots. What number is this? Find a group of objects in the center that has the same amount. Tell your partner what you found." Repeat this several times with different subitizing cards.
- Now focus only on the cards and not the objects in the center. Show the subitizing card for a few seconds and then place it face down. Ask students to think about how the dots were arranged and what number they saw. Then have students share with their partners.
- The goal is to provide practice seeing different patterns or arrangements, and for students to recognize it as a quantity.
- Distribute the booklet *We Go Camping.* Have students share camping experiences that they have had. After reading the first page, have students count the birds.
- **?** "How many birds did the girl see?" Model how to write the number 3 using the verbal pathway, "pull around and in, around and stop." Have students repeat the verbal pathway as they trace the number 3 in the book and again in the air.
- Repeat this for the four trees using the verbal pathway, "pull down a little, across and stop, pull down."
- Students should return to their seats with their booklets.

? Teaching Prompt   ⊙ Learning Target

Learning Target: Understand and write the numbers 3 and 4.

Explore and Grow

Directions: Use counters to show how many trees and how many birds are in the story *We Go Camping*. Write how many trees and how many birds are in the story.

© Big Ideas Learning, LLC

Chapter 1 | Lesson 4

Explore and Grow

? "Let's use counters to show the number of birds that were in the story *We Go Camping*. Place your counters on the first tree. How many counters did you place on the tree? Write the number on the tree to the right."

• Repeat this process to show the number of trees the boy sees.

• **Note:** Review the verbal pathway for each number several times, as both numbers can be challenging to write.

• **Supporting Learners:** Hold up, or point to, three or four objects at a time. Have students identify the amount shown. Have students air write the number modeled using the verbal pathway.

Think and Grow

Getting Started

- Use the subitizing cards for 3 and 4, displaying 3 and then 4. Do students see a group of three plus one more when they view four?
- There is a group, a dot model, and a traceable numeral for each number 3 and 4 on this page.
- As you lead students through the exercises, remember that we want them to see the collection and know how many there are without counting. Some students may still need to count, placing their fingers on each object.

Teaching Notes

- **Model:** Have students use their index fingers to trace each number as they say the verbal pathway. After tracing the number several times they will write the number on their own.
- **Note:** Some students may not have the fine motor skills to form the number 3. Do they recognize the numeral? Can they use their fingers to trace the number in the air? Continue to provide support.
- **Turn and Talk:** "Tell your partners how you write the number 3. Tell them how to write the number 4."
- Circulate and ask students how they know there are three apples and four eggs. Are they counting? Do they see a group of three (or four)? Do they recognize the pattern of dots as being similar to what they see on dice? Do students understand that they can count the objects in any order, meaning that it doesn't matter which egg they start with? Are students able to tell the verbal pathway for writing each number?
- ⊙ Judge whether it is time for students to assess their proficiency with identifying groups of three or four objects, and in writing the numbers 3 and 4. Restate the learning target and review both success criteria. See sample language to use on page T-10.
- **Extension:** Have students make a model of the numbers 1 to 4 and write each numeral.
- **Supporting Learners:** Use a five frame to assist students having difficulty counting the objects. Have students place a counter on each object and then move the counters to a five frame as they count.
- **Supporting Learners:** Students can practice air writing the numbers, or you can use your finger to write the numbers in a student's palm.

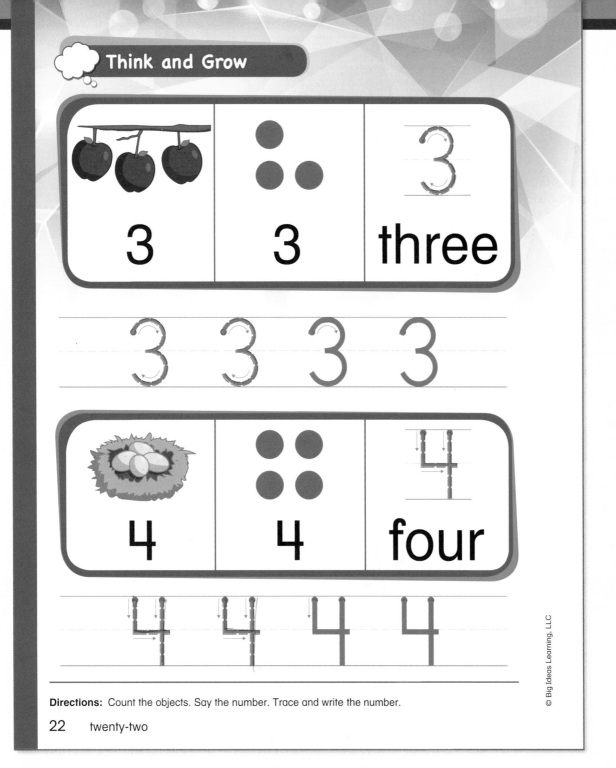

3

3

three

3 3 3 3

4

4

four

4 4 4 4

Directions: Count the objects. Say the number. Trace and write the number.

22   twenty-two

Meeting the needs of
all learners.

ELL Support

Teach the words *cube, butterfly, bookbag and backpack, cranberry,* and *acorn* by pointing to each and stating its name. Have students use vocabulary cards to check for understanding of the numbers 3 and 4. Ask, "How many cubes are there?" Have students hold up the appropriate card to indicate the answer. Repeat for the other objects.

Laurie's Notes

Apply and Grow: Practice
MAKING INSTRUCTIONAL DECISIONS

Students are now familiar with four numbers. They can count to 4, write the numbers 1 to 4, and identify how many are in a collection of 1 to 4. We need to remember that the way in which the objects are displayed, whether in a line, an array, or scattered does influence the students' ability to recognize the amount. Objects arranged in a line are easiest to count, though students are working towards recognizing quantities without counting. Now that we have three or four objects in an arrangement, recognizing quantity becomes more difficult.

Orientation is another aspect to consider when showing real-life objects. For instance, when you move three apples, the new orientation of the apples does not change the total number of objects. A big idea for students to understand is that orientation and arrangement do not affect quantity.

EMERGING students may need more practice with subitizing patterns if they do not recognize small groups without having to count the objects.

- These students can practice matching the number, subitizing, and dot cards.

PROFICIENT students can recognize common subitizing patterns. They are able to follow the verbal pathways in tracing the numbers 3 and 4.

Supporting Learners

- Provide linking cubes to cover the objects on the page as students count them.
- The reversal of numbers may occur when students are working too quickly. Prompt them to stop and fix the number.
- Consistent reversals may occur when writing the numbers. Provide hand-over-hand assistance, or write the number with a highlighter and have the student trace over it.

Extensions: Adding Rigor

- Support subitizing by providing each student with four counters and a piece of paper or whiteboard. Hold up commonly recognized dot patterns made for the numbers 3 and 4. Students must replicate the dot pattern shown and write the number. Display the dot patterns slowly at first and then move to a faster pace. Add in the dot cards for numbers 1 and 2 as a review. Add dot patterns as each new set of numbers is learned.
- Show patterns for the numbers 2 to 4 that involve two parts, or two colors. Conceptual subitizing is when students can see the two parts (2 blue and 2 red) and know the quantity is 4.

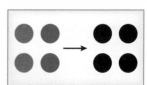

Name _____

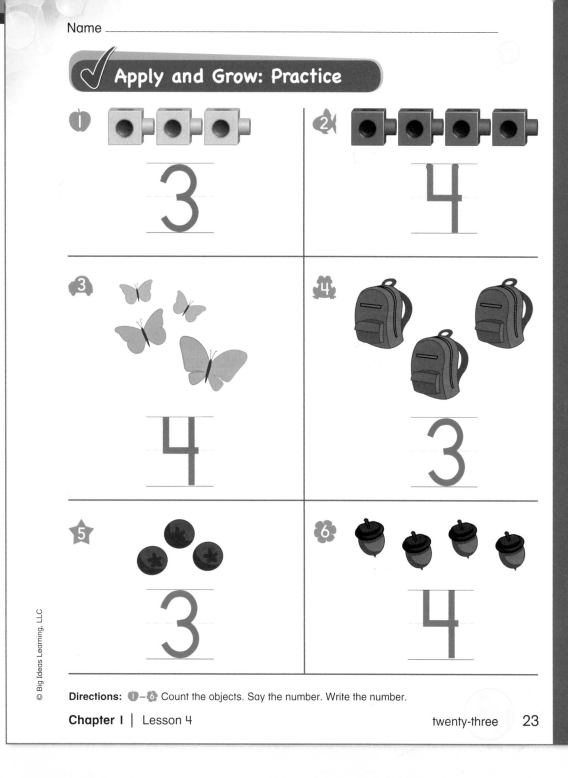

1. 3

2. 4

3. 4

4. 3

5. 3

6. 4

Directions: 1–6 Count the objects. Say the number. Write the number.

© Big Ideas Learning, LLC

Laurie's Notes

Think and Grow: Modeling Real Life

This application is cumulative. It helps students to identify groups of one to four objects, and to write the numbers 1 to 4.

- **Preview:** "What do you see on the page? What do you think is happening in the picture? Have you ever been camping? What do you do when you're camping?"

? Have students point to and count the logs. "How many logs are there?" Have students write the number 4 as they say the verbal pathway.

- **Supporting Learners:** Some students may still need to cross out the objects as they count.

- Repeat these steps for each object.

⊙ You want students to do a self-assessment. How proficient are they at recognizing, or identifying, a group of three or four objects and writing the numeral for it? To help them assess this, show a card with three dots for several seconds. "Tell me what number it was by using your finger to draw the number in the air" Observe students' drawings. "Now say aloud the name of the number you saw." Explain to students that if they knew it was the number 3, that would be a thumbs up. If they were not able to tell, or they thought it was a different number, have students show a thumbs down. Assure students they can all be a thumbs up with more time and practice. "I know you can all learn math!"

? **Extension:** Ask comparison questions. "Are there more tents or lanterns?" Alternately, ask whether there is a lantern for each tent.

Closure

- **Turn and Talk:** Have students present one to four counters for their partners to count. The other partners will identify and record the numbers on their whiteboard.

 4

 3

 1

 2

Directions: Count the objects in the picture. Say the number. Write the number.

24   twenty-four

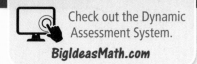

Connect and Extend Learning

Practice Notes

See page T-7 for general information about the Practice.

- **Exercises 1 and 2:** Have a dot to indicate where to start writing the number. Exercises 3 and 4 do not.
- **Exercise 9:** Preview the exercise using the following questions. "What do you see in the picture? What time is it? How do you know?"

Cross-Curricular Connections

Language Arts

- *Three Little Firefighters* by Stuart J. Murphy; Count the number of firefighters in the story. Count the number of ways they sort the mixed up buttons. Practice sorting into categories including size, shape, and color.

Social Studies

- When discussing family units or communities, count the number of people or pets in a family or the number of buildings, houses, or stores in a community.

Name _____

Learning Target: Understand and write the numbers 3 and 4.

three

3

four

4

Directions: Count the linking cubes. Say the number. Write the number.

 4

 3

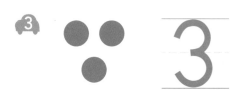 3

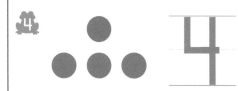 4

Directions: ❶–❹ Count the dots. Say the number. Write the number.

Chapter 1 | Lesson 4

twenty-five 25

Connect and Extend Learning

Extend Student Learning

Logical-Mathematical

- When lining students up at the door, dismiss them from their seats by the colors that they are wearing, by their table or group name, or by the first letter of their name. Choose characteristics that will make groups of three or four students. Ask each group to stand in front of you and count the number of people in that group. Have them air write the number with their fingers, and then get in the line. Repeat for the remaining groups of students.

Linguistic

- Write a new page in the story *We Go Camping.* Ask students what other things they could see when they go camping. Draw the characters and the three or four items they would see.
- Create a second classroom book called *Our Number Walk: 3 and 4* to go along with the book made for the numbers 1 and 2 in Lesson 1.2.

Lesson Resources	
Surface Level	**Deep Level**
Resources by Chapter • Extra Practice • Reteach Differentiating the Lesson Skills Review Handbook Skills Trainer	Resources by Chapter • Enrichment and Extension Graphic Organizers Dynamic Assessment System • Lesson Practice

5 3

6 4

7 4

8 2

9

4   3   1

Directions: **5** – **8** Count the objects. Say the number. Write the number.
9 Count the objects in the picture. Say the number. Write the number.

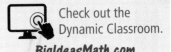
1.5

Learning Target

Show and count the
number 5.

Success Criteria

- Name the number 5.
- Count one object for
  each number to 5.
- Tell the number of
  objects in a group.

Warm-Up

Practice opportunities
for the following
are available in the
Resources by Chapter
or at *BigIdeasMath.com.*

- Daily skills
- Vocabulary
- Prerequisite skills

ELL Support

Have students practice
pronouncing the word
five by repeating
after you. Review the
numbers *one* through
four using the same
method. Then count
aloud as you extend
each finger of one
hand. Have students
do the same.

Laurie's Notes

Preparing to Teach

Five and ten are two key benchmark numbers in kindergarten.
They are very important in developing number concepts and
operations. In this lesson, students model and count the number
five. Students need to be able to show and count the number 5
to build the necessary background knowledge for composing and
decomposing numbers. Students observe that there are no empty
spaces on the five frame, and all of their fingers on one hand are
used to show five! This lesson is similar in design to the previous
"Model and Count" lesson and the theme is having a picnic.

Materials

- linking cubes
- rekenrek
- two-color counters

Dig In (Circle Time)

Introduce the number 5 without using words. You might play five
consecutive notes on an instrument, tap a pencil on a desk five
times, or clap your hands rhythmically for five beats. You want
students to hear one more beat after four. Many will know the
name of the number that follows four even when they have not
made sense of the quantity five.

- **?** Have students count to 5 with you as they clap for each count.
  "What are you doing when you say 1, 2, 3, 4, 5?"
- Model counting to 5 using your fingers. Have students count
  to 5 while they show the corresponding fingers. Model 5 using
  linking cubes. Have a student point to each cube as the class
  counts aloud. You could also show 5 on a rekenrek.
- Count other objects or collections in the room that are grouped
  as a quantity of five, such as weekdays on the calendar, points
  on a star, or hooks on a coat rack.
- **⊙** "You have counted to 5. How are you doing with your learning?
  Tell your partner."

? Teaching Prompt   **⊙** Learning Target

Learning Target: Show and count the number 5.

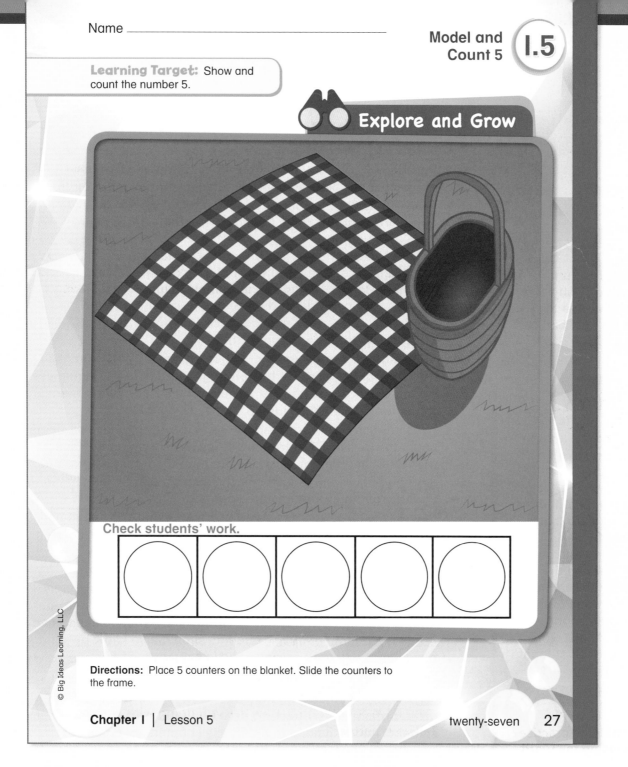

Explore and Grow

Check students' work.

Directions: Place 5 counters on the blanket. Slide the counters to the frame.

Explore and Grow

- Distribute counters. Say, "I went on a picnic to the park. I set out five plates on the blanket. Use counters to show the plates on the blanket."
- "Use counters to tell your partner a story about five things you take on a picnic." Solicit stories from several students as they use their counters to show the stories.
- Have students choral count as they move each counter onto the frame.
- "Use a whisper voice to count the number in the frame. Now, use your fingers to show the same number." Ask questions to assess the students' understanding that the five frame is full and that they use all of the fingers on one hand to count to 5.

Think and Grow

Getting Started

- Introduce the vocabulary card for **five**. Show the five frame model and consider adding this to an anchor chart for 5.
- **Probe:** "How many counters are in the five frame? How are they arranged? Can you show five fingers? What comes after 4 when counting?"

Teaching Notes

- **Model:** Count the flying discs. Students can place a linking cube as they count each disc. Slide the counters to the five frame. Use a very excited voice to confirm students' observation that the frame is full.
- Some students may not want to use the linking cubes. Instead they may prefer to count by pointing. Whether the students use linking cubes or not, they must color one section of the five frame for each object counted.
- **Reason Abstractly and Quantitatively:** Be sure to have students count the flies and watermelon slices more than once. Have them start at different locations. Remind them that neither the arrangement of the objects nor the starting place changes the quantity of the group they are counting.
- ◉ Review the three success criteria with students. They have had time to explore and demonstrate their proficiency with naming and counting 5, and telling how many.
- **Big Idea:** Students are seeing three arrangements for the quantity of five. They are also filling the five frame completely. You want your students to be very familiar with this visual image. You want them to automatically know that a filled in five frame is a quantity of five. Students should also know by sight that all of the fingers on one hand is a quantity of five.
- ? **Extension:** "How many seeds are on each watermelon slice?" 5
- **Supporting Learners:** Some students may now be able to count groups of objects by tracking each object with their eyes. Other students may still need to point, use counters, or cross out objects to count. Allow students to show their understanding in different ways as you guide them to the next counting phase.
- **Supporting Learners:** Use a rekenerek to support students' understanding of the benchmark of five by moving five beads of the same color.

ELL Support

Teach the words *flying disc, fly,* and *watermelon slice* by pointing to each and stating its name. Have students repeat the words. Explain that the word fly describes both a thing and an action. Remind them that when describing more than one of these objects, the sound at the end of each word changes. Have students practice language by stating the answer to each example.

Beginner students may count aloud, "one, two, three, four, five" as they point to the objects.

Intermediate students may answer "five" and name the objects being counted.

Advanced students may use a complete sentence, such as, "There are five flying discs."

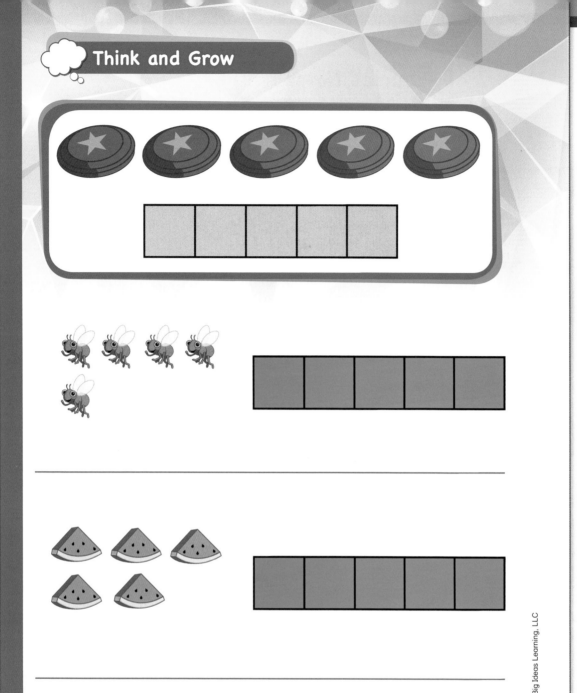

Directions: Count the objects. Color the boxes to show how many.

MATH MUSICALS

You can use the song
Fish Crackers
as students learn to count to 10!

Fish Crackers

Laurie's Notes

Apply and Grow: Practice

MAKING INSTRUCTIONAL DECISIONS

Students have developed an understanding of 5 through visual models, sounds, fingers, and drawings. A firm understanding of the quantity five is necessary in order to develop addition and subtraction fluency within 5. Some students easily see and count five, while others still need additional time and practice. Through observation and listening, you will determine the appropriate support and instruction to help students move from one counting phase to the next. Refer to page T-17 for a description of each type of counter to assist you in making instructional decisions.

EMERGING students may not consistently demonstrate cardinality or may not remember that the last number in the counting sequence tells how many. They may still be reciting the number words. They need more interaction and support with counting.

- Assist emerging students by counting aloud to 5 while holding up the corresponding fingers. Show a number, 1 through 5, using your fingers and ask the students how many are being shown.
- Use the subitizing and dot cards as flash cards. Have students practice identifying the number with a partner.

PROFICIENT students do not hesitate when counting and are more confident when telling how many objects are in a group. They understand that the number of objects in a group is not affected by their arrangement or orientation. They may emphasize the last number word said.

? To assist a figurative counter in becoming a counting-on counter, give the student five counters that he or she can line up on the desk. Have the student take two counters and push them under his or her left hand. Ask, "How many counters are under your left hand?" Then point to the counters on the table and model counting by saying, "Let us count on by saying three, four, five." Continue to practice using different starting points.

Extension: Adding Rigor

- Use masking tape to outline five squares on the floor. Have students work with partners. One student holds up one to five fingers on one hand. The other student hops that number of squares. Students take turns showing a number and hopping.

Meeting the needs of all learners.

ELL Support

Check for understanding of Lesson 1.5 by asking the following questions and having students answer silently with a thumbs up for *yes* and a thumbs down for *no*. Teach the words *dragonfly* and *nets* by pointing to each and stating its name before doing this check.

1. Are there four butterflies? Are there five butterflies?
2. Are there four dragonflies? Are there five dragonflies?
3. Are there four nets? Are there five nets?

Name _____

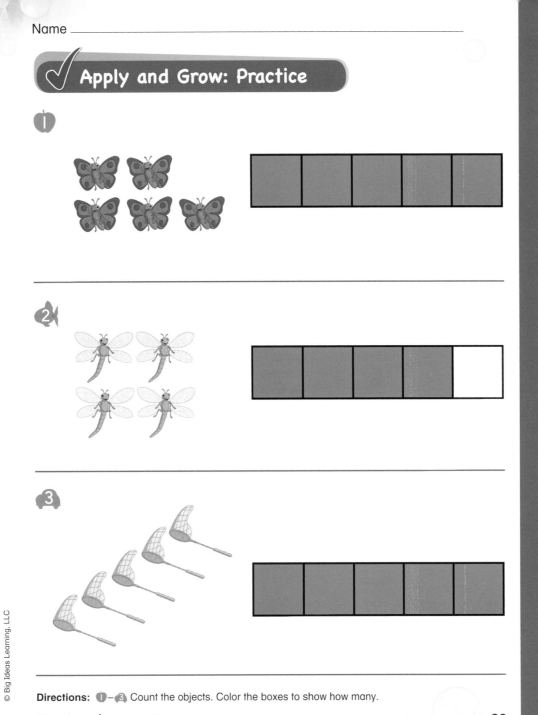

1

2

3

Directions: **1**–**3** Count the objects. Color the boxes to show how many.

© Big Ideas Learning, LLC

Laurie's Notes

Think and Grow: Modeling Real Life

This application helps students count to answer "how many" questions with numbers up to 5.

◉ Students should now be more familiar with discussing the learning targets and success criteria. Establish a daily routine in which students describe the learning target and tell what they've learned. You may hear students say they are confused, or fuzzy about how to count to 5. Listen closely to their discussions because students can often identify what is clear and what is not clear. When you are able to understand this, you are better able to support their learning. Students need to be clear about what they need to learn and when they have been succesful in their learning. Have students use their thumb signals to show where they are in their learning.

❓ **Preview:** "What do you think is happening in the picture? This picnic is different than the last one we saw because it is at a picnic table. What kinds of food are being eaten at this picnic?"

❓ "Think to yourself. How can you find the number of plates and forks on the picnic table? How can you show the number?" Solicit answers and connect students' ideas to the learning target.

❓ **Make Sense of Problems and Persevere in Solving Them:** The apples and sandwiches may distract students as they count the number of plates. Because the plates don't have identical food items, students may question whether they can be counted together. Ask, "When you count the students at your table, does the clothing they are wearing matter?" Remind students to focus only on the items that they are being asked to count.

❓ "Without counting them, how many forks do you think there are? How does what you know about the picture help you predict the number of forks?" I counted five plates and each plate has a fork next to it.

• **FYI:** The orientation of the forks on the top row is different. The aerial view shows people sitting on different sides of the table.

❓ **Extension:** "Close your eyes and picture an orange on each plate. How many oranges do you see? Use your pencil or crayon to draw an orange on each plate. Is the number of oranges the same as the number you pictured?"

• **Extension:** Have students count the number of apples, and then the number of sandwiches.

Closure

• Prompt students to use objects, drawings, fingers, or actions to show their partners a number from 1 to 5. Their partners say the number. Alternate turns.

 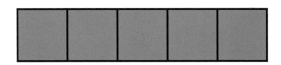

Directions: Count the objects in the picture. Color the boxes to show how many.

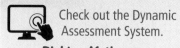
Connect and Extend Learning

Practice Notes

See page T-7 for general information about the Practice.

- **Exercises 1–3:** Be sure students are not counting the green number icons (apple, fish, and car), only the objects.
- **Exercise 4:** Ask if there are the same number of bubbles as jars.

Cross-Curricular Connections

Language Arts

- *Who Sank the Boat?* by Pamela Allen; Count the animal characters including the cow, donkey, sheep, pig, and tiny mouse. Have students retell the story including the details of who, what, where, and when. Have them explain why the lightest animal made the boat sink.
- Have students count the words in sentences containing five words or less.

Science

- Discuss the five food groups. Have students try to name and count five different kinds of food for each group.

Fruits	Veggies	Dairy	Protein	Grains

Practice **1.5**

Learning Target: Show and count the number 5.

Directions: Count the pieces of chalk. Color the boxes to show how many.

1

2

Directions: **1** and **2** Count the objects. Color the boxes to show how many.

Chapter 1 | Lesson 5

Connect and Extend Learning

Extend Student Learning
Musical

- Have a small group of students sit in a circle. Give each student four cubes of the same color. Students can count the cubes and lay them in a pile in front of them. Add a different-colored cube to the group. Tell students to pass it around the circle as you clap. When you say "stop and count" have students stop passing the cube and count their piles. The student holding the different-colored cube in his or her hand is able to include it in the count.

? Reason Abstractly and Quantitatively: Ask, "How many cubes do you have now? Did the number change? Why or why not?" The number of cubes stayed the same because I did not get the different-colored cube; the number of cubes changed because I have one more cube in my pile.

- Have students make up a song about counting the numbers 1 to 5. If students need additional guidance, relate the task to *Five Little Monkeys Jumping on the Bed* or *1, 2, Buckle My Shoe.* They can use the Newton or Descartes puppet to act out the song.

Lesson Resources	
Surface Level	**Deep Level**
Resources by Chapter • Extra Practice • Reteach Differentiating the Lesson Skills Review Handbook Skills Trainer Math Musicals	Resources by Chapter • Enrichment and Extension Graphic Organizers Math Musicals Dynamic Assessment System • Lesson Practice

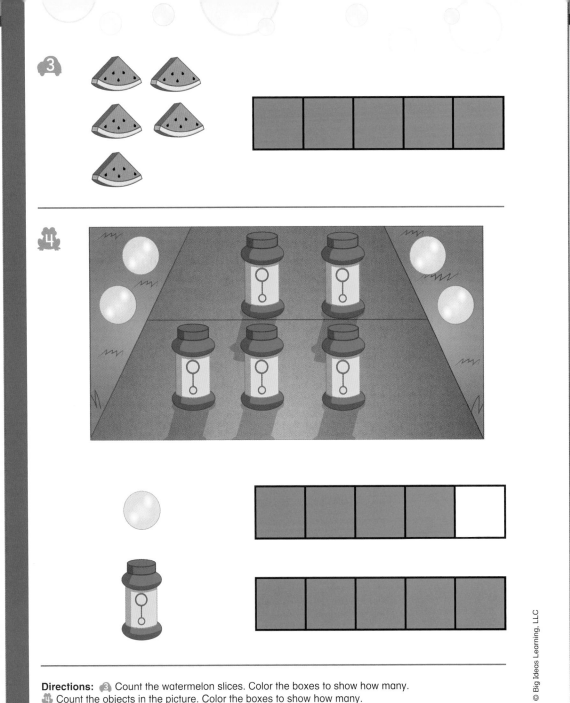

Directions: ③ Count the watermelon slices. Color the boxes to show how many.
④ Count the objects in the picture. Color the boxes to show how many.

1.6

Laurie's Notes

Learning Target

Understand and write
the number 5.

Success Criteria

• Identify a group of
  five objects.
• Write the number 5.

Warm-Up

Practice opportunities
for the following
are available in the
Resources by Chapter or
at *BigIdeasMath.com.*

• Daily skills
• Vocabulary
• Prerequisite skills

ELL Support

Preview the words
turtle and *pond* by
pointing to each and
stating its name.
Explain to students
that, as you read, they
should listen carefully
for the word *five* and
decide which objects
are named after the
number 5.

Preparing to Teach

In this lesson, the focus is on understanding a quantity of five,
so it is important to have many visual models of five available.
Students also write the number 5 using a verbal pathway, so
look for places in the classroom where the number is written.
Allow and encourage students to use their fingers to count and
show five. This lesson also reviews and displays the numbers
1 through 4 in different arrangements to help build students'
exposure to subitizing.

The lesson is similar in design to the previous "Understand and
Write" lessons and the theme focuses on a pond.

Materials

• Five Frame Cards 0–5*
• Dot Cards 0–5 Set 1*
• Subitizing Cards 0–5*
• Number Cards 0–5*
• *At the Pond*
• two-color counters

**Found in the Instructional Resources*

Dig In (Circle Time)

• Discuss three familiar dot arrangements
  for 5: a full five frame, an array, and a
  die model.

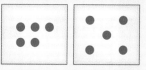

? "What do you see when you look at
  the five frame?" five dots; no empty
  spaces; It is more than 4. There are
  no wrong answers. You want to hear
  what they see, which often leads to
  what they are thinking.

• "Tell your partner what you see in this model." Hold the array.
  Listen for 3 dots and 2 dots, or 4 dots and 1 dot. Students are
  saying partner numbers for 5.

? "What does the die model look like?" an x or cross; two eyes,
  a nose, and a mouth; a box with one in the middle Again, there
  are no wrong answers.

• Distribute the booklet *At the Pond.* As you read each page, say
  "We have 5 [name an item]." Then describe how to write the
  number 5 using the verbal pathway, "pull down a little, around
  and stop, pull across." Students trace the number 5 in the book
  and write it in the air.

• Students should return to their seats with their booklets.

? Teaching Prompt   ⊙ Learning Target

Name _____

Learning Target: Understand and write the number 5.

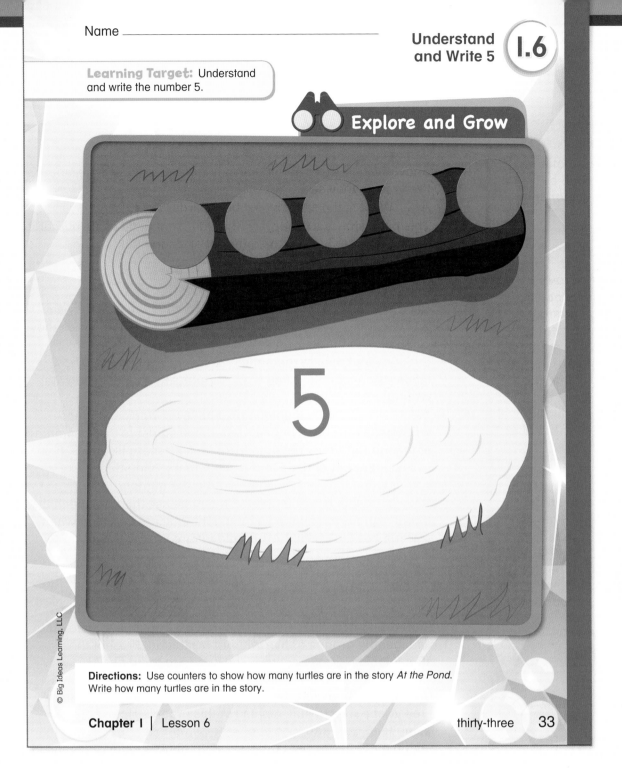

Explore and Grow

Directions: Use counters to show how many turtles are in the story *At the Pond*. Write how many turtles are in the story.

© Big Ideas Learning, LLC

Explore and Grow

? Refer to *At the Pond*. Ask, "How many turtles are on the log? Use your counters to show the number of turtles on the log." Monitor students' understanding. Have students explore how to write the number 5 by practicing in the pond.

• Students may wish to share personal experiences similar to the story.

• Hold up, or point to, five objects. Have students identify the amount shown and air write the number being modeled using the verbal pathway.

Chapter 1 | Lesson 6   **33**

ELL Support

Say the name of each object pictured as you point, *"flamingo, goose, lily pad."* Explain that when you describe more than one goose, you use the word *geese.* Have students practice language in groups of three. One student asks another, "How many geese are there?" Then have them rotate roles for the next example. Each student should ask a question and give an answer once.

Beginner students may only answer "five."
Intermediate students may answer "five" and name the objects being counted.
Advanced students may answer using complete sentences, such as, "There are five flamingos."

Think and Grow

Getting Started

- Show the subitizing card and number card for 5 and talk about the models they see.
- **?** Ask, "What is the same about both cards?" both show 5
- This page shows a group, a dot model, and a traceable numeral for the number 5. Note the different arrangements of the flamingos, geese, and lilypads.

Teaching Notes

- Have students use their index finger to trace the 5 as they say the verbal pathway. After tracing the number several times they will write the number on their own.
- Circulate and restate the directions as needed. Observe how students are counting and what supports they may need with writing 5.
- **Teaching Tip:** Some students may have previous experience writing the number 5 in one motion. Tell students that beginning at the top right may result in the 5 looking more like an *S*. Point to the upper left of the 5 and explain that it should look like a corner when they are finished writing the number.
- ◉ When students have completed the page ask them to use their thumb signals to show how confident they are in telling when a group has 5 objects. How confident are they with writing the number 5?
- **Extension:** Cover a portion of the group. Can students tell how many are under your hand? Cover 3 geese so that only 2 are visible. Students tell how many geese are under your hand.
- **?** **Supporting Learners:** Some students may be able to write 5 and identify groups of five without hesitation. Present these students with three counters and ask, "Are there five? How can you make it five?" Have students answer using counters. Continue this process using different starting numbers each time. Make sure to stay within five.
- **Supporting Learners:** Provide counters and a copy of the Five Frames Instructional Resource for students having difficulty counting the quantity of five in different arrangements.

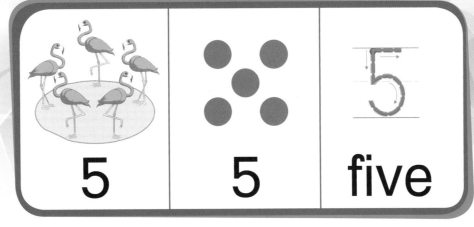

Directions:
- Count the objects. Say the number. Trace and write the number.
- Count the objects. Say the number. Write the number.

34   thirty-four

Meeting the needs of all learners.

ELL Support

Remind students that they already learned the word *cube.* Preview the words *cattails, snails,* and *raindrops* by pointing to each and stating its name. Check for understanding of the number five by asking about the objects in Exercises 1–4. "How many cubes are there?" Explain to students that they should hold up the number of fingers that match the number of objects you ask about.

Laurie's Notes

Apply and Grow: Practice

MAKING INSTRUCTIONAL DECISIONS

It is reasonable for students to have more difficulty with counting as the number of objects increases. In this lesson, students also learned to count objects in various arrangements which also takes more practice. Linear, circular, arrays, and scattered are all important arrangements for students to recognize. When the arrangement is scattered, or random, be sure that the objects are not too far apart. Help students develop a tracking system so they count each object only once.

EMERGING students may count the objects without using a system for tracking. This can cause rows or columns to be repeated as students count objects in an array. It also leads to students counting scattered objects in an illogical fashion, leaving out objects, or counting some objects more than once. Having no tracking system can also make it difficult to identify their starting point when counting circular arrangements.

PROFICIENT students develop some type of system for tracking. They count objects in rows and columns in a logical progression without repeating a count. They stop counting before the object they started with in circular arrangements. They follow a single logical path through all objects in a scattered arrangement.

Supporting Learners

- Reinforce writing the previously learned numbers by providing baggies filled with shaving cream, hair gel, or paint. Students push down gently on the outside of the bag with their finger to write the numbers and then swipe their hand across the bag to clear the writing. This helps create muscle memory while reciting each verbal pathway.
- The verbal pathway for the number may need to be chorally said. Ask, "What words do we say to write 5?"
- Encourage students to work from left to right and top to bottom when counting a group of objects. Demonstrate how they might cross out objects as they are counted.

Extension: Adding Rigor

- Have students take turns arranging objects in different configurations. Have partners count and write the numbers.

Name _____

1

5

2

5

3

3

4

5

Directions: **1**–**4** Count the objects. Say the number. Write the number.

Chapter 1 | Lesson 6   thirty-five   35

Laurie's Notes

Think and Grow: Modeling Real Life

This application helps students count and write the numbers 1 through 5.

- **Preview:** Explain that ponds are home to many animals and insects. Discuss activities that can take place at a pond such as swimming, fishing, boating, and skipping rocks.
- ⊙ Take time to talk with students about what they have learned regarding the numbers 1 through 5. Can they count a group of objects and tell how many? Can they draw a picture or use manipulatives to show a number? Can they write each number? Students with little prior experience may be feeling a bit overwhelmed or confused at this time. Assure all students that they will continue to work with and practice these numbers.
- You may want to wait until students have completed this page before you ask them to judge their proficiency considering many of the numbers are reviewed.
- "There are many objects in the picture. Talk with your partner about how you will count each object." You want students to have a strategy for locating and keeping track of which objects have been counted. Solicit ideas from students.
- **Look for and Make Use of Structure:** If possible, display the picture using a document camera. Ask volunteers to share their strategies for counting. Compare the different approaches. Remind students that the quantity stays the same regardless of the order in which the objects were counted.
- Ask to see whether students found it easier to count the ducklings because they are in a straight row.
- ⊙ When students have completed the page ask them to use their thumb signals to judge their understanding of the success criteria. "Are you comfortable telling how many are in a group by counting or sight, making a group of five, and writing the number 5?" You could ask additional questions about the numbers 1 through 4.
- **? Extension:** "How many ladybugs are there? Is there another group of five?" Yes, there are five ducks.
- **Extension:** Prompt students who have mastered identifying and writing the number of animals in the scene to draw additional animals so that there are five of each in the picture.

Closure

- Call four students up to the front of the room. Have the class identify the number of students standing there. "How can we make this five students?" After students decide to have one more student join the group, recount the students. Continue this process using different starting numbers.

 3

 5

 5

 2

Directions: Count the objects in the picture. Say the number. Write the number.

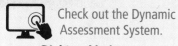
Connect and Extend Learning

Practice Notes

See page T-7 for general information about the Practice.

- **Exercises 1–6:** Note that there are different arrangements. How do students count each type? Are they starting to subitize small quantities?
- **Exercise 7:** Note that the lily pads are different sizes.

Cross-Curricular Connections

Language Arts

- *Room On The Broom* by Julia Donaldson; Count the characters each time one joins the broom.

Social Studies

- As you discuss communities and good citizenship, have students identify five things that they could do to help the people around them.

Name _____

Learning Target: Understand and write the number 5.

five

Directions: Count the linking cubes. Say the number. Write the number.

①

5

②

5

③

3

④

5

Directions: ①–④ Count the dots. Say the number. Write the number.

Connect and Extend Learning

Extend Student Learning

Linguistic

- Create a third classroom book called *Our Number Walk: 5.* Add this book to the collection of number books already created in Lessons 1.2 and 1.4.

Logical-Mathematical

- Make sets of *Subitizing Spoons* for students to match.

Lesson Resources	
Surface Level	**Deep Level**
Resources by Chapter • Extra Practice • Reteach Differentiating the Lesson Skills Review Handbook Skills Trainer	Resources by Chapter • Enrichment and Extension Graphic Organizers Dynamic Assessment System • Lesson Practice

5 5

6 4

7

🐟 5   🪷 4   🗿 2

Directions: **5** and **6** Count the objects. Say the number. Write the number.
7 Count the objects in the picture. Say the number. Write the number.

38   thirty-eight

1.7

Laurie's Notes

Learning Target

Understand, name, and write the number 0.

Success Criteria

- Name the number 0.
- Explain that 0 means having no objects.
- Identify a group of zero objects.
- Write the number 0.

Warm-Up

Practice opportunities for the following are available in the Resources by Chapter or at *BigIdeasMath.com.*

- Daily skills
- Vocabulary
- Prerequisite skills

ELL Support

Explain that there are many ways to describe zero. When someone says one of these sentences, you know they mean *zero.*

- There are no toys.
- There are none.
- There aren't any.

Preparing to Teach

Understanding the quantity of zero can be confusing for students. It may not make sense to them that there is a number to represent nothing. Students may wonder how you can count when there is nothing to count. You need to build this concept intentionally through models. An empty dot card or empty five frame can help students associate the number 0 to having nothing. Fingers can also be used, particularly, if you represent numbers in reverse order, 5, 4, 3, 2, 1, 0. Guide students to understand that zero is the number we write to show none of something. This means there are no objects to count.

Materials

- Dot Cards 0–5 Sets 1–3*
- *My Toys**
- two-color counters
- linking cubes

Found in the Instructional Resources

Dig In (Circle Time)

Use the dot card models to display numbers 1 through 5. Flash the card. Have students guess the number they saw. After a few rounds, insert the 0 card so it is displayed. Many students will say, "There isn't anything" or, "There are no dots."

? "What can we call it when we have nothing?" At least one student in the class will know the number name zero. Have them explain what it means.

? Discuss examples of the quantity zero: how many giraffes are in the room; how many pencils are in your empty hand; how many students can jump to the ceiling; how many purple noses are in the room. Say, "Zero is what we say and write to show none, meaning there are no objects to count."

- Call out random numbers, 1 to 5, and have students show them with their fingers. At some point include the quantity of zero.

- Distribute the booklet *My Toys.* Have students point to the box and count the number of toys. Make sure to note that there is nothing in the box to count. Have students trace the number 0 using the verbal pathway, "pull back and around." Have students draw 0 in the air to practice.

- Students should return to their seats with their booklets.

Name _____

Learning Target: Understand, name, and write the number 0.

Explore and Grow

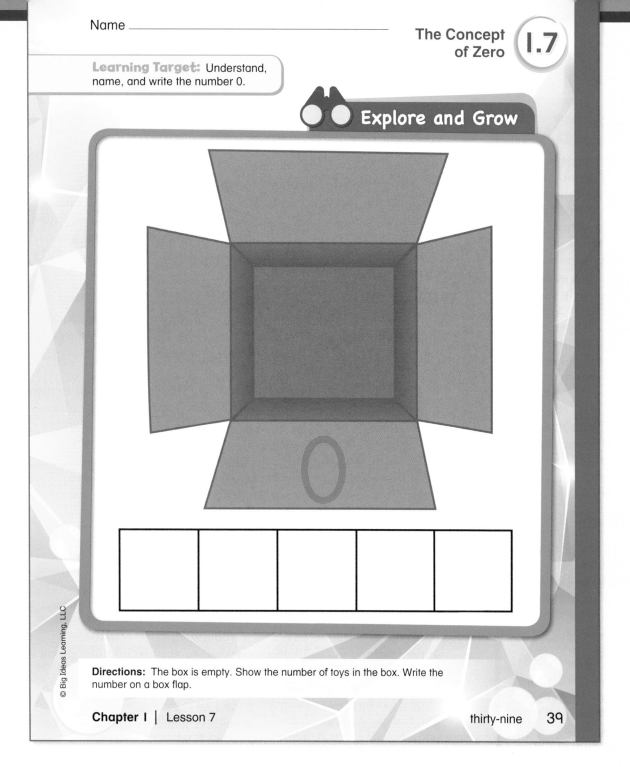

© Big Ideas Learning, LLC

Directions: The box is empty. Show the number of toys in the box. Write the number on a box flap.

Explore and Grow

? **Story Time:** "Oh look, a box for my toys! The box is empty. Can I use counters to show the number of toys in the box?" You don't need any counters to show zero. "How can I show the number of toys in the box on the frame?" Leave it empty. Have students explore writing 0 on a box flap.

• **Supporting Learners:** Some students may recognize the number 0 is written the same way as the letter O. Acknowledge their connection while discussing the difference in meaning.

• "Use your hand to show zero counters." Students may form the number 0 or they may use a fist with no fingers up.

ELL Support

Teach the words *leaf* and *sheep* by pointing to each and stating its name. Have students repeat each word. Remind students that when describing more than one of an object, normally the sound at the end of the word changes, but sometimes a different word is used. When describing more or less than one leaf, the word *leaves* is used. The word *sheep* does not change. Have students describe the number of objects counted in each example.

Beginner students may only count aloud as they point to the pictures.

Intermediate students may state the number and name of each object such as "one leaf"

Advanced students may use simple sentences to describe the number of objects, such as "There are zero leaves."

Think and Grow

Getting Started

- Introduce the vocabulary card for *zero* and have students brainstorm examples of 0 with partners. Share as a class.
- Note: For students to understand a contextual picture of 0, it is helpful to compare it to a similar picture that models a quantity. On this page there are two tree limbs, one with one leaf and one with no leaves. There is a circular pen with two sheep and a circular pen with no sheep.

Teaching Notes

- Let students talk about the picture of the tree limb. Have them share what they know about autumn and why leaves fall from the trees. Not all students will have the background knowledge or experiences to answer.
- Model: Have students describe the two tree limbs. "Point to the limb with no leaves or zero leaves." "How many linking cubes do we need to show zero?" none; zero Be clear with students that when there are no counters, you are representing the quantity of zero. Zero is a number.
- Now that students have identified zero, have them practice tracing and writing the number 0. Students can repeat the verbal pathway "pull back and around."
- ? "How many sheep are in each pen?" Listen for an understanding that each answer is a number representing a quantity.
- ⊙ There are four success criteria in the lesson and now students should have a sense of their understanding of zero. Allow them to share what they know about the number 0 by having them discuss it with partners. Circulate and listen to their conversations. If students seem unsure, ask probing questions such as "What does 0 mean? Can you show me zero pencils? How do you write 0? Show me zero fingers." End the partner conversations and ask students to use their thumb signals to show if they know what zero means. You could have them signal their ability to write the number 0 as well.
- Supporting Learners: Review the counting sequence with students as needed.
- Supporting Learners: Students may have trouble understanding that zero means there is nothing to point to or physically touch. Provide examples using other numbers and 0 to help students understand the difference.

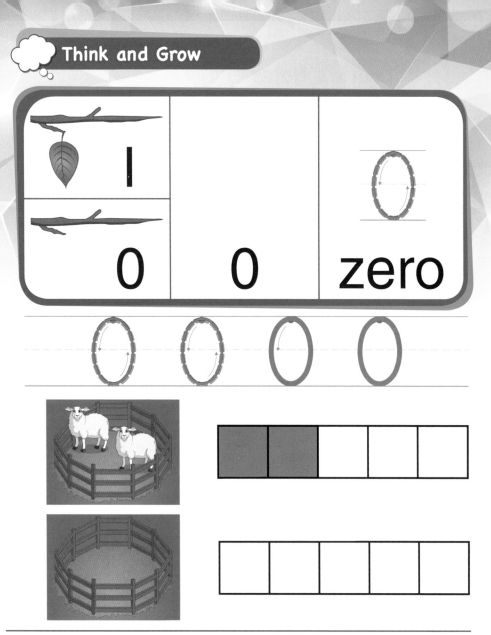

1		0
0	0	zero

Directions:
- Count the leaves on the bottom branch. Say the number. Trace and write the number.
- Count the sheep in each pen. Color the boxes to show how many.

40   forty

Laurie's Notes

Meeting the needs of all learners.

Apply and Grow: Practice

MAKING INSTRUCTIONAL DECISIONS

Zero is an important number in our base ten number system. Conceptually it is difficult for students to think about and understand that 0 is a number. Students have come to understand that the numbers they write tell how many objects there are when they count. Now there are no objects to count. Students will say, "There are no objects to count, so I can't count." They may also ask, "How can I write a number when there is nothing to count?" Students need many experiences with identifying a group of zero. Understanding 0 as a number takes time. Ask questions to get students to answer "how many" and name the number in a group of zero objects. See the Dig In examples on page T-39.

EMERGING students may still be confused about how to count when there is nothing to count. Acknowledge that zero means there is nothing to count, and to represent having no objects by using the written number symbol 0.

- Put five manipulatives in a basket and count them. Put the number card 5 next to the basket and write the numeral. Remove one manipulative, count again, put the number card 4 next to the basket, and write the numeral. Repeat this process until you get to 0. Ask students how many are left, show the 0 card, and write the numeral. Ask students to describe what 0 is and what it means.

PROFICIENT students have an understanding that zero is the quantity we say where there are none. They can write the number and explain what zero means.

- Play an action game. Show a number card and have students complete a specific action that many times. Show the numbers 5 through 0 in descending order. Emphasize 0.

Extension: Adding Rigor

- Extend the lesson by having students make their own number book using the numbers 0 through 5. Have them make their numbers on six sheets of paper. Tell them to draw the corresponding amount of dots or pictures for each number. Another option is to have students cut out pictures from a magazine to glue on the pages. As students write each number on the page, be sure to review its verbal pathway. Ask, "What will we see on the 0 page?" Consider putting the books together with a ring so students can easily flip through them and add more numbers.

✓ Apply and Grow: Practice

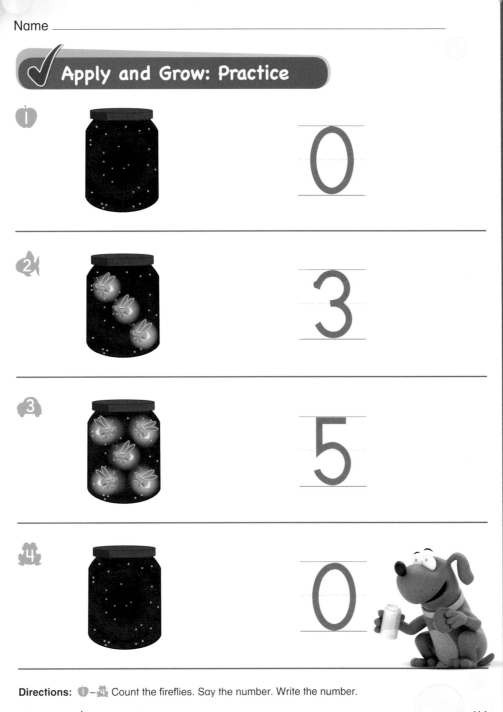

1. 0

2. 3

3. 5

4. 0

Directions: ①–④ Count the fireflies. Say the number. Write the number.

© Big Ideas Learning, LLC

Laurie's Notes

Think and Grow: Modeling Real Life

This application helps students count to answer "how many" questions including the numbers 0 through 5.

- **Preview:** Have students look at the picture and talk with their neighbors about what they see. Let them share stories about their experiences.
- **?** "Think to yourself. How will you find how many starfish toys, shovels, rakes, and buckets are in the sandbox picture? How will you show the number?"
- **?** Have students point to the green shovel and tap as they count. "How many green shovels are there?" Have students write the number 2 as you say the verbal pathway.
- Repeat this type of language to have students count the number of rakes, buckets, and starfish toys in the picture. Chant the verbal pathway as students write each number.
- **Teaching Strategy:** Remind students to review the picture and only look for the items that they are being asked to count.
- **? Teaching Tip:** Students may have trouble noticing that there are zero rakes in the scene. Ask, "Where would the rake be in the scene?" around or in the sandbox "Do you see the rake? What number can we use to show there are no rakes?"
- **Note:** Make sure to document and support any students who are having difficulty with the orientation of the objects.
- **Extension:** Have students make up a story to tell their partners about the picture. Students should use the objects at the bottom of the page in their story. Listen for students to mention the number of objects in their stories. They could use the Newton and Descartes puppets to help tell the story.
- ⦿ When students have completed the page, ask them to use their thumb signals as you review each success criterion. Ask additional questions about the numbers 1 to 5 if you have noticed some confusion on this page with a particular number.
- **Supporting Learners:** Have students think of a time when something was empty or they had none of something. Common examples are no cookies remaining, or no people in a parked car. Relating the concept of zero to students' background knowledge helps students make important connections.

Closure

- Prompt students to have partners guess how many fingers are behind their backs. Once their partners guess, both students should count the fingers together to check the answer. Then have the partners switch roles.

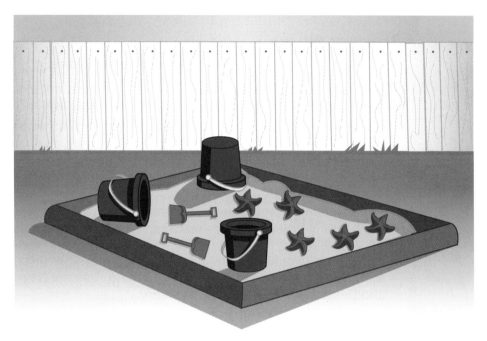

 2

 5

 0

 3

Directions: Count the objects in the picture. Say the number. Write the number.

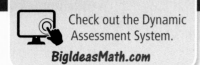
Connect and Extend Learning

Practice Notes

See page T-7 for general information about the Practice.

- **Exercises 1 and 2:** Students are counting flowers, not vases.
- **Exercises 3 and 4:** Students are counting fireflies, not jars.
- Common Error: Students may write "0" in the five frame to answer Exercise 2. Remind students that an empty five frame is a model of (it means) 0.

Cross-Curricular Connections

Language Arts

- *Zero Is The Leaves On The Tree* by Betsy Franco; Have students create their own story titled *Zero Is* by drawing or writing about scenes in which there is none of something. Use the Newton and Descartes puppets to tell the story.

Science

? Show students a visual representation of the life cycle of a frog. Ask students to count the number of legs shown in each phase. Ask, "In what phases do the frogs have zero legs?" eggs phase and the early stages of tadpoles phases

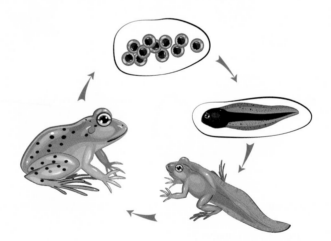

Practice (**1.7**)

Learning Target: Understand, name, and write the number 0.

zero

Directions: Count the flowers. Say the number. Write the number. Color the boxes to show how many.

❶

❷

Directions: ❶ and ❷ Count the flowers. Color the boxes to show how many.

Chapter 1 | Lesson 7

forty-three **43**

Connect and Extend Learning

Extend Student Learning

Intrapersonal

• Draw a grid of squares on a piece of paper. Write a number between 0 and 5 inside each square. Have students create towers out of linking cubes, and place each tower on the corresponding number square. Students must recognize that they do not put any linking cubes on the squares that have 0 written on them.

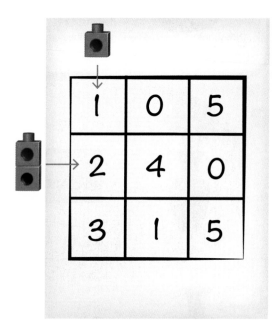

Lesson Resources	
Surface Level	**Deep Level**
Resources by Chapter • Extra Practice • Reteach Differentiating the Lesson Skills Review Handbook Skills Trainer	Resources by Chapter • Enrichment and Extension Graphic Organizers Dynamic Assessment System • Lesson Practice

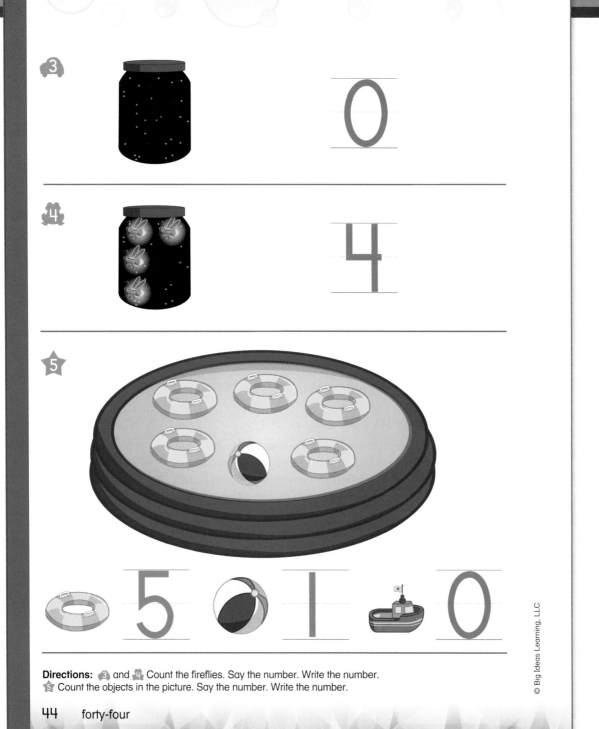

Directions: 3 and 4 Count the fireflies. Say the number. Write the number.
5 Count the objects in the picture. Say the number. Write the number.

1.8

Laurie's Notes

Learning Target

Count and order numbers to 5.

Success Criteria

- Count from 1 to 5.
- Identify the starting number.
- Order numbers up to 5.

Warm-Up

Practice opportunities for the following are available in the Resources by Chapter or at *BigIdeasMath.com.*

- Daily skills
- Vocabulary
- Prerequisite skills

ELL Support

Review the numbers 0 to 5 by saying each number and having students hold up their card that corresponds to each. Have them repeat the name of each number.

Preparing to Teach

Students have learned to count, model, and write the numbers 0 to 5. In this lesson, students will order the numbers from 0 to 5. It is important to distinguish between knowing the sequence of the words *zero, one, two,* and so on, and ordering numbers. When students need to repeat the sequence of words to be able to order numbers, their understanding of quantity is not secure. You want students to recognize that when counting in order, the quantity is changing each time. This is the beginning of understanding *one more* and *one less* in the next chapter.

Materials

- linking cubes
- Number Cards 0–5*

Found in the Instructional Resources

Dig In (Circle Time)

Have students crouch low to the ground. Tell students to count to 5 and stand a little taller each time they say the next number. When counting in reverse, students start in a standing position and crouch a little lower each time. You want students to focus on changing their heights each time to correspond with the increasing or decreasing numbers. They are also practicing their number sequence.

- **?** Try a second activity in which you or students hold a number of linking cubes. Ask, "What number is this? How can you show the next number?" Start with a different amount of cubes each time.

- Give each trio of students a collection of cubes. Hold up two fingers and ask each group to make a model of this number. Then ask them to make a model of the number that comes before and after this. Talk about what it means to put things in order. Have the trio put their towers in order.

- **?** "What do you notice about your towers?" Each one is longer, or taller; students may also mention stairs.

- Note: *Tower* and *train* are used interchangeably throughout depending on if students hold them upright or flat.

- Ask a volunteer in each group to take the number cards for 1, 2, and 3 and place them with their matching towers.

- Repeat this process for the numbers 3 and 4. You want students to make the connection that the names of the towers are in the same order as when counting.

- **?** "Where would the 0 card go?" before the 1 "What is the first number you say when you count forward?" 1 "Which number would you start with if you counted backward?" 5

Name _____

Learning Target: Count and order numbers to 5.

Explore and Grow

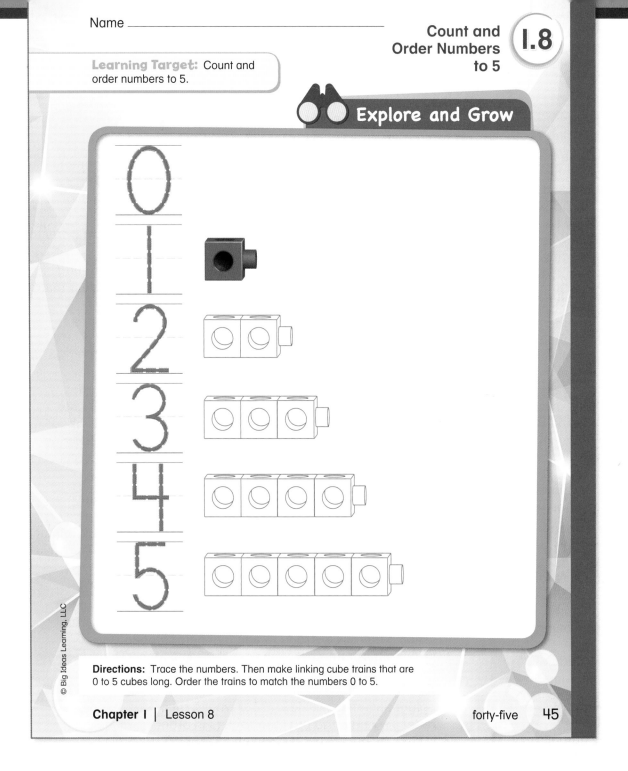

Directions: Trace the numbers. Then make linking cube trains that are 0 to 5 cubes long. Order the trains to match the numbers 0 to 5.

Chapter 1 | Lesson 8   forty-five   **45**

Explore and Grow

- Students build linking cube trains with lengths of 0 to 5.
- Discuss what a train with zero linking cubes would look like. Acknowledge that there is nothing to show when you model zero.
- Continue this process with the numbers 1 through 5. Say the number and model it with cubes to build a train. Keep the train models on the page.
- "What number do I say after 2? What number do I say before 5?"

Laurie's Notes

Think and Grow

Getting Started

- Have students put away their linking cube trains by counting backwards for each train. They should say 0 each time to indicate there are no cubes left. Begin with the 5 train, then 4, and so on.
- Introduce the vocabulary card for **order**. Relate the term *order* to the counting sequence.
- Call out a number within 5. Have students practice counting forward and backward from a given number. Make it clear that they are saying the numbers in order.

Teaching Notes

- On this page, students count objects and write the number. Then they practice writing them in order.
- ⊙ When students have finished writing the numbers in order, have them explain to their partners how they know they are correct. Students' explanations should provide insights about their understanding of ordering numbers, which is the second success criterion.
- ❓ **Extension:** "What number comes after _____ ? before _____?"
- ⊙ To assess the second success criterion, ask questions such as, "If the starting number is 2, then what number comes next? For the number set 5, 4, 3, 2, 1, what is the starting number? Tell me what you know about the number pattern 5, 4, 3, 2, 1, 0" Five is the starting number; it is counting backwards to 0.
- ❓ **Extension:** "Where would the number 0 go?"
- **Supporting Learners:** If students have difficulty ordering the numbers, they should manipulate the five frame cards. The visual pattern is a strong image that helps students see one more for each number in the counting sequence. The five frame cards should be available in a Center activity for students to work with.
- ⊙ Take time to be very intentional in reviewing the success criteria for this lesson. There have been many activities and learning opportunities that can be referenced and connected to the success criteria. You want students' understanding and learning of the success criteria to be visible to them. When you ask students to use their thumb signals to communicate their understanding of a skill or concept, they need to be clear about what successful learning looks like.
- Give students regular practice at counting forward and backward from a given number. This helps prepare students as they compare numbers and develop addition and subtraction strategies.

2

4

5

1

3

●	●			

○	○	○	○	

●	●	●	●	●

○				

●	●	●		

1   2   3   4   5

Directions:
- Count the objects in each five frame. Say the number. Write the number.
- Write the numbers in order. Start with the number 1.

46   forty-six

Laurie's Notes

Apply and Grow: Practice

MAKING INSTRUCTIONAL DECISIONS

We want to be sure students understand the order of numbers, and how the numbers are related to each other. Rote recitation of the words *one, two, three,* and so on is not enough. Students should have visual images of these numbers and models that can be compared. When linear models are arranged in order, students should be able to explain that when counting, the model has one more dot. The quantity increases by one. With practice, students will become more fluent with the number-word sequence in forward and reverse order.

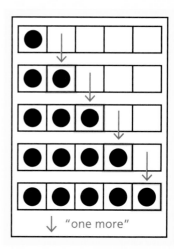

↓ "one more"

EMERGING students are not consistent in their ability to count and order numbers to 5 in forward and reverse order. They may say number words in the correct order but not attach meaning to the numbers. Counting in reverse order is more difficult for most students.

- Match subitizing cards to their corresponding number cards to practice counting and ordering.
- Have students use linking cubes to build each number from Number Cards 0–5. Have students place the cards in order.

PROFICIENT students accurately count and order the numbers to 5 in forward order and, frequently, in reverse order. They understand that the quantity increases by one as they count forward. Given a start number, they know the next number.

- Use number cards, immediately followed by subitizing cards, to order in a forward sequence. As students progress and become more fluent, order the cards in reverse.

Extensions: Adding Rigor

- Students create subitizing dot patterns using bingo markers, or regular markers, on blank paper. Students write a number and show two different dot patterns for the number.
- Provide number and subitizing cards for students to place in forward and reverse order. One student orders the numbers and the other student orders the subitizing cards. Students trade shuffled cards and order the new set. Next, students take turns closing their eyes as partners remove a card from the order. Students open their eyes and identifiy the missing number, and then take a turn removing a number from the newly ordered set for their partners.

ELL Support

Teach the words star, alien, cloud, moon rock, and sun by pointing to each and stating its name. Then check for understanding of Lesson 1.8 by asking, "How many stars are there?" Have students hold up the appropriate card from their deck of number cards to answer.

Name _____

1   5

2   3

3   2

4   4

5 |

6 | 2 3 4 5

Directions: 1 – 5 Count the objects. Say the number. Write the number.
6 Write the numbers in order. Start with the number 1.

Chapter 1 | Lesson 8   forty-seven   47

Laurie's Notes

Think and Grow: Modeling Real Life

This application helps students count and write the numbers 1 through 5. They will also write the numbers in reverse order.

- **Preview:** Have students talk with their partners about what they see. The concept of rockets flying into space may not be familiar to all students. As a class, discuss what students think about rockets, flying in space, and stars.
- **?** "When do you see stars?" Listen for many answers, including those other than just at night. Explain that stars can also be different colors.
- Read the directions. Have students discuss strategies they can use to count the stars. Solicit responses.
- **Construct Viable Arguments and Critique the Reasoning of Others:** Encourage students to count and then check with partners to see whether they agree about the number of each color of star. Students should feel comfortable talking with partners and then self-correcting when they recognize a mistake.
- Read the directions for the last example. Check for understanding of what *reverse order* and *starting number* mean.
- **Note:** If students are not ready to write the numbers in reverse order, have them write the numbers in order starting with 1.
- **?** **Extension:** "How many brown stars are there? Where would you place this number in the order?" Count backward again as a class, "5, 4, 3, 2, 1, 0 blast off!"
- ⊙ When students have completed the page, ask them to use their thumb signals as you review each success criterion. Use additional language so students are clear about the difference between counting numbers and ordering numbers. Counting in order needs to be assessed separately from counting in the reverse order.
- **Supporting Learners:** Use shuffled number cards and linking cubes to have partners build each number and then order the number cards.
- **Supporting Learners:** Some students may not need the visual representation to order numbers. Circulate and ask students to explain their understanding (strategy) for ordering the numbers 1 through 5.

Closure

- Write number sequences on the board from 0 to 5. Leave out one number each time. Have students identify which number is missing in the sequence. Choose a student to come to the board to complete the number sequence or have students record the missing number on their whiteboards.

3 1 4 5 2

5 4 3 2 1

Directions:
• Count the stars in the picture. Say the number. Write the number.
• Write the numbers in reverse order. Start with the number 5.

48   forty-eight

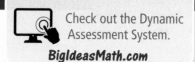
Connect and Extend Learning

Practice Notes

See page T-7 for general information about the Practice.

- **Exercise 2:** The direction each bird is flying does not influence the count.
- **Exercise 5:** Students are counting each color of flag without regard to direction flag is flying.

Cross-Curricular Connections

Language Arts

- *Five Little Ducks* by Annie Kubler; Count the baby ducks each time one leaves the group.

Social Studies

- To help students get to know each other, have them interview a peer. Prompt them to ask questions involving the numbers 0 through 5. "What is something you have zero of, that you might like to have someday? Tell me about one special person in your life. What is something you have two of? Tell me three things you like to eat. What are your four favorite colors? Name five things you have in your pencil box."
- Notice the various patterns in our world. Look for different arrangements of objects like cars in a parking lot, stop lights, lines on the street, vegetables in a row, or building and house arrangements.

Name _____

Learning Target: Count and order numbers to 5.

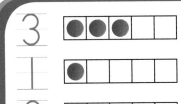
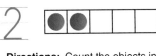

Directions: Count the objects in each five frame. Say the number. Write the number. Then write the numbers in order. Start with the number 1.

① 2

② 3

③ 1

④ 1 2 3

Directions: ①–③ Count the birds. Say the number. Write the number. ④ Write the numbers in order. Start with the number 1.

© Big Ideas Learning, LLC

Connect and Extend Learning

Extend Student Learning

Linguistic

- Read the *Our Number Walk* classroom stories that were made for the numbers 1 through 5 in Lessons 1.2, 1.4, and 1.6.

Visual-Spatial

- Have students make a themed number poster to hang in the classroom. Choose a setting such as a farm with animal pens, a playground scene, a forest, a lake, a beach, or a bedroom. Have students create a scene that has groups of zero to five objects in each.

Lesson Resources	
Surface Level	**Deep Level**
Resources by Chapter • Extra Practice • Reteach Differentiating the Lesson Skills Review Handbook Skills Trainer	Resources by Chapter • Enrichment and Extension Graphic Organizers Dynamic Assessment System • Lesson Practice

⑤ 3 2 4 5 1

⑥ 1 2 3 4 5

⑦ 5 4 3 2 1

Directions: ⑤ Count the flags in the picture. Say the number. Write the number.
⑥ Write the numbers in order. Start with the number 1.
⑦ Write the numbers in reverse order. Start with the number 5.

50   fifty

Performance Task

In this task, students work with different arrangements of objects up to 5. They are asked to count groups of objects, write the numbers, order the numbers, and draw and write to show 5 in two different ways. Not all students will understand that writing 5 is showing the number a different way. You can use their responses to gauge their thinking about modeling, counting, understanding, and writing numbers to 5.

- Decide ahead of time whether students will be working independently, in pairs, or in groups.
- Pause between direction lines for students to complete each step.
- Have students share their work and thinking with others. Discuss as a class.

Exercise	Answers and Notes	Points
1	3; 0; 2; 4; 1 0, 1, 2, 3, 4	10
2	five dots or drawings of eggs in any arrangement	1
3	Write the number 5.	1
	Total	12

①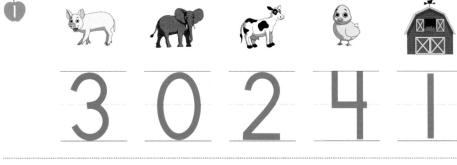

3 0 2 4 1

0 1 2 3 4

②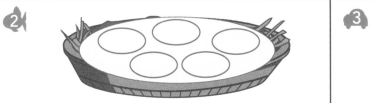

③ 5

Directions: ① Count the objects in the picture. Say the number. Write the number. Write the numbers in order. Start with the number 0. ② A chicken lays five eggs. Draw to show how many eggs. ③ Show how many eggs in another way.

Chapter 1   fifty-one **51**

Laurie's Notes

Number Land

Materials

- 1 manipulative per student to use as a playing piece
- 1 copy of Subitizing Cards 0-5* per student

*Found in the Instructional Resources

Students can work in pairs or small groups.

- **?** "What numbers do you see on this page? Are the numbers on the game board in order? How do you know?"
- **Note:** This may be the first time students have been exposed to a pattern. They may be confused why` 0 is shown after 5. Focus on one string of numbers on the board and cover the rest to help students understand that 0 does not come after 5. Then repeat the question.
- Read the directions at the bottom of the page. Decide how many times you want students to go around the board.
- Model how to draw a card and move a manipulative clockwise to the closest corresponding number. When they run out of cards, shuffle and replace the deck with the blank side facing up.
- When game play concludes, the discussion should center on student reasoning about how they moved around the board.
- **?** **Attend to Precision:** "As you played the game, how did you know what number to put your piece on?" I counted the dots on the card and matched them to the number on the board; I moved my playing piece to that number.

  FYI: Students may subitize the amount shown on the card and express this by saying, "I just knew the number."
- **Supporting Learners:** Provide students with counters and a five frame to use to build each card's number.

Closure

- Ask students, "How else can you show the numbers?" draw pictures; write the number; model with counters

Number Land

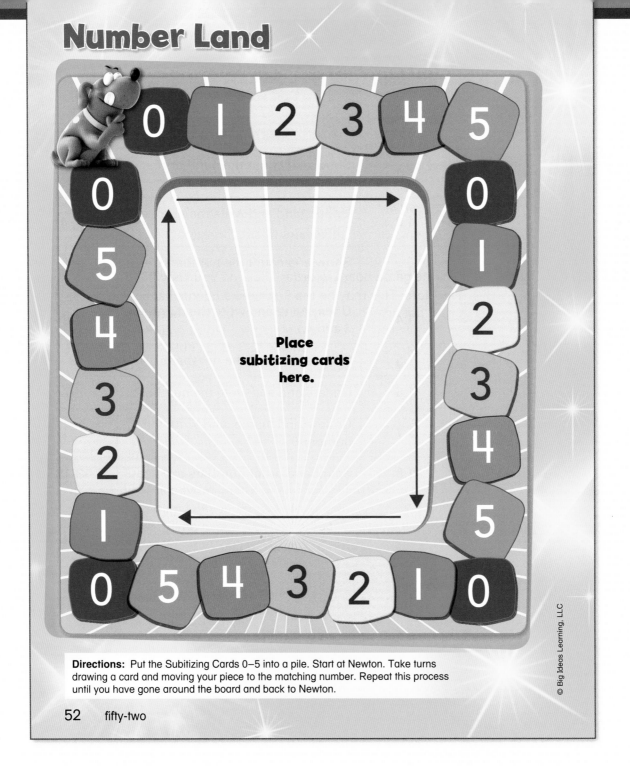

Place subitizing cards here.

Directions: Put the Subitizing Cards 0–5 into a pile. Start at Newton. Take turns drawing a card and moving your piece to the matching number. Repeat this process until you have gone around the board and back to Newton.

Learning Target Correlation

Lesson	Learning Target	Exercises
1.1	Show and count the numbers 1 and 2.	1, 2
1.2	Understand and write the numbers 1 and 2.	3, 4
1.3	Show and count the numbers 3 and 4.	5, 6
1.4	Understand and write the numbers 3 and 4.	7, 8
1.5	Show and count the number 5.	9
1.6	Understand and write the number 5.	10
1.7	Understand, name, and write the number 0.	11, 12
1.8	Count and order numbers to 5.	13-18

Chapter Practice

1.1 Model and Count 1 and 2

1.2 Understand and Write 1 and 2

I

2

Directions: and Count the objects. Color the boxes to show how many.
Count the objects. Say the number. Write the number.

Chapter 1   fifty-three **53**

Chapter Resources		
Surface Level	**Deep Level**	**Transfer Level**
Resources by Chapter • Extra Practice • Reteach Differentiating the Lesson Skills Review Handbook Skills Trainer Game Library Math Musicals	Resources by Chapter • Enrichment and Extension Graphic Organizers Game Library Math Musicals	Dynamic Assessment System • Chapter Test Assessment Book • Chapter Tests A and B

1.3 Model and Count 3 and 4

5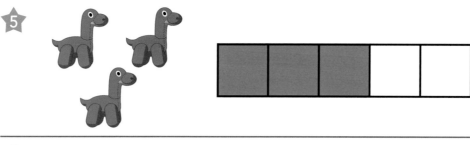

6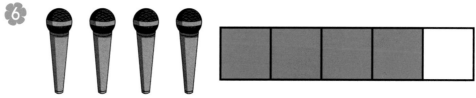

1.4 Understand and Write 3 and 4

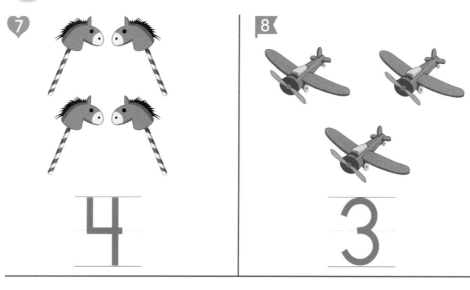

7

4

8

3

Directions: **5** and **6** Count the objects. Color the boxes to show how many.
7 and **8** Count the objects. Say the number. Write the number.

1.5 Model and Count 5

 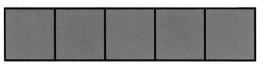

1.6 Understand and Write 5

5

1.7 The Concept of Zero

3

0

Directions: Count the ears of corn. Color the boxes to show how many.
Count the beavers. Say the number. Write the number.
and Count the owls. Say the number. Write the number.

1.8 Count and Order Numbers to 5

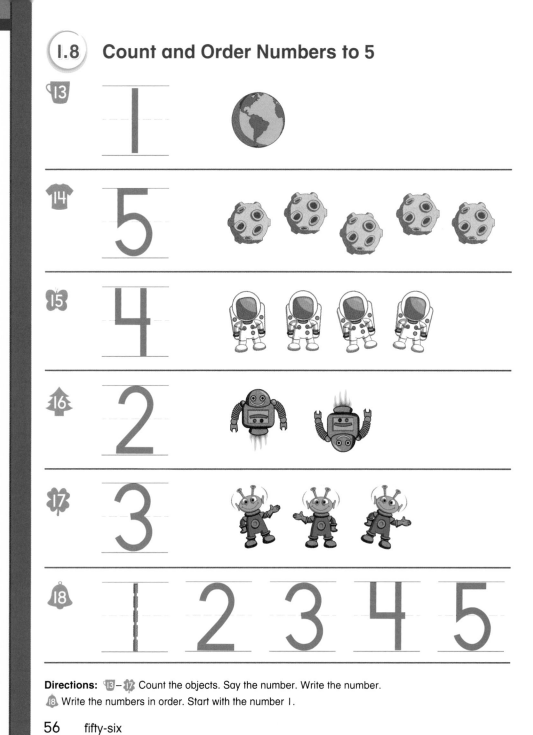

Directions: 13 – 17 Count the objects. Say the number. Write the number.

18 Write the numbers in order. Start with the number 1.

Math Musicals can be used with current topics, to review previous topics, or to preview upcoming topics.

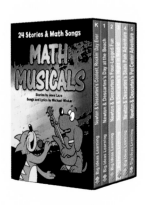

© Big Ideas Learning, LLC

Centers

Center 1: Number Land

Materials: Student Edition page 52, 1 manipulative per student to use as a playing piece, and 1 copy of Subitizing Cards 0–5* per student

Have students complete the Number Land activity. See page T-52 for the directions.

Center 2: Skills Trainer

Materials: computers or devices with Internet access

Have students go to *BigIdeasMath.com* to access the Skills Trainer.

Center 3: Flip and Find

Materials: Number Cards 0–5*, Subitizing Cards 0–5*

Arrange the cards face down in four rows and three columns. Students take turns flipping over two cards at a time. When a student flips two cards with the same value, they keep the match. Students continue to play until all cards have been matched.

Center 4: Color by Numbers

Materials: Color by Numbers 0–5*, crayons

Students use the key to color the picture. You may need to show students an example to get them started. For students who are unable to read color names, color the crayons with the given color.

Center 5: Number Poster

Materials: Five Frames*, construction paper, crayons, scissors, glue or tape, stamps or stickers

Create a sample poster for students to reference. Fold a piece of construction paper into fourths so there is one column with four rows. Students will model a number between 1 and 5 in four ways: write the number, model the number in a five frame, draw a picture to represent the number, and use stickers or stamps to model the number.

Found in the Instructional Resources

Chapter Assessment Guide

Chapter tests are available in the Assessment Book. An alternative assessment option is listed below.

Visual-Spatial

Direct students to draw a picture that models the numbers 1 to 5. Allow students to choose the setting and objects being counted. Have students identify how many of each object there are in their drawing by writing the numeral or stating the number. Reference the Think and Grow: Modeling Real Life pages for ideas. This could also be used as a partner activity with one partner identifying the number of objects in each group drawn by the other partner. Use the rubric below to assess students' current level of understanding.

Teaching Tip: Make sure to walk students through choosing the scene and drawings for each number. Multi-step directions can be difficult for students. You do not want the students' understanding to be misrepresented because of confusion with the directions.

Note: Some students may need to use classroom objects, linking cubes, or counters versus drawing a picture.

Task	Points
Students can show the numbers 1, 2, 3, 4, and 5.	1 point per number; 5 points total
Students can correctly identify the quantity for the numbers 1, 2, 3, 4, and 5 (written or verbally).	1 point per number; 5 points total
Total	10 points

My Thoughts on the Chapter

What worked...

What did not work...

What I would do differently...

Teacher Tip

Not allowed to write in your teaching edition? Use sticky notes to record your thoughts.

2 Compare Numbers 0 to 5

Chapter Overview

Lesson	Learning Target	Success Criteria
2.1 Equal Groups	Show and tell whether two groups are equal in number.	• Match objects from two groups. • Tell whether the numbers of objects in two groups are the same or not the same.
2.2 Greater Than	Show and tell whether one group has a greater number of objects than another group.	• Match objects from two groups. • Identify the group that has more objects.
2.3 Less Than	Show and tell whether one group has a lesser number of objects than another group.	• Match objects from two groups. • Identify the group that has fewer objects.
2.4 Compare Groups to 5 by Counting	Use counting to compare the numbers of objects in two groups.	• Compare the numbers of objects in two groups using the words *greater than*, *less than*, or *equal to*. • Explain how to compare two groups by counting.
2.5 Compare Numbers to 5	Compare two numbers.	• Tell whether two numbers are the same. • Use *greater than* and *less than* to describe two numbers that are not the same. • Draw to show how one number compares to another.

Chapter Learning Target:
Understand grouping.

Chapter Success Criteria:
- Identify groups of objects.
- Match objects.
- Compare groups.
- Draw groups of obects.

Progressions

Through the Grades	
Kindergarten	**Grade 1**
• Use matching and counting to tell whether the number of objects in a group is greater than, less than, or equal to the number of objects in another group. • Count the number of objects in different arrangements. • Compare two written numerals between 0 and 5.	• Compare 2 two-digit numbers based on the meanings of the tens and the ones digits. • Use the >, =, and < symbols. • Answer questions about the number of objects in a category, and how many more or less are in one category than another. • Relate counting to addition and subtraction. • Understand the meaning of the equal sign, and determine whether equations involving addition and subtraction are true or false.

Standard	Through the Chapter				
	2.1	2.2	2.3	2.4	2.5
Identify whether the number of objects in one group is greater than, less than, or equal to the number of objects in another group, e.g., by using matching and counting strategies.	●	●	●	●	●
Count to answer "how many?" questions about as many as 20 things arranged in a line, a rectangular array, or a circle, or as many as 10 things in a scattered configuration; given a number from 1–20, count out that many objects.				●	●
Compare two numbers between 1 and 10 presented as written numerals.				●	●

Key: ▲ = Preparing ● = Learning ★ = Complete

Laurie's Overview

About the Math

The concepts of same, more, and less are relationships that build children's basic number sense. It is essential that you assess students' understanding of counting to five to scaffold instruction to meet all levels of understanding.

In this chapter, students learn to compare numbers 1 to 5. This learning begins with deciding whether two quantities are the same or not the same. Students at this stage of cognitive development are influenced by many attributes unrelated to quantity. For example, put three unlike crayons in your hand and ask a pre-operational learner to count how many crayons you have. Their processing and understanding of the question can be influenced by attributes such as the crayon's color, length, and paper wrapping. For that reason, you need to be careful when showing students two quantities of objects that you want them to compare. Equally important is how you display or arrange objects when students need to match or count. Some students may think two quantities are always different when they are not shown in the same arrangement. Encourage students to count or subitize to determine whether two groups of objects are the same.

The concepts of more and fewer (less) are introduced early in the chapter. These concepts are logically connected. If group A has more objects than group B, then group B has less objects than group A. Students enter school having experience with the concept of more and are able to decide which group has more, particularly when the difference in quantity is great. Students have had less experience with the concept of *fewer* or *less*, and for that reason, it is important to ask pairs of comparative questions.

Group A   Group B

Which group has more objects? Which group has less objects?

There is language, or vocabulary terms associated with more and less. Students learn the terms *greater than* and *less than* in order to compare numbers. The symbols for greater than (>) and less than (<) are not introduced. A concrete and visual way to compare the quantities in two groups is to match items. Students can pair the objects from two groups by moving them, or lines can be drawn when students are looking at a picture. When all of the items in each group are not paired (matched), one group has a greater/lesser quantity than the other.

Once students have used matching to understand what it means to compare two groups, they can use counting to compare. Students are familiar with the counting sequence and should be able to visualize numbers 1 to 5. Understanding the counting sequence allows students to compare two groups by counting.

Three has one *more* counter than two.
Two has one *less* counter than three.

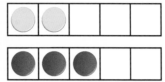

Finally, students are able to compare written numerals because of their understanding of quantity and their ability to visualize the numbers. In order to show how they know 3 is less than 5, they must draw a model of each. Comparing numbers that are closer in quantity may be more difficult so students may still need to use the strategies of matching or counting in order to compare.

Models

- Students are familiar with using their fingers to show numbers. Students can use two hands to show numbers that are equal or not equal. Fingers can be paired tip to tip, and students can count aloud when comparing the two quantities. For example, "Show three fingers on one hand. Use the other hand to show the number that is more than three."

- Many students are able to subitize the amount of counters in a five frame and will not need to count to know *how many*. Comparing the two quantities shown, students can reason that there is one more counter on the second five frame, and so, that quantity is greater.

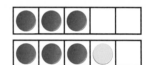

- Students can easily see when quantities are different by using linking cubes arranged in towers. Because it is often more difficult to determine when a number is less than another, linking cubes offer a great visual and tactile way for students to learn.

- A rekenrek is another tool that you can use to compare quantities.

- Create an anchor chart to show the concepts learned in the chapter. Include vocabulary and illustrations as each concept is taught.

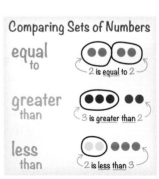

Comparing Sets of Numbers

equal to — 2 is equal to 2

greater than — 3 is greater than 2

less than — 2 is less than 3

Chapter Materials and Resources

The primary materials and resources needed for this chapter are listed below. Other materials may be needed for the additional support ideas provided throughout the chapter.

Check out the virtual manipulatives.
BigIdeasMath.com

Classroom Materials	Chapter Opener	2.1	2.2	2.3	2.4	2.5	Connect and Grow
scissors	•						*
two bags or two socks		•					
linking cubes		•	•	•	•	•	
two-color counters		•	•	•	•	•	•
collections of objects to match			+	+			
whiteboards and markers						•	•
5 paper clips							*
10 bear counters							*
clothes pins							•

Instructional Resources	Chapter Opener	2.1	2.2	2.3	2.4	2.5	Connect and Grow
Vocabulary Cards	+	+	+	+	+		
Number Cards 0–5							*
Toss and Compare Numbers from 0–5 Recording Sheet							*
Five Frames							*
Number Paths 1–5							*
Lion Cards 0–5							*
Lion Cards Recording Sheet							•

• class set   + teacher only   * per pair/group

Suggested Pacing

Day 1	Chapter Opener	Performance Task Preview		Vocabulary			
Day 2	Lesson 2.1	Warm-Up	Dig In	Explore	Think	Apply: Practice	Think: Modeling Real Life
Day 3	Lesson 2.2	Warm-Up	Dig In	Explore	Think	Apply: Practice	Think: Modeling Real Life
Day 4	Lesson 2.3	Warm-Up	Dig In	Explore	Think	Apply: Practice	Think: Modeling Real Life
Day 5	Lesson 2.4	Warm-Up	Dig In	Explore	Think	Apply: Practice	Think: Modeling Real Life
Day 6	Lesson 2.5	Warm-Up	Dig In	Explore	Think	Apply: Practice	Think: Modeling Real Life
Day 7	Connect and Grow	Performance Task		Activity		Chapter Practice	
Day 8		Centers					
Day 9	Chapter Assessment	Chapter Assessment					

Year-to-Date: 21 Days

Laurie's Notes

Performance Task Preview

- Ask students to talk about games they have played or games they may have made up. Students may name games that they play in your class. Discuss the rules.
- **?** "What does it mean to follow the rules of a game? Why do we have rules? Look at the picture. How many blue game pieces are there? How many green pieces? Are there more blue game pieces or green game pieces shown here?"
- In the Performance Task at the end of the chapter, students will compare the number of dots on a domino to the number of dots on a die and the number of Xs to the number of Os on a tic-tac-toe board.

2 Compare Numbers 0 to 5

- What does it mean to follow the rules of a game?

- Are there more blue game pieces or green game pieces shown here?

Chapter Learning Target:
Understand grouping.

Chapter Success Criteria:
- I can identify groups of objects.
- I can match objects.
- I can compare groups.
- I can draw groups of objects.

© Big Ideas Learning, LLC

fifty-seven   57

Check out the
digital flash cards.
BigIdeasMath.com

Laurie's Notes

ELL Support

Students should understand the words *count* and *number*. Check understanding by asking students to count from 1 to 5, first chorally as a class, and then one student at a time. Point to each number and say, "One is a number. Two is a number." Use all five numbers shown. Teach the words *swing*, *dinosaur*, *cloud*, and *slide* by pointing to each and stating its name. Have students report their answers by using sentences, such as, "I see four swings."

Vocabulary Review

? "What do you see on the page? What do you do on a playground? Are there playground rules? How do you know how many people can swing at a time?"

? "What do you notice about the dinosaurs?" Listen for students to use the review words *count* and *number*.

• Direct students to count each group of objects. Evaluate students' skill levels as they count aloud and write the numbers.

• **Extension:** Model how to draw simple objects, such as a circle for a bird or a thick line for a seesaw. Discuss and compare the numbers of objects drawn.

Chapter 2 Vocabulary

• Front-load the new vocabulary by having students draw more objects on the playground or in the sky and comparing the numbers of objects in the picture.

Activity

• **Show and Tell:** Students lay their vocabulary cards in front of them with the picture side facing up. Show students a vocabulary card, say the word, and describe the picture definition. Students find the corresponding card. Students tell their partners how they know the picture is a match to the vocabulary word.

  Supporting Learners: Limit the number of cards the students lay out in front of them.

Math Musicals can be used with current topics, to review previous topics, or to preview upcoming topics. There are many *Math Musicals* to choose from!

Use your hand puppets to act out new stories and have students sing the songs several times to take full advantage of the power of music to learn math!

2 Vocabulary

Review Words
count
number

Directions: Count the objects. Say the number. Write the number.

© Big Ideas Learning, LLC

Chapter 2 Vocabulary Cards

compare

equal

fewer

greater than

less than

more

same as

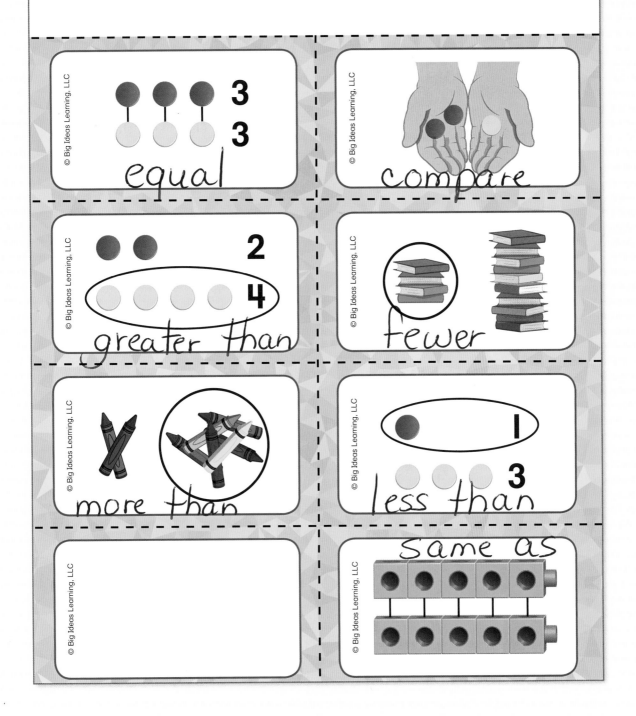

equal

compare

greater than

fewer

more than

less than

same as

Laurie's Notes

Learning Target

Show and tell whether two groups are equal in number.

Success Criteria

• Match objects from two groups.
• Tell whether the numbers of objects in two groups are the same or not the same.

Warm-Up

Practice opportunities for the following are available in the Resources by Chapter or at *BigIdeasMath.com*.

• Daily skills
• Vocabulary
• Prerequisite skills

ELL Support

Explain that the word *equal* means *the same as*. It is a cognate of some other languages. Students whose first language is Spanish may know *igual* and those whose first language is French may know *égal*. Point out the similarities in the sounds of the words.

Preparing to Teach

Give two students unequal amounts of snacks and they will know it! They can usually tell when the quantities are the same as, or equal. Students compare groups of objects by matching each object from one group to an object from the other group. When matching, students can see if each object has a "partner." The term *partner* helps students recognize when two groups of quantities are the same. This also prepares students to recognize quantities that are odd or even.

Materials

• two bags or two socks
• linking cubes
• two-color counters

Dig In (Circle Time)

Two students compare the quantity of linking cubes in their bags or socks. This is repeated with different amount of cubes each time.

• Prepare two socks or bags with 3 linking cubes in each. Hand them to two students. "Take out your cubes and count them. Do you have the same amount? How do you know?"

• Repeat this several times and include unequal amounts such as 1 and 4 so that the unequal amounts are obvious. Eventually use amounts that differ by only 1 such as 4 and 3. Observe and comment on how students are deciding whether the numbers of cubes are the same or not.

• **Note:** Students may describe the heights of the towers as taller or shorter. Students gain more experience with measurement terms in a later chapter.

• **Supporting Learners:** Some students may have difficulty visualizing whether the quantities of each group of counters are the same or not the same. Have students make a linking cube tower and compare to see whether the numbers of objects in each group are the same.

⊙ Model the same number of fingers on each hand and say, "Show me the same number of fingers on each hand. Show me fingers on each hand that are not the same number."

❓ Teaching Prompt   ⊙ Learning Target

Name _____

Learning Target: Show and tell whether two groups are equal in number.

Explore and Grow

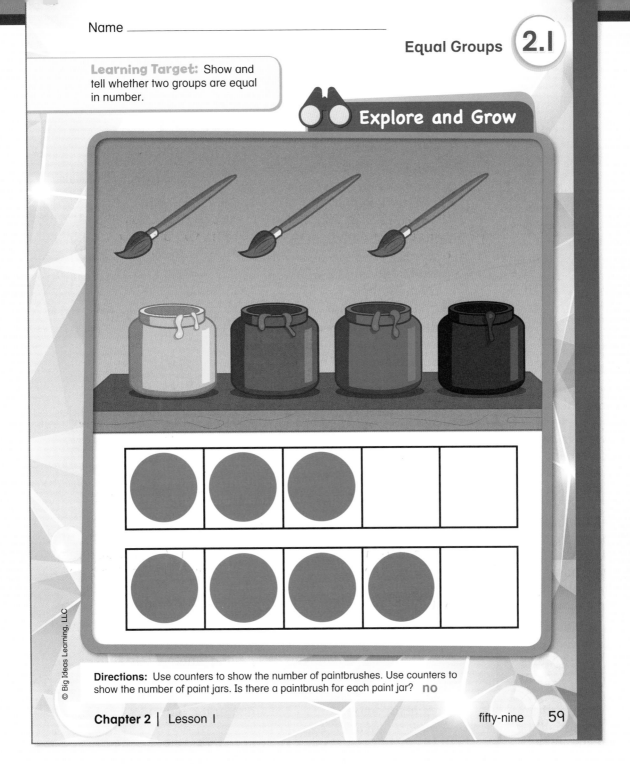

Directions: Use counters to show the number of paintbrushes. Use counters to show the number of paint jars. Is there a paintbrush for each paint jar? **no**

© Big Ideas Learning, LLC

Chapter 2 | Lesson 1   fifty-nine   59

Explore and Grow

- Students count the number of paintbrushes and jars using counters. Use the red side of the counters to cover one group and the yellow side of the counters to cover the other group. Push red and yellow counters together to find partner matches. Slide each row of counters to the appropriate frame.
- ? Turn and Talk: "Is there a paintbrush for each jar of paint? How do you know?" Listen for how students are deciding that the quantities are not the same.
- You could introduce the idea of showing a thumbs up signal when the groups are the same amount or a thumbs down signal when the groups are not the same amount.

Laurie's Notes

Think and Grow

Getting Started

- Introduce the vocabulary cards for **same as** and **equal**. Discuss the picture definitions and model each using cubes or your fingers.
- Start an anchor chart for these words. "I want to hear these words as you talk with your partner today."
- "Tell your partner about two groups of objects in this room that have the same number of objects."

Comparing Sets of Numbers

equal to — 2 is equal to 2

greater than — 3 is greater than 2

less than — 2 is less than 3

Teaching Notes

- The groups of objects on the page are arranged so that lines can easily be drawn to match and compare.
- Model: Together as a class, trace the dotted lines between the red and blue crayons. "Each red crayon has a blue crayon partner. There are the same numbers of each. Circle the picture of the thumbs up to show that both groups are equal."
- Compare the green and purple crayons. There are two green crayons that do not have a purple crayon partner. The groups are not the same amount. Circle the picture of the thumbs down.
- Circulate as students decide whether there are the same numbers of buttons as there are colored pencils.
- Note: Students may draw two lines from one object. Remind them that each object has only one partner.
- Ask, "How good are you with telling whether two groups are equal in number?" Restate this using the phrase 'the same number as' so students can build the understanding of what equal means.

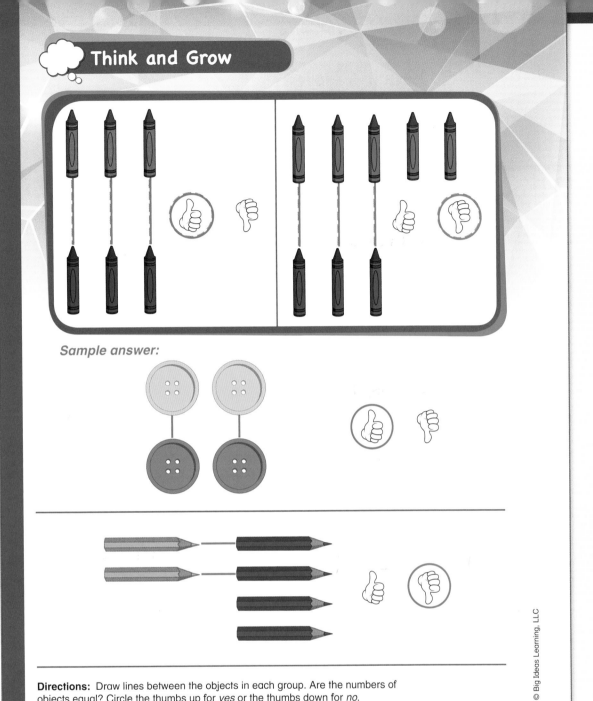

Sample answer:

Directions: Draw lines between the objects in each group. Are the numbers of objects equal? Circle the thumbs up for *yes* or the thumbs down for *no*.

60   sixty

Meeting the needs of
all learners.

Apply and Grow: Practice

MAKING INSTRUCTIONAL DECISIONS

When comparing numbers, the concept of *same as* is a basic number relationship that students need to understand before moving on to *more* and *fewer*. Use the terms *equal* and *same as* interchangeably to help students' understanding. This prepares students to use the equal sign to show that two quantities are the same later on.

Students may count objects to see how many are in each group when the method of matching to compare is not possible. This may also happen when the student's number sense is not strong enough to compare the numbers. Both methods allow students to decide whether two groups have the same number of objects.

EMERGING students may have difficulty identifying when two groups are the same or not the same in quantity. They are not at the subitizing stage yet and therefore have to count each group. These students may lose track or get lost during the number sequence.

- Display number cards 0 to 5 and subitizing cards 0 to 5 randomly, and have students match them.
- Line counters up in two rows and connect the counters with pieces of string to show one-to-one correspondence.

PROFICIENT students can identify when two groups are the same quantity or not the same quantity.

- Have students choose a subitizing card and use counters to create a number that is equal to the number on the card.

Extension: Adding Rigor

- For answers that are thumbs down, have students explain how to make the quantities the same.

✓ Apply and Grow: Practice

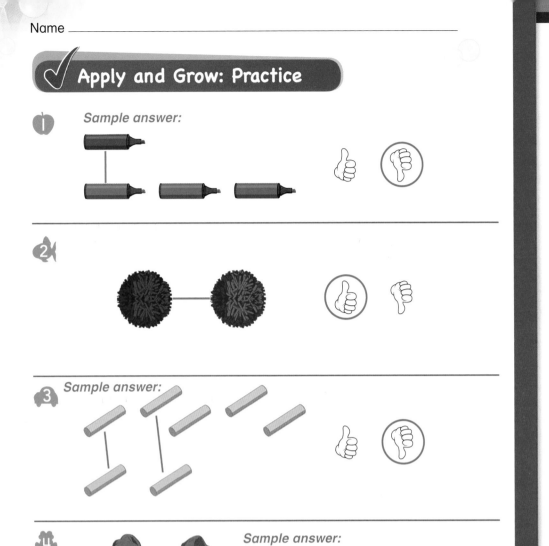

1 Sample answer:

2

3 Sample answer:

4 Sample answer:

Directions: 1–4 Draw lines between the objects in each group. Are the numbers of objects equal? Circle the thumbs up for *yes* or the thumbs down for *no*.

© Big Ideas Learning, LLC

Chapter 2 | Lesson 1   sixty-one   61

Laurie's Notes

Think and Grow: Modeling Real Life

This application allows students to show their understanding of equal and not equal. You want students to know when two quantities are equal, not just when two numerals look the same.

? **Preview:** "What do you see on this page? Have any of you ever painted? What colors do you like to use?" Allow students to share their experiences with partners.

- "Imagine that you squeeze some paint out of each tube. Draw one spot of paint for each tube."

? When they finish, ask, "How can we show that there is a spot of paint for each paint tube?" Listen for a strategy such as drawing lines.

- **Note:** Students may be concerned with their ability to draw a paint spot. Reassure them that quick drawings, such as circles or blobs, are fine.

- "In the next exercise, you will show that you understand the meaning of *not equal*, or *not the same as*. There are three tubes of orange paint. Make paint spots that are not the same amount."

? Students may ask whether they can make more than three spots, or make only one spot. Direct the question back to them. "Is 1 the same as 3 or is it not equal to 3?"

? Use the Descartes puppet. "If Descartes has four paint brushes and says the number of brushes is not equal to the number of paint tubes, then is he correct?" yes "How do you know?" Four and three are not the same.

⊙ Revisit the learning target. Have students signal their ability to show and tell whether the number of objects in one group is equal to the number of objects in another group.

? **Extension:** "What are some ways you can show whether two groups are equal or not equal?" Draw lines to connect partners; count each group; model with counters.

- **Supporting Learners:** Some students may have difficulty modeling *the same as* and *not the same as* without a five frame. Allow students to use counters and a copy of Five Frames to build the numbers. They can drag the counters to their page to create their drawings.

Closure

- Have partners take turns. One partner presents a random number of counters from 0–5. The other partner builds a group that is equal in number and a group that is not equal in number. The students explain how they know which group is equal and which group is not equal.

💭 Think and Grow: Modeling Real Life

Sample answer:

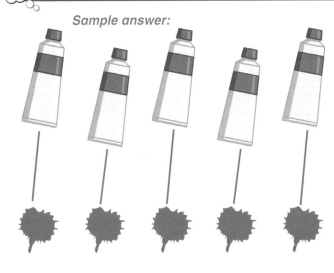

Sample answer:

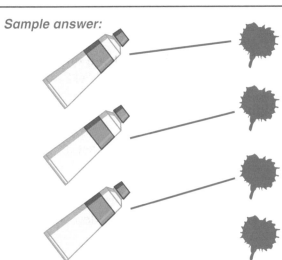

Directions:
- Draw paint spots so that the numbers of paint tubes and paint spots are equal. Draw lines between the objects in each group to show that you are correct.
- Draw paint spots so that the numbers of paint tubes and paint spots are not equal. Draw lines between the objects in each group to show that you are correct.

62   sixty-two

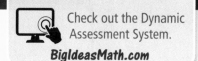
Connect and Extend Learning

Practice Notes

- **Exercises 1–4:** Remind students to draw a line between the closest two picture parts. Their thinking is clearer than when lines cross over each other.
- **Exercise 5:** Demonstrate how to quick draw a pencil.

Cross-Curricular Connections

Language Arts

- *Bear Counts* by Karma Wilson; Have students draw two groups of living things from the story. Make sure that the groups are equal in number. Students can also turn the paper over and draw two groups of living things from the story that are not equal in number.

Science

? Keep track of the weather for a few days. Create pictures or use a calendar set to represent each type of weather. After there are a few different types, post them on the board. Say, "Let's compare the number of sunny days to the number of cloudy days. Are the numbers the same?"

Name _____

Learning Target: Show and tell whether two groups are equal in number.

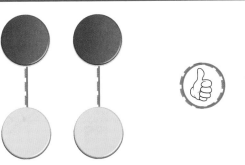

Directions: Draw lines between the counters in each group. Are the numbers of counters equal? Circle the thumbs up for *yes* or the thumbs down for *no*.

I and 2. Sample answers are given.

1

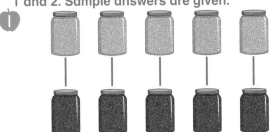

2

© Big Ideas Learning, LLC

Directions: ❶ and ❷ Draw lines between the objects in each group. Are the numbers of objects equal? Circle the thumbs up for *yes* or the thumbs down for *no*.

Chapter 2 | Lesson I

sixty-three 63

Connect and Extend Learning

Extend Student Learning

Intrapersonal

- Give students number cards from 0 to 5 and 10 linking cubes. Have students pick a card and build a tower with the linking cubes, and then build a second tower that is equal to the first tower. Students can check each other's work for accuracy.

3

Lesson Resources	
Surface Level	**Deep Level**

Resources by Chapter
  • Extra Practice
  • Reteach
Differentiating the Lesson
Skills Review Handbook
Skills Trainer
	Resources by Chapter
	  • Enrichment and Extension
	Graphic Organizers
	Dynamic Assessment System
	  • Lesson Practice

3–5. Sample answers are given.

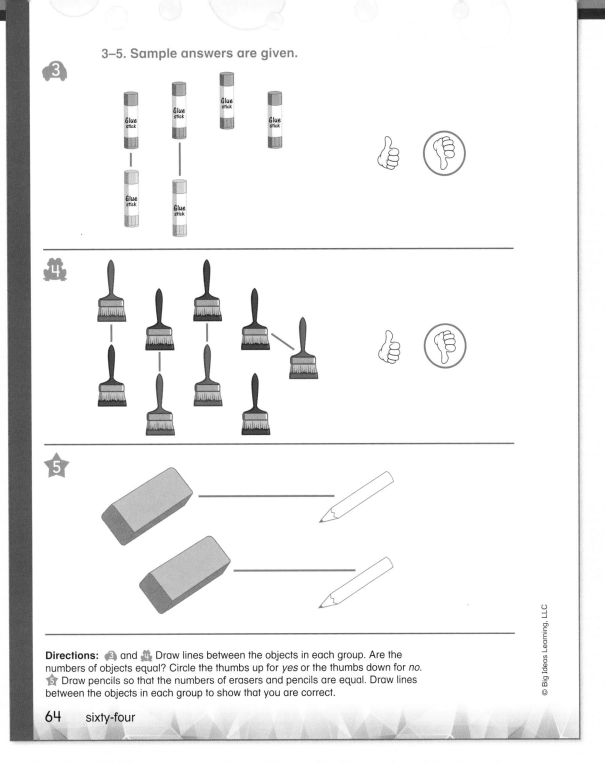

Directions: 3️ and 4️ Draw lines between the objects in each group. Are the numbers of objects equal? Circle the thumbs up for *yes* or the thumbs down for *no*.
5️ Draw pencils so that the numbers of erasers and pencils are equal. Draw lines between the objects in each group to show that you are correct.

2.2

Learning Target

Show and tell whether one group has a greater number of objects than another group.

Success Criteria

- Match objects from two groups.
- Identify the group that has more objects.

ELL Support

Explain to students that the word *greater* can mean more than one thing. If something is great, then it is very good. Something that is greater than something else is better. Explain that in math the phrase *greater than* means *more than*, instead of *good* or *better*.

Laurie's Notes

Preparing to Teach

Give a student one more treat than another student and you will hear, "They have more." You want students to have the understanding that the quantity of objects in one group is greater than the quantity of objects in another group. Be careful about how you display the objects in the two groups. Place them so that they are easily matched to be sure students are comparing quantities and not the size of the objects.

Materials

- collections of objects to match
- linking cubes
- two-color counters

Dig In (Circle Time)

Gather a collection of objects that students will recognize go together, such as cups and saucers, pairs of shoes, or crayons and coloring books. The goal is to have students match objects from one group (cups) with objects from the other group (saucers).

- Give 4 cups to one student and 4 saucers to a second student.
- **?** Ask "How many do you have? Do you have the same number of objects?" Students match each cup with a saucer.
- **?** Use unequal amounts, such as three left shoes and two right shoes. After students say how many they have ask, "Do you have the same number of objects? Tell your partner what you think will happen if we match the left shoes to the right shoes." Listen for an understanding that one group has more, and so, there will be a shoe left over.
- Repeat this process several times by using a series of equal and unequal amounts. Students compare by matching.
- ◉ Can students identify unequal groups? Can they match objects from each group and tell which group has more?

? Teaching Prompt   ◉ Learning Target

Name _____

Learning Target: Show and tell whether one group has a greater number of objects than another group.

Explore and Grow

Directions: Use counters to show the number of suitcases. Use counters to show the number of stuffed animals. Are there more suitcases or more stuffed animals? **suitcases**

© Big Ideas Learning, LLC

Explore and Grow

❓ Students cover each suitcase with a yellow counter and each stuffed animal with a red counter. Ask, "How many suitcases are there? How many stuffed animals?" Students slide the counters to the five frames.

❓ Ask, "Do we have a stuffed animal for each suitcase? How do you know?" There are more suitcases than stuffed animals; there is one more yellow counter than red counters.

• **Big Idea:** In the last lesson, students identified that two and three do not represent the same amount. In this lesson, the relationship to focus on is that a group of three objects is *more than*, or *greater than*, a group of two objects. They are not equal.

• **Extension:** Draw one more stuffed animal to make the quantities equal.

Laurie's Notes

Think and Grow

Getting Started

- Introduce the vocabulary cards for **more** and **greater than**. Refer to the pictures for each. Have students talk about the meaning.
- Use both vocabulary words interchangeably to relate the two. Add the vocabulary and examples to the anchor chart if you created one.
- Have students look around the room to give examples of a set that has more objects than another set.

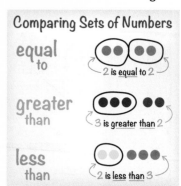

Comparing Sets of Numbers

equal to — 2 is equal to 2

greater than — 3 is greater than 2

less than — 2 is less than 3

Teaching Notes

- There are two groups of objects in each exercise. In the example, lines are provided for students to trace to help match the objects between groups. If an object in one group doesn't have a match, then that group must have more objects. Circle the group that has more objects.
- **?** **Model:** Together as a class, trace over the dotted lines between the backpacks and bus tickets. "Is there a backpack for each ticket? Are there more backpacks or tickets? To show there is a greater number of tickets, circle the group of bus tickets."
- Repeat for the cameras and binoculars. Show students that the lines are always drawn between the closest objects.
- Circulate as the students match to decide which group has more.
- **Extension:** For each exercise, ask students to count *how many* in each group. Example: Students may say, "Four is more than two" or "four is greater than two."
- Tell your neighbor how you decided which group of objects to circle.
- ◉ When students have finished the page, take the time to discuss how they've matched the objects from group to group. Some students may already know that a group of four is greater than a group of two without doing a one-to-one match, but many students will still need to match objects in order to know which group has more objects.
- **Supporting Learners:** Use linking cubes to represent the quantity in each group. Students can build towers and then compare the heights of the towers.

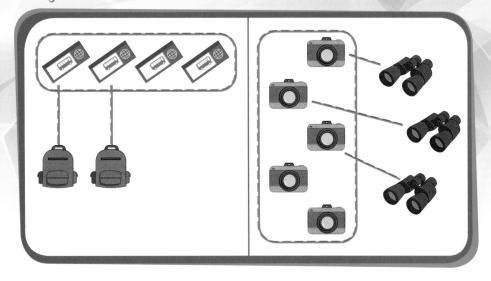

Sample answer:

Sample answer:

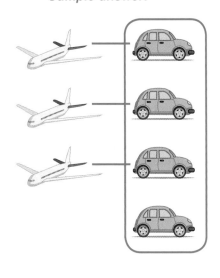

Directions: Draw lines between the objects in each group. Circle the group that is greater in number than the other group.

66   sixty-six

Laurie's Notes

Apply and Grow: Practice

MAKING INSTRUCTIONAL DECISIONS

In this lesson, students used matching to decide which group has more. The arrangement of the objects affects the students' ability to subitize and visually identify which group has more. Matching the objects one-to-one is necessary for many students.

EMERGING students may have difficulty identifying the number of objects in a group. They may also compare attributes such as size versus counting the quantity of the objects in each group. If students are not secure with the counting sequence, then it may be more difficult to identify a group of four objects as being more than a group of three objects.

PROFICIENT students can identify the number of objects in a group and use a strategy for deciding which group has more. These students may be using the counting sequence to say that a group of four objects is more than a group of three objects because four is greater than three.

Supporting Learners

- Provide two types of markers, such as fine-line and thick. Have one student select a random amount of fine-line markers to hold. The other student should select more thick markers than the thin-line markers. Each student counts their markers and states the amount.
- Read the directions to students, allowing time between sentences. This time will allow students to complete each step, one at a time.

Extension: Adding Rigor

- Roll two dice. Students tell which die has more dots on its face.

Meeting the needs of
all learners.

Name _____

1–4. Sample answers are given.

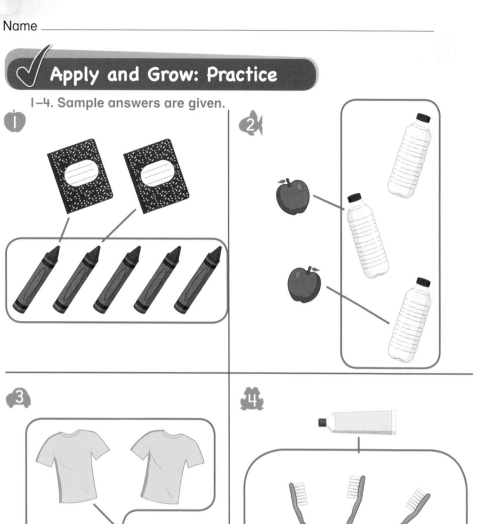

①

②

③

④

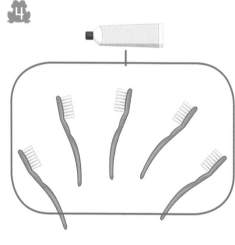

Directions: ❶–❹ Draw lines between the objects in each group. Circle the group that is greater in number than the other group.

Chapter 2 | Lesson 2

sixty-seven 67

© Big Ideas Learning, LLC

Laurie's Notes

Think and Grow: Modeling Real Life

This application allows students to show their understanding of one group having more objects than another group. Keep in mind that, although students have formally studied numbers to five, they may show a group of more than five when drawing their pictures.

? **Preview:** "Do you like to take pictures? When do you take pictures?" Allow students to share their experiences with partners or the class.

? Discuss the top part of the page that shows two stickers and one photo. "I want you to think about what it would look like if there were more photos than stickers. How many more photos would you need to draw? Explain to your neighbor." Students are likely to say that they need to draw lots of photos. Probe to see whether they can reason about a more precise amount of photos. Listen for an understanding that at least two more photos need to be drawn. Remind students to draw lines between the objects to show they are correct.

• **Supporting Learners:** When students are hindered by the need to draw, have them use physical materials, such as counters. Use the red side to represent the photos and the yellow side to represent the stickers. Can they use physical materials to model their understanding of one group having more objects than another group?

? **Critique the Reasoning of Others:** Look for examples of four or five photos drawn for the bottom portion of the page. Pair these students or display both samples under a document camera. "Do both examples show a group that has more than three objects? How do you know?"

◉ When students are shown two groups of objects with unequal amounts, can they determine which group has more? How are they deciding? Do they count? Are they matching one-to-one? Can they tell by eyesight? Be sure to use groups that differ in quantity by only one or two.

Closure

• Have students work with partners. Students hold up a random number of fingers on one hand. Partners tell how many fingers they see and hold up more fingers on their own hands. Partners should explain how they know that they are showing more fingers. Reverse roles.

First Student   Second Student

Sample answer:

Sample answer:

Directions: Draw photos on the scrapbook so that the number of photos is greater than the number of stickers. Draw lines between the objects in each group to show that you are correct.

68   sixty-eight

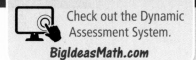

Connect and Extend Learning

Practice Notes

- **Exercises 3 and 4:** The objects are scattered so remind students to draw lines to partner the objects that are closest to each other.
- **Exercise 5:** Students may draw many more than 5 photos.

Cross-Curricular Connections

Language Arts

- Show sight words that students have learned so far. Compare the number of letters in each word. Tell which word has more letters.
- Have students fold a piece of paper in half. On the left side of the paper, have students draw or write a story about something they can do alone. On the right side of the paper, have students draw or write a story about an activity that requires more than one person.

Learning Target: Show and tell whether one group has a greater number of objects than another group.

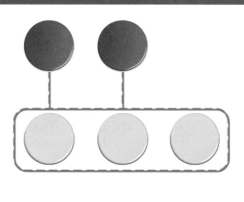

Directions: Draw lines between the counters in each group. Circle the group that is greater in number than the other group.

I and 2. Sample answers are given.

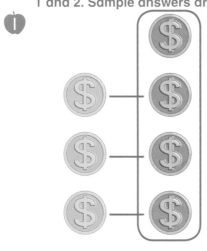

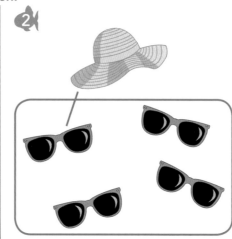

Directions: ❶ and ❷ Draw lines between the objects in each group. Circle the group that is greater in number than the other group.

Chapter 2 | Lesson 2

sixty-nine 69

Connect and Extend Learning

Extend Student Learning

Logical-Mathematical

- Play "Apples in a Basket." Cut out two basket shapes from brown construction paper for each student or pair of students. Label the paper baskets with the words *number* and *greater than*. Have students choose a number from 0 to 5, and place it on the *number* basket. Students build that number using the red sides of two-color counters. Then, students can build a number that is greater than the number card on the *greater than* basket.

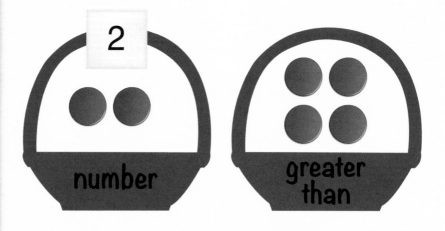

Lesson Resources	
Surface Level	**Deep Level**
Resources by Chapter • Extra Practice • Reteach Differentiating the Lesson Skills Review Handbook Skills Trainer	Resources by Chapter • Enrichment and Extension Graphic Organizers Dynamic Assessment System • Lesson Practice

3–5. Sample answers are given.

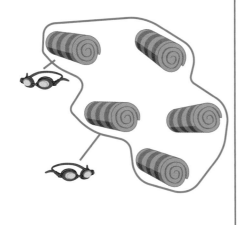

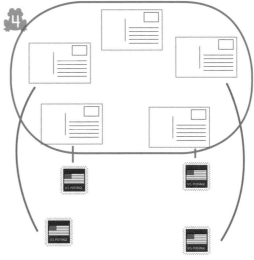

Directions: 3 and 4 Draw lines between the objects in each group. Circle the group that is greater in number than the other group. 5 Draw photos on the scrapbook so that the number of photos is greater than the number of stickers. Draw lines between the objects in each group to show that you are correct.

Check out the
Dynamic Classroom.

BigIdeasMath.com

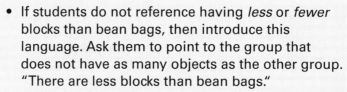

Laurie's Notes

Preparing to Teach

In the previous sections, students were able to show and tell when two groups had the same numbers of objects or when one group had more objects than another group. The last comparative relationship is one group has less, or fewer, objects than another group. Students will make the comparison by again matching objects from the two groups.

Materials

• collections of objects to match
• linking cubes
• two-color counters

Dig In (Circle Time)

Place two groups of objects in the center of the circle, for instance one block and four bean bags. Students will compare the quantity of objects in each group. Give students time to share what they see.

• If students do not reference having *less* or *fewer* blocks than bean bags, then introduce this language. Ask them to point to the group that does not have as many objects as the other group. "There are less blocks than bean bags."

• Add another block and repeat the discussion. Make sure students can visually match the objects by arranging as shown.

• Repeat with a group of three blocks and four bean bags.

• **Extension:** Add a fourth block to assess students' recall of equal, or the same amount.

• Remove one block at a time and ask whether there are still less blocks than bean bags. Continue until you have one block.

• **Extension:** Some students may talk about a group of zero blocks. Acknowledge their good thinking.

⊙ Discuss the learning target and the two success criteria. "You pointed to the group of blocks because there were less blocks than bean bags."

❓ Teaching Prompt   ⊙ Learning Target

Name _____

Learning Target: Show and tell whether one group has a lesser number of objects than another group.

Explore and Grow

Directions: Use counters to show the number of rabbits. Use counters to show the number of holes. Are there fewer rabbits or fewer holes? **holes**

© Big Ideas Learning, LLC

Chapter 2 | Lesson 3

seventy-one **71**

Explore and Grow

? Students cover each rabbit with a yellow counter and each hole with a red counter. Ask, "How many rabbits are there? How many holes?" Students slide the counters to the five frames.

? Ask, "Do we have a hole for each rabbit? How do you know?" No, there are two rabbits with no hole; there is not a match for each yellow counter; there are five yellow counters and only three red.

• Students can visually compare, or manipulate their counters to compare.

• Probe students' reasoning. If there are *more* yellow counters than red counters, then there are *less* red counters than yellow counters. Alternately, if five is greater than three, then three is less than five. Discuss this connection.

Laurie's Notes

Think and Grow

Getting Started

- Introduce the vocabulary cards for **fewer** and **less than**. Refer to the circled group of books as having less than the other stack of books and the circled group of counters as having fewer counters.

- Students may relate to statements such as, "You have too many crackers. Take fewer." Fewer relates to quantity, not size or length. Add the vocabulary and examples to the anchor chart if you've created one.

- Have students find examples in the classroom of a set that has fewer, or less, objects than another set.

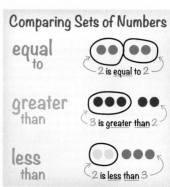

Comparing Sets of Numbers

equal to — 2 is equal to 2

greater than — 3 is greater than 2

less than — 2 is less than 3

Teaching Notes

- There are two groups of objects in each exercise. In the example, lines are provided for students to trace to help match the objects between groups. The group that has all of its objects matched is the group with fewer or less objects than the other group. Draw a line through the group that has fewer objects.

- **? Model:** Together as a class, trace over the dotted lines between the owls and the trees. "Is there an owl for each tree? Are there less owls or trees? To show that there is a lesser number of owls, draw a line through the group of owls."

- Repeat for the guinea pigs and cage. You may hear students say, "There are not enough cages for all of the guinea pigs." Make sure they understand that *not enough* means there are less of them.

- **? Reason Abstractly and Quantitatively:** Say, "If three is more than one, then one is less than three. Is this correct? How do you know?"

- There are different ways in which students will match the fish and fish bowls. They may even match two fish to a bowl. Remind students that only one fish goes to a bowl.

- ◉ Some students may visually decide which group has fewer objects. Other students may need to match the objects first. The arrangement of the objects also influences how students are making their decision. Discuss each success criterion by referencing each example. Have students use their thumb signals to show how confident they are with each criterion.

- **Supporting Learners:** Use linking cubes to represent each quantity. Linking cube towers can be used to decide which quantity is less.

Sample answer:

Sample answer:

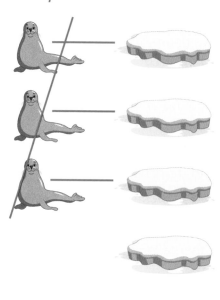
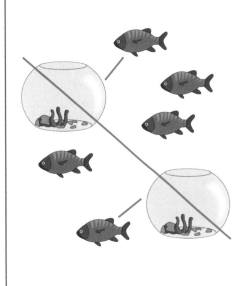

Directions: Draw lines between the objects in each group. Draw a line through the group that is less in number than the other group.

MATH MUSICALS

Fish Crackers

You can use the song
Fish Crackers
as students learn to count to 10!

Laurie's Notes

Apply and Grow: Practice

MAKING INSTRUCTIONAL DECISIONS

Students may have greater difficulty with the concept of *fewer* than with the concept of *more*. You want students to be able to connect these two concepts. Use the examples for this purpose while comparing living objects to their habitats. Students can practice statements such as, "There are more horses than barns, so there are fewer barns than horses."

Students develop number sense gradually through exploration, practice, and real-life experiences with numbers and their relationships. Students can give examples of similar contexts, such as dogs and a doghouse to show their understanding.

EMERGING students may have difficulty identifying the number of objects in a group. They may also find the context confusing. They may say that both horses can fit into the barn, which of course is true. Remind students that they are only matching one object from each group and not making a decision about how many objects might fit.

- Students may need more number sense practice. Provide activities that support students with modeling numbers, associating the numeral with the quantity, identifying the same amounts, and working with *more* before focusing on *less*.

PROFICIENT students are able to identify the number of objects in a group and have a strategy for deciding which group has fewer. Students may even be using the counting sequence to say that a group of two objects is less than a group of three objects because two is less than three.

- **Construct Viable Arguments:** Have students explain how they know one group has less objects than another group.

Extensions: Adding Rigor

- Have students pick one of the examples and tell their partners a story about what they see. The stories should include the vocabulary words from this chapter. They can use the Newton and Descartes puppets in their story telling.
- Have students choose a number from 1–5 and draw that many objects on the paper. On the back, they can draw another group that has a fewer number of objects.

Meeting the needs of all learners.

Name _____

1–4. Sample answers are given.

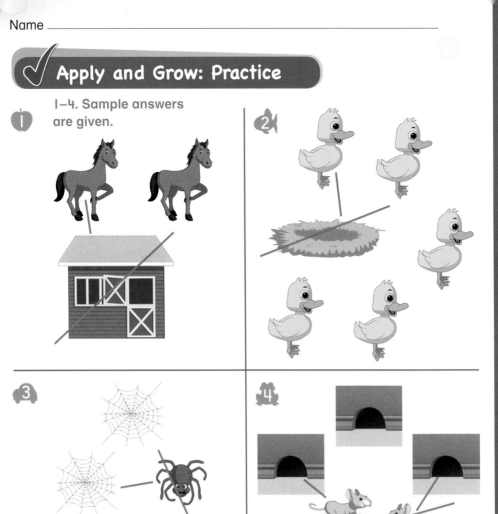

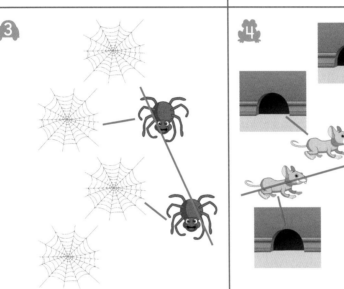

Directions: ❶–❹ Draw lines between the objects in each group. Draw a line through the group that is less in number than the other group.

Chapter 2 | Lesson 3

seventy-three   73

Laurie's Notes

Teach the words *hummingbird*, *flower*, and *bush*, if necessary. Ask students, "How many hummingbirds are in the top picture?" Have students hold up the appropriate number of fingers to indicate that there are two. Then ask, "How many flowers did you draw?" Students should hold up two or more fingers. Ask students, "How many hummingbirds are in the bottom picture?" Have students hold up the appropriate number of fingers to indicate that there are five. Then ask, "How many flowers did you draw?" Students should hold up three or fewer fingers.

Think and Grow: Modeling Real Life

This application allows students to show their understanding of one group having fewer objects than another group.

- **Preview:** Ask, "What type of birds have you seen? Do you know the names of different birds? What do you wonder about birds?" Allow students to share their experiences with partners or the class.
- Discuss the exercise that shows two birds and one flower.
- Make sure students account for the flowers that are already pictured as they respond to and answer the questions. "Which group has fewer objects, the birds or the flowers? Could you draw more flowers so there are less birds than flowers? How many more flowers would you need to draw? Explain to your neighbor." Students are likely to say that they need to draw lots of flowers. Probe to see whether they can reason about a more precise amount of flowers. Listen for an understanding that at least two more flowers need to be drawn.
- **Model with Mathematics:** Students can use counters or linking cubes to cover and create objects to match before they draw.
- After students draw, each bird will have a flower to land on. Draw lines to match the objects. Notice that the directions are different for the bottom picture. Now there will not be enough flowers for each bird.
- **Reason Abstractly and Quantitatively:** "In the bottom picture I want to have *less* flowers than there are birds. Talk with your neighbor. Can you draw more flowers and still have less than the number of birds?" Give students think time and, if necessary, relate this to the Dig In time when objects were removed (versus added).
- Display the page under a document camera. Students can model their thinking. Drawing one or two more flowers will still show a quantity less than five. Some students may mention that there are already less. Acknowledge that this is great thinking, but remind them that the directions say they need to draw some flowers.
- Have students tell their partners what they have learned today. Do they discuss matching objects between two groups? Are they using vocabulary correctly?
- **Supporting Learners:** Provide two-color counters, paper clips, or string to help students match objects.

Closure

- Hold up four objects that are visible to all students. Ask them to use their fingers to show a group that is less than four.

Sample answer:

Sample answer:

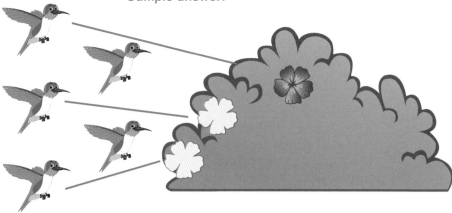

Directions:
- Draw flowers on the bush so that the number of hummingbirds is less than the number of flowers. Draw lines between the objects in each group to show that you are correct.
- Draw flowers on the bush so that the number of flowers is less than the number of hummingbirds. Draw lines between the objects in each group to show that you are correct.

74   seventy-four

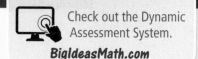
Connect and Extend Learning

Practice Notes

- **Exercise 1:** Students may say that all of the ants can fit in the hole. Clarify "What are the two groups?"
- **Exercise 5:** There is one berry in the bush to encourage students to represent a number other than 0. Emphasize the direction to draw berries and not to leave just one berry.

Cross-Curricular Connections

Language Arts

- *Monster Musical Chairs* by Stuart J. Murphy; This book covers the beginning stage of subtracting one from a given number. The story begins with six monsters and five chairs. After each round of musical chairs, there are fewer and fewer chairs and monsters. Write or illustrate a silly story using the prompt, "What would happen if the classroom had fewer tables or desks?" Use your Newton and Descartes puppets to tell the story or sing the song.

Social Studies

- Discuss different modes of transportation. Have students think about how having fewer seats on a bus or on a subway train could affect the passengers. What if there were fewer buses going to and from school? Will a car move if it has less than four tires?

Name _____

Learning Target: Show and tell whether one group has a lesser number of objects than another group.

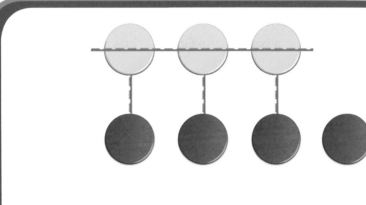

Directions: Draw lines between the counters in each group. Draw a line through the group that is less in number than the other group.

① **I and 2. Sample answers are given.**

②

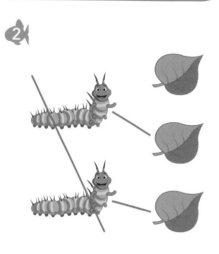

Directions: ① and ② Draw lines between the objects in each group. Draw a line through the group that is less in number than the other group.

Chapter 2 | Lesson 3

seventy-five **75**

Connect and Extend Learning

Extend Student Learning

Visual-Spatial

- Hand out a copy of the Greater Than or Less Than Instructional Resource to each student. Have students color in the corresponding number of boxes for each number in the table. For Exercises 1–4, students circle the number that shows more than the other number. For Exercises 5–8, students draw a line through the number that shows less than the other number.

Logical-Mathematical

- Play "Apples in a Basket" again and include another basket with the label *less than*. See page T-70 for a description of the game.

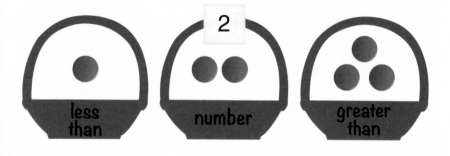

Lesson Resources	
Surface Level	**Deep Level**

Resources by Chapter
  • Extra Practice
  • Reteach
Differentiating the Lesson
Skills Review Handbook
Skills Trainer
Math Musicals
	Resources by Chapter
	  • Enrichment and Extension
	Graphic Organizers
	Math Musicals
	Dynamic Assessment System
	  • Lesson Practice

3–5. Sample answers are given.

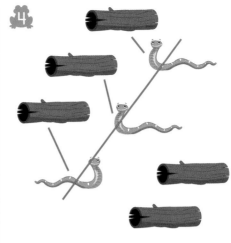

Directions: 3 and 4 Draw lines between the objects in each group. Draw a line through the group that is less in number than the other group.
5 Draw berries on the bush so that the number of berries is less than the number of bears. Draw lines between the objects in each group to show that you are correct.

76   seventy-six

Laurie's Notes

Learning Target

Use counting to compare the numbers of objects in two groups.

Success Criteria

• Compare the numbers of objects in two groups using the words *greater than*, *less than*, or *equal to*.

• Explain how to compare two groups by counting.

Warm-Up

Practice opportunities for the following are available in the Resources by Chapter or at *BigIdeasMath.com*.

• Daily skills
• Vocabulary
• Prerequisite skills

ELL Support

Review the terms learned in this chapter. Draw sets of circles and squares that illustrate the concepts of *greater than*, *less than*, and *equal to* on the board. Number them 1, 2, and 3. Ask, "Which drawing shows that the number of circles is greater than the number of squares?" Have students hold up the number of fingers to indicate the appropriate drawing. Repeat for each phrase.

Preparing to Teach

Students have used matching to compare the quantities of objects in two groups. In this lesson, they will use counting to compare two groups. Language is especially important in this lesson. While showing students two red crayons and four blue crayons, you want them to count and make three correct statements: "Four is more than two. Two is less than four. Two and four are not the same amount."

Materials

• linking cubes
• two-color counters

Dig In (Circle Time)

Use two groups of linking cubes, either loose or in towers, as models for students to count. Using a different color of cubes for each group helps students to reference the group.

• **Big Idea:** You want students to recognize that when counting groups of unequal amounts, the last numbers said will be different. When counting equal amounts, the last numbers said will be the same.

• Hold a different number of linking cubes in each hand, and put one hand behind your back. Students must see both sets of linking cubes in order to compare by matching. If only one group is visible at a time, then students must use a different strategy to solve.

? "I have red cubes in this hand and blue cubes in the hand behind my back. You can only ask to see one group at a time. Do I have more red, more blue, or the same number of cubes?" Have students talk with each other to decide on a strategy.

? Some students will suggest counting. "How can counting the linking cubes help us to compare?" The students' language may not be precise, but you want to hear their explanations.

• If time permits, give each pair of students two sets of different colored cubes. Ask one partner to make the number 2. Ask the other partner to make a number greater than 2. "Count each amount to show you are correct." Change the students' roles, the starting number, and the comparison term each time.

? Teaching Prompt   ⊙ Learning Target

Learning Target: Use counting to compare the number of objects in two groups.

Explore and Grow

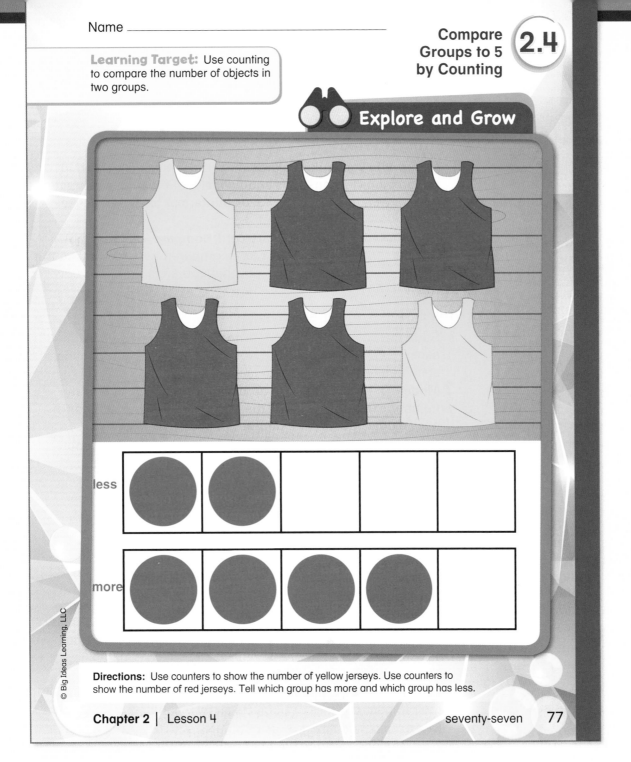

less

more

Directions: Use counters to show the number of yellow jerseys. Use counters to show the number of red jerseys. Tell which group has more and which group has less.

Chapter 2 | Lesson 4 seventy-seven **77**

© Big Ideas Learning, LLC

Explore and Grow

- **Use Appropriate Tools Strategically:** Have students cover each yellow jersey with a yellow counter and each red jersey with a red counter. Have students slide the yellow counters to one five frame and the red counters to the other five frame.

- "Tell your partner how many jerseys you have of each color."

- **? Model with Mathematics:** Ask, "What color jersey do you have more of? What color jersey do you have less of? Tell your neighbor how you knew which color jersey was more or less." Listen for students to mention counting, or that four is more than two.

Check student understanding of the words *racket*, *ball*, *hockey stick*, and *puck* by saying each word and asking students to point to the appropriate picture. Hockey may be something an ELL has not seen before, so explain that it is a sport played on ice in which you try to score goals, similar to soccer. Read the instructions aloud and have students complete the page as you demonstrate the actions to take, if needed. Then have students practice language in pairs as they did before. One student says to the other, "Describe the number of rackets and balls." Then have them alternate roles for the hockey exercise.

Beginner students may answer using a sentence, such as, "Rackets are greater than balls." **Intermediate** and **Advanced** students may answer using sentences, such as, "The number of rackets is greater than the number of balls."

Think and Grow

Getting Started

- Review the vocabulary words that students have learned in the previous lessons. This should include *equal, more, greater than, fewer,* and *less than*. Use counters or linking cubes to model each.
- Introduce the new vocabulary card, **compare**. Give examples of contexts where students have compared two amounts in the last three lessons. Make it clear that you are comparing *how many* are in two different groups.

Teaching Notes

- Students need to count and write the number of objects in each group. There are three problems and three comparison statements. Pause between each direction line.
- **? Model:** Chorally count the number of purple dots. Write the number 5. Do the same for the green dots. "Is the number of purple dots equal to the number of green dots?"
- **? Attend to Precision:** "How do you know the groups are not equal?" Listen for five is greater than two, or there are more purple dots than green dots.
- Discuss how counting is being used to compare *how many* objects are in two groups. When comparing two numbers, count and listen to which number comes first. This is the lesser number.
- You could have students circle the two numbers on a number path and visually see which number comes first.
- In the second problem, students are showing which group has more objects by circling the greater number. Expect many students to be able to subitize and know how many without counting.
- The arrangement of the objects in the third problem makes subitizing more challenging. Expect that students will point with their fingers or cross out objects as they count.
- **? Extension:** "Are any groups of objects equal? How can you make the hockey sticks and hockey pucks equal?"
- ◉ Have students use their thumb signals to show how well they can compare the numbers of objects in two groups. Probe to see that students are also able to explain how counting is used when comparing.
- **Supporting Learners:** Have students count as they place a counter on each object. Then have students explain for which group they used more (or less) counters to cover. Physically placing counters can help students relate the numbers of objects to the counting sequence.

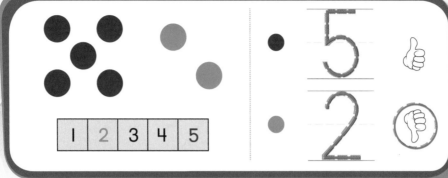

1 | 2 | 3 | 4 | 5

Directions: Count the objects in each group. Write each number.
- Is the number of purple dots equal to the number of green dots? Circle the thumbs up for *yes* or the thumbs down for *no*.
- Compare the numbers of tennis rackets and tennis balls. Circle the number that is greater than the other number.
- Compare the numbers of hockey sticks and hockey pucks. Draw a line through the number that is less than the other number.

78   seventy-eight

Meeting the needs of
all learners.

Apply and Grow: Practice

MAKING INSTRUCTIONAL DECISIONS

Students must understand one-to-one correspondence and be proficient with the counting sequence in order to successfully compare two quantities by counting. The vocabulary in the first three lessons may cause confusion for students. The statements, "There are fewer nets than soccer balls" and "The number of nets is less than the number of soccer balls" are good examples of this. Both statements convey the same comparison, yet, *fewer* and *less than* cannot be interchanged in the statements. You may need to rephrase questions in order to assess a student's understanding of comparing by counting.

EMERGING students may not be secure with the counting sequence and need additional experience with counters or linking cubes. They may also need more practice with comparative vocabulary.

- Students need more practice with seeing objects arranged in lines when comparing.
- Give students extra time to practice the vocabulary terms by using them in sentences. An example of this is to say, "I have *more* buttons on my shirt than my pockets," or "I have the *same* number of shoes as feet." Model the counting process as you look at two groups of objects.

PROFICIENT students are able to compare the quantities in two groups by counting. They may not be able to explain different strategies related to how objects are displayed, but can successfully compare two groups.

- Encourage students to think about how they are comparing groups, and how they can explain their thinking.

Additional Support

- Provide students with objects in simple formations. Allow them to use Number Paths 1–5 found in the Instructional Resources. Students can explain how they identify and compare numbers.

Extension: Adding Rigor

- Play "Can You Guess My Number?" Put five or less small objects behind your back. Give students a series of comparison clues about the hidden number of objects. After hearing each clue, students should write their ideas on a whiteboard. For example, if your number is three, you could give clues, such as "My number is less than four. My number is greater than one. My number is not the same as two." Once they feel they have the answer, they write their number.

Name _____

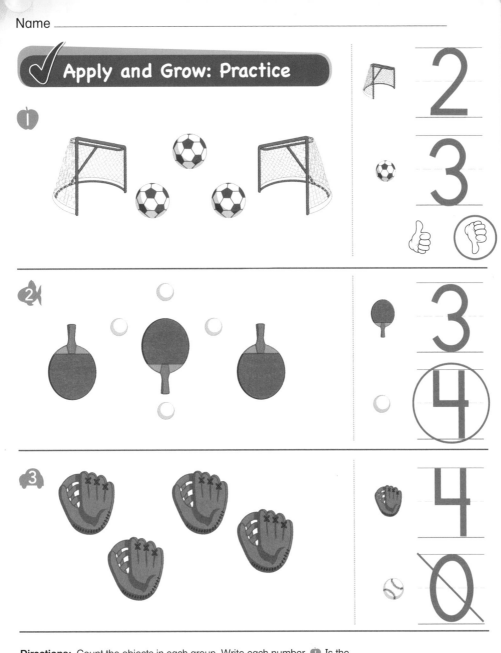

Directions: Count the objects in each group. Write each number. ① Is the number of soccer balls equal to the number of soccer goals? Circle the thumbs up for *yes* or the thumbs down for *no*. ② Circle the number that is greater than the other number. ③ Draw a line through the number that is less than the other number.

© Big Ideas Learning, LLC

Chapter 2 | Lesson 4   seventy-nine   79

Think and Grow: Modeling Real Life

This application allows students to show their understanding of greater than and less than. It is important that students draw objects for each comparison. You will have a better understanding of students' thinking when viewing their drawings.

- **Preview:** There may be students who are not familiar with golf or miniature golf. Ask a student who is familiar to explain the game to the class.
- Begin each exercise by asking students to count the number of golf clubs on the ground.
- Read the directions as stated and rephrase as needed. The first direction line could be, "You want more golf balls than golf clubs." Have students write the numbers of golf balls and golf clubs. Observe and note whether students write the number first or draw the golf balls first.
- **Look for and Make Use of Structure:** Have students show their pictures to one another. You want them to notice that their neighbors may have a different number of golf balls but that they are both correct.
- **Note:** The directions tell students to draw golf balls on the ground in the second exercise. Students may say that they can draw zero balls. Can they explain why it is less than four? If students can successfully explain their answers, then they have grasped the concept.
- **? Extension:** "How many golf clubs do you need to draw in the first exercise to have an equal amount? How many golf balls do you need to draw in the second exercise to have an equal amount?"
- ◉ Revisit the learning target. Have students signal their ability to use counting to tell whether the number of objects in one group is greater than, less than, or equal to the number of objects in another group.
- **Supporting Learners:** Some students may confuse the meaning of greater than and the meaning of less than. Display the vocabulary cards for students to see. If necessary, place a set of vocabulary cards on their desks.

Closure

- Review counting to 5. Then show three linking cubes, and have students count them. Ask students to model a number that is greater than three. Allow students to share their answers. Repeat this process several times, having students show numbers greater than, less than, or equal to the initial number modeled.

Sample answer:

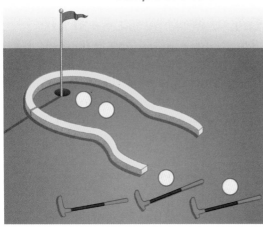

Sample answer:

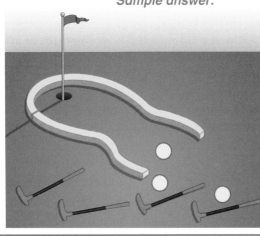

Directions:

- Draw golf balls on the ground so that the number of golf balls is greater than the number of golf clubs. Write the number of each object. Circle the number that is greater than the other number.
- Draw golf balls on the ground so that the number of golf balls is less than the number of golf clubs. Write the number of each object. Draw a line through the number that is less than the other number.

80   eighty

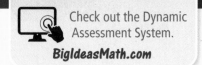
Connect and Extend Learning

Practice Notes

- **Exercises 1 and 2:** Remind students that they are not drawing lines to match objects but are counting the number of objects, writing the number, and comparing the numbers.
- **Exercise 3:** Students may want to draw one set of pom-poms to represent the pom-poms. Refer them to the picture next to the writing line showing one pom-pom as the object.

Cross-Curricular Connections

Language Arts

- *Bears on Wheels* by Stan and Jan Berenstain; As you read the story, have students compare the two groups of bears using comparative vocabulary terms.

Social Studies

- Select five students at a time to tell how they get to school. Count and write the number of students who get to school by car, bus, subway train, walking, or riding a bike. Use *greater than*, *less than*, and *equal to* for comparing.
  Note: Multiple comparisons can be made if the five students use more than two types of transportation.

Learning Target: Use counting to compare the numbers of objects in two groups.

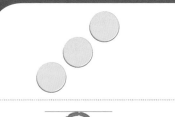 

 3 3

Directions: Count the objects in each group. Write each number. Is the number of yellow counters equal to the number of red counters? Circle the thumbs up for *yes* or the thumbs down for *no*.

   2

 4

Directions: ① Count the objects in each group. Write each number. Is the number of basketball hoops equal to the number of basketballs? Circle the thumbs up for *yes* or the thumbs down for *no*.

Chapter 2 | Lesson 4

eighty-one 81

Connect and Extend Learning

Extend Student Learning

Bodily-Kinesthetic

❓ Place number cards in a pile. Hold up a number card for students to see. Without saying the number aloud, ask students to show the number using manipulatives. Have students place their manipulatives on top of a whiteboard. Hold up another card and ask them to show that number of manipulatives in a line below their first group. Have students count and record how many in each group. Ask, "How many do you have in each group? Use *greater than*, *less than*, or *equal* to compare your groups." I have five bears in my first group and three bears in my second group. Five is greater than three.

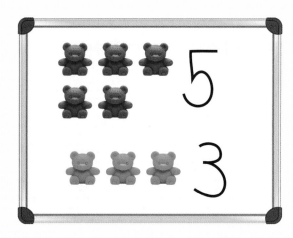

Lesson Resources	
Surface Level	**Deep Level**
Resources by Chapter • Extra Practice • Reteach Differentiating the Lesson Skills Review Handbook Skills Trainer	Resources by Chapter • Enrichment and Extension Graphic Organizers Dynamic Assessment System • Lesson Practice

⑤

4

Sample answer:

③

3

2̸

Directions: ② Count the objects in each group. Write each number. Circle the number that is greater than the other number. ③ Draw pom-poms on the floor in the picture so that the number of pom-poms is less than the number of megaphones. Write the number of each object. Draw a line through the number that is less than the other number.

82   eighty-two

2.5

Learning Target

Compare two numbers.

Success Criteria

- Tell whether two numbers are the same.
- Use *greater than* and *less than* to describe two numbers that are not the same.
- Draw to show how one number compares to another.

Warm-Up

Practice opportunities for the following are available in the Resources by Chapter or at *BigIdeasMath.com.*

- Daily skills
- Vocabulary
- Prerequisite skills

ELL Support

Review numbers 1 through 5 in a variety of ways. Have students listen as you count aloud. Then have them count aloud. Next, have them count off one-by-one in sequence. Have students watch as you write each number on the board. Point to one number and have the class say its name. Repeat for each number.

Laurie's Notes

Preparing to Teach

Students previously compared two groups by matching and counting. The objects in each group were seen and manipulated by students. In this lesson, students compare two written numerals. To provide support for all students, make sure the five frame models for each number are visible.

Materials

- linking cubes
- whiteboards and markers
- two-color counters

Dig In (Circle Time)

Students write on whiteboards and use linking cubes to model numbers.

- Write a number on your whiteboard but do not reveal it to the students.
- **Directions:** "Write a number from 1 to 5 on your whiteboard. Use your cubes to show the number."
- Show your number to the students. "If you think your number is less than my number, then hold up your whiteboard." Select a few students to explain how they know their numbers are less. What reasoning are students using? Do they talk about counting or number order? Do they mention the visual model?
- "If you think your number is greater than my number, then hold up your whiteboard." Solicit explanations.
- **?** "Has everyone held up their whiteboards? Why not?" Listen for an understanding that the remaining numbers are equal.
- Students will want to repeat the activity in hopes of matching your number! Be sure to write 1 and 5 as one of your number choices.
- ⊙ Linking cube models are one way for students to explain the relationship (greater than, less than, or equal) between two numbers.
- **Extension:** Repeat the activity and add movement. Designate three different areas in the room for students to stand based on whether their numbers are greater than, less than, or equal to the number on your board. Have students discuss the numbers in the three areas of the room.

? Teaching Prompt   ⊙ Learning Target

Learning Target: Compare two numbers.

Explore and Grow

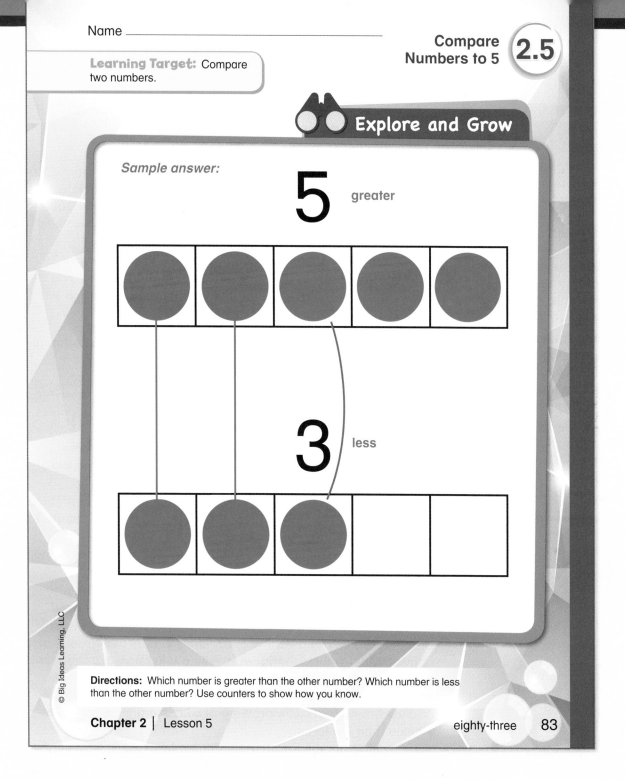

Sample answer:

5 greater

3 less

Directions: Which number is greater than the other number? Which number is less than the other number? Use counters to show how you know.

© Big Ideas Learning, LLC

Chapter 2 | Lesson 5

eighty-three 83

Explore and Grow

- **Model with Mathematics:** Have students use counters to model the number 5 and then the number 3 in the five frames.
- "Tell your partner which number is greater, 5 or 3. Use your five frame models to explain why you are correct." Select a few students to share their reasoning with the class.
- Change the comparison term to *less than* and repeat.

Laurie's Notes

Think and Grow

Getting Started

? Hold up two whiteboards with two different numbers from 1 to 5 so that the numbers you've written are not visible to students. "How can you tell when two numbers are equal?" Listen for an understanding that the numerals are the same. Show the numbers on the whiteboards and compare them.

? "If the numbers are not equal, then how can you tell which number is greater?" You know when one number comes after the other when counting; one number is farther on the number path.

Teaching Notes

? **Model:** "In the first example, we want to compare the numbers 2 and 2. Are they equal? Can you draw to show how you know?" Students may not initially know how to *show they know.* The dotted circles are shown to suggest that by drawing counters you can show there are the same amount of counters for each number. The numbers are the same.

- **Reason Abstractly and Quantitatively:** Watch for students who need to draw first. You want students to understand the quantities and then draw to show their thinking.

- "In the next exercise, we want to know which number is greater than the other. Circle the greater number. Now draw a picture to show how you know."

- In the last exercise, the comparison term changes. "Draw a line through the number that is less than the other number."

- **Think-Pair-Share:** "Talk with your partner about the numbers you compared. Tell how you determined which number was greater and which number was less." Solicit responses.

⊙ Students are working with two numerals versus two groups of objects. Most will be confident in telling when two numbers are equal, but when the numbers are not equal, some may not be as confident. Can they explain which is greater or less? Do they understand how to use a drawing or the counting sequence to explain their reasoning?

- **Extension:** Write the number 4 on the board. "What is a number greater than 4? less than 4? equal to 4?" Have students write or say each answer.

- **Supporting Learners:** Students may have trouble comparing written numerals. Have students draw, imagine, or use manipulatives to represent objects to relate the quantity to the numeral.

2 ◯ ◯
_____
2 ◯ ◯

👍 👎

1 ◯   *Sample answer:*
_____
⑤ ◯ ◯ ◯ ◯ ◯
_____
4 ◯ ◯ ◯ ◯   *Sample answer:*
_____
3̸ ◯ ◯ ◯
_____

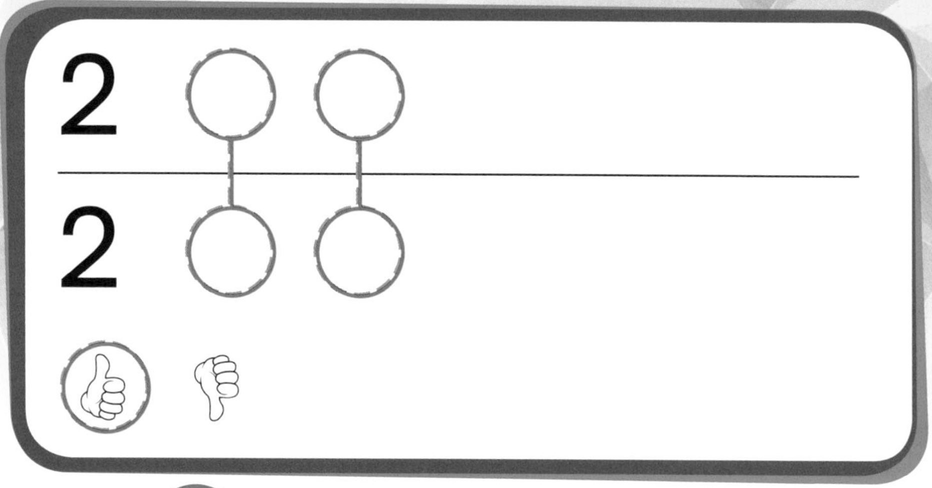

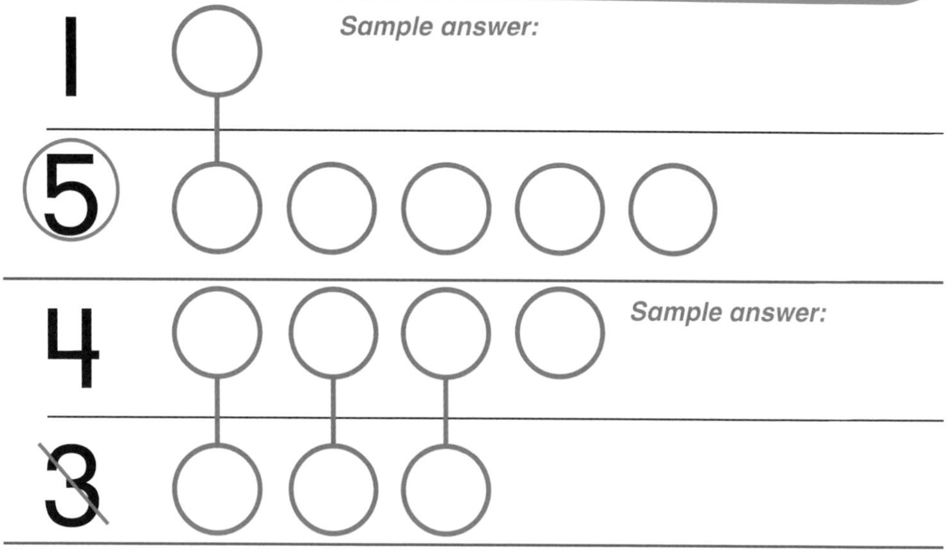

Directions: Compare the numbers.
• Are the numbers equal? Circle the thumbs up for *yes* or the thumbs down for *no*. Draw to show how you know.
• Circle the number that is greater than the other number. Draw to show how you know.
• Draw a line through the number that is less than the other number. Draw to show how you know.

84 eighty-four

© Big Ideas Learning, LLC

Laurie's Notes

Apply and Grow: Practice

MAKING INSTRUCTIONAL DECISIONS

Students have practiced comparing numbers by matching and counting. In these exercises, you want to see whether students are independent in comparing written numerals. The numbers differ by one in each exercise. The exercises may be modified by making the difference between the numbers greater than one.

Look for and Express Regularity in Repeated Reasoning: Students draw objects corresponding to the numbers shown to prove their comparisons. Remember to focus on the "how" when asking students to explain their answers. This helps you learn how they think and address any misconceptions. This helps students to develop their reasoning.

EMERGING students may have difficulty telling and showing how a number is greater than, less than, or equal to another number.

- Provide students with manipulatives, such as linking cubes or two-color counters to compare the numbers.

PROFICIENT students are able to explain how they are comparing two numbers. They can tell whether a number is greater than, less than, or equal to the second number.

- Put two sets of number cards, 1 to 5, in a box or a bag. Have students work in pairs and each draw one number card. Students flip over their cards and use their number paths to determine the comparison.

Additional Support

- Have students move counters forward or backward on the number paths to help compare numbers. The farther to the right the number is on the number path, the greater the number.

Extension: Adding Rigor

- Provide students with five blue and five red linking cubes. Have students use the linking cubes to make their own comparison problems for their partners to solve. The solving partners use whiteboards to write the numbers, and circle or underline the numbers when asked to compare.

Meeting the needs of all learners.

Name _____

1–3. Sample answers are given.

① 2 ◯ ◯

3 ◯ ◯ ◯

👍 👎

② 1 ◯

②̂ ◯ ◯

③ 5 ◯ ◯ ◯ ◯ ◯

4̸ ◯ ◯ ◯ ◯

Directions: Compare the numbers.
① Are the numbers equal? Circle the thumbs up for *yes* or the thumbs down for *no*. Draw to show how you know. ② Circle the number that is greater than the other number. Draw to show how you know. ③ Draw a line through the number that is less than the other number. Draw to show how you know.

© Big Ideas Learning, LLC

Chapter 2 | Lesson 5

eighty-five 85

Laurie's Notes

Think and Grow: Modeling Real Life

This application allows students to show their understanding of comparing written numerals. Students have previously compared two given numbers. Now, they must decide what number to write based on a comparison term, and then draw to show their understanding.

- **Preview:** Ask students whether they know why there are numbers on the sides of the cars. Allow students to discuss their knowledge and experiences of racing within their groups.
- "Write the number that is equal to the number on the blue car." Pause while students write. "Draw to show how you know your numbers are equal." You want students to draw the quantities for the number on the car and the number they wrote.
- **? Think-Pair-Share:** Have students explain their drawing to their partners. "How do you know the number is equal to 4?" Solicit several responses.
- **Teaching Tip:** Prompt students to write the number first and then draw to show their understanding.
- In the next two problems, students write numbers that are greater or less than the numbers on the cars. In each problem, they draw models to explain how they know the comparisons are correct.
- **Note:** Students may write 0. Can they explain why it is less than 5? If students can successfully write and explain their answers, then they have grasped the concept.
- ⊙ Have students use their thumb signals to show their understanding of how to compare two numbers.

Closure

- Write the number 3 on the board. Have all students stand. Show number cards from 0 to 5 in random order. Have students jump when the number is greater than 3, squat when the number is less than 3, and stand still when the number is equal to 3. Allow for time between each answer.

Think and Grow: Modeling Real Life

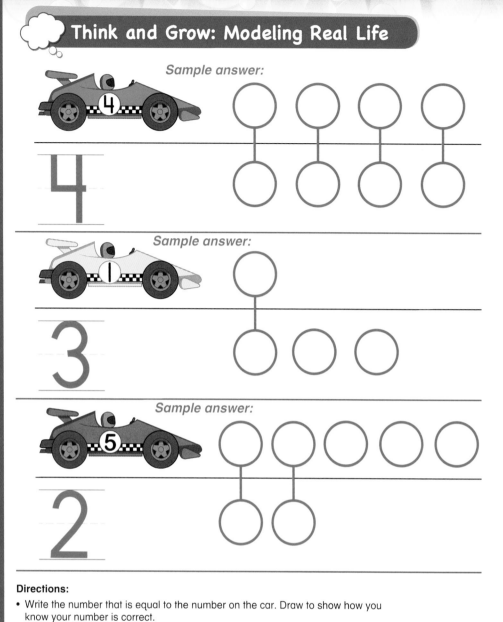

Sample answer:

4

Sample answer:

3

Sample answer:

2

Directions:
- Write the number that is equal to the number on the car. Draw to show how you know your number is correct.
- Write a number that is greater than the number on the car. Draw to show how you know your number is correct.
- Write a number that is less than the number on the car. Draw to show how you know your number is correct.

86   eighty-six

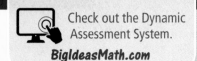
Connect and Extend Learning

Practice Notes

- **Exercises 1–3:** Point out that each number has its own space to draw and show how a number is greater than, less than, or equal to another number.
- **Exercises 1–4:** Different colored crayons can be used for each number when students draw to show how they know. A cover sheet may help students focus on one exercise at a time.
- **Exercise 4:** Read the directions. Students write a number greater than the number on the jersey. Clarify that drawing to show does not mean to draw another jersey. Students should still draw counters.

Cross-Curricular Connections

Language Arts

- Choose two different pages in a book and show students the page numbers. The page numbers are within 5. Discuss which page number is less than or greater than the other page number. Talk about which way you would turn the page to get to a number that is greater than the page you are on.

Science

- Observe objects in nature. For example, students may observe and collect leaves of different colors in the fall. Group the leaves by color and then compare the number in each group.

Learning Target: Compare two numbers.

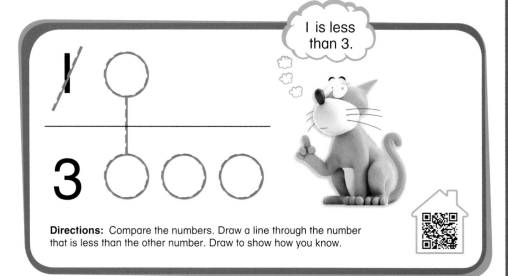

Directions: Compare the numbers. Draw a line through the number that is less than the other number. Draw to show how you know.

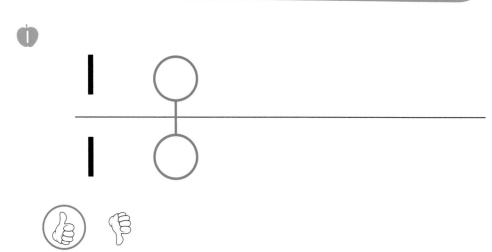

Directions: ❶ Compare the numbers. Are the numbers equal? Circle the thumbs up for *yes* or the thumbs down for *no*. Draw to show how you know.

Connect and Extend Learning

Extend Student Learning

Bodily-Kinesthetic

- Play "Number Freeze." Give each student a number card from 0 to 5. Have students hold their cards and walk around the room until you call, "Freeze." Students stop where they are and then look to find a partner standing near them. Be sure to help students find a partner, or partner with a student when there is an odd number of students. Have partners compare their number cards using the comparison words. Have students switch cards with their partners and walk around the room again. You can have students complete the activity several times.

| 2 | 5 |

Lesson Resources	
Surface Level	**Deep Level**
Resources by Chapter • Extra Practice • Reteach Differentiating the Lesson Skills Review Handbook Skills Trainer	Resources by Chapter • Enrichment and Extension Graphic Organizers Dynamic Assessment System • Lesson Practice

2 4

2

3 2

5

4

3

4

Directions: **2** Compare the numbers. Are the numbers equal? Circle the thumbs up for *yes* or the thumbs down for *no*. Draw to show how you know. **3** Compare the numbers. Draw a line through the number that is less than the other number. Draw to show how you know. **4** Write a number that is greater than the number on the jersey. Draw to show how you know your number is correct.

Laurie's Notes

ELL Support

Have students work in groups to practice language, discuss, and complete the page. Provide the names of the objects pictured, if needed. Expect students to perform as described.

Beginner students may provide one-word answers by stating only the number that answers each statement.

Intermediate students may provide single sentence answers that compare numbers, such as, "One is less than four."

Advanced students may use multiple sentences to answer, such as, "I drew a line through number 1. One is less than four."

Performance Task

In this task, students demonstrate their understanding of comparison words by writing and drawing to show a number that is less than, greater than, or equal to another number. In Exercise 1, each side of the domino is counted separately. In Exercise 2, you may need to explain how Tic-Tac-Toe is played. The empty spaces in this sample will need to be filled with Os.

- Decide ahead of time whether students will be working independently, in pairs, or in groups.
- Pause between direction lines for students to complete each step.
- Have students share their work and thinking with others. Discuss as a class.

Exercise	Answers and Notes	Points
1	1, 4; a line through 1	3
2	5 drawn Os; 4, 5, a circle around 5	4
3	3, 3, 4; circles around both 3s	5
	Total	12

Performance Task **2**

①

②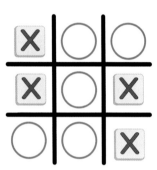

③

© Big Ideas Learning, LLC

Directions: ① Count the dots on each side of the domino. Write the 2 numbers. Draw a line through the number that is less than the other number. ② Draw O's on the game board so that the number of O's is greater than the number of X's. Write each number. Circle the number that is greater than the other number. ③ Write each number. Circle the numbers that are equal.

Chapter 2   **89**

Laurie's Notes

Toss and Compare

Materials

- 1 two-color counter per student
- 1 copy of Toss and Compare Numbers from 0–5 Recording Sheet* per pair of students

*Found in the Instructional Resources

Students can work in pairs or small groups.

- **?** "What do you see on this page?" numbers and dot patterns for the numbers 0 to 5 This question helps students strengthen their recognition of written numbers, as well as their ability to subitize.
- Hand out the two-color counters and a Toss and Compare Numbers from 0–5 Recording Sheet to each pair of students.
- Read the directions at the bottom of the page. Model how to gently toss a counter to keep it from rolling off of the game board. Let students know that when their counter rolls off of the page, they can toss again.
- When the game concludes, focus the discussion on the students' reasoning about which number was greater.
- **?** **Attend to Precision:** "How did you know which number was greater?" used the number path; counted to the greater number; compared the written numbers
- **?** "How did you know which number to choose when your counter landed on Newton or Descartes? Why did you choose 5?" Five is the greatest number. Students may have chosen a different number and could still be correct. Their explanations would need to be that it was greater than their partners' number.
- **?** "Which number on the board is greater than all of the other numbers? less than all of the other numbers?"
- **Supporting Learners:** Give students additional manipulatives to build each number.
- **Supporting Learners:** Allow students to draw dots on the Toss and Compare Numbers from 0–5 Recording Sheet to show their numbers and to help them compare.

Closure

- "How did you compare two numbers when one was written and one was drawn as a dot pattern?" I counted the dots and wrote that number. Then I used the number path to compare the two numbers; I counted to the greater number; I drew dots for the written number. Then I matched the dots to find which number was greater.

Toss and Compare

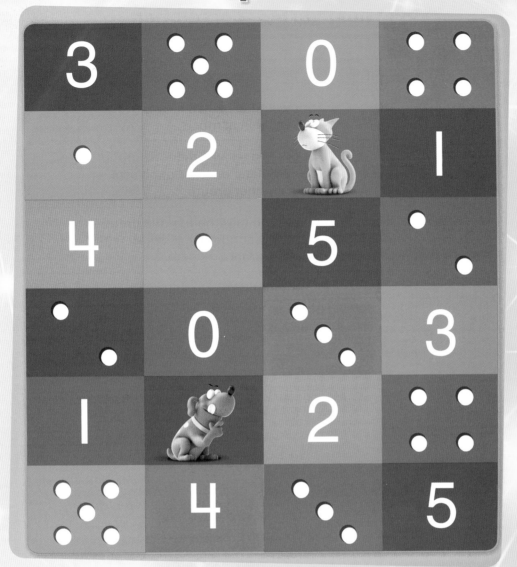

Directions: Take turns tossing a counter onto the board. If the counter lands on Newton or Descartes, choose any number from 0 to 5. Write the numbers on your Toss and Compare Numbers from 0 to 5 Recording Sheet. Circle the number that is greater than the other number. Circle both numbers if they are equal. Repeat this process until you fill your sheet.

Learning Target Correlation

Lesson	Learning Target	Exercises
2.1	Show and tell whether two groups are equal in number.	1–3
2.2	Show and tell whether one group has a greater number of objects than another group.	4
2.3	Show and tell whether one group has a lesser number of objects than another group.	5
2.4	Use counting to compare the numbers of objects in two groups.	6–8
2.5	Compare two numbers.	9–11

2.1 Equal Groups

1–3. Sample answers are given.

1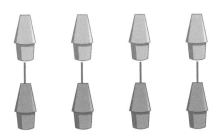

2

3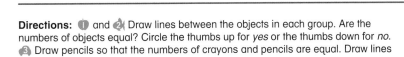

Directions: **1** and **2** Draw lines between the objects in each group. Are the numbers of objects equal? Circle the thumbs up for *yes* or the thumbs down for *no*. **3** Draw pencils so that the numbers of crayons and pencils are equal. Draw lines between the objects in each group to show that you are correct.

© Big Ideas Learning, LLC

Chapter Resources		
Surface Level	**Deep Level**	**Transfer Level**
Resources by Chapter • Extra Practice • Reteach Differentiating the Lesson Skills Review Handbook Skills Trainer Game Library Math Musicals	Resources by Chapter • Enrichment and Extension Graphic Organizers Game Library Math Musicals	Dynamic Assessment System • Chapter Test Assessment Book • Chapter Tests A and B

2.2 Greater Than

4 and 5. Sample answers are given.

2.3 Less Than

Directions: Draw lines between the objects in each group.
 Circle the group that is greater in number than the other group.
 Draw a line through the group that is less in number than the other group.

Compare Groups to 5 by Counting

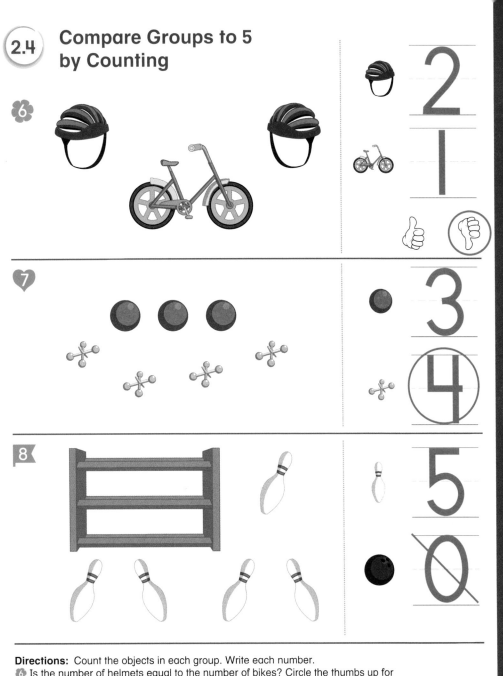

Directions: Count the objects in each group. Write each number.
6 Is the number of helmets equal to the number of bikes? Circle the thumbs up for *yes* or the thumbs down for *no*. **7** Circle the number that is greater than the other number. **8** Draw a line through the number that is less than the other number.

Chapter 2

ninety-three   93

9–11. Sample answers are given.

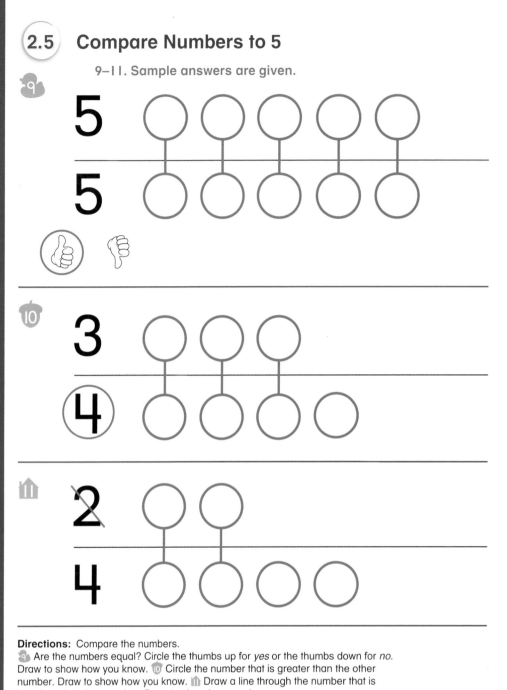

Directions: Compare the numbers.
9 Are the numbers equal? Circle the thumbs up for *yes* or the thumbs down for *no*. Draw to show how you know. 10 Circle the number that is greater than the other number. Draw to show how you know. 11 Draw a line through the number that is less than the other number. Draw to show how you know.

Math Musicals can be used with current topics, to review previous topics, or to preview upcoming topics.

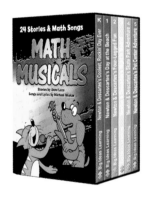

Centers

Center 1: Toss and Compare

Materials: Student Edition, page 90, 1 copy of Toss and Compare Numbers from 0–5 Recording Sheet* per pair, and 1 two-color counter per student

Have students complete the Toss and Compare activity. See page T-90 for the directions.

Center 2: Skills Trainer

Materials: computers or devices with Internet access

Have students go to *BigIdeasMath.com* to access the Skills Trainer.

Center 3: Bear Match-Up

Materials per pair: Five Frames*, Number Cards 0–5*, 5 paper clips, 10 bear counters, 1 whiteboard, and 1 dry-erase marker

Each student chooses a number card and puts that many bears on a five frame. Have one student lay a paper clip between each match. The other student writes both numbers on the whiteboard. Have students compare the numbers.

Center 4: Number Path Clip

Materials per pair: Number Paths 1–5* printed on cardstock or laminated, Number Cards 0–5*, 2 clothespins, whiteboards and markers

Each student chooses a number card and places a clothespin on that number on the number path. Each student writes both numbers on a whiteboard. Students circle the number that is greater and draw a line through the number that is less. Have students clap when the numbers are equal.

Center 5: Compare Lion Cards

Materials: Lion Cards 0–5*, scissors, Lion Cards Recording Sheet*

Cut apart the Lion Cards. Each student chooses a lion card and both students write the numbers on their recording sheets. Have students use their thumbs to tell whether the numbers are equal. Students can circle the number that is greater or draw a line through the number that is less.

*Found in the Instructional Resources

Chapter Assessment Guide

Chapter tests are available in the Assessment Book.
An alternative assessment option is listed below.

Musical

Play music while flashing a number card. Have students perform a
dance move, the number of times shown on the card. For the next
round, call out "greater than" or "less than" and flash a number
card. See whether students can perform the dance move the
number of times that corresponds to the comparison word.
Note: You may have students that choose not to dance. Have
them clap, stomp, or tap a beat instead.

Task	Points
Students use movement to identify numbers equal to the numbers 1, 2, 3, 4, and 5.	1 point per number; 5 points total
Students use movements to identify numbers greater than the numbers 0, 1, 2, 3, and 4.	1 point per number; 5 points total
Students use movements to identify numbers less than the numbers 1, 2, 3, 4, and 5.	1 point per number; 5 points total
Total	15 points

My Thoughts on the Chapter

What worked...

Teacher Tip

Not allowed to write in your teaching edition? Use sticky notes to record your thoughts.

What did not work...

What I would do differently...

3 Count and Write Numbers 6 to 10

Chapter Overview

Lesson	Learning Target	Success Criteria
3.1 Model and Count 6	Show and count the number 6.	• Name the number 6. • Count one object for each number to 6. • Tell the number of objects in a group.
3.2 Understand and Write 6	Understand and write the number 6.	• Identify a group of six objects. • Write the number 6.
3.3 Model and Count 7	Show and count the number 7.	• Name the number 7. • Count one object for each number to 7. • Tell the number of objects in a group.
3.4 Understand and Write 7	Understand and write the number 7.	• Identify a group of seven objects. • Write the number 7.
3.5 Model and Count 8	Show and count the number 8.	• Name the number 8. • Count one object for each number to 8. • Tell the number of objects in a group.
3.6 Understand and Write 8	Understand and write the number 8.	• Identify a group of eight objects. • Write the number 8.
3.7 Model and Count 9	Show and count the number 9.	• Name the number 9. • Count one object for each number to 9. • Tell the number of objects in a group.
3.8 Understand and Write 9	Understand and write the number 9.	• Identify a group of nine objects. • Write the number 9.
3.9 Model and Count 10	Show and count the number 10.	• Name the number 10. • Count one object for each number to 10. • Tell the number of objects in a group.
3.10 Understand and Write 10	Understand and write the number 10.	• Identify a group of 10 objects. • Write the number 10.
3.11 Count and Order Numbers to 10	Count and order numbers to 10.	• Count to 10. • Identify the starting number. • Order numbers to 10.

Chapter Learning Target:
Understand numbers.

Chapter Success Criteria:
▦ Identify numbers.
▦ Name numbers.
▪ Order numbers.
▦ Write numbers.

Progressions

Through the Grades	
Kindergarten	**Grade 1**
• Name, count, and write numbers within 10. • Pair each number name with an object. • Determine that the last number stated names the total. • Count objects in different arrangements. • Count starting from any number within 10. • Order numbers within 10 both forward and backward. • Understand that the next number stated is one number greater.	• Represent, write, and solve "Add To" and "Put Together" problems with unknowns. • Write and solve addition number sentences. • Solve addition word problems. • Represent, write, and solve "Take From" and "Take Apart" problems with unknowns. • Write and solve subtraction number sentences. • Solve subtraction word problems. • Solve addition and subtraction comparison problems.

Standard	Through the Chapter										
	3.1	3.2	3.3	3.4	3.5	3.6	3.7	3.8	3.9	3.10	3.11
When counting objects, say the number names in the standard order, pairing each object with one and only one number name and each number name with one and only one object.	●		●		●		●		●		
Understand that the last number name said tells the number of objects counted. The number of objects is the same regardless of their arrangement or the order in which they were counted.	●		●		●		●		●		
Count to answer "how many?" questions about as many as 20 things arranged in a line, a rectangular array, or a circle, or as many as 10 things in a scattered configuration; given a number from 1–20, count out that many objects.	●	●	●	●	●	●	●	●	●	●	●
Write numbers from 0 to 20. Represent a number of objects with a written numeral 0–20.		●		●		●		●		●	●
Count forward beginning from a given number within the known sequence.											●
Understand that each successive number name refers to a quantity that is one larger.											●

Key: ▲ = Preparing   ● = Learning   ★ = Complete

Laurie's Overview

About the Math

Students have been working with the numbers 0 to 5 in the last two chapters and are becoming more secure with the benchmark of 5. This is a goal for the year and it occurs at different rates for different students. Recognize that some students will still need to deepen their understanding with numbers to 5, even though in this new chapter students must count, write, and understand numbers to 10. Support for emerging learners is suggested in each lesson.

Students see a ten frame for the first time in this chapter. Placing 2 five frames together as an array will help students start to understand the benchmark of 10. Relating the new numbers in this chapter to the benchmarks of 5 and 10 help students build their number sense.

In Chapter 1 we used four different and notable arrangements: linear, array, circular, and scattered. The same arrangements are used in this chapter. Counting objects shown in the circular or scattered form is more challenging and strategies need to be intentionally taught to help students keep track of which objects they have counted. Students can use counters, cross out, or point with their fingers to keep track of the objects they have counted. Some students may count the objects in a logical order or they may count on from a smaller group they see. We also use dot models during the Dig In time and for center activities. The dot models help students recognize patterns.

Linear

Array

Circular

Scattered

     Dot models for 5

The reason we pay so much attention to how groups of objects are arranged and how number quantities are modeled is so that students have sufficient experiences to develop a conceptual understanding of what counting means. Students learn the number names and recite them in order, which is a rote procedure. Understanding how to count is conceptual.

Students may have successfully learned to count within 5 but the transfer of this understanding is not immediate for numbers within 10. They still need to learn the number names in order, and they need to connect these names in one-to-one correspondence with the objects being counted. Seeing a pattern of five dots, as *four dots and one more*, helps students associate the order of four and five when counting.

Students first learn to model and count each number before they associate the numeral to the number name and quantity. In this chapter, students learn to write the numbers 6 through 10 using verbal pathways. The verbal pathways are short action statements on how to form each number. The pathways for 6 through 10 are listed below.

6 - pull back, around, and in
7 - pull across and slant down
8 - pull back, around, back around, and connect
9 - pull back, around, pull down
10 - pull down; pull back and around

A special note about writing the number 10 is needed. This is the first time two numerals are needed to represent a number. We want students to understand the quantity of 10 and know how to represent it symbolically. This is not the time to discuss place value! Place value concepts are introduced in Grade 1. To help students make sense of this say, "The number 10 has two parts, a 1 and a 0." Point out that a small space is needed between each part.

At the end of the chapter, students learn to order numbers from 0 to 10. Having a firm understanding of the counting sequence helps prepare students for comparing numbers.

Models

- Children, and adults, often use their fingers to show quantities. Students quickly learn that they can use their fingers when counting numbers. Numbers introduced in this chapter require using fingers from both hands.

- The numbers that are introduced in this chapter require 2 five frames, and so the ten frame is introduced. The ten frame is a good organizational tool that allows students to show each number and build their understanding with the benchmarks of 5 and 10. Modeling numbers on the ten frame also helps students develop subitizing skills.

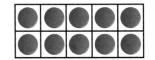

- Have students use linking cubes to model and count a given number of objects to 10. Using two colors, such as five blue and two yellow, can be related to how 7 is represented on a ten frame.

- Number cards can be used in a variety of ways and help students associate the numeral with the quantity.

- Subitizing cards and dot cards are provided in the Instructional Resources so that students become familiar with the dice and domino representations of numbers 0–10.

Chapter Materials and Resources

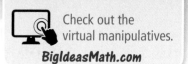

Check out the virtual manipulatives.
BigIdeasMath.com

The primary materials and resources needed for this chapter are listed below. Other materials may be needed for the additional support ideas provided throughout the chapter.

Classroom Materials	Chapter Opener	3.1	3.2	3.3	3.4	3.5	3.6	3.7	3.8	3.9	3.10	3.11	Connect and Grow
objects to compare	+												
scissors	•												•
two-color counters	*	•	•	•	•	•	•	•	•	•	•	•	
linking cubes		+		+	•	•		•		•	•		
rekenrek								•		+			
dice with dots		+	*										
5 dice with numbers			*										
instrument to make a beat					+		+						
objects to model 9									+				
manipulatives for game pieces													•
green paint													*
glue sticks													•

Instructional Resources	Chapter Opener	3.1	3.2	3.3	3.4	3.5	3.6	3.7	3.8	3.9	3.10	3.11	Connect and Grow
Vocabulary Cards	+	+		+		+		+		+			
Five Frame Cards 0–5		+											
Ten Frame Cards 5–10		+									+		
Ten Frames		•											
Music Class			•										
Subitizing Cards 5–10			+		+		+		+	+			•
Number Cards 5–10			+		+				+				•
Rainy Day					•								
Bugs, Bugs, Bugs							•						
Dot Cards 5–10 Set 1							+						
In the Water										•			
Number Cards 0–5											+		
Caterpillar Prints													•
Missing Numbers													•
Missing Number Strips													•
My Baseball Game									•				

• class set   + teacher only   * per pair/group

Suggested Pacing

Day 1	Chapter Opener	Performance Task Preview		Vocabulary			
Day 2	Lesson 3.1	Warm-Up	Dig In	Explore	Think	Apply: Practice	Think: Modeling Real Life
Day 3	Lesson 3.2	Warm-Up	Dig In	Explore	Think	Apply: Practice	Think: Modeling Real Life
Day 4	Lesson 3.3	Warm-Up	Dig In	Explore	Think	Apply: Practice	Think: Modeling Real Life
Day 5	Lesson 3.4	Warm-Up	Dig In	Explore	Think	Apply: Practice	Think: Modeling Real Life
Day 6	Lesson 3.5	Warm-Up	Dig In	Explore	Think	Apply: Practice	Think: Modeling Real Life
Day 7	Lesson 3.6	Warm-Up	Dig In	Explore	Think	Apply: Practice	Think: Modeling Real Life
Day 8	Lesson 3.7	Warm-Up	Dig In	Explore	Think	Apply: Practice	Think: Modeling Real Life
Day 9	Lesson 3.8	Warm-Up	Dig In	Explore	Think	Apply: Practice	Think: Modeling Real Life
Day 10	Lesson 3.9	Warm-Up	Dig In	Explore	Think	Apply: Practice	Think: Modeling Real Life
Day 11	Lesson 3.10	Warm-Up	Dig In	Explore	Think	Apply: Practice	Think: Modeling Real Life
Day 12	Lesson 3.11	Warm-Up	Dig In	Explore	Think	Apply: Practice	Think: Modeling Real Life
Day 13	Connect and Grow	Performance Task		Activity		Chapter Practice	
Day 14		Centers					
Day 15	Chapter Assessment	Chapter Assessment					

Year-to-Date: 36 Days

Laurie's Notes

Performance Task Preview

? Preview the page to gauge students' prior knowledge about numbers from 5 through 10. Ask, "What kinds of animals do you see here? How many animals are there? Where might you see these animals?"

• Relate the safari animals to animals they may have seen at the zoo, circus, or as pictures in science class. Allow students to share personal connections or stories with the class.

• In the Performance Task at the end of the chapter, students will count and tell the numbers of safari animals in a picture.

- What kinds of animals do you see here?
- How many animals are there?

Chapter Learning Target:
Understand numbers.

Chapter Success Criteria:
☐ I can identify numbers.
☐ I can name numbers.
☐ I can order numbers.
☐ I can write numbers.

© Big Ideas Learning, LLC

ninety-five 95

Laurie's Notes

Vocabulary Review

- ❓ **Preview:** "What do you see on the page? How many lions are there? How do you know? Write the number on the line." Observe how students count to determine whether they use one-to-one correspondence or subitize.

- ❓ "Without counting, how many cars do you think there are? How do you know?" Listen for students to say that they see one more car than the lions they counted. "Count the cars and write the number."

- Use classroom objects to ask comparative questions using the terms *same as, equal, more, fewer, greater than,* and *less than* to review the word *compare*. Now have students compare the number of lions and number of cars, the second direction line.

- **Extension:** Have students draw one more roller coaster car. They can write the new number of roller coaster cars.

Chapter 3 Vocabulary

Activity

- **Word/Picture Toss:** Lay out a set of vocabulary cards on the floor with the word side up. Students take turns gently tossing a counter onto a card. Read the word and have the student repeat the word. The student turns over the card to see the ten frame model and shows it to the class. Repeat this process until all of the cards show the ten frame model.

MATH MUSICALS

Math Musicals can be used with current topics, to review previous topics, or to preview upcoming topics. There are many *Math Musicals* to choose from!

Use your hand puppets to act out new stories and have students sing the songs several times to take full advantage of the power of music to learn math!

(3) Vocabulary

 3   **4**

Directions:
- Count the objects. Say the number. Write the number.
- Compare the number of lions to the number of cars. Circle the number that is greater than the other number.

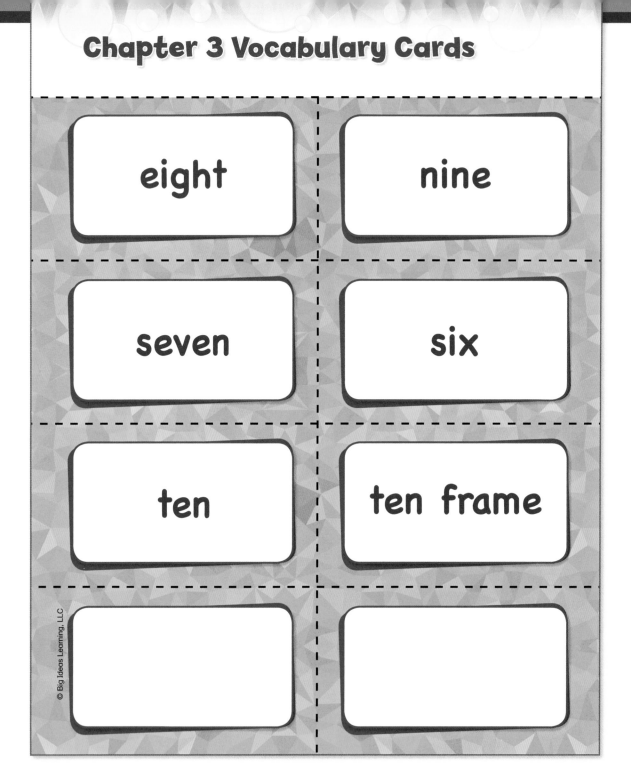

eight

nine

seven

six

ten

ten frame

© Big Ideas Learning, LLC

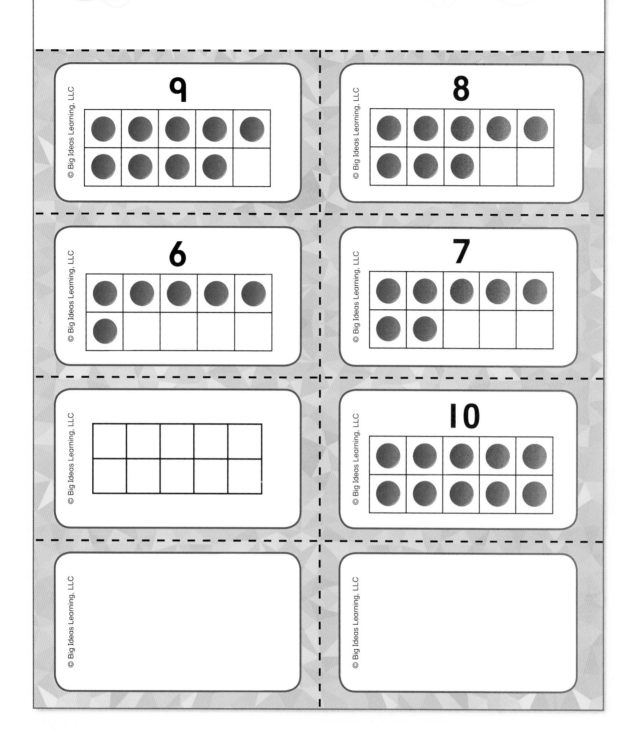

3.1

Learning Target

Show and count the number 6.

Success Criteria

- Name the number 6.
- Count one object for each number to 6.
- Tell the number of objects in a group.

ELL Support

Review the numbers 1 through 5 and then introduce the number 6. As you say each number in the sequence, have students repeat each number aloud. Then have students say the sequence on their own. One student says "one," the next student says "two," and so on. Repeat the sequence as needed.

Laurie's Notes

Preparing to Teach

Use the concept of *one more* to introduce the number six. A ten frame is 2 five frames put together. Show five on the first and one more on the second. Relate this to fingers on their hands. Before, it only took one hand to model the numbers 1 through 5. Now students need to use fingers from both hands. You will see different models for 6: five fingers plus the thumb or index finger on the other hand or three fingers on each hand.

All of the "Model and Count" lessons in this chapter have the same design but a different theme. The theme of this lesson is transportation.

Materials

- Five Frame Cards 0–5*
- Ten Frame Cards 5–10*
- Ten Frames*
- dice with dots
- two-color counters
- linking cubes

Found in the Instructional Resources

Dig In (Circle Time)

? Show the five frame card for 5. "What would one more look like? Tell your partners." Have counters and linking cubes available for students to explain their thinking.

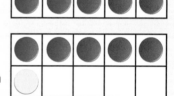

? Display the ten frame card for 5. Explain the model as 2 five frames. "How could we show one more than five on this?" Solicit volunteers to use counters or linking cubes to show one more than five.

- Introduce the number 6 and show a die with the six dots facing up. "Describe the pattern to your partner." Give students time to share and then discuss as a class.

- Now that students have seen the quantity of six, chorally count to 6 several times. Students can clap, tap their knee, or bob their head for each count. The last time they count, have students hold up six fingers. Make sure students understand that it takes fingers on both hands to model the number 6!

Name _____

Learning Target: Show and count the number 6.

Check students' work.

Explore and Grow

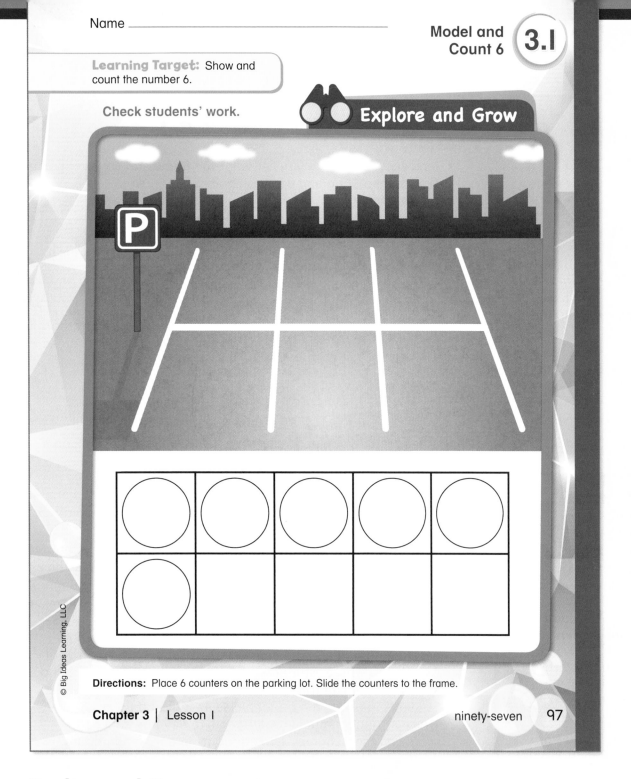

Directions: Place 6 counters on the parking lot. Slide the counters to the frame.

Chapter 3 | Lesson 1

ninety-seven 97

Explore and Grow

- Distribute counters. Say, "I went to the airport. I saw six cars in the parking lot. Use counters to show the cars in the parking lot."
- "Tell your partner a story about the six cars, or about six things you see while sitting in your car. Count to show you have six."
- ? Have students count aloud as they slide the counters to the ten frame. "What do you notice about the counters on the frame? The top row or first five frame is full and the second one only has one.
- Have students point to each counter as they count. Look for students to demonstrate one-to-one correspondence as they point and count to 6.

Laurie's Notes

Think and Grow

Getting Started

- Introduce the vocabulary cards for **ten frame** and **six**. Consider creating and discussing an anchor chart for 6.
- Model six linking cubes and a ten frame as shown. Using two colors helps make the connection that six is one more than five which develops number sense.

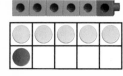

- ❓ "What do you know about the number *six*?" six family members; six pets; eating at 6 o'clock
- ❓ **Sample Questions:** How many counters are in the ten frame? How are they arranged? Can you show 6 fingers? What comes after 5 when counting? Do we have 6 pillows in the reading center?

Teaching Notes

- The cars are arranged with the top row filled and one underneath, which is similar to the standard model for six on a ten frame.
- **Model:** Together as a class, count each car. As students say the counting sequence, they place a counter on each car. Slide the counters to the ten frame boxes to count how many. Color each box that has a counter.
- Circulate as students count the helicopters and motorcycles and restate directions as needed. Note which students are placing counters on the objects, pointing at the object with their fingers, or saying the number words aloud as they track the objects with their eyes.
- **Big Idea:** Make sure students notice the arrangements for each quantity of six. The helicopters are shown in an array of two rows of three. Students may know the quantity is six and see two groups of three or count on from one group of three. Students may see the motorcycles as four and two more. These arrangements allow students to develop conceptual subitizing by recognizing the quantity in parts and putting them together.
- **Note:** Model placing the counters in the ten frame going from left to right in the top row and then left to right in the bottom row. This helps develop their number sense with the benchmarks of 5 and 10.
- ◉ Students have had time to explore various models and arrangements for six. Can they show a model of six? Do they know when a group has a quantity of six? Have students use their thumb signals to show their confidence levels for each.
- **Attend to Precision:** Students may miscount or recount because they forget where they start or they miss an object. Have students lay counters or cross out each object as they count.

Think and Grow

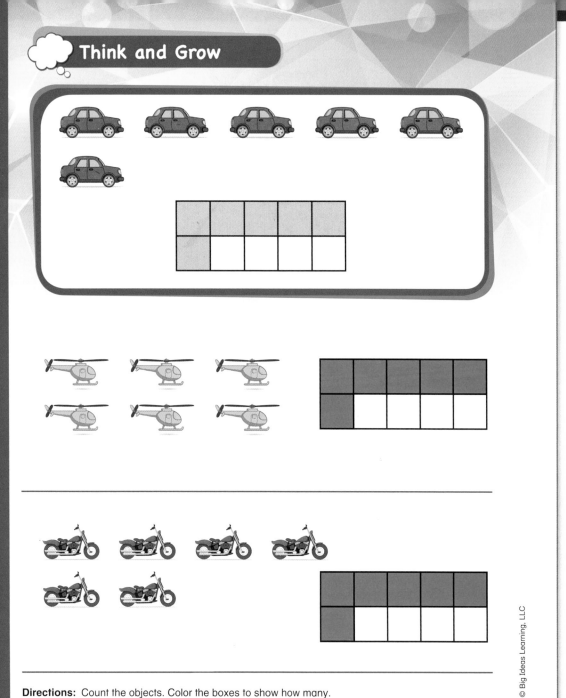

Directions: Count the objects. Color the boxes to show how many.

Laurie's Notes

Apply and Grow: Practice
MAKING INSTRUCTIONAL DECISIONS

Students are now counting longer number sequences which can require more practice based on the students' understanding of the numbers 0 through 5. The focus of this lesson, and all of the other "Model and Count" lessons in this chapter, is on the students' development of number sequence, one-to-one correspondence, and cardinality. These lessons do not focus on writing the numeral.

Keep in mind that the previous Apply and Grow: Practice components can be revisited as you work through the book. This chapter is similar to Chapter 1 but explores a different set of numbers, therefore many of the supports still apply.

EMERGING students may need direct support or an alternative approach. They can be perceptual counters, who need to see the objects in order to count, or emergent counters, who have difficulty associating one number word with one object when counting.

* Have students cross out objects as they count.
* Students may benefit from using a rekenrek. Students build on their understanding of the benchmark of five as they move five beads of the same color, and then one more of a different color.

PROFICIENT students are able to count and show a group of six objects. These students are often non-count-by-ones counters, counting-on counters, or figurative counters.

* Have students model the quantity of six in different arrangements.

Additional Support

* Encourage students to count the numbers out loud and repeat the last number they counted in a complete sentence. Have students count "1, 2, 3, 4, 5, 6" and say "I have six counters."

Extensions: Adding Rigor

* Provide students with six counters and ten frames. Tell students to put two counters on a ten frame. Have them count on from 2 until they reach 6. Repeat this process with different starting numbers that are less than 6.
* ? Increase critical thinking by asking questions such as, "How do you know?" and "Can you show me?"

Meeting the needs of
all learners.

Name _____

①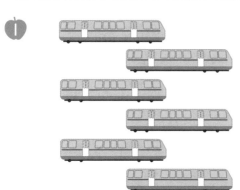

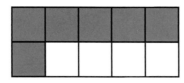

②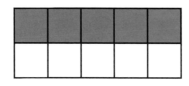

③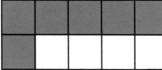

Directions: ① – ③ Count the objects. Color the boxes to show how many.

Chapter 3 | Lesson 1   ninety-nine   99

© Big Ideas Learning, LLC

Laurie's Notes

Think and Grow: Modeling Real Life

This application helps students count to answer "how many" with the number 6. Numbers 4 and 6 are used in a contextual setting.

- Have students tell their partners what they have learned today. You may hear students say they are confused, or that they forget some of the numbers when they count. They may also say they are not sure whether they have counted an object or not. When students can identify what is not clear, you are better able to support their learning. The goal is for students to be clear about what they need to learn and when they have been successful in their learning.

- Have students use their thumb signals to show where they are in their learning.

- **Preview:** "What do you think is happening in the picture? Have you ever walked on a sidewalk with other children? Talk to your partner about what you see." Students are probably walking to school or to the library.

- Students unfamiliar with a city scene may not know what a taxi is. It is important that they can identify the objects in the picture in order to be able to count the correct objects.

- Read the directions. "What objects are we counting? How do you know what objects to count?" Taxis and then students; There is a picture of each next to the ten frame.

- **Think-Pair-Share:** "How will you count the taxis and bookbags?"

- **Connection:** Ask a comparative question that connects to the last chapter such as, "Are there the same number of taxis as children?"

- **Extension:** "Imagine two more taxis in the picture." Pause for students to visualize. "How many taxis are on the street now?" Have students draw the taxis to show their thinking.

- **Supporting Learners:** Students can use counters or linking cubes to practice counting six objects.

Closure

- Prompt students to choose a number from 0 through 6 and show partners using objects, drawings, fingers, or actions. Have the partners say the number.

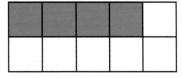

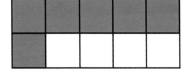

Directions: Count the objects in the picture. Color the boxes to show how many.

100   one hundred

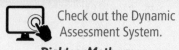

Connect and Extend Learning

Practice Notes

- **Exercises 1–5:** Preview the pages and state the names of each object. Discuss the different arrangements. Do students see any smaller numbers as a collection inside the larger group?
- **Exercises 1–5:** Students can cross out objects or place counters over them as they count.
- **Exercises 1–5:** Remind students to color the boxes on the top row completely, then begin on the second row.

Cross-Curricular Connections

Language Arts

- Count the number of words in a sentence or the number of letters in a word.

Social Studies

- Identify any students who are six years old or those who have six letters in their name.

Name _____

Learning Target: Show and count the number 6.

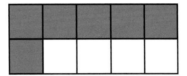

Directions: Count the trucks. Color the boxes to show how many.

①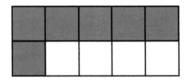

②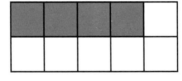

Directions: ① and ② Count the objects. Color the boxes to show how many.

Chapter 3 | Lesson 1

one hundred one 101

© Big Ideas Learning, LLC

Connect and Extend Learning

Extend Student Learning

Visual-Spatial

- Play "Roll and Draw". Create a simple picture that can be drawn in parts. Assign a number on a die to each part of the picture. The picture can be a drawing of a person, animal, car, truck, airplane, or bus. You may also decide to create a seasonally themed picture. Have students roll the die and draw the assigned piece.

  Teaching Tip: If a student rolls the same number twice and that part of the picture is not needed, then he or she should roll again.

Bodily-Kinesthetic

- On a piece of paper, have students draw six silly things that they can act out. Assign each action to a number on the die. Roll the die and have students count to six while they perform each action. Use examples such as crawl like a crab, waddle like a penguin, or flap your arms like a bird.

Lesson Resources	
Surface Level	**Deep Level**
Resources by Chapter • Extra Practice • Reteach Differentiating the Lesson Skills Review Handbook Skills Trainer	Resources by Chapter • Enrichment and Extension Graphic Organizers Dynamic Assessment System • Lesson Practice

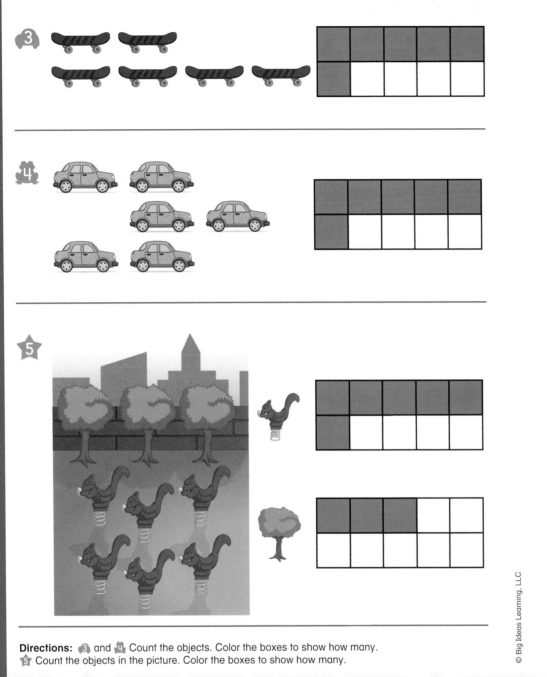

Directions: 3 and 4 Count the objects. Color the boxes to show how many.
5 Count the objects in the picture. Color the boxes to show how many.

3.2

Check out the Dynamic Classroom.

BigIdeasMath.com

Laurie's Notes

Learning Target

Understand and write the number 6.

Success Criteria

• Identify a group of six objects.
• Write the number 6.

Warm-Up

Practice opportunities for the following are available in the Resources by Chapter or at *BigIdeasMath.com*.

• Daily skills
• Vocabulary
• Prerequisite skills

ELL Support

Teach the word drum by pointing to the drum and stating its name. Have students repeat the word. Tell students to listen carefully for the number 6 as well as for the name of the object that is being counted.

Preparing to Teach

In the previous lesson, students learned to model and count the number 6. Now the focus is on recognizing the quantity of six in any arrangement. Students have seen the ten frame arrangement for six and in this lesson, they will see groups of six arranged in different formations. Students can explore arrangements of six using an interactive whiteboard, a felt board, or magnetic board. All of these experiences help students become flexible in their understanding of the quantity of six.

All of the "Understand and Write" lessons in this chapter have the same design but a different theme. The theme of this lesson is musical instruments.

Materials

• dice with dots and numbers
• *Music Class**
• two-color counters
• Subitizing Cards 5–10*
• Number Cards 5–10*

**Found in the Instructional Resources*

Dig In (Circle Time)

• Each pair of students needs one die with dot patterns. One student rolls and the partner names the number. Students reverse roles. Let them play several times before the die with numerals is introduced.

⊙ Introduce the new die with numerals versus dots. Share the learning target and success criteria as you show students the die face that has the number 6.

• Play the *Roll and Name* game again with the number die so students become familiar with what the number 6 looks like.

❓ Distribute the *Music Class* booklets. "What happens in music class? Talk to your partner." Have students identify the various instruments on the cover before turning the page. Read and discuss the booklet.

❓ "How many drums are in the story?" Observe the counting process. Are students pointing with their fingers and saying the number words aloud?

• "There are six drums." Model as you say, "This is how you write the number 6. Pull back, around, and in." Have students finger trace 6 in the booklet several times as you repeat the verbal pathway. Practice air writing 6.

• Students should return to their seats with their booklets.

❓ Teaching Prompt   ⊙ Learning Target

Name _____

Learning Target: Understand and write the number 6.

👓 Explore and Grow

© Big Ideas Learning, LLC

Directions: Use counters to show how many drums are in the story *Music Class*. Write how many drums are in the story.

Chapter 3 | Lesson 2   one hundred three   103

Explore and Grow

◉ Refer to the *Music Class* booklet. "Use your counters to show the number of drums." Are students able to count and place six counters or do they need to count the drums in the story again? The first success criterion is identifying a group of six. Are they confident with what a group of six looks like?

• If their one-to-one correspondence is still a problem, have students put a counter on each drum in the story. These counters can then be moved to the large drum on the Explore and Grow page.

• Chorally say the verbal pathway for writing 6 as they practice it in the air. Then write the number 6 on the small drum.

Point to the trumpets, guitars, and maracas as you say the name of each. Have students repeat each word. Explain that there are all types of instruments that make music and then have them repeat the word *instrument*. If possible, play recordings of their sounds. Have students practice language as they did in the previous lesson. One student asks the other, "How many trumpets are there?" Then have them switch roles for the other exercises.

Beginner students may only answer with "six."

Intermediate students may answer "six" and the instrument being counted.

Advanced students may answer using a simple sentence, such as, "There are six trumpets."

Think and Grow

Getting Started

- Show students the subitizing card and number card for 6. Have students talk about the cards with partners. Do they understand that both cards show 6?
- The die dot pattern should be familiar and although they described the die dot pattern in the previous lesson, ask again today. How do students describe the pattern?
- There is a group, a dot model, and a traceable numeral for 6 on this page. Note the different arrangements of the trumpets, guitars, and maracas.

Teaching Notes

- **Model:** Together as a class, count the group of six trumpets. Finger trace the numeral 6. Count the dot model and finger trace the numeral 6. Say the verbal pathway "pull back, around, and in," as students trace and then practice writing 6.
- Students may ask why the dots are not shown as they are on a ten frame, with five on the top row and one below. Acknowledge that they are doing some good thinking. Explain that there are different ways we show the number 6. If you chose to make an anchor chart, this would be a good time to add to it.
- Circulate as students complete the page. State directions as needed. Count and say how many, then write the number.
- For any of the groups of six on this page, have students count the objects in different ways such as right to left or bottom to top to help them recognize that the quantity stays the same.
- ⊙ Show a common dot model of six. "Is this a group of six? Tell your partner how you know." Can they subitize and see a group of six, or do they have to count to know there are six?
- **Supporting Learners:** Some students may have difficulty writing the number 6. Provide textured number cards for students to trace with their finger.
- ❓ **Supporting Learners:** Place six counters or objects on a table. Show them in different arrangements. Use models such as arrays, linear, circular, and scattered. Each time ask, "How many are there?" Listen to students count the collection. Check for understanding that the quantity remains the same.

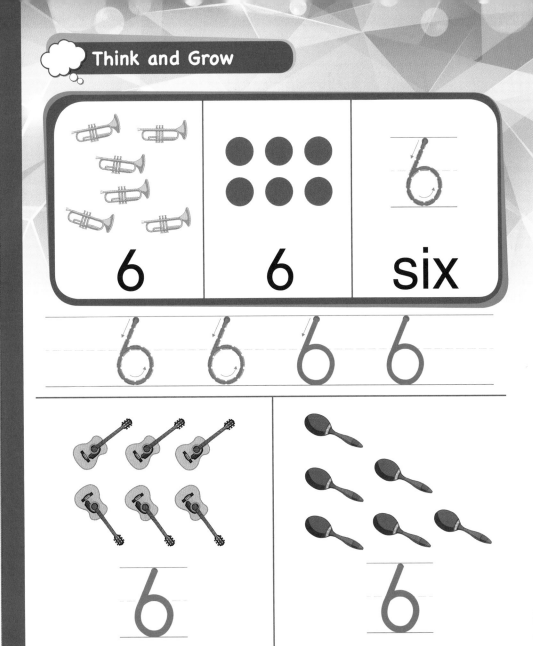

6   6   six

Directions:
- Count the objects. Say the number. Trace and write the number.
- Count the instruments. Say the number. Write the number.

Laurie's Notes

Meeting the needs of all learners.

Apply and Grow: Practice

MAKING INSTRUCTIONAL DECISIONS

Counting to 6, understanding the quantity of six, and writing the number 6 are all different skills. Students may be able to write 6, but have difficulty counting. Your own observations and a student's self-assessment will influence what support or extensions each student needs.

EMERGING students may have difficulty associating one number word with one object when counting, or they may not know the correct number sequence. Lacking fine motor skills can also influence their ability to write numbers.

- Show the array model for six and clap the pattern: clap three times, pause briefly, and clap three more times.

PROFICIENT students are able to identify a group of six objects and write the number 6.

- Have students walk around the classroom and identify objects that have the number 6 on them, such as a poster, number line, clock, and room number. Students can draw these objects on paper.

Additional Support

? Prepare a large number 6 poster. Trace the number with glue and let it dry. Have students finger trace the dry, textured number and then ask students, "When making the number 6, did you use curved or straight lines?"

- Provide counters and ten frames to students who need a more organized, hands-on experience. Consider using counters to place in the frames or over the pictures.
- Have students practice making curves and straight lines on writing paper.

Extensions: Adding Rigor

? As students work with different arrangements of six, some will develop the visual sense that a number can be made up of different parts. Some students may say, "six is five and one," or "six is three and three." Acknowledge these observations and extend the learning by asking, "What other numbers make up six?" two and four

- Choose a number card from 0 through 6. Place linking cubes or counters on a ten frame. Use the linking cubes to build a tower.

Name _____

✓ Apply and Grow: Practice

1    6

2   6

3   4

4   6

Directions: ❶–❹ Count the objects. Say the number. Write the number.

Chapter 3 | Lesson 2   one hundred five   105

Laurie's Notes

Think and Grow: Modeling Real Life

This application helps students count to identify the size of a group and write the number they count. The numbers 4 and 5 are revisited.

? **Preview:** Discuss prior knowledge of the instruments shown. Ask, "Have you ever played an instrument?" Students may enjoy trying to make the sound of each instrument.

◉ The learning target today was to understand and write the number 6. In this application you'll observe students counting groups of 4, 5, or 6 objects. Incorrect answers do not necessarily mean that students do not know the counting sequence or understand cardinality. They may not have counted all of the objects due to their scattered location on the page. Ask students, regardless if the answer is correct or incorrect, to explain how they counted. Students should practice explaining their thinking regularly.

? **Think-Pair-Share:** "How will you count the instruments?" Are students making rows? Are they counting left to right and top to bottom? Have a small group share and then discuss strategies as a class.

• You may need to count the triangles as a class before having students work independently. If students become stuck, ask guiding questions that lead them to find a pattern or logical order to count.

• Circulate and observe as students determine the numbers of each type of instrument. Students may count each object and track their counting, or subitize part and count on to find the quantity. Encourage students to share their thinking.

◉ Revisit the learning target. Have students use their thumb signals to show their understanding of the number 6 and their ability to write the number 6.

? **Reason Abstractly and Quantitatively:** Make connections to the previous chapter. "Is there any group that has the same number of instruments as another group? Which group has a number greater than 5? Which group has one less than another group?"

• **Supporting Learners:** Some students may have difficulty focusing on one set of instruments at a time. Have students cover the instruments they are not counting at the time.

Closure

• Have three students stand at the front of the room. "How many students are standing? Air write 3." Pause. "I want a group of six students standing. What can we do?" Have more students stand. Add one student at a time, identify how many, and practice air writing the numbers until there are six students standing.

Directions: Count the instruments in the picture. Say the number. Write the number.

106   one hundred six

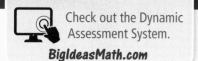
Connect and Extend Learning

Practice Notes

- **Exercises 1–5:** Preview the pages and state the names of each object. Remind students that most of the problems do not have the dot to show them where to begin writing the number.
- **Exercise 5:** Ask students to compare the two numbers they wrote.

Cross-Curricular Connections

Language Arts

- *The Noisy Counting Book* by Susan Schade and Jon Buller; Create a classroom book about a group of six animals that make noisy sounds.
- Have students write the number and word form each time a new number is introduced. This practice can be repeated throughout the year.

Science

- All insects have six legs. Look at pictures of insects and count the legs.

Name _____

Learning Target: Understand and write the number 6.

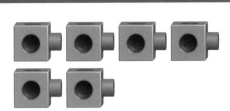

six

Directions: Count the linking cubes. Say the number. Write the number.

1

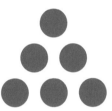

6

2

6

Directions: **1** and **2** Count the dots. Say the number. Write the number.

Chapter 3 | Lesson 2

one hundred seven   107

Connect and Extend Learning

Extend Student Learning

Linguistic

- Start a classroom book, *Our Number Walk: 6 to 10* by drawing items for the number 6. See page T-14 for a refresher on how to make the book.

Logical-Mathematical

- Create a playing board with subitizing patterns. Students take turns rolling a die and covering the correct subitizing dot arrangement with a counter. The first person to fill a row or column wins.

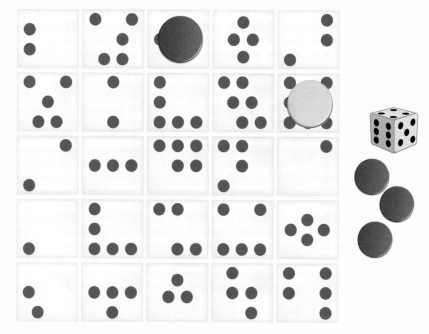

- **Teaching Tip:** Have students recognize and associate numerals to their corresponding quantities by having them use number cards 1 to 6 instead of rolling a die.

Lesson Resources	
Surface Level	**Deep Level**
Resources by Chapter • Extra Practice • Reteach Differentiating the Lesson Skills Review Handbook Skills Trainer	Resources by Chapter • Enrichment and Extension Graphic Organizers Dynamic Assessment System • Lesson Practice

3  6

4  5

5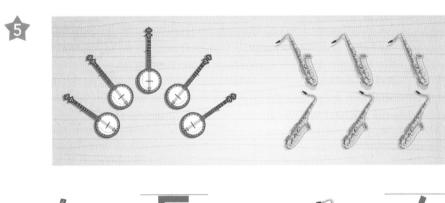

 5   6

Directions: **3** and **4** Count the objects. Say the number. Write the number.
5 Count the instruments in the picture. Say the number. Write the number.

108   one hundred eight

3.3

Learning Target
Show and count the number 7.

Success Criteria
- Name the number 7.
- Count one object for each number to 7.
- Tell the number of objects in a group.

Warm-Up
Practice opportunities for the following are available in the Resources by Chapter or at *BigIdeasMath.com*.
- Daily skills
- Vocabulary
- Prerequisite skills

ELL Support
Review the numbers 1 through 6 and then introduce the number 7. As you say each number in the sequence, have students repeat each number aloud. Then have students say the sequence on their own. One student says "one," the next student says "two," and so on. Repeat the sequence as needed.

Laurie's Notes

Preparing to Teach
In this lesson, the number seven is introduced. A calendar and linking cubes are used. I like to have each group use only one or two colors of linking cubes. Using one color focuses students' attention on the total quantity. Two colors, such as five blue and two yellow, helps develop their conceptual subitizing skills. The lesson is similar in design to the previous "Model and Count" lessons and the theme is wildlife.

Materials
- linking cubes
- two-color counters

Dig In (Circle Time)
A calendar is used to introduce the number 7. Volunteers point to and say the names of the days. Students count slowly as you point to each day and perhaps increase the volume a bit as you approach the number 7. "There are seven days in a week!"

SEPTEMBER

Sunday	Monday	Tuesday	Wednesday	Thursday	Friday	Saturday
					1	2
3	4	5	6	7	8	9
10	11	12	13	14	15	16
17	18	19	20	21	22	23
24	25	26	27	28	29	30

- Have the students count to 7 again. This time, have them clap, tap their knee, or nod their head for each count. Judge readiness for counting to 7 from a given number.
- Model counting to 7 using your fingers. Then have students count to 7 while they show the corresponding fingers. Some students have difficulty controlling the movement of their fingers. When they finish counting, are there seven fingers up?
- **?** Hold up seven linking cubes. Ask, "How many cubes am I holding? How do you know?" Have a student point to each cube as the class counts aloud. If a calendar can be placed on the floor, the linking cubes can be put on each day, Sunday through Saturday.
- **◉** Connect the calendar work and counting to 7 to the first two success criteria. "Now let's see what a group of seven objects looks like!"

? Teaching Prompt   **◉** Learning Target

Name _____

Learning Target: Show and count the number 7.

Check students' work.

Explore and Grow

Directions: Place 7 counters in the forest. Slide the counters to the frame.

© Big Ideas Learning, LLC

Chapter 3 | Lesson 3

one hundred nine   109

Explore and Grow

- Distribute counters. "I was walking through the forest when I stopped and looked around. I saw seven animals. Use counters to show the animals."
- Turn and Talk: "Tell your partner a story about the forest animals. Count to show you have seven." Students who are less confident will often share if you relate the work to a story. This is a good way to get them to talk about the number 7 in a way that may be less stressful. Using the Newton and Descartes puppets also helps.
- Have students orally count as they move each counter onto the frame.
- ? Slide each of the two bottom counters over one space. "Do you still have seven counters?" Listen for an understanding that the quantity has not changed.

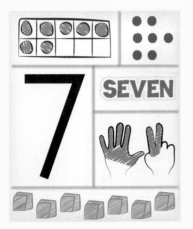

SEVEN

Laurie's Notes

Think and Grow

Getting Started

- Introduce the vocabulary card for **seven** and discuss your anchor chart. How do students see the dot pattern? Perhaps 5 plus 2 more, seven dots, or 3 are empty

- ? **Turn and Talk:** "What do you know about the number seven?" seven days of the week, bedtime is 7 o'clock, a sibling is 7 years old

- ? **Sample Questions:** How many counters are in the ten frame? How are they arranged? What comes after 6 when counting? What grade are your reading buddies in? Can you show seven with your fingers?

Teaching Notes

- The fish are arranged as counters would be on a ten frame. Students will still use counters, saying one number word for each object.

- **Model:** Together as a class, count each fish. As students say the counting sequence, they place a counter on each fish. Slide the counters to the ten frame boxes to count how many. Color each box that has a counter.

- Circulate as students count the eagles and rabbits, making note of how students are counting. Some may see six eagles and one more, some may see the top row of four and count on from there, and others may point to or place counters on each object as they count.

- ◎ Throughout their work on this page, listen for the understanding that when students finish counting and say the number, they know how many objects are in the group.

- Stop at a group of desks and ask the students to use their fingers to show each number as they count to 7. Small group assessments may reveal needed support or extension.

- **Connection:** All of the groups on this page have the same number of objects. "The number of fish *is the same as* the number of eagles."

- ◎ Students have had time to explore various models and arrangements for seven. Can they show a model of seven? Do they know when a group has a quantity of seven? Have students use their thumb signals to show their confidence levels for each.

- **Extension:** Because all of the groups have a quantity of seven, ask about the students' observations of the numbers of empty boxes in each ten frame.

Think and Grow

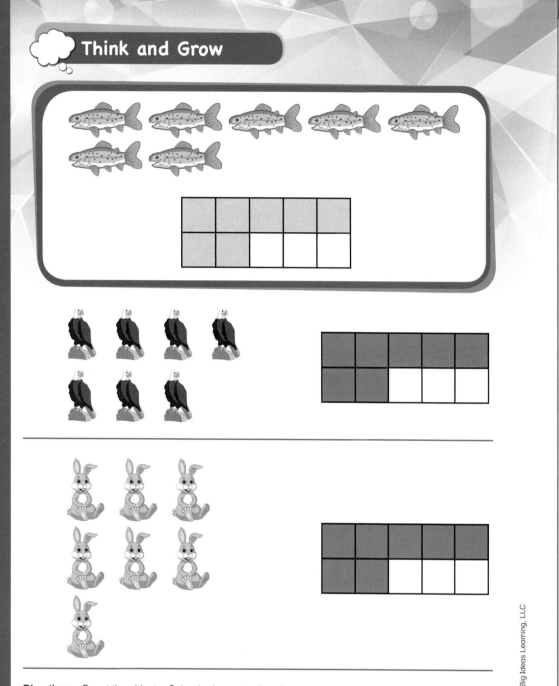

Directions: Count the objects. Color the boxes to show how many.

110   one hundred ten

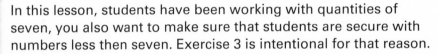

Laurie's Notes

Apply and Grow: Practice

MAKING INSTRUCTIONAL DECISIONS

The answers to the questions below can help determine each student's proficiency level as well as their needed supports.

- Are the students counting in order to seven? How often?
- Are students using one-to-one correspondence as they count? Do they point or use their eyes to track?
- Do they demonstrate cardinality? Do they remember what they counted?

In this lesson, students have been working with quantities of seven, you also want to make sure that students are secure with numbers less then seven. Exercise 3 is intentional for that reason.

EMERGING students may have difficulty counting seven objects. They may hesitate or get lost during the number sequence.

- Remind students to use their finger to point to each object as they say the number name. Students can also use counters.

PROFICIENT students are able to count and show a group of seven objects.

- Show two groups of different quantities, such as, a group of five and a group of seven. "Explain how you know which group has seven."

Additional Support

- Some students may not fully understand that each number name should be counted separately. They may point to two objects as they say two-syllable counting words such as "seven." Support these students by showing the vocabulary card for 7 and clap the syllables as you say the word.
- Students, who lose track while counting or get different answers when they recount, need more practice with the number sequence or one-to-one correspondence. They may even need more practice with numbers 0 through 5.

Extensions: Adding Rigor

- To support students with counting on to 7, have students roll a die and fill in a ten frame with the corresponding number of counters. Have students use the opposite side of the two-color counter to fill in the rest of the frame to 7.
- Perhaps during quiet time today you could read a story about the seven dwarfs.

Meeting the needs of
all learners.

Name _____

Apply and Grow: Practice

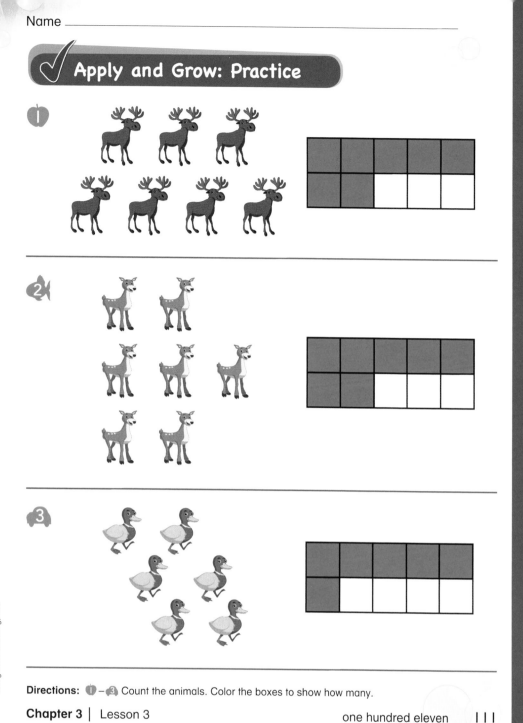

Directions: ❶ – ❸ Count the animals. Color the boxes to show how many.

Chapter 3 | Lesson 3

© Big Ideas Learning, LLC

Think and Grow: Modeling Real Life

This application helps students count to answer "how many" with the number 7. Numbers 5 and 7 are used in a contextual setting.

- ⊙ "Tell your partner what you have learned today." Listen for comments such as, "I learned to count to 7" and "I can make a group of 7."
- **?** Preview: "What do you think is happening in the picture? Have you ever been for a walk near a stream? Talk to your partner about the picture."
- **Think-Pair-Share:** Ask students to think about how they will count the birds and the bears and share their thoughts with their partners. Have a class discussion to determine all of the strategies used.
- **?** Read the directions. "What objects are we counting? How do we know what objects to count?" birds and bears; There is a picture of each next to a ten frame.
- **?** Extension: "Do you know what bears like to eat? How many fish would we need in the stream so each bear would get one fish?" Have students draw 7 fish.
- ⊙ Revisit the learning target with students. Have students signal their confidence levels with showing and counting seven objects.
- **Extension:** Students can draw additional birds in the picture to make seven.

Closure

- Prompt students to choose a number from 0 to 7 and show that number to their partners using objects, drawings, fingers, or actions. Have the partners say the number.

Think and Grow: Modeling Real Life

 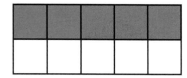

 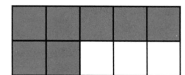

Directions: Count the animals in the picture. Color the boxes to show how many.

112   one hundred twelve

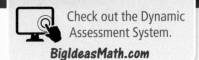
Connect and Extend Learning

Practice Notes

- **Exercises 1 and 2:** Ask students to discuss how the skunks and eagles are arranged. "Does this make them easier to count?"
- **Exercises 1–5:** Preview the pages and state the names of each animal.

Cross-Curricular Connections

Language Arts

- *Bear Snores On* by Karma Wilson; Discuss the seven friends that come to visit bear while he sleeps. Retell the order that the characters come to see him.

Social Studies

- Discuss fire safety with students and show a picture of a fire truck. Have students point to seven items that are part of the fire truck or used to fight fires.

Learning Target: Show and count the number 7.

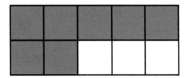

Directions: Count the badgers. Color the boxes to show how many.

1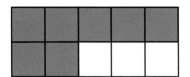

2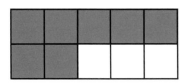

Directions: **1** and **2** Count the animals. Color the boxes to show how many.

© Big Ideas Learning, LLC

Connect and Extend Learning

Extend Student Learning

Musical

- Focus on counting and emphasizing the number of days in a week. Have students sing the "Days of the Week" song to the tune of "Oh My Darling."

Logical-Mathematical

- Create a set of dot cards using two different colors to identify subitizing patterns in each dot arrangement. This helps students identify parts of a number. While looking at the dot cards, you may hear students say, "There is one blue dot and two red dots and that makes three." You can also have students represent each quantity with counters on a ten frame. Provide markers and notecards for students to make their own.

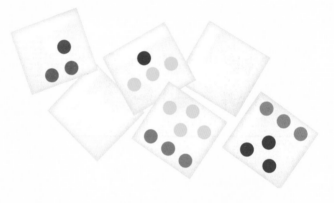

Lesson Resources	
Surface Level	**Deep Level**
Resources by Chapter • Extra Practice • Reteach Differentiating the Lesson Skills Review Handbook Skills Trainer	Resources by Chapter • Enrichment and Extension Graphic Organizers Dynamic Assessment System • Lesson Practice

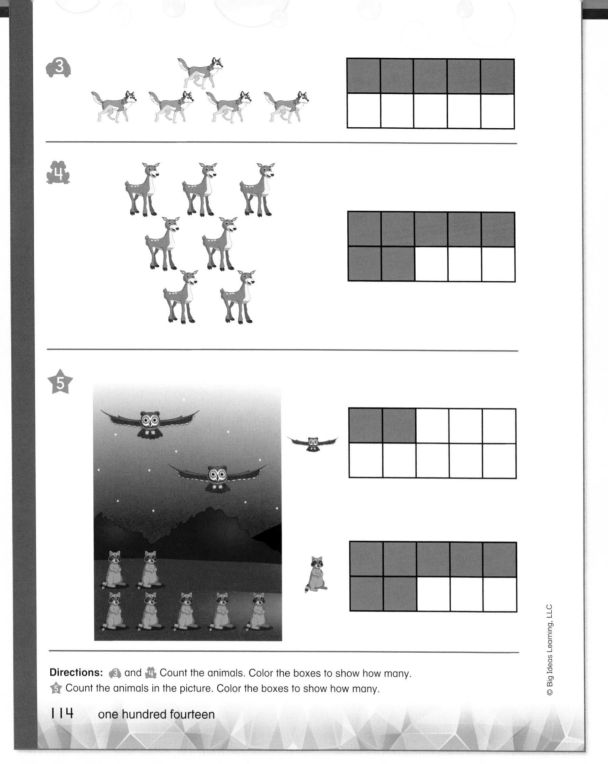

Directions: ❸ and ❹ Count the animals. Color the boxes to show how many.
⭐ Count the animals in the picture. Color the boxes to show how many.

114   one hundred fourteen

3.4

Learning Target

Understand and write the number 7.

Success Criteria

• Identify a group of seven objects.
• Write the number 7.

Laurie's Notes

Preparing to Teach

In this lesson, students count and recognize the quantity seven. Students see seven represented in a variety of arrangements, and understand that the collection is the quantity of seven. Students can make a group of seven objects and write the numeral to represent it.

The lesson is similar in design to the previous "Understand and Write" lesson and the theme is weather.

Materials

• instrument to make a beat
• linking cubes
• two-color counters
• *Rainy Day**
• Subitizing Cards 5–10*
• Number Cards 5–10*

**Found in the Instructional Resources*

Dig In (Circle Time)

Use a recorder, hand symbols, or another similar object to make seven notes or beats with a pause between each. You want students to listen and count the number of sounds they hear. "Listen, count, and think the number to yourself." Pause and then ask students how many notes they heard. Introduce the learning target and success criteria. Repeat, but leave less time between notes.

• When students have practiced counting to 7, tell them that when you play less than seven notes, they should clap to finish counting to 7. An example would sound like *note, note, note, note, note, clap, clap.*
• **Teaching Tip:** Tell students to clap using the same rhythm as the notes so they don't rush and can stay together.
• Give each pair of students seven linking cubes, and have them point to a cube each time they hear a note. When you stop playing before the number 7, they should say the next number words for counting to 7. An example would sound like *note, note, note, note, note, six, seven.*
• Distribute the booklet *Rainy Day.* Have students share their rainy day experiences. Read and discuss the booklet.
• ❓ "How many raindrops are in the story?" seven Students may be concerned by the different sizes of raindrops. "Count all of the raindrops even when they are different sizes."
• "There are seven raindrops. This is how you write 7. Pull across and slant down." Have students finger trace and air write the 7 several times as you repeat the verbal pathway. Students can count the puddles and practice writing 7.
• Students should return to their seats with their booklets.

Warm-Up

Practice opportunities for the following are available in the Resources by Chapter or at *BigIdeasMath.com.*

• Daily skills
• Vocabulary
• Prerequisite skills

ELL Support

Point to the raindrop and say, "raindrop." Have students repeat the word. Explain that the word raindrop is made by putting two words together. Rain is water that comes from the sky. The word drop means to fall down. A raindrop is one bit of water that falls from the sky. Tell students to listen carefully for the number 7 as well as the name of the object being counted.

Learning Target: Understand and write the number 7.

Explore and Grow

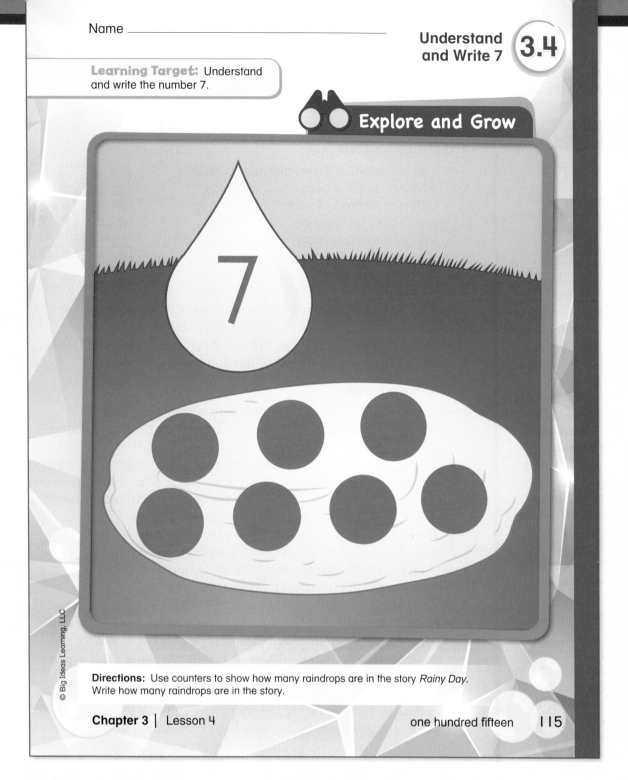

Directions: Use counters to show how many raindrops are in the story *Rainy Day*. Write how many raindrops are in the story.

Explore and Grow

⊙ "Use your counters to show the number of raindrops in the *Rainy Day* booklet." Do they immediately show a group of seven counters in the large puddle or do they need to go back and count the raindrops in the booklet? Ask, "Is this a group of seven?" The first success criterion is to identify a group of seven.

- Say the verbal pathway as they practice air writing the number 7. Now explore writing the number 7 on the large raindrop.

- **Supporting Learners:** Write the number 7 on a whiteboard and have students use a finger to trace and erase as they say the verbal pathway.

Laurie's Notes

Think and Grow

Getting Started

- Use the subitizing and number cards for seven to begin a conversation about different models of seven. Students may notice that six and one more is seven, or that five and two more is seven. You want students to be familiar with dot models (dice, dominos, and ten frames) for numbers.

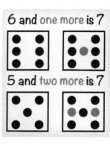

? Ask, "What is the same about both cards?" They both show seven.

- Make sure students know the names of each object. Ask what the weather would be like when you see each object.

Teaching Notes

- **Teaching Tip:** If a document camera is available, student volunteers can point to objects projected on the board as the class counts.
- **Model:** Count the group of seven umbrellas together as a class. Finger trace the numeral 7. Count the dot model and finger trace the numeral 7. Say the verbal pathway, "pull across and slant down," as students trace and write the number 7.
- The angle of the slanted portion of the number 7 is challenging for students. Draw three versions of a 7. Discuss the goal of making it look like the 7 in the middle versus having the slant being straight down or overly slanted.

- **Note:** In some countries the 7 is written with a horizontal segment across the slant to distinguish it from the number 1. Students may see this at home.

- **Teaching Tip:** Provide additional images of seven objects placed in recognizable patterns. Display them under a document camera, draw them on the board, or manipulate them on an interactive board. This helps students develop the subitizing skill of seeing and recognizing the quantity seven.
- ◉ State each success criteria and have students use their thumb signals to show where they are in their learning.
- **Supporting Learners:** Some students may count and write groups of seven without hesitation. Provide these students one to six objects at a time. Ask them, "How many do you have?" Students can add objects to make the group equal to seven.
- **Supporting Learners:** Provide a copy of ten frames for students having difficulty counting seven in different configurations.

ELL Support

Point to the umbrellas, rainbows, and snowflakes as you say the name of each. Have students repeat each word. Tell students that these are words they may use when talking about the weather. A snowflake may be something an ELL has not seen before. Explain that it is an individual bit of snow, like a raindrop is an individual bit of rain. Have students work in groups to describe the numbers of objects counted in each exercise. Have one student ask, "How many umbrellas are there?" Then have them switch roles for the other exercises.

Beginner students may only answer with "seven."
Intermediate students may answer "seven" and the item counted.
Advanced students may answer using a simple sentence, such as, "There are seven umbrellas."

7

7

7

seven

Directions:
- Count the objects. Say the number. Trace and write the number.
- Count the objects. Say the number. Write the number.

116   one hundred sixteen

© Big Ideas Learning, LLC

Laurie's Notes

Meeting the needs of all learners.

Apply and Grow: Practice

MAKING INSTRUCTIONAL DECISIONS

Consider the following questions as you decide whether additional supports or extensions are needed for each student.

- Are students able to say the names of each number?
- Are they able to draw or identify a quantity that corresponds to each numeral?
- Do they write the numerals on their own or do they refer to the drawing arrows or models in order to write the numerals?

Remember, we are looking for students to understand that a numeral is a label that represents a quantity. If students have not made this connection, make sure they have the associated quantity to count when they practice writing numerals. Some students will need more practice with the quantity number cards before they can move on to the symbol number cards.

EMERGING students may not associate the correct numeral to its corresponding quantity. They may still be confused about the counting sequence, need to use counters, or need to use their fingers when deciding the number of objects in a group.

- Prepare a tactile number 7 cut out of felt or sandpaper. Have students finger trace and answer the question, "What kind of lines make up the number 7?" Straight and slanted lines
- Show a number card to students and have them show that same number on their fingers.
- Show a subitizing card and have students write the numeral on a whiteboard or paper.

PROFICIENT students are able to consistently identify a group of seven objects and write the number 7. They are also confident in counting to 7 given a starting number.

- Have students help a peer by modeling how to fill in the sentence, "I counted _____ objects. I did this by _____."
  Sample answer: seven; pointing to each object as I counted

Extension: Adding Rigor

- Have students place seven cubes on a piece of black paper to represent stars in the night sky. Students can use any arrangement. Talk with students about constellations or star patterns and have them design their own using seven cubes. The Big Dipper and Little Dipper are made up of seven stars each. The Big Dipper is a star pattern found in the constellation Ursa Major, otherwise known as The Big Bear. The Little Dipper is a star pattern found in the constellation Ursa Minor, otherwise known as The Little Bear.

Name _____

1 7

2 7

3 5

4 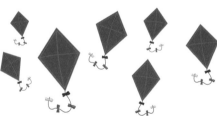 7

Directions: 1 – 4 Count the objects. Say the number. Write the number.

Laurie's Notes

Think and Grow: Modeling Real Life

This application helps students count to identify the size of each group and write the number to represent the quantity. The numbers 2, 5, 6, and 7 are revisited.

- **Preview:** Ask students whether they have ever seen a weather chart. Students may relate this to tracking the weather in class or seeing a weather forecast in a newspaper or on television.
- Have groups of students discuss what the various symbols mean. The partly cloudy symbol can be confusing to some students. They may think of it as a sun with some clouds or a cloud with the sun. Either way, they want to count it with the sunny symbol and the cloudy symbol. Be sure they can distinguish each of the four symbols.
- ? **Think-Pair-Share:** Read the directions. Ask, "How will you find the numbers of each type of weather symbol?" Students may track across the rows or down the columns. Some may cross out the symbols as they count.
- ? "How many sunny days are on the chart?" seven Have students write the number 7.
- Have students identify the numbers of each type of weather symbol.
- ⊙ Have students assess their learning for today. If students move to centers at this time, match them to the center that has the most appropriate support. All center activities should be engaging and appropriate to the needs of the learner.
- **Supporting Learners:** Some students may be proficient in counting and writing the number 7. Have these students tell a story about the weather chart or create their own weather charts and write the numbers of each symbol. They can use the Newton or Descartes puppet when telling the story.
- ? **Extension:** "Are there more sunny days or rainy days? sunny How do you know?" 7 is greater than 2.
- **Note:** Students have not compared numbers past 5, but have learned the term *greater than*.

Closure

- **Turn and Talk:** Have students take turns showing one to seven counters to partners. Ask the partners to add counters to make the group equal to seven. A ten frame, rekenrek, or linking cubes can be helpful.

Think and Grow: Modeling Real Life

Weather Chart

Monday	Tuesday	Wednesday	Thursday	Friday

Directions: Count the objects in the picture. Say the number. Write the number.

118   one hundred eighteen

© Big Ideas Learning, LLC

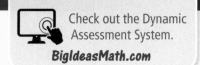

Connect and Extend Learning

Practice Notes

- **Exercises 1–5:** Discuss the arrangements of the objects.
- **Exercise 3:** Students may say there are three pairs of boots. Tell them to count each individual boot.
- **Exercises 3 and 4:** Preview the pages and state the names for each object.
- **Exercise 5:** Check to see that students can distinguish between the two types of weather symbols.

Cross-Curricular Connections

Language Arts

- *Froggy Bakes A Cake* by Jonathan London; Count the number of items that Froggy uses for his recipe. He uses flour, sugar, chocolate, milk, eggs, butter, and baking powder. Count the number of eggs Froggy uses.

Science

- Discuss the weather. Have students fold a piece of blue construction paper in half and leave it folded. Have students write the number 7 by the fold. Give students a container of cotton balls and have them count seven. Glue seven cotton balls below the number to make clouds in the sky. Have students cut and glue seven raindrops underneath the clouds. Use the other half to follow the same process for another number.

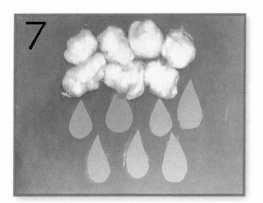

Name _____

Learning Target: Understand and write the number 7.

seven

Directions: Count the linking cubes. Say the number. Write the number.

①

7

②

7

Directions: ① and ② Count the dots. Say the number. Write the number.

© Big Ideas Learning, LLC

Chapter 3 | Lesson 4   one hundred nineteen   119

Connect and Extend Learning

Extend Student Learning

Linguistic

- Continue the classroom book, *Our Number Walk: 6 to 10* by drawing objects for the number 7. See page T-14 for a refresher on how to make the book.

Logical-Mathematical

- Place magnetic tape on seven craft sticks. Write a number from 0–7 on the bottom of each stick. Have students place the corresponding number of paperclips on each magnetic strip. Have partners count each stick to check.

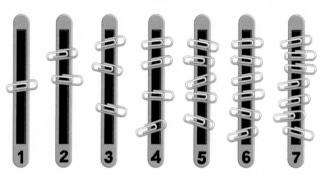

- Have a treasure hunt inside or outside. Prepare by finding a given number of objects that have a specific characteristic. A few examples are listed below.

  Find one large object.

  Find two tall objects.

  Find three objects that are the same.

  Find four objects that are different.

  Find five objects that are on a shelf.

  Find six small soft objects.

  Find seven green objects.

  Change the game by choosing new objects or limiting the colors of objects.

  Teaching Tip: Have students draw what they find. Encourage students to label their drawings.

Lesson Resources	
Surface Level	**Deep Level**
Resources by Chapter • Extra Practice • Reteach Differentiating the Lesson Skills Review Handbook Skills Trainer	Resources by Chapter • Enrichment and Extension Graphic Organizers Dynamic Assessment System • Lesson Practice

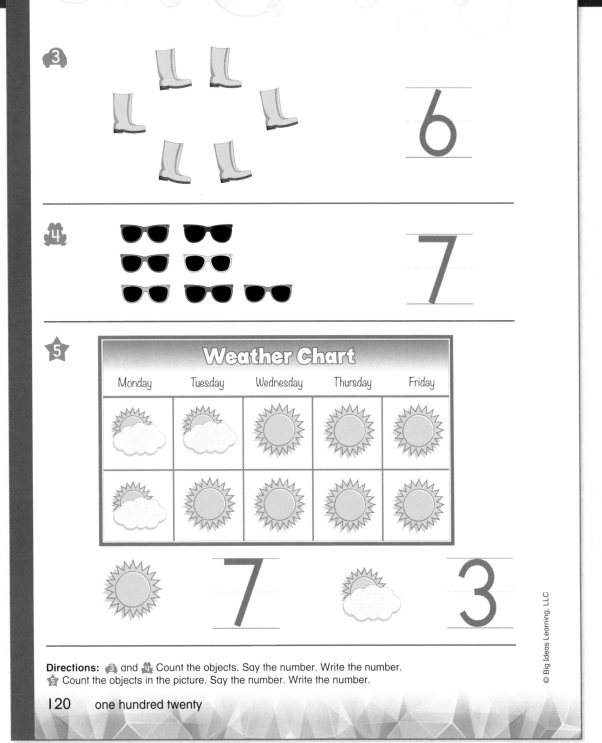

3 6

4 7

5

Weather Chart				
Monday	Tuesday	Wednesday	Thursday	Friday

7

3

Directions: **3** and **4** Count the objects. Say the number. Write the number.
5 Count the objects in the picture. Say the number. Write the number.

3.5

Learning Target
Show and count the number 8.

Success Criteria
- Name the number 8.
- Count one object for each number to 8.
- Tell the number of objects in a group.

ELL Support
Homophones are words that sound alike and have different meanings. These words are particularly challenging for ELLs. The word *eight* has the homophone *ate*. Tell students to listen to everything being said to be sure they understand which word is being used.

Laurie's Notes

Preparing to Teach
The number 8 is introduced today. Eight can be a confusing word because it is a homophone. Children may confuse it with the word *ate*. As always, think about what connections your students may have to the number 8. When students connect counting to something contextual, it helps them make the quantity of eight less abstract. The lesson is similar in design to the previous "Model and Count" lessons. The theme is a desert or arid climate.

Materials
- linking cubes
- two-color counters

Dig In (Circle Time)
Have seven students stand in the center of the circle in two rows (four and three). Point out that there are three groups of partners and then count seven people altogether.

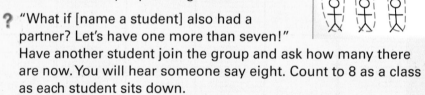

- ❓ "What if [name a student] also had a partner? Let's have one more than seven!" Have another student join the group and ask how many there are now. You will hear someone say eight. Count to 8 as a class as each student sits down.
- Have children count to 8 again as they clap for each count. They can also tap, nod, or do some other motion. Have students count to 8 from a given number when they are ready.
- ❓ Model counting to 8 using your fingers. Then have students count to 8 while they show the corresponding fingers. Hold up eight fingers and ask, "Can you show the same number of fingers?" Some students find four and four fingers are easier to model than five and three fingers.
- If students are not yet ready to move on to the Explore and Grow, spend time working with linking cube models as a whole class or in pairs.
- ⊙ Students have named the number 8 and counted to 8 as they pointed to objects. The second success criterion reinforces the concept of one-to-one correspondence.

❓ Teaching Prompt   ⊙ Learning Target

Learning Target: Show and
count the number 8.

Check students' work.

Explore and Grow

Directions: Place 8 counters in the desert. Slide the counters to the frame.

© Big Ideas Learning, LLC

Explore and Grow

? "Who can tell us something about a desert? What would you see in
a desert?" Listen for objects such as cactuses, lizards, sage brush,
tumbleweed, snakes and so on.

- Distribute counters. "I saw eight desert cactuses ready to bloom. Use
  counters to show each cactus."

- Call on different students to count the cactuses in the desert. Count together
  as students slide the counters to the ten frames.

- **Supporting Learners:** Have students practice counting to 8 from a given
  number. This helps students when they subitize a smaller group and *count
  on* to find the quantity.

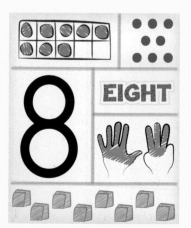

Laurie's Notes

Think and Grow

Getting Started

- Introduce the vocabulary card for **eight** and show eight on the ten frame. You may want to create an anchor chart including different subitizing patterns for eight. Remember, when you ask students to describe how they see the dots, there is not a correct answer. You want students to describe what they see.
- ? "What do you know about the word *eight*?" legs on a spider; limbs on an octopos; the time school starts
- ? Sample Questions: How many counters are in the ten frame? How many are empty? What is our room number? How many computers are in the lab?

Teaching Notes

- Notice the three arrangements of eight objects. The mice are in the standard ten frame arrangement and then there are two rectangular arrays. One has two rows of four and the other one has a group of six and two more. This helps build students' conceptual subitizing skills.
- Model: Together as a class, count each mouse. As students say the counting sequence, they place a counter on each mouse. Slide the counters to the ten frame boxes to count how many. Color each box that has a counter.
- Give directions as needed, while students count the cactuses and tortoises. Count, say how many, slide, and color.
- You will still have students who cover the objects with counters as they count aloud and others who will want to just point and count. Some may track with their eyes or just see the group of eight objects.
- FYI: Students develop their understanding of counting at different rates so, it is necessary to support and to extend learning.
- ⊙ For students still making sense of counting, do not minimize how powerful it is to point out what successful learning looks like. Ask volunteers to demonstrate counting to 8 as they point to each object in a group of 8, the second success criterion. Ask students, "How many are in the group?" When they associate the last number they counted with the number of objects in the group, they are demonstrating the third success criterion.
- Extension: Give partners a set of number cards from 0 to 7. One student draws a card and the other student counts forward to 8 or backwards to 0.
- ? Connection: When all have finished ask, "Are the number of mice and the number of cactuses the same?"

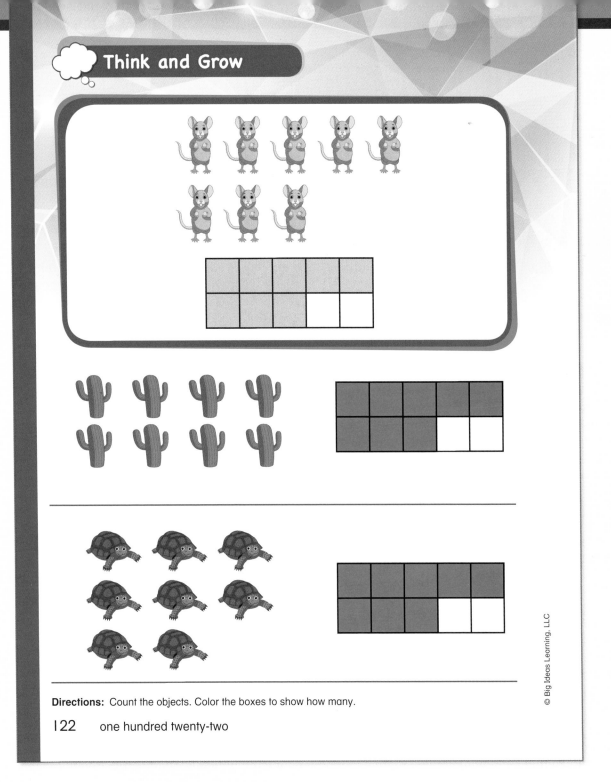

Directions: Count the objects. Color the boxes to show how many.

122   one hundred twenty-two

Meeting the needs of all learners.

Apply and Grow: Practice

MAKING INSTRUCTIONAL DECISIONS

Refer to the list of different types of student counters found on page T-17 for a refresher of the descriptions and to re-evaluate students. Show students a subitizing card for the number 8. Have the students count and tell how many. Monitor to see whether the student can count accurately the first time without recounting. Use the same number card and ask students to get the same amount of counters out of a basket. Observe whether the student needs to recount the dots on the card to determine the number of objects to pull from the basket. Repeat this process with other numbers.

EMERGING students may have difficulty counting the objects even when they are shown in a familiar arrangement. They may hesitate or get lost during the number sequence.

- Model how to count to 8 by holding up your fingers one-by-one as you count. Do it again with students, and then encourage the students to do it on their own. They can also practice with partners.

PROFICIENT students are able to count and show a group of eight objects.

- When the objects are shown in a scattered arrangement, can students explain a strategy for keeping track of what objects they have counted and the ones that still need to be counted?

Additional Support

? **Attend to Precision:** Have students use precise language to explain how they count. Ask, "How can you find out whether there are eight objects in a group?" Count the objects. The last number I say tells how many are in the group. "How can you use counters to help you count the objects?" I can place them over each picture one-by-one as I count.

Extensions: Adding Rigor

- Have students count forward and backward from any given number within eight.
- Demonstrate counting a group of eight objects without being able to see them all. Arrange eight counters so that students can see them. Use your hand to cover two counters. Can students still tell how many counters there are? Are they able to visualize the two that are covered?

Name _____

1

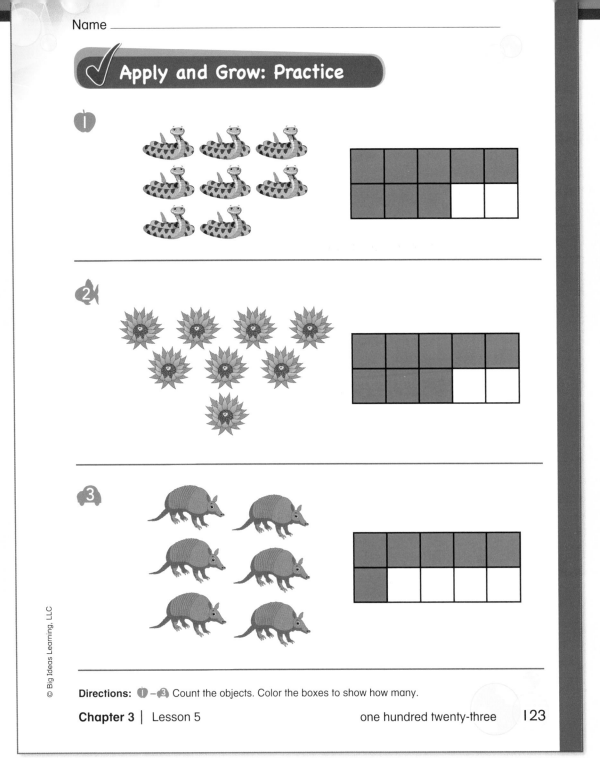

2

3

Directions: ❶ – ❸ Count the objects. Color the boxes to show how many.

© Big Ideas Learning, LLC

ELL Support

Review the word cactus, and teach the word lizard by pointing to each and stating its name. Explain that when there is more than one lizard, you add –s to the word. Check for understanding of Lesson 3.5 by asking the following questions and having students answer silently with a thumbs up for *yes* and thumbs down for *no*. Give them time to count each before they answer.

- Are there eight cactuses? Are there six?
- Are there eight lizards?

Think and Grow: Modeling Real Life

This application helps students count to answer "how many" with the number 8.

? **Preview:** "What do you think is happening in the picture? Have you ever seen a cactus or lizard? Talk to your partner about the picture."

- **FYI:** There are six types of terrestrial ecosystems. These include taiga, tundra, deciduous forest, grasslands, tropical rain forests, and deserts. Use student friendly language to explain a bit about deserts.

- **Think-Pair-Share:** "How will you count the cactuses and lizards?" Have students share with their partners and then with the class.

? Read the directions. "What objects are we counting?" cactuses and lizards Students have fun saying cactuses. You can also say cacti.

? **Extension:** "Are there the same number of cactuses as lizards?" no "How do you know?" 6 and 8 not the same "Draw more cactuses so there are the same number of cactuses as lizards."

◉ After reviewing the learning target with students, have them signal their understanding of showing and counting the number 8.

- **Supporting Learners:** Students can use counters or linking cubes to practice counting eight objects.

Closure

- Prompt students to choose a number from 0 to 8 and show that number using objects, drawings, fingers, or actions. Have partners say the number.

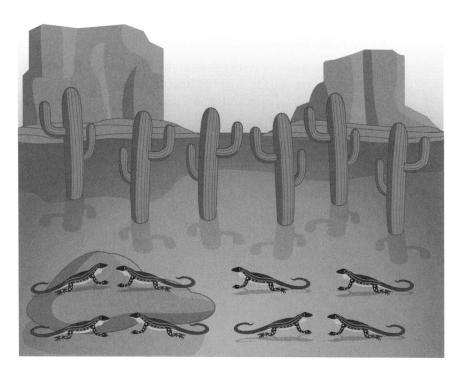

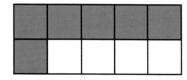

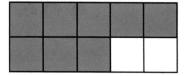

Directions: Count the objects in the picture. Color the boxes to show how many.

124   one hundred twenty-four

Connect and Extend Learning

Practice Notes

- **Exercises 1–4:** Preview the pages and state the names of the objects. Use words such as lizards, meerkats or prairie dogs, cactus flowers, tarantulas, aloe vera plants, tumbleweed, and scorpions.
- **Exercise 5:** Remind students not to count the tumbleweed and scorpion outside of the picture.

Cross-Curricular Connections

Language Arts

- *The Itsy Bitsy Spider* by Iza Trapani; Sing the song "The Itsy Bitsy Spider" and perform the hand movements as you sing. After the spider climbs up the water spout, have students count to eight as you touch fingers together.

Science

- Explore and discuss spiders. Students are familiar with spiders but may not know that they have eight legs, and six or eight eyes. Provide time to look at different types and facts about spiders.

eye arrangement of a spider

Name _____

Learning Target: Show and count the number 8.

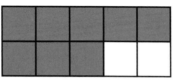

Directions: Count the lizards. Color the boxes to show how many.

①

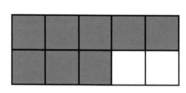

②

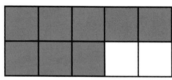

Directions: ① and ② Count the objects. Color the boxes to show how many.

Chapter 3 | Lesson 5

one hundred twenty-five   125

© Big Ideas Learning, LLC

Connect and Extend Learning

Extend Student Learning

Intrapersonal

- Cut out enough large half circles for each student to use as an octopus body. Provide each student with a pair of googly eyes to glue to the body. Prepare enough strings for each student to use as octopus limbs. These should all be knotted at the end so that students can thread beads on each one. Increase the numbers of beads on each string starting with one and ending with eight. Attach the threaded strings to the octopus body with tape. Have students count the numbers of beads on each string and write the corresponding numbers above each one.

Lesson Resources	
Surface Level	**Deep Level**
Resources by Chapter • Extra Practice • Reteach Differentiating the Lesson Skills Review Handbook Skills Trainer	Resources by Chapter • Enrichment and Extension Graphic Organizers Dynamic Assessment System • Lesson Practice

3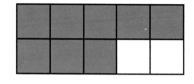

4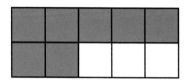

5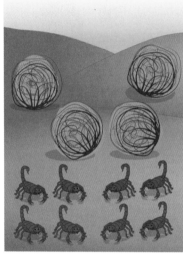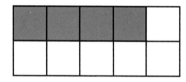

 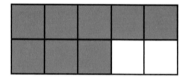

Directions: **3** and **4** Count the objects. Color the boxes to show how many.
5 Count the objects in the picture. Color the boxes to show how many.

Check out the Dynamic Classroom.

BigIdeasMath.com

Laurie's Notes

Preparing to Teach

In this lesson, students review the numbers 0 to 7 as they understand and write the number 8. A circular arrangement will be shown for the first time in this lesson. Be sure to share a strategy for counting objects in this type of arrangement. Listen for students using subitizing skills with smaller numbers. Some students may even move from perceptual to conceptual subitizing. They may say, "I see five," and then count on to eight.

All of the "Understand and Write" lessons in this chapter have the same design but a different theme. The theme of this lesson is bugs and insects.

Materials

- instrument to make a beat
- two-color counters
- *Bugs, Bugs, Bugs**
- Subitizing Cards 5–10*
- Dot Cards 5–10 Set 1*

Found in the Instructional Resources

Dig In (Circle Time)

Repeat the activity described on page T-115 using an instrument to create eight beats. Students love music and making sounds to practice the counting sequence. Be sure to use the second and third version of the activity as well, in which you play five notes and then they clap or count aloud three times to finish the counting sequence to 8.

- ? Distribute the booklet *Bugs, Bugs, Bugs.* "What kinds of bugs have you seen? Talk to your partner." This might be a scary topic for students, so watch for any distressed reactions. Have students identify the various objects on the cover before reading and discussing the booklet.
- ? "How many bees are in the story?" eight Students may be distracted and want to tell stories about being stung by a bee.
- "There are eight bees flying. Write the number 8." Use the verbal pathway "pull back, around, back around, and connect." Have students finger trace the 8 in the booklet several times as you repeat the verbal pathway. Practice air writing 8. Students can count the spots on the ladybug and practice writing 8.
- ? "How many legs does the ladybug have? How do we write a 6?"
- Students should return to their seats with their booklets.

Learning Target

Understand and write the number 8.

Success Criteria

- Identify a group of eight objects.
- Write the number 8.

Warm-Up

Practice opportunities for the following are available in the Resources by Chapter or at *BigIdeasMath.com*.

- Daily skills
- Vocabulary
- Prerequisite skills

ELL Support

Preview the words bug, ladybug, and spots by showing or drawing visuals to explain each. If possible, allow students to hold and examine a variety of toy bugs. Tell students to listen carefully for the word eight as you read and decide what the number eight is being used to count.

? Teaching Prompt   ⊙ Learning Target

Learning Target: Understand
and write the number 8.

Explore and Grow

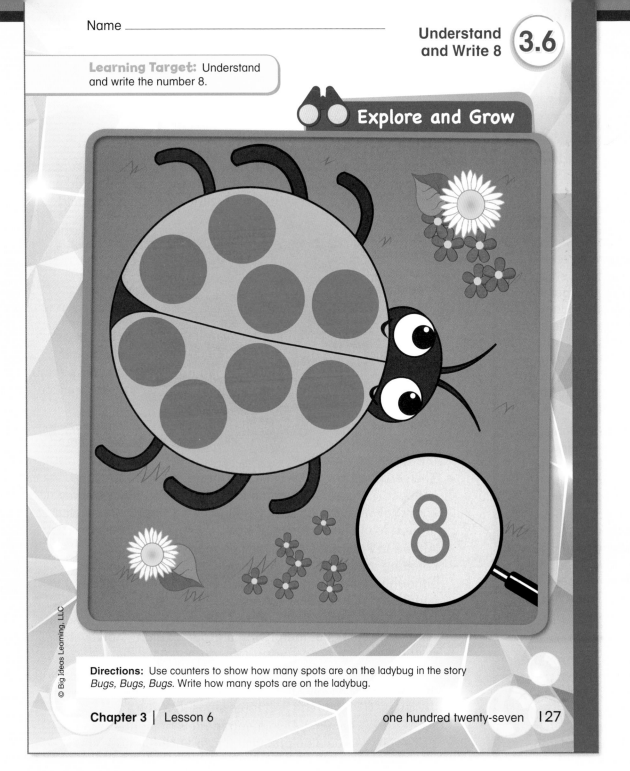

Directions: Use counters to show how many spots are on the ladybug in the story
Bugs, Bugs, Bugs. Write how many spots are on the ladybug.

Explore and Grow

◉ Refer to the *Bugs, Bugs, Bugs* booklet. "Use your counters to show the
number of spots on the ladybug." When students count and say "8" to
represent the number of spots, they are demonstrating the first success
criterion. Be intentional in pointing this out. "You can identify a group of
eight. Thumbs up!"

• Chorally say the verbal pathway as they practice air writing the number 8.
Now explore writing the number 8 on the magnifying glass.

• **Supporting Learners:** Some students begin to write the 8 in a clockwise
versus counterclockwise direction. When they do this and the 8 looks the
same, I do not try to change the motion.

Point to the spiders, centipedes, and praying mantises (milipedes or grasshoppers) as you say the name of each. Have students repeat each word. Tell students these are all types of bugs. Have students work in pairs. Have one student ask the other, "How many spiders are there?" Then have them switch roles for the other exercises.

Beginner students may only answer "eight."
Intermediate students may answer using the number and name of each object, such as, "eight spiders."
Advanced students may answer using simple sentences, such as, "There are eight spiders."

Think and Grow

Getting Started

- Show students the subitizing card and dot card for 8. Talk about the two dot patterns and what the students see. You could ask what other types of arrangements they have seen, or could make, for 8.
- Displaying this page under a document camera could be helpful. The arrangement of spiders (scattered) and grasshoppers (circular) may be challenging for students. Model a strategy for counting these two arrangements.

Teaching Notes

- **Model:** Count the group of eight spiders together as a class. Finger trace the numeral 8. Count the dot model and finger trace the numeral 8. Say the verbal pathway, "pull back, around, back around, and connect," as students trace and then practice writing 8.
- **?** "Were the spiders or dots easier to count? Why?" Answers may vary, but most students will say dots are easier to count because "they are lined up."
- The verbal pathway, "pull back, around, back around, and connect," is hard for students to remember even when they know how to write an 8. Say the pathway aloud, as you walk around to observe students' work.
- **Attend to Precision:** "Tell your partner your method for counting the bugs." You want students to understand that although their partners may have used a different strategy to count, the quantity is still the same.
- ⊙ Discuss and assess each success criterion separately. Students may be proficient at identifying a group of eight, however they may still need practice writing the number 8.
- **Supporting Learners:** Some students may have difficulty writing the number 8 because it has four steps. If the class has learned the letter "S," relate the first three steps to writing an "S."
- **Supporting Learners:** Displaying models of eight around the classroom can be a helpful visual reference for students.

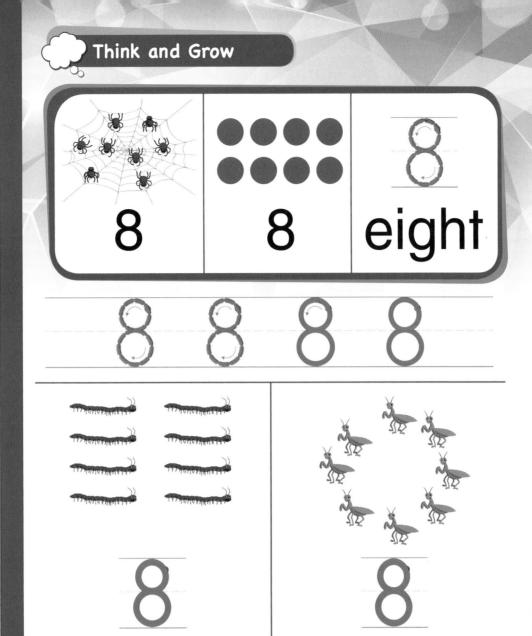

8

8

eight

8 8 8 8

Directions:
- Count the objects. Say the number. Trace and write the number.
- Count the bugs. Say the number. Write the number.

Meeting the needs of
all learners.

Laurie's Notes

Apply and Grow: Practice

MAKING INSTRUCTIONAL DECISIONS

Many of your students have probably made observations about number relationships by now. Some students may recognize objects or pictures in specific arrangements and tell how many without counting one-by-one. The most common patterns used in the book so far are found on dice and on a ten frame. To get more practice with subitizing, show students many different arrangements and have them draw these same patterns on a whiteboard or piece of paper. Use them like flashcards and quickly show the arrangement to students. See whether students are able to recognize the number without counting one-by-one.

EMERGING students may not consistently associate one number word with one object when counting, or they are only confident about counting when the objects are arranged in one way, such as linear.

- Have students close their eyes and visualize the number 8. What do they see? Do they see the numeral? Do they see dots? How are the dots or objects arranged? Students may say things such as, "I see the number 8 that you write" or "I see eight dots on a domino." Ask students to describe their mental images.

PROFICIENT students are able to identify a group of eight objects and write the number 8. They are starting to see the quantity of eight as a large group made up of two smaller parts, such as four and four.

Additional Support

- Students should recognize that the number 8 has curves. Have students practice writing the number 8 on a whiteboard without the restriction of handwriting lines. This will allow them to explore and develop their muscles and coordination with writing 8.
- Students can practice writing the numbers using thicker pencils, crayons, or chalk.

Extensions: Adding Rigor

- Provide modeling clay for students to build the number 8. Model how to make snakes with the clay and pinch them together to make 8.
- Provide students with sets of number cards, whiteboards, and counters. One student draws a number card and places that number of counters on a desk. The other student writes the corresponding number on the whiteboard. Students should check each other's work and then switch roles.

Name _____

1 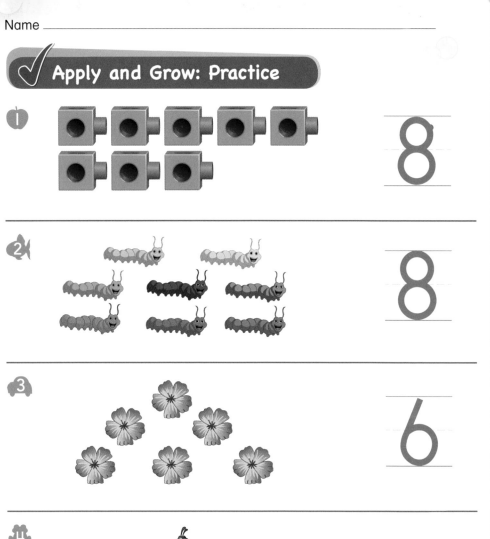 8

2 8

3 6

4 8

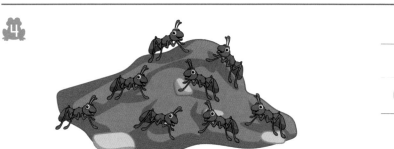

© Big Ideas Learning, LLC

Directions: 1 – 4 Count the objects. Say the number. Write the number.

Chapter 3 | Lesson 6

one hundred twenty-nine 129

Laurie's Notes

Think and Grow: Modeling Real Life

This application helps students count to identify the sizes of each group and write the numbers they count. The numbers 4, 6, 7, and 8 are revisited.

- **? Preview:** "Tell your partner what you see in the picture. Would you like to play outdoors in an area like this?"
- **Think-Pair-Share:** Read the directions and have students think about how they will count the objects. The scattered arrangement of the objects invites students to have a counting strategy. Crossing out the object or placing a counter on it will be necessary for most students.
- **?** Encourage students to work together to count the objects. Each student counts the butterflies and checks with their partners. "What will you do if you each count a different number?" The social skills developed during partner work should include knowing what to do when you do not agree!
- Discuss the quantities of each group of objects found. When displayed under a document camera, students can take turns modeling how they counted.
- **? Connection:** "Did any of the groups have the same number of objects?" Students have compared numbers 0 through 5 and will compare numbers 6 through 10 in the next chapter. Can they apply their understanding of less than to numbers greater than 5?
- **? Extension:** Ask, "How many more" of a particular object "would you need to have 8?"
- **Supporting Learners:** Have students use ten frames to show eight in different ways. Have students explain what they notice each time they show eight. For example, students may notice a row of five and a row of three or two rows of four.
- ⊙ Have students use their thumb signals to show their understanding of what they learned today.

Closure

- Review the vocabulary cards for 0 through 8. Have students say each number and stand up when an 8 is shown. Flip through the cards several times.

 7

 8

 6

 4

Directions: Count the objects in the picture. Say the number. Write the number.

130   one hundred thirty

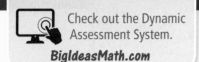
Connect and Extend Learning

Practice Notes

- **Exercises 1–5:** Discuss the arrangements of the dots and objects on each page.
- **Exercise 3:** Remind students to mark which snail they count first. Some students will cross out the snails as they count.
- **Exercise 5:** Tell students not to count the worm and bird outside of the picture.

Cross-Curricular Connections

Language Arts

- *My Octopus Arms* by Keith Baker; Count all of the objects that are, or can be, held by each octopus limb. Have students write or draw a story about what it might be like to have eight limbs. Remind students that humans have four limbs and discuss what they are used for.

Science

- Students should close their eyes, listen, and count as you drop a specific number of objects into a container. The containers used can be made of metal, plastic, or glass. Choose a few students to identify the number of objects that they believe they heard hit the container. You could also add water to a container to vary the sounds. Drop things like coins, washers, bolts, manipulatives, or other small classroom objects.

Learning Target: Understand and write the number 8.

eight

Directions: Count the linking cubes. Say the number. Write the number.

1

8

2

8

Directions: 1 and 2 Count the dots. Say the number. Write the number.

© Big Ideas Learning, LLC

Connect and Extend Learning

Extend Student Learning

Visual-Spatial

- Continue the classroom book, *Our Number Walk: 6 to 10* by drawing objects for the number 8. See page T-14 for a refresher on how to make the book.

Logical-Mathematical

- Create simple spider webs on orange paper plates, or use white plates and have students color them. Place a number 0–8 on each plate. Provide students with beads or counters to represent spiders in the webs. Have students put the spiders in different arrangements on the plates. Make sure the number of spiders matches the number on the plate.
- Teaching Tip: Instead of using beads or counters, make paper spiders to use in the webs. Another option is to use spider rings.

Lesson Resources	
Surface Level	**Deep Level**
Resources by Chapter • Extra Practice • Reteach Differentiating the Lesson Skills Review Handbook Skills Trainer	Resources by Chapter • Enrichment and Extension Graphic Organizers Dynamic Assessment System • Lesson Practice

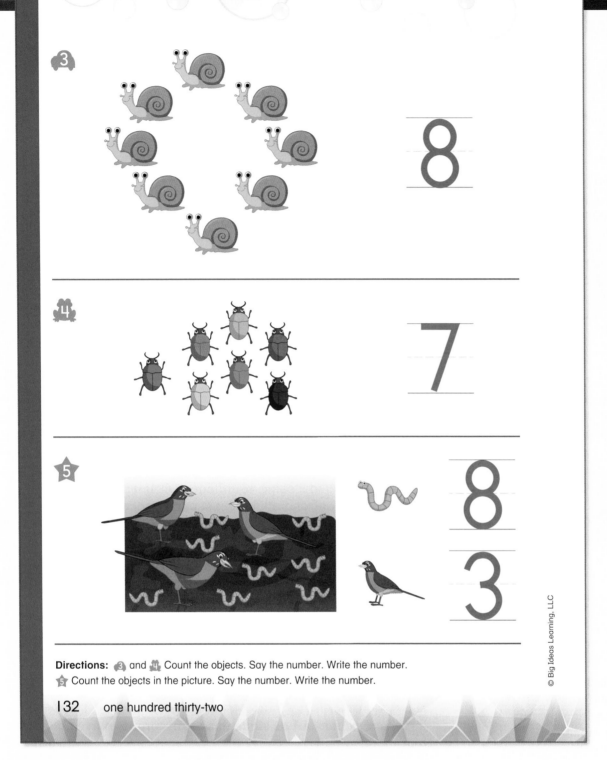

③ 8

④ 7

⑤ 8
3

Directions: ③ and ④ Count the objects. Say the number. Write the number.
⑤ Count the objects in the picture. Say the number. Write the number.

132 one hundred thirty-two

© Big Ideas Learning, LLC

Laurie's Notes

Preparing to Teach

Nine is a number that may be familiar to students if someone has taught them to dial 9-1-1. This practice is often part of Fire Prevention Month in October. When students model the quantity of nine on a ten frame they often comment about having only one empty box. They are anxious to fill the frame! The lesson is similar in design to previous "Model and Count" lessons and the theme is the beach.

Materials

- linking cubes
- rekenrek
- two-color counters

Dig In (Circle Time)

Story Time: Tell students that you ate some strawberries during dinner last night. "Do you know how many I ate? More than 1. More than 2." Continue until you get to eight. "Does anyone know what comes after eight?" nine "I ate nine strawberries!"

- Have children count to 9 with you as they clap for each count.
- Model counting to 9 using your fingers. Count slowly so students can control putting up just one finger at a time. My students like to see if they can hold down one finger to show nine in different ways. Two examples are shown.

⊙ Students have counted to 9 and modeled nine with their fingers. Use linking cubes or a rekenrek so that students can point to one object as they say each number name. If you use linking cubes, consider five of one color and four of another. Like with the rekenrek, this allows students to see a group of five and four more.

Learning Target

Show and count the number 9.

Success Criteria

- Name the number 9.
- Count one object for each number to 9.
- Tell the number of objects in a group.

ELL Support

Have students practice pronouncing the word *nine* by repeating after you. Review the words *one* through *eight* using the same method. Then count aloud as you extend nine fingers. Have students do the same.

? Teaching Prompt   ⊙ Learning Target

Name _____

Learning Target: Show and count the number 9.

— Check students' work.

👀 **Explore and Grow**

Directions: Place 9 counters on the beach. Slide the counters to the frame.

Chapter 3 | Lesson 7   one hundred thirty-three **133**

© Big Ideas Learning, LLC

Explore and Grow

❓ Distribute counters. "I saw nine baby turtles on the beach. Use counters to show the turtles on the beach." Pause. "What do you think they are doing? Tell your partner what you are thinking."

❓ "Count your turtles as you slide them to the ten frame. What do you notice when you show nine on a ten frame?" I need two rows; there is an empty box; there are four more than a five frame.

• **Supporting Learners:** Students work with partners. One partner calls out a number 0 through 5. The other counts on from that number to 9. Students need to practice counting on. This can be done with counters or cubes.

Laurie's Notes

Think and Grow
Getting Started

- Introduce the vocabulary card for **nine**. Consider creating an anchor chart for nine.
- **Turn and Talk:** "What do you know about the number *nine*?" nine innings; September; a tic-tac-toe board You could have students tell their partners how they see the nine dots on the vocabulary card.
- **? Sample Questions:** How many counters are in the ten frame? What comes after 8 when counting? Do we have reading time at 9 o'clock? Do you have a brother who is 9 years old?

Teaching Notes

- **Look for and Make Use of Structure:** Point out the arrangements of the balls, pelicans, and towels. All of these arrangements help to build students' subitizing skills. When you ask students to tell how they are counting the objects, do you hear evidence of students seeing smaller parts that are combined to make nine?
- **Model:** Together as a class, count each ball. As students say the counting sequence, they place a linking cube or counter on each ball. Slide the counters to the ten frame boxes to see how many. Color each box that has a counter.
- Give directions as needed, while students count the pelicans and beach towels. Count, say how many, slide, and color.
- The arrangement of the towels is set up so that students can count the objects in different ways. For instance, students could start with the last towel in the bottom row, or the top row at the right. They could also subitize and see a dice pattern group of six and count on three more.
- **Big Idea:** The number of towels does not change when you count them in a different order.
- ⊙ "How good do you think you are at counting to 9? Show me with your thumb signals."
- **? Extension:** Have students count a quantity of nine shown in a circular arrangement. Model this by having nine students stand in a circle. Select one student to start. The first squats and says, "One." The next student squats and says, "Two." Continue around the circle and make sure students are able to see the importance of where you start when counting a circular arrangement. Ask, "What do you think might happen if we did not squat as we counted?"

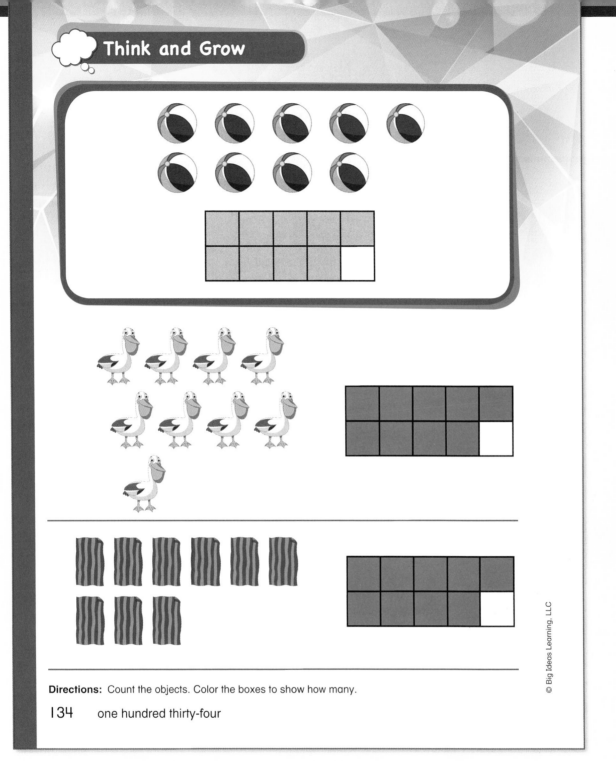

Directions: Count the objects. Color the boxes to show how many.

134   one hundred thirty-four

Meeting the needs of
all learners.

Laurie's Notes

Apply and Grow: Practice

MAKING INSTRUCTIONAL DECISIONS

As students count greater numbers, the process becomes more complex. Take note of how students naturally keep track of what they are counting. Ask students, "What can you do to help you count?" I cross out objects as I count; I use my finger to point as I count; I see groups and count on.

EMERGING students may have difficulty remembering all of the number names or saying them in order.

- Have students work with different dot patterns for 9. When there are three rows of three dots, cover up two rows and see whether they can start counting on from 3 versus 1.

PROFICIENT students are confident in counting to 9 when the objects are in different arrangements.

- Count to 9 beginning at a start number less than 9.

Additional Support

- Have students drop marbles or small rocks into a container one-by-one. Have them listen to the sound that the object makes as it falls to the bottom. Have students count the objects or each sound. Add water to the container to change the sound.

Extensions: Adding Rigor

- Get students to think more critically by asking, "How many more do you need to have a full ten frame? How do you know? How many are in the ten frame now? How do you know?"
- Have students create coloring sheets with multiple groups of nine objects. Each group of nine is made up of the same object. Suggest a theme for the page, or draw common figures such as circles, lines, curves, hearts, or flowers. Students can then trade their papers with friends to count.

Name _____

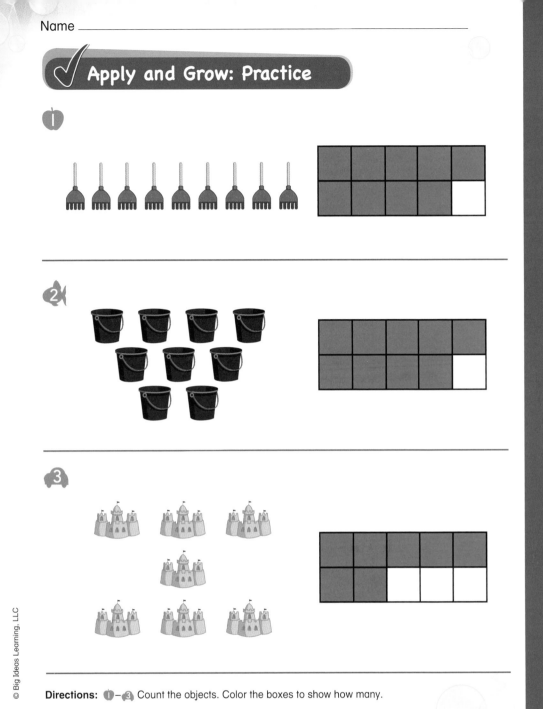

1

2

3

Directions: ❶–❸ Count the objects. Color the boxes to show how many.

© Big Ideas Learning, LLC

Laurie's Notes

Think and Grow: Modeling Real Life

This application helps students count to answer "how many" with the number 9. The numbers 8 and 9 are used in a contextual setting.

? **Preview:** "What do you think is happening in the picture? Talk to your partner about the picture."

? Read the directions. "What objects are we counting?"

? **Think-Pair-Share:** Have students think about how they will count the turtles and boats and then talk to partners. Share as a whole class.

- The arrangement of the turtles and boats should enable students to count them without confusion.

- **Supporting Learners:** Place counters or linking cubes on each object as the number word is said. You can also show examples of dot patterns for 9 and have students describe how they see each pattern.

- **Extension:** Have students tell stories about the picture. Make sure students say the number of objects when telling their stories.

- The learning target today was to show and count the number 9. Have students signal their understanding of the learning target using their thumb symbols.

Closure

- Prompt students to choose a number from 0 to 9 and show that number to partners using objects, drawings, fingers, or actions. Have the partners say the number.

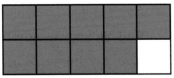

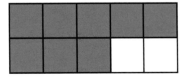

Directions: Count the objects in the picture. Color the boxes to show how many.

136   one hundred thirty-six

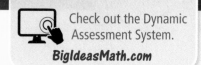
Connect and Extend Learning

Practice Notes

- **Exercises 1–5:** Some students may need to place counters on each object and move the counters to a ten frame to count. Others may prefer to cross out the objects as they count.

- **Exercise 5:** Remind students not to count the seagull and seal that are outside of the picture.

Cross-Curricular Connections

Language Arts

- *Engine, Engine, Number Nine* by Stephanie Calmenson; Use this story to emphasize the number 9 and to have a class discussion about trains. Then use the chant below to initiate transitions during the day. After the chant, when you say "one," students should count forward to 9. When you say "nine," students should count in reverse from 9.

    Whoo, whoo!

    Engine, engine, number nine

    Rolling, rolling, down the line

    See it sparkle, see it shine

    Engine, engine, number nine

    One, two, three, four, five, six, seven, eight, nine!

- Make a three by three array on the floor with tape. Have students count and discover that there are nine boxes on the floor. The array needs to be large enough to put a notecard, with a sight word written on it, inside each box. A student throws a beanbag into the box, reads the word, and spells the word on the card.

Name _____

Learning Target: Show and count the number 9.

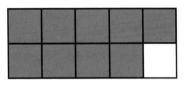

Directions: Count the shells. Color the boxes to show how many.

1

2

Directions: **1** and **2** Count the objects. Color the boxes to show how many.

Chapter 3 | Lesson 7   one hundred thirty-seven   137

© Big Ideas Learning, LLC

Connect and Extend Learning

Extend Student Learning

Bodily-Kinesthetic

- Play "Hide and Search". Place an empty coffee can in the center of the room. Prepare nine pictures of seasonal fruit or plants. Clip a clothespin to each picture. Hide the clipped pictures in the room. Be sure part of the picture is visible so it is not too hard to find. Have students search the room for the clothespin pictures. Once they find a picture, students can take off the clothespin and drop the clothespin into the coffee can. Have students count out loud the number of times they hear a clothespin drop into the can. Have students hold on to their pictures until all are found. These students can hide their pictures for the next round.

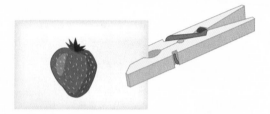

Lesson Resources	
Surface Level	**Deep Level**
Resources by Chapter • Extra Practice • Reteach Differentiating the Lesson Skills Review Handbook Skills Trainer	Resources by Chapter • Enrichment and Extension Graphic Organizers Dynamic Assessment System • Lesson Practice

3

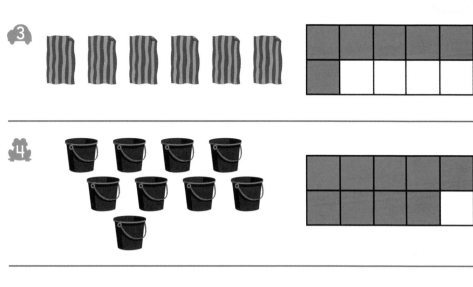

4

5

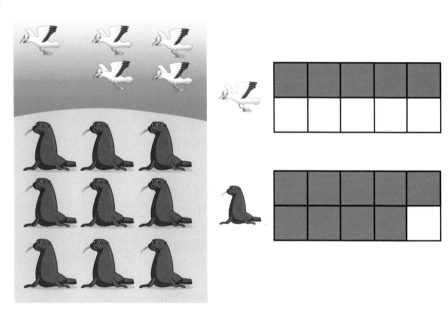

Directions: **3** and **4** Count the objects. Color the boxes to show how many.
5 Count the animals in the picture. Color the boxes to show how many.

138　　one hundred thirty-eight

Laurie's Notes

Preparing to Teach

We are getting close to the end of this chapter and students have learned to count, model, and write many numbers. Eight was a challenging number to write and 9 can be challenging for different reasons, such as confusing it with the number 6 or the letter P.

The design of this lesson is the same as other "Understand and Write" lessons in this chapter. The theme of this lesson is athletic equipment.

Materials

- objects to model 9
- *My Baseball Game**
- two-color counters
- Subitizing Cards 5–10*
- Number Cards 5–10*

*Found in the Instructional Resources

Dig In (Circle Time)

A collection of nine objects, perhaps with a sports theme, are placed in a circle. They are used to model 9.

- **?** Place a few of the objects in the circle. "How many are there?" Add another object and repeat. Continue asking until students agree that there are nine objects in the circle.
- **?** Change the arrangement of the objects and ask, "How many do you see now?" Have student volunteers point and count. Have the remaining students signal whether they agree with the amount stated. Repeat this process using a new arrangement each time.
- Distribute the booklet *My Baseball Game*. "Tell me what you know about baseball or softball." Have students share a few ideas. Read and discuss the booklet.
- **?** "How many baseballs are in the story?" nine Are students counting with their fingers or tracking with their eyes?
- "There are 9 baseballs." Model how to write the number 9 as you say the verbal pathway "pull back, around, pull down." Have students finger trace the number 9 in the booklet several times as they repeat the verbal pathway. Practice air writing 9. Count the bats and repeat.
- Students should return to their seats with their booklets.

Learning Target

Understand and write the number 9.

Success Criteria

- Identify a group of nine objects.
- Write the number 9.

Warm-Up

Practice opportunities for the following are available in the Resources by Chapter or at *BigIdeasMath.com*.

- Daily skills
- Vocabulary
- Prerequisite skills

ELL Support

Explain the game of baseball to students. Tell students that the picture is of a field where the game of baseball is played. It is called a *baseball diamond* because of its shape. The word *baseball* is a combination of *base*, which is the name of each square spot on the field, and *ball*, which is the object players throw and hit. If possible, allow students to hold and examine a baseball glove, bat, and ball. Remind students they are learning and listening for the number 9.

? Teaching Prompt   Learning Target

Learning Target: Understand and write the number 9.

Explore and Grow

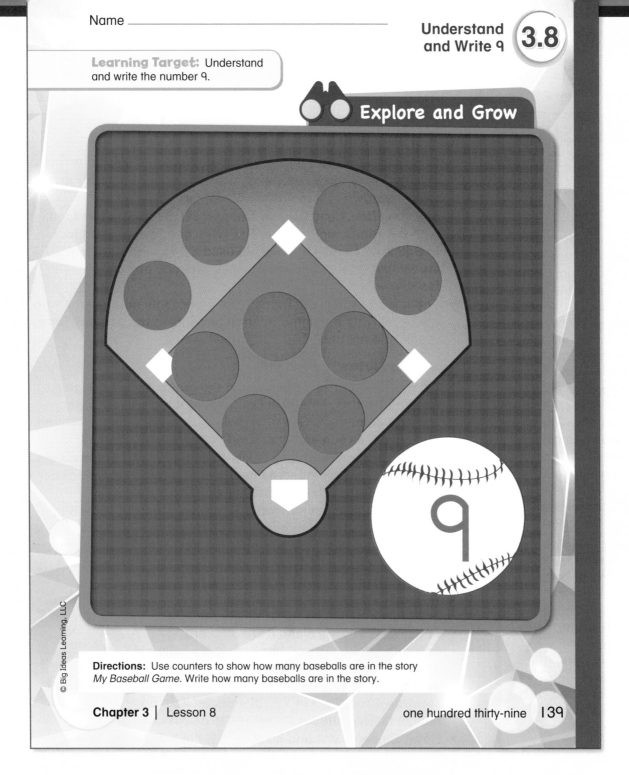

© Big Ideas Learning, LLC

Directions: Use counters to show how many baseballs are in the story *My Baseball Game.* Write how many baseballs are in the story.

Chapter 3 | Lesson 8

one hundred thirty-nine 139

Explore and Grow

- Refer to the *My Baseball Game* booklet. "Use your counters to show the baseballs on the baseball field."
- **Note:** Students who have played baseball or softball may want to position their counters on the field representing the defensive position of players.
- Have students chorally say the verbal pathway for writing the number 9 as they practice air writing a 9. Now explore writing the number 9 on the baseball.
- Students often mix up the number 9 with the number 6. Supports for this are given in the Think and Grow.

Think and Grow

Getting Started

- Show students the subitizing card and number card for 9. Students may recognize the domino pattern or they may just see three rows of three dots.
- **Preview:** Name each image. Some students may not be familiar with the sports represented. The swim goggles may just look like glasses. They may not have used a jump rope. You want students to share their experiences with any objects they are familiar with.
- There is a group, a dot model, and a traceable numeral for 9 on the page. Note the different arrangements of the goggles, jump ropes, and helmets.

Teaching Notes

- **Model:** Together as a class, count the group of nine goggles. Finger trace the numeral 9. Count the dot model and finger trace the numeral 9. Say the verbal pathway "pull back, around, pull down," as students trace and then practice writing 9.
- **?** "Were the goggles or dots easier to count? Why?" The answers will vary but listen for students to say that the dots were easier to count because they are in lines or a box.
- If a student hasn't commented about the 9 looking like a 6 that is turned around, bring it up. Write the two numbers beside one another and ask students to describe how they are alike and how they are different. Some students will turn their papers 180° and exclaim they are the same!
- **Supporting Learners:** Have students create their own mnemonic devices to remember how the 9 and 6 are different. You could draw the number 6 having a belly and the number 9 having a head. You can also refer to the 6 as being a silly sock with six stripes and the 9 as a nutty necktie with nine nuts. Give the students time to discuss and draw.
- **Note:** Students will find it funny that the jump ropes look like the number 9. They may also comment on the arrangement of the helmets looking like a cross or an X. I love these observations. It tells me that students are looking for and observing patterns.
- **Common Error:** Students may count each line of helmets and count the middle helmet twice. They need a strategy for counting this type of arrangement.
- **◉** "How confident are you at telling whether a group has nine objects? in writing the number 9?"

ELL Support

Preview the words *s*wim goggles, jump ropes, and football helmets. Explain that each is used in a sport or game. If possible, bring in examples of each and demonstrate. Students may not be familiar with American football. Tell them that it is known as football in the United States, while the football they may be familiar with is known as soccer. Have students work in pairs. Have one student ask the other, "How many swim goggles are there?" Then have them switch roles for the other exercises.

Beginner students may only answer "nine."
Intermediate students may answer "nine" and name the object counted, such as, "nine swim goggles."
Advanced students may answer using simple sentences, such as, "There are nine swim goggles."

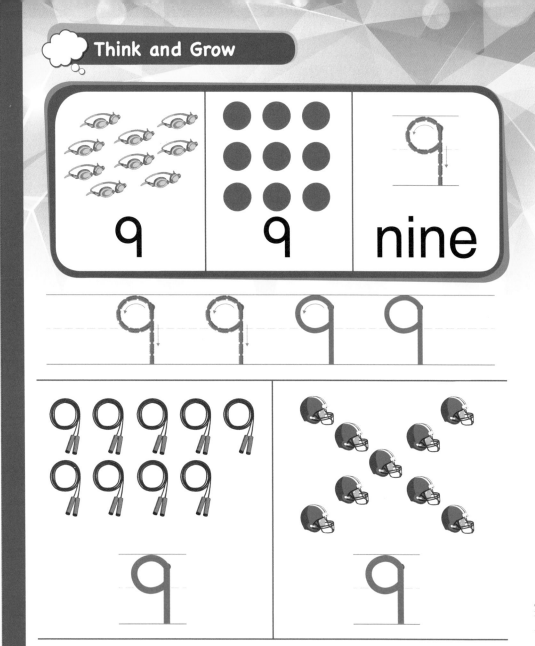

9

9

nine

9

Directions:
- Count the objects. Say the number. Trace and write the number.
- Count the objects. Say the number. Write the number.

140   one hundred forty

© Big Ideas Learning, LLC

Laurie's Notes

Meeting the needs of
all learners.

Apply and Grow: Practice

MAKING INSTRUCTIONAL DECISIONS

Hopefully you have had the opportunity to hear each student count a group of objects aloud. Do you have evidence that they are conceptually subitizing numbers 6 through 9? You will know when students understand this type of counting because they chunk quantities together and continue counting on. For example, students may see the dot pattern of three and just know that it is three. They may use this information when counting the dot pattern of nine and see a three or six and then count on. Encourage students to explain what they see when viewing different dot patterns of nine or when the nine is shown in a ten frame.

EMERGING students may be in one of the early phases of counting. They may need more practice remembering the names of some of the numbers or with writing some of the numbers. Students may reverse the number 9 or confuse it with the number 6 when writing the numeral.

PROFICIENT students are able to identify a group of nine objects and write the number 9. They do not reverse the number 9 or confuse it with the number 6. They should be able to count a group of nine objects shown in a circular arrangement.

Supporting Learners

- A telephone can be a fun way to have students practice recognizing and naming numbers.
- Use ten-sided dice with the numerals 0 through 9 on the die faces. Partners can take turns rolling and naming the numbers. This is random practice at number recognition.

Extension: Adding Rigor

- Hand out number and subitizing cards, 0 through 9. Make sure to distribute matching sets, but only give one card to each student. Have students walk around the room to find a matching card. Each number card should match a subitizing card and vice versa. If you have fewer than 20 students, omit pairs of cards, beginning with 0, then 1, and so on. If you have more than 20 students, include additional dot patterns for selected numbers.

✓ Apply and Grow: Practice

1 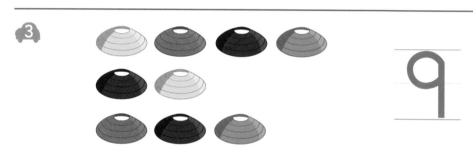 9

2 8

3 9

4 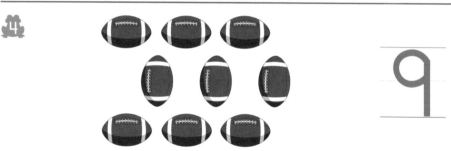 9

Directions: ❶–🐸 Count the objects. Say the number. Write the number.

Chapter 3 | Lesson 8   one hundred forty-one   141

Think and Grow: Modeling Real Life

This application helps students to count and identify the numbers of objects in each group and to write the numbers they count. The numbers 5, 6, 7, and 9 are revisited.

? Preview: "Wouldn't this be a fun place to play? Have you ever used any of these balls with [name of the physical education teacher]? Tell your partner what you know about the different types of balls."

- If possible, display the page under a document camera. Discuss the strategies students can use to count each group. Make sure they mention to cross out each ball as they count, use their fingers or eyes to count the objects in rows or columns, or count on from a smaller group.
- Read the directions and assist students as they get started.
- Discuss which type of ball was the easiest to count and why.
- ⊙ "Tell your partner what you have learned today." Give students time to share their learning with partners before asking them to use their thumb signals.
- **? Extension:** There will be students that are able to count the total number of balls. "Draw two more volleyballs. What is the total now?"
- **Supporting Learners:** Make a physical model of the three ball racks using four colors of linking cubes. Ask students to count how many cubes there are of each color. Students can manipulate, or move, the cubes. They can sort them into groups according to color and then count. Practice this several times. Now ask them to count without moving the cubes. Can they point with their finger and count each color?

Closure

- Have students take turns with their partners. One partner shows a group of counters using a number from 0 to 9. The other partner adds counters to the group to make it equal to nine. This can also be done using a ten frame or rekenrek.

 7

 9

 6

 5

Directions: Count the balls in the picture. Say the number. Write the number.

142   one hundred forty-two

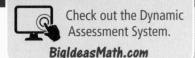
Connect and Extend Learning

Practice Notes

- **Exercises 3–5:** Preview the pages so students are familiar with the objects. Have students repeat the words scooters, stopwatches, and bowling balls.
- **Exercise 4:** Students may say that the stopwatches are different colors so they are not sure which ones to count.
- **Exercise 5:** Point out the difference between this exercise and the last. The bowling balls are being grouped and counted by color.

Cross-Curricular Connections

Language Arts

- *The Berenstain Bears and the Tic-Tac-Toe Mystery* by Stan and Jan Berenstain; Tic-Tac-Tom always wins the game tic-tac-toe. The bears need to figure out how he does it. As you read the story, discuss the author's message about playing fair. Discuss the strategies, or tricks, that Tom is using as he plays on the nine spaces of the playing board.

Social Studies

- Show visuals of a number pad used on a phone, remote control, calculator, or computer keyboard. Discuss with students the arrangement of the numbers. Call out a number and have students practice pressing that number on the visual.
- Write each student's name and phone number on their own piece of paper. Have students say, trace, and rewrite their phone number. Allow students to write or draw about why it is important to know their phone number on the back of the paper.
- **Teaching Tip:** Inform parents that students are using their phone numbers to identify and write numbers 0–9.

computer

phone

calculator

Name _____

Learning Target: Understand and write the number 9.

nine

Directions: Count the linking cubes. Say the number. Write the number.

9

9

Directions: ❶ and ❷ Count the dots. Say the number. Write the number.

Extend Student Learning

Linguistic

- Continue the classroom book, *Our Number Walk: 6 to 10* by drawing items for the number 9. See page T-14 for a refresher about how to make the book.

Musical

- Play "Number Stew". Bring in a small pot and wooden spoon. Place number cards 1-9 in the pot. Call on a student to be the first person to choose a number from the pot as you say the chant below.

  Bubble, bubble, boil and brew
  Let us make a number stew
  Choose a number from the pot
  Count to the number that you got
  Stir the pot once again
  Pass it along to a friend

- **Teaching Tip:** Have students pass the spoon to the person sitting next to them instead of passing it to any friend in the room. Model how to make safe passes.

Bodily-Kinesthetic

- Play "Listen and Move". Have students stand in a circle or line. Give each student a number card to see and hold. Give the directions for a specific number to perform a task. Tell students they must listen closely so they know when to move. After each number is called, pass the number to the person to the right and play again. Try to move faster each time.

Listen and Move

0	Nod Head
1	Tap Toe
2	Swing Arms
3	Turn Around
4	Touch Toes
5	Clap Hands
6	Jump Up
7	Stomp Feet
8	Kick Foot
9	Wave Hand

Lesson Resources

Surface Level	Deep Level
Resources by Chapter • Extra Practice • Reteach Differentiating the Lesson Skills Review Handbook Skills Trainer	Resources by Chapter • Enrichment and Extension Graphic Organizers Dynamic Assessment System • Lesson Practice

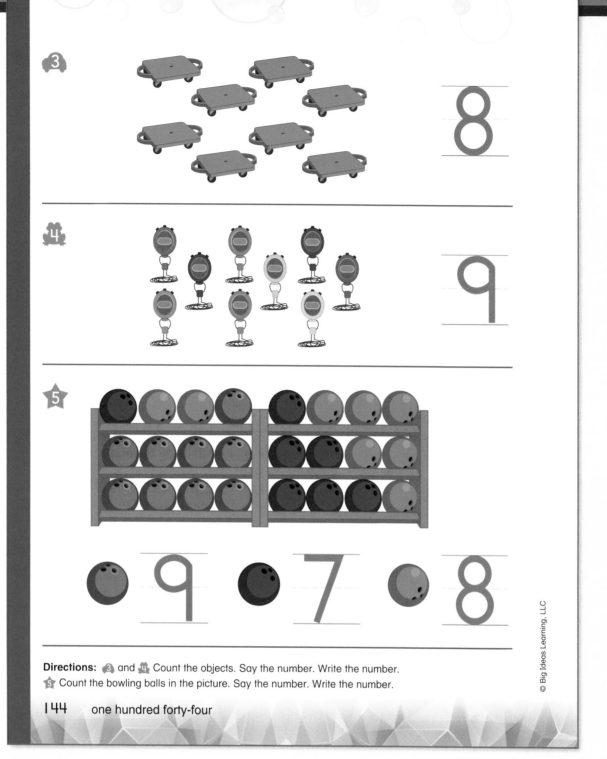

③ 8

④ 9

⑤ 9 7 8

Directions: ③ and ④ Count the objects. Say the number. Write the number.
⑤ Count the bowling balls in the picture. Say the number. Write the number.

144   one hundred forty-four

© Big Ideas Learning, LLC

3.9

Learning Target

Show and count the number 10.

Success Criteria

- Name the number 10.
- Count one object for each number to 10.
- Tell the number of objects in a group.

Warm-Up

Practice opportunities for the following are available in the Resources by Chapter or at *BigIdeasMath.com*.

- Daily skills
- Vocabulary
- Prerequisite skills

ELL Support

Have students practice saying the word *ten* by repeating after you. You may want to have them practice distinguishing the sounds of *ten*, *tin*, and *tan*, because the vowel sounds in each word are not easily distinguished. Explain that tin is a type of metal and tan is a light brown color. If each word is not clearly understood, they should try to understand from the context. Then explain that *soil* is the dirt in which you can plant fruits, vegetables, flowers, or other plants.

Laurie's Notes

Preparing to Teach

Students will be excited that the ten frame is completely filled in and that all of their fingers are needed to count! Ten is an important benchmark in working up to Grade 1 skills. It is related to early number operations, number sense, and place value. The lesson is similar in design to the previous "Model and Count" lessons and the theme is gardening.

Materials

- linking cubes
- rekenrek
- two-color counters

Dig In (Circle Time)

Ask the students to mimic you as you hold up and wiggle all of your fingers. Ask whether they know what number they are going to count today.

- Have students count to 10 with you as they clap for each count.
- Model counting to 10 using your fingers. Extend one more finger for each count. This can be challenging for little hands that don't have sufficient fine motor skills. If this is the case, pair students and have one student point to each finger on his or her partner's hand as they count. Then have them switch roles.
- Practice counting with fingers several times. When you get to the number 10, it's fun to have them wiggle all of their fingers!
- ? Hold up 10 linking cubes. Ask, "How many cubes am I holding? How do you know?" Ask a volunteer to point to each cube as the class counts aloud. You can also use a rekenrek to model 10. A volunteer can slide over one bead as each number is said.
- ◉ Students have named the number 10 and counted to 10 by pointing to each object. This reinforces one-to-one correspondence.

? Teaching Prompt   ◉ Learning Target

Name _____

Learning Target: Show and
count the number 10.

Check students' work.

Explore and Grow

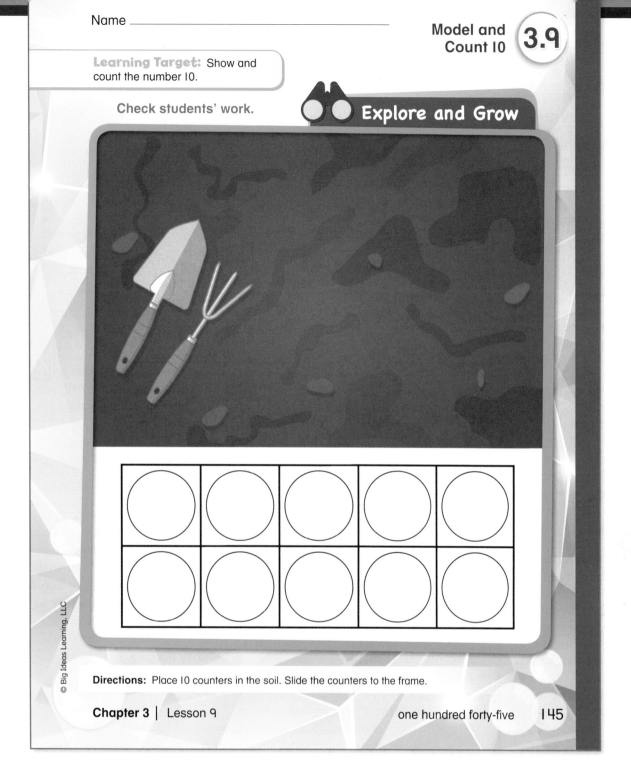

Directions: Place 10 counters in the soil. Slide the counters to the frame.

© Big Ideas Learning, LLC

Explore and Grow

- Distribute counters. "I want to grow plants for a community garden. I planted 10 seeds in the dirt. Use counters to show the seeds."
- "Tell your partner a story about the seeds. Be sure to tell them what you are growing. Count to show you have 10." Use the Newton and Descartes puppet to tell what is growing.
- ? Have students count aloud as they slide the counters to the ten frames. "What do you notice about the counters on the frame? The frame is full. There are no empty boxes. Relate this to showing all 10 fingers and all the beads on a rekenrek. Note that each model shows two groups of five.

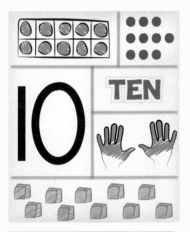

Laurie's Notes

Think and Grow

Getting Started

- Introduce the vocabulary card for **ten**. Consider creating an anchor chart for 10.
- ? "What do you know about the number ten?" 10 toes; 10 bowling pins; a 10 dollar bill
- ? **Sample Questions:** How many counters are in the ten frame? How many fingers do you have? Do you have 10 toes? Do you have a snack break at 10 o'clock? Do you have a sister who is 10 years old?

Teaching Notes

- The arrangement of the worms should remind students of a ten frame.
- Model: Together as a class, count each worm. As students say the counting sequence, they place a counter on each worm. Slide the counters to the ten frame boxes to count how many. Color each box that has a counter.
- Give directions as needed, while students count the strawberry signs and scarecrows. Count, say how many, slide and color.
- Extension:
  - ? "How many boxes are empty in each frame?" zero
  - As students finish, you could have them count to 10 using their fingers, count the strawberry signs starting at the bottom row to see that the quantity is still 10, or draw a picture of 10 objects.
- ⊙ "Think to yourself. I can use my fingers or linking cubes to show what 10 looks like. If you are sure you can do that, then show a thumbs up. If you are not sure, then show a sideways thumb. If you know you cannot show 10, then put your thumbs down." Group students according to their thumb signals.
  - Thumbs up – Have students show one another.
  - Sideways thumb – Students talk to each other and see whether they can figure it out.
  - Thumbs down – Students explain what they are confused about. What numbers can they show?

ELL Support

Tell students that the animals shown are worms. Explain that worms live in the ground and are placed on hooks when fishing. Teach the words strawberry sign and scarecrow by pointing to each and stating its name. Explain that these are two things found in a garden where plants are grown. A strawberry sign is used to show where the strawberries are planted. A scarecrow is placed in a garden to scare away unwanted animals that will eat the plants. Have students tell the number of objects counted in each exercise.

Beginner students may only count aloud as they point to the pictures.
Intermediate students may say the number and name of each object, such as, "10 worms."
Advanced students may use simple sentences to describe the number of objects, such as, "There are 10 worms."

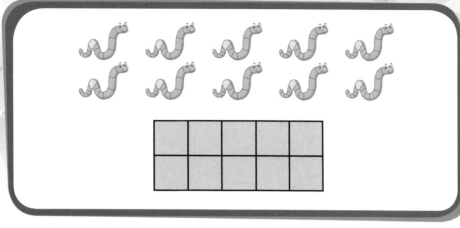

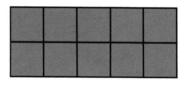

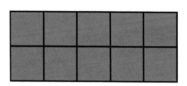

Directions: Count the objects. Color the boxes to show how many.

Fish Crackers

MATH MUSICALS

Use the story *Fish Crackers* from the book
Newton & Descartes's Coolest, Rockin' Day Ever to help
students with counting to 10! In this story, Newton
and Descartes find treats while Miss Polly is away. By
counting, they discover that there are 10 fish crackers and
10 dog biscuits. Turn to Appendix A for the music
and lyrics to the song *Fish Crackers?*

Laurie's Notes

Meeting the needs of
all learners.

Apply and Grow: Practice

MAKING INSTRUCTIONAL DECISIONS

One-on-one questioning may still be necessary to support emerging learners. If you show a linear arrangement of 10 counters to students, can they count them accurately? If yes, can they give you the same number of linking cubes? Have they understood that the last number word said means how many? Can they give you the 10 linking cubes without matching them to the counters? Emerging learners may need additional experiences and time to understand counting.

EMERGING students are not fluent in using the number names to count and show how many.

- Provide counters or linking cubes for students to complete the exercises.
- Show a number from 1 to 10 with your hands. Have students count the number of fingers you hold up and then move that many steps. They are still practicing the counting sequence.

PROFICIENT students are able to count and show a group of 10 objects.

- Show a ten frame with nine or less counters and ask students how many are needed to make 10.

Additional Support

- Put 10 small objects, such as blocks or toy cars, under a towel. Hand the student one object from underneath the towel and have students count that object. Keep the remaining objects covered. Continue to pull out objects one-by-one and have students count them. Determine whether students start back from one each time or whether they count on. For students who struggle with the activity, repeat it except have ten frames available for students to place their counters on. Does the visual model help them as they count? Can they use the frames so they don't need to start over each time?

Extension: Adding Rigor

- Have students create board games by drawing 10 circles as spaces on pieces of paper or cardboard. Provide pairs of students with one die to roll and two bear counters as their playing pieces. Have students determine why the bears should try to get across the boards. Do their bears need to get to the tree or to meet their friends? Take turns rolling the die and moving that many spaces.

Name _____

 1

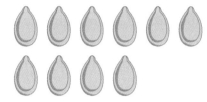 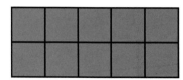

 2

 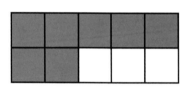

3

 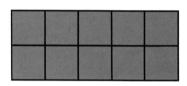

Directions: ❶–❸ Count the objects. Color the boxes to show how many.

Chapter 3 | Lesson 9   one hundred forty-seven   147

© Big Ideas Learning, LLC

Think and Grow: Modeling Real Life

This application helps students count to answer "how many" with the number 10. Numbers 6 and 10 are used in a contextual setting.

- **Preview:** "What do you think is happening in the picture? Have you ever planted a garden? Talk to your partner about the picture."
- Read the directions. "What objects, or vegetables, are we counting?" carrots and cauliflower
- **Think-Pair-Share:** Have students think about how they will count carrots and cauliflower, and then talk to their partners. Share as a whole class.
- Make sure the students are counting the carrots separately from the heads of cauliflower. When students are having difficulty focusing on just one group, use paper to cover the other group as they count.
- **Supporting Learners:** Provide counters or linking cubes to cover each object in a group as they are counted.
- "Explain to your partner how you found the number of objects in each group."
- **Extension:** Have students draw additional cauliflower in the picture to make 10.
- **Connection:** If appropriate, ask comparative questions in advance of the next chapter. "Which vegetable do you have more of? How many more? Which vegetable do you have less of? How many less?"
- "Talk to you partner about what you have learned today. If you think you need a little more practice with something, tell them that also." Listen as students share their learning with others.

Closure

- Prompt students to choose a number from 0 to 10 and show that number to partners using objects, drawings, fingers, or actions. Have the partners say the number.

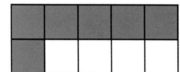

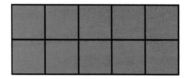

Directions: Count the objects in the picture. Color the boxes to show how many.

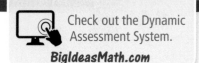
Connect and Extend Learning

Practice Notes

- **Exercises 1–5:** Preview the pages so students are familiar with the objects.
- **Exercise 5:** Remind students not to count the lawn gnome, or garden gnome, and the bush or shrub, outside of the picture.

Cross-Curricular Connections

Language Arts

- *The Very Hungry Caterpillar* by Eric Carle; Have students draw the food items on white paper plates. Then have them count and write the numbers of items.

Science

- Show a visual of a crab with 10 legs and discuss its characteristics. Have students count the legs on the crab. Note, not all of the legs are the same size.

Name _____

Learning Target: Show and count the number 10.

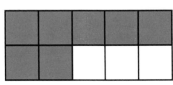

Directions: Count the peppers. Color the boxes to show how many.

①

②

Directions: ① and ② Count the objects. Color the boxes to show how many.

Chapter 3 | Lesson 9   one hundred forty-nine   149

Connect and Extend Learning

Extend Student Learning
Bodily-Kinesthetic
- Use 10 empty water bottles and set them in a bowling pin triangle. Have students take turns rolling a ball and counting the number of water bottles they knock down.
- Have students draw and color a brown empty flower pot on white paper. Provide each student with 10 seeds. Have students place their flower pots on the floor and pretend to put some soil into the pots. Tell students to drop all of their seeds over the flower pots and then count how many land in it. The goal of the game is to try to get all 10 seeds in the pot.

Lesson Resources	
Surface Level	**Deep Level**
Resources by Chapter • Extra Practice • Reteach Differentiating the Lesson Skills Review Handbook Skills Trainer Math Musicals	Resources by Chapter • Enrichment and Extension Graphic Organizers Math Musicals Dynamic Assessment System • Lesson Practice

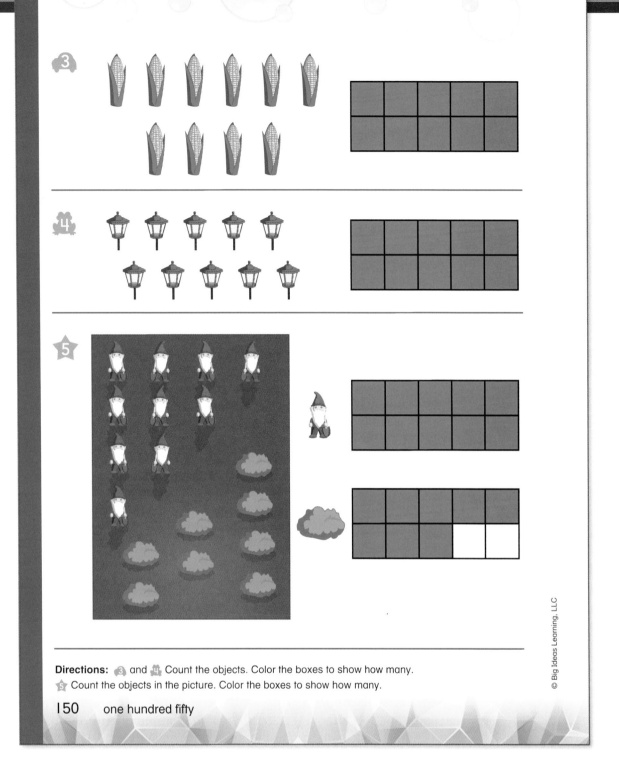

Directions: ③ and ④ Count the objects. Color the boxes to show how many.
⑤ Count the objects in the picture. Color the boxes to show how many.

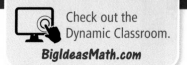

Learning Target

Understand and write the number 10.

Success Criteria

- Identify a group of 10 objects.
- Write the number 10.

Warm-Up

Practice opportunities for the following are available in the Resources by Chapter or at *BigIdeasMath.com*.

- Daily skills
- Vocabulary
- Prerequisite skills

ELL Support

Preview the word starfish as you point to its picture. Tell students that a starfish is a sea animal shaped like a star. It is actually not a type of fish and is sometimes referred to as a sea star. The word *starfish* combines the words *star* and *fish* to create the name of the animal. Have students listen carefully for the word *ten* as you read. Have them decide what the number 10 is being used to count.

Laurie's Notes

Preparing to Teach

This is an exciting lesson! This is most students' first experience writing a two-digit number. Students need to understand that even though there are two parts to write, it is only one number and represents one quantity. The term *part* is used when writing 10 instead of *digit*. The focus here is not on place value, but on learning to write the number that represents the quantity of 10.

The design of this lesson is similar to the other "Understand and Write" lessons in this chapter. The theme is things found in the water.

Materials

- linking cubes
- two-color counters
- *In the Water**
- Subitizing Cards 5–10*
- Ten Frame Cards 5–10*

**Found in the Instructional Resources*

Dig In (Circle Time)

Students have seen visual images of 10. They have their fingers to show 10 and have seen a full ten frame. To help reinforce the benchmarks of 5 and 10, use two colors of linking cubes. Make sure to use five of each color.

- Put all 10 linking cubes together. Have students count as you point to each cube. Then split the cubes making a model similar to a ten frame. Again, students count as you point to each cube.

- ? "Are there other ways that we can show a group of 10?" Ask students to model a group of 10 using cubes or counters. If no student puts them in a circular fashion, create one for them. Choose a student to point to and count each object. Have the remaining students signal whether or not they agree with the amount counted.
- Distribute the booklet *In the Water*. "Tell your partner what you like about playing in the lake or the ocean." If a student has not had this experience, they can talk about pet fish or toys they use in a bathtub. Read and discuss the booklet.
- **Big Idea:** "The number 10 is made up of two *parts* that you already know how to write." Ask students to think about how they wrote the numerals 1 and 0 and discuss with their partners. Have students trace the number 10 using the verbal pathway of "pull down" for 1 and "pull back and around" for 0. Practice writing 10 in the air.
- Students should return to their seats with their booklets.

Learning Target: Understand
and write the number 10.

Explore and Grow

Directions: Use counters to show how many starfish are in the story *In the Water*.
Write how many starfish are in the story.

© Big Ideas Learning, LLC

Explore and Grow

- "Use your counters to show the number of starfish in the story *In the Water*.
  Put your counters in the water." Students may arrange the counters so that it
  is easy to count to 10. This is fine as long as they show 10.
- Say the verbal pathway for 10 as they practice writing it in the air. Now
  explore writing the number 10 on the starfish.
- **Supporting Learners:** When reading the number 10, some students may say
  "one, zero." Remind students that this is the number 10, because the 1 and 0
  are close together.

Laurie's Notes

Think and Grow

Getting Started

- Show students the subitizing card and ten frame card for 10. Students may be less familiar with seeing the domino pattern for 10 but they will certainly recognize the filled ten frame!
- Ten is an important benchmark. You want students to have multiple mental images of 10. Take time to have students talk about the anchor chart for 10.
- Preview the images on the page by naming each one. Focus on the arrangements and recognizing the quantity, and just smile when students refer to the jellyfish as purple mushrooms.

Teaching Notes

- **Model:** Students will be familiar with the structure of the Think and Grow, however you still want to review the verbal pathways for 1 and 0 with them. Make sure to refer to the 1 and 0 as the parts that make the number 10.
- Because there are two parts in writing the number 10, point out that there are two starting points.
- Have a few students explain how they counted the different groups. You may hear students reference a full ten frame when discussing the lobsters, or two rows of five. Students may see a collection of nine jellyfish plus one more, or a smaller group of six and count on.
- ⊙ The arrangements for a group of 10 on this page do not include a linear or circular pattern. Before you ask students to share their thumb signals for how good they are at identifying a group of ten, specifically mention the different arrangements. Students should now understand that the way in which objects are arranged can make it easier or more difficult to count and recognize quantity.
- **Supporting Learners:** Watch to make sure students write 10 with very little space between the 1 and the 0.

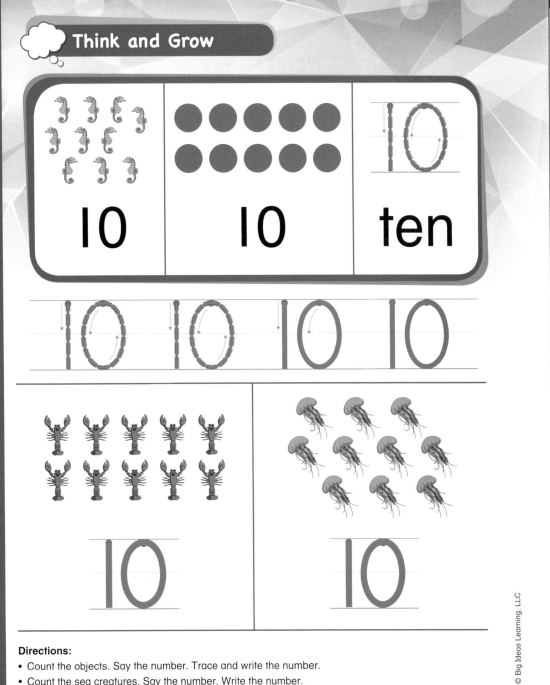

10

10

ten

Directions:
- Count the objects. Say the number. Trace and write the number.
- Count the sea creatures. Say the number. Write the number.

Meeting the needs of
all learners.

Apply and Grow: Practice

MAKING INSTRUCTIONAL DECISIONS

The discussion has not been on place value in this lesson or chapter. At this time, students should only understand that the quantity of the number 10 is one more than 9. They know that it fills up a ten frame and matches the number of fingers we have. The ways in which they see 10 as a visual image and model are very important. In representing 10 as a written numeral, students know there are two parts. All of the other numbers before 10 only had one part.

EMERGING students may still be in the early phases as a counter. They are counting by ones and do not yet see smaller parts that combine to make the whole.

- Provide additional experiences with subitizing cards, dot model cards, and number cards. When they write the numerals, do they associate it with the correct quantity?

PROFICIENT students are able to identify a group of 10 objects and write the number 10.

Additional Support

- Students can trace their hands, count each finger, and label them with the numeral.
- Have students fish for numbers. Write the numerals 0 through 10 on fish cutouts. Put a magnetic strip on the back of each fish. Attach a paper clip to a string to represent the hook and add a pencil to the other end to represent the handle of a pretend fishing pole.

Extensions: Adding Rigor

- Play *Number Party*. Have students walk around the room until you call out a number from 0 to 10. The students must put themselves into groups made up of the particular number that was called. Students who are left over get to do a fun type of action such as frog hopping or worm wiggling. The action should be stated by the teacher and for the same amount of times as the original number. Once the students complete the actions, play a new round with a new number.
- Teaching Tip: Use starting and stopping signals to clarify when students should move to a group or to stop. Begin by playing the game with numbers 1–5. Once students demonstrate their understanding, then use numbers 6–10.

Name _____

10

2

10

3

9

4

10

Directions: 1 – 4 Count the objects. Say the number. Write the number.

© Big Ideas Learning, LLC

Think and Grow: Modeling Real Life

This application helps students count to identify the sizes of each group and write the numbers they count. The numbers 7, 8, 9, and 10 are revisited.

? **Preview:** "Have you ever seen fish swimming together? Do you know what a group of fish that swims together is called?" a school

- Read the directions and give sufficient guidance for students to begin their work. Have counters or linking cubes available to use as needed.

- Each group of 7 to 10 sea creatures were placed to create noticeable patterns which makes this a helpful culminating exercise. Make sure students are pointing out smaller subitizing groups and explaining how they count.

- Observe how students are counting. If they are not using counters or pointing with their fingers, ask them how they counted a collection.

- Take time as a class for students to share how they counted each group. It is most effective when the page can be displayed so that students can point as they explain.

- **Connection:** Students have compared smaller quantities and know what *one more than* and *one less than* mean. Can they apply that understanding to the quantities they counted on this page?

⊙ Have students use their thumb signals to show their understanding of identifying quantities of 10 seen in many different arrangements. Ask how good they are at writing the number 10.

- **Supporting Learners:** If students have difficulty distinguishing between the types of fish, use a sheet of paper or your hand to cover all but one collection of fish.

? **Extension:** "What would you tell an adult about the number 10? You want to tell them everything you know! Turn and tell your neighbor to practice what you would say."

Closure

- Review the vocabulary cards for 0 to 10. Have students say each number, use their fingers to show the quantity, and wave both hands when 10 is shown. Go through the cards several times. You can also practice with the subitizing cards.

Think and Grow: Modeling Real Life

 9

 10

 8

 7

Directions: Count the sea creatures in the picture. Say the number. Write the number.

154   one hundred fifty-four

© Big Ideas Learning, LLC

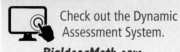

Check out the Dynamic
Assessment System.

BigIdeasMath.com

Connect and Extend Learning

Practice Notes

- **Exercises 1–5:** Each arrangement now contains a large number of objects. Remind students to be neat and controlled when crossing out objects as they count.
- **Exercise 3:** The bubbles are different sizes which may concern students. We can count a group of objects even when they are not the same size.
- **Exercise 5:** Have students use a brightly colored crayon instead of a pencil to help them keep track of counted objects. Explain that the picture is of an aquarium tank or ocean that is being viewed from the top. Remind students not to count the stingray, fish, and eel that are seen outside of the picture.

Cross-Curricular Connections

Science

- Have students name 10 animals that can be found on a farm. Discuss with students the characteristics of these animals and what they need to survive.
- Have students draw a crazy ocean creature that models the number 10 by representing each body part multiple times. Include eyes, ears, noses, antennas, hairs, arms, legs, or feet.
- **Teaching Tip:** Have students work with partners. One student identifies the number of body parts and the other student sketches. Alternate turns.

Name _____

Learning Target: Understand and write the number 10.

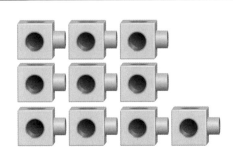

ten

Directions: Count the linking cubes. Say the number. Write the number.

①

10

②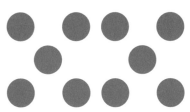

10

Directions: ① and ② Count the dots. Say the number. Write the number.

Chapter 3 | Lesson 10   one hundred fifty-five   155

Connect and Extend Learning

Extend Student Learning

Linguistic

- Continue the classroom book, *Our Number Walk: 6 to 10* by drawing items for the number 10. See page T-14 for a refresher on how to make the book.

Visual-Spatial

- Prepare a stencil of a fish bowl and a fish for students to trace and cut out. The fish bowl should be made from large blue construction paper. The fish can be made with any color. Have students cut a couple wavy strips of green for the seaweed. Students write a number on each fish and glue them onto the paper. Have students make fingerprint air bubbles to match the number on the fish. Guide students to think about how to arrange their bubbles.

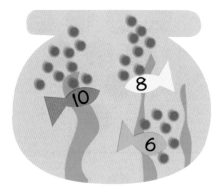

Lesson Resources	
Surface Level	**Deep Level**
Resources by Chapter • Extra Practice • Reteach Differentiating the Lesson Skills Review Handbook Skills Trainer	Resources by Chapter • Enrichment and Extension Graphic Organizers Dynamic Assessment System • Lesson Practice

3

10

4

9

5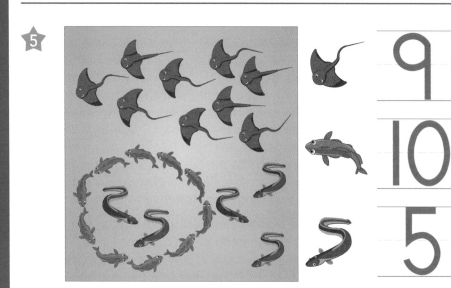

9

10

5

Directions: **3** and **4** Count the objects. Say the number. Write the number.
5 Count the sea creatures in the picture. Say the number. Write the number.

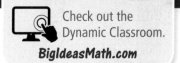

3.11

Learning Target
Count and order numbers to 10.

Success Criteria
- Count to 10.
- Identify the starting number.
- Order numbers to 10.

ELL Support
Review the numbers 0–10 by saying each number and having students hold up their corresponding number cards. Have them repeat aloud the name of each number. Review the numbers that have homophones: one, won; two, too, to; four, for; eight, ate. Review the meanings of the different words.

Laurie's Notes

Preparing to Teach
In this lesson, students order numbers 0 to 10. You want their understanding to be more than just reciting the number names. There were opportunities throughout this chapter to make connections to the concepts of *greater than* and *less than* which were presented in Chapter 2. These comparative concepts support students' understanding of ordering numbers 0 to 10.

Materials
- Number Cards 0–10*
- counters

Found in the Instructional Resources

Dig In (Circle Time)
Play "Mingle-Mingle-Mingle" before students come to circle time. Distribute one number card to each student. The first time you might use the cards 0–5, then 0–7, and finally 0–10. Any student holding a card mingles about until you say, "Order in the class!" Students like to use a cha-cha-cha voice and say "mingle, mingle, mingle" as they move around the room. Students with a card then need to order themselves from 0 to the last number. Remind students that *order* refers to the counting sequence. Pick different students to mingle each time, or have everyone mingle and only cardholders need to arrange themselves as others watch.

- **Note:** The same activity can be done using ten frame models or linking cube models instead of the number cards.
- **Extension:** Omit a number and do the same activity. Have students explain which number is missing and how they know.
- ⊙ Invite the students to circle time. Exhibit any visual models of the numbers 0 to 10 that you have available. You could display anchor charts, number posters, linking cubes, or your collections of number and subitizing cards. Share the learning target and success criteria.
- ❓ **Turn and Talk:** "How will we know that we can order numbers to 10?" Listen for students to talk about knowing how to count, seeing one more dot on each ten frame, adding another linking cube to each tower, or holding up another finger.
- ⊙ Now have students listen to you count to 10. Omit a number and mix them up slightly by saying, "1, 2, 3, 6, 4, 7, 9, 10." Then ask, "Did I count correctly? How do we count to 10?" Counting to 10 is the first success criterion.

❓ Teaching Prompt   ⊙ Learning Target

Learning Target: Count and
order numbers to 10.

Explore and Grow

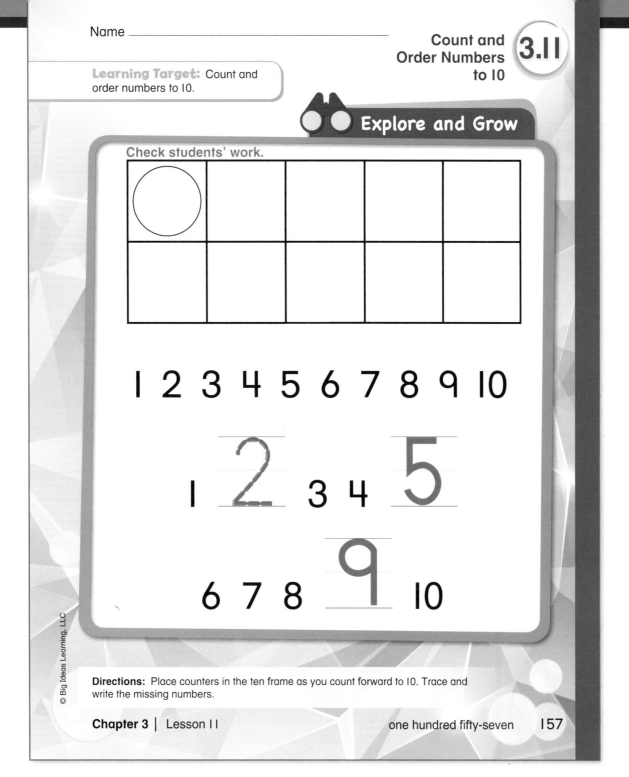

Check students' work.

1 2 3 4 5 6 7 8 9 10

1 2 3 4 5

6 7 8 9 10

Directions: Place counters in the ten frame as you count forward to 10. Trace and
write the missing numbers.

Explore and Grow

- Have the students point to and count the numbers 1 to 10. Students place
  the counters on the ten frames one at a time as they count aloud. Pause after
  each number and have students finger write the number in the air. Say the
  verbal pathways as you write.
- When the frame is full, ask students to fill in the missing numbers.
- **?** Ask questions such as, "What number would I say after 8? What number
  would I say before 6? Close your eyes and picture the number after 4. What
  is that number? Picture the number before 10. What is that number?"

ELL Support

Remind students that the objects on the page can be called counters, dots, disks, or circles. They should recognize that when someone uses any of those words they could be referring to the same thing. Review the colors red, green, yellow, and blue, if necessary. Have students work in pairs. Have one student ask the other, "How many red dots are there?" Have them switch roles for each exercise.

Beginner students may answer using only a number.
Intermediate students may answer with the number, color, and name of the object counted, such as, "seven red dots."
Advanced students may answer using a complete sentence, such as, "There are seven red dots."

Think and Grow

Getting Started

- Practice counting to 10. Now call out a number within 10. Have students practice counting forward and backward from that number. "We call this the start number."
- There are two parts to each problem. Students write the numbers for each ten frame shown. Then order those numbers starting with the number shown.

Teaching Notes

- **Model:** Have students identify and record the numbers of counters in each ten frame on the top row. Again, observe and ask questions to determine how students are counting. Make note of which students need support in writing the numbers. Are they looking at posters or other supports in the room to recall how numbers are written?
- ? "Look at the numbers you wrote. Which number comes first when counting? Trace the 4." Identify this as the starting number.
- **Teaching Tip:** If students do not easily identify 4 as the starting number, count slowly starting from 0. Have students look for each number as you count, until you say 4.
- **Turn and Talk:** "Tell your partner what number in the list comes next when counting." Repeat until all of the numbers are named. Have students write the numbers as they go.
- ? "How do you know this is the correct number order?" The numbers are in counting order; there's one more dot each time.
- Consider pairing students to complete the bottom exercise.
- ? **Extension:** "Where would the number 5 go? the number 10? How do you know?"
- ◉ Be very intentional in reviewing each success criterion. Ask students to demonstrate what it means to count to 10, and to count to 10 from a certain start number. First students should *count in their head* and then they should *count out loud*. "Was your thinking correct?" This helps students understand what successful learning looks like. It is visible to them. For the third success criterion ask them to describe to their partners how they know they can order numbers to 10. Students need clarity about what we want them to learn and how they will know whether they have learned it.
- **Supporting Learners:** Have students cross out each number as they record them.
- **Supporting Learners:** Provide linking cubes so that students can make a model of each number. Students may find it helpful to compare the lengths of the linking cube trains.

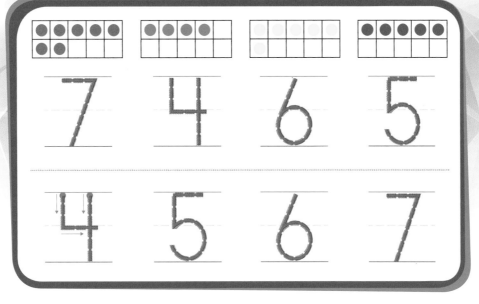

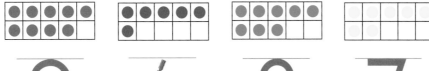

Directions: Count the dots in each ten frame. Say the number. Write the number.
Write the numbers in order. Start with the given number.

158   one hundred fifty-eight

Meeting the needs of all learners.

Laurie's Notes

Apply and Grow: Practice

MAKING INSTRUCTIONAL DECISIONS

Acknowledge the connections students made with ordering the numbers 0 to 5 and what they are learning with the numbers 6 to 10. Remember, the number 0 is not a counting number. We count with the numbers 1, 2, 3, and so on. Zero can be included when we order numbers, but we do not count with the number 0.

EMERGING students may find it difficult to count and order numbers to 10. Students need additional experiences with counting and naming numbers.

- Use the number cards, immediately followed by the subitizing cards, to order in a forward sequence. As students progress and become more fluent, order the cards in reverse.

PROFICIENT students are confident when they count and order the numbers to 10 in forward and reverse order. They can identify the start number when they count forward to 10, or count in reverse order to 0.

- Write each number 1 to 10 in order on the board. Say each number. Then repeat this process but leave out a number or two. As you say the numbers, pause and have students state the missing number and write it on the board.

Additional Support

- Show a number on a rekenrek. Now show the quantity that is one more than the original number. Keep showing a quantity that is one more until you reach 10. You can also involve the students with sliding the beads. Either way you want to associate the sliding of a bead with *one more than*, which tells the next number in the counting sequence.
- Have students work together to hang the number cards in order using clothespins on a string.

Extension: Adding Rigor

- Pair students and have them work together to order Number Cards 0–10. One student closes his or her eyes while the other student removes a card. The first student opens his or her eyes and names the missing number. Alternate turns. This can also be done with the subitizing cards.

Apply and Grow: Practice

1

3   2   5   4

2   3   4   5

2

9   10   8   7

7   8   9   10

Directions: **1** and **2** Count the dots in each ten frame. Say the number. Write the number. Then write the numbers in order.

Laurie's Notes

Think and Grow: Modeling Real Life

In this application, students write the numbers 0 through 10 in reverse order.

- Students may be familiar with a timer that counts down and then buzzes, such as an oven timer, microwave oven, or a score clock at an athletic event. The buzzer signals that there is no time remaining. In this application, students will count in reverse order, and in the absence of a buzzer, they will write the number 0!

- **?** Preview: "Have you ever seen a timer like this? When do we count backward or count down?" when playing games; while cleaning up; when counting down with a microwave or oven timer.

- Have students hold up 10 fingers. Count backward from 10 to 0 while putting one finger down at a time. For students having difficulty, use numbered finger puppets.

- Technology: There are many online timers that you can display to assist students in visualizing a countdown.

- **?** Ask, "What number do you see on the timer? 10 What is our starting number?" 10

- **?** Read the directions and start counting backward from 10. Be sure to emphasize the word *backward* as you ask, "When counting backward from 10, what number comes next?" 9 Have students record the number. Repeat this process for the number 8.

- Extension: Call out different numbers within 10 and have students count backward from that number.

- Extension: Have students write, draw, or tell stories using a countdown. Have students explain what happens when they get to 0. Allow students to use the Newton and Descartes puppets to share their stories with the class.

- ⊙ Have students tell their partners what they learned today and how well they think they have learned it.

- **?** Supporting Learners: Relate counting backward to a familiar activity such as eating grapes. Students use counters to represent 10 grapes. Have students pretend to eat one grape at a time. After they remove a counter ask, "How many do you have now?"

Closure

- Write number sequences on the board from 0 to 10, leaving out one to three numbers each time. Have students identify and record the missing numbers on their whiteboards or by whispering to partners.

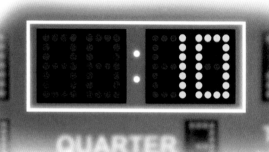

10 9 8 7
——————————————————➤

6 5 4 3
——————————————————➤

2 1 0
——————————————➤

Directions: Count backward from the number on the timer. Write the numbers.

160 one hundred sixty

© Big Ideas Learning, LLC

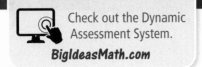

Connect and Extend Learning

Practice Notes

- **Exercise 2:** Preview with students. Tell them that they need to count all of the dots on each domino. Write the number on the line.
- **Exercise 3:** Discuss the game of hide-and-seek so students know how it is played.

Cross-Curricular Connections

Language Arts

- *How Do Dinosaurs Count To Ten?* by Jane Yolen; Have students talk about things they would like to count if they were a dinosaur.

Science

- Discuss *balance and motion* with students. Have students balance on one foot as they count forward to 10 and the other foot as they count backward from 10. For motion, have students count forward to 10 as they move in one direction and backward as they move in another direction.

Learning Target: Count and order numbers to 10.

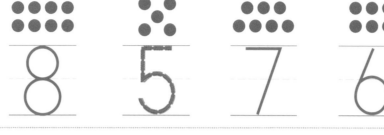

Directions: Count the dots. Say the number. Write the number. Then write the numbers in order. Start with the given number.

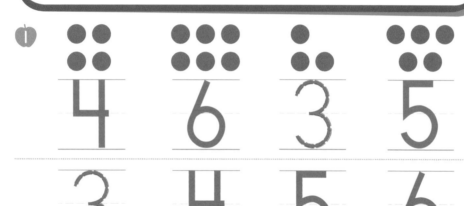

Directions: ❶ Count the dots. Say the number. Write the number. Then write the numbers in order.

Chapter 3 | Lesson 11

one hundred sixty-one 161

© Big Ideas Learning, LLC

Connect and Extend Learning

Extend Student Learning

Linguistic

- Read the *Our Number Walk: 6 to 10* classroom book, made in Lessons 3.2, 3.4, 3.6, 3.8, and 3.10, with students.

Visual-Spatial

- Have students create their own connect-the-dots design. Model how to draw a simple design on regular paper using a pencil. Go over the design with a dark marker or crayon. Use tracing paper to place over the design page. Draw 10 dots on the lines that are showing through. These dots will be connected to make the design. Have students label the dots in sequential order.
- Teaching Tip: Remind students to make simple designs or have students create connect-the-dot lines instead of designs.

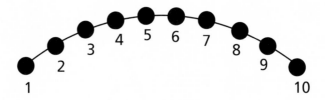

| Lesson Resources ||
Surface Level	**Deep Level**
Resources by Chapter • Extra Practice • Reteach Differentiating the Lesson Skills Review Handbook Skills Trainer	Resources by Chapter • Enrichment and Extension Graphic Organizers Dynamic Assessment System • Lesson Practice

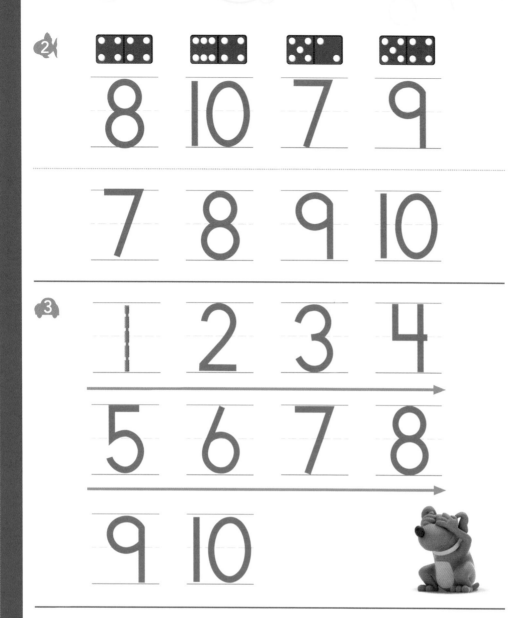

2

8	10	7	9

7	8	9	10

3

1	2	3	4
5	6	7	8
9	10		

Directions:

2 Count the dots on each domino. Say the number. Write the number. Write the numbers in order. Start with the number 7. **3** You are playing hide-and-seek. Count forward from 1. Write the numbers.

162   one hundred sixty-two

Laurie's Notes

Performance Task

In this task, students will count different arrangements of numbers from 6 to 9. They will write these numbers and then put the numbers in order. They are also asked to show the number 10 in two different ways by drawing and writing the number. You may need to remind students that writing 10 is showing the number a different way. Use their responses to gauge their understanding about modeling, counting, and writing numbers to 10.

- Decide ahead of time whether students will be working independently, in pairs, or in groups.
- Pause between direction lines for students to complete each step.
- Have students share their work and thinking with others. Discuss as a class.

Exercise	Answers and Notes	Points
1	7; 9; 8; 6 6, 7, 8, 9	8
2	10 boxes filled in	2
3	numeral 10	2
	Total	12

Performance Task ③

①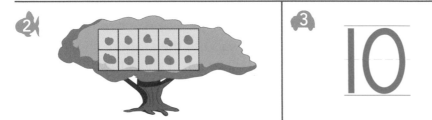

7 9 8 6

6 7 8 9

②

③ 10

Directions:
① Count the animals in the picture. Say the number. Write the number. Then write the numbers in order. ② Draw dots to show 10 birds in the tree. ③ Show how many birds in another way.

Chapter 3   one hundred sixty-three   163

Laurie's Notes

Number Land

Materials

- 1 manipulative per student to use as a playing piece
- 1 copy of Subitizing Cards 5–10* per student

*Found in the Instructional Resources

Students can work in pairs or small groups.

- ❓ "What numbers do you see on this page? Are the numbers on the Number Land board in order?" Listen to student explanations. Short strings of numbers are in order, but they are repeated. Five does not come after ten.
- Read the directions at the bottom of the page. Decide how many times you want students to go around the board.
- Model how to draw a card and move a manipulative clockwise to the closest corresponding number. Be sure students shuffle the cards and put them back on the draw pile with the blank side facing up any time they run out.
- When game play concludes, the discussion should center on students' reasoning about how they moved around the board.
- ❓ **Attend to Precision:** "As you played the game, how did you know what number to put your piece on?" I counted the dots on the card and matched them to the number on the board; I knew the number and moved the playing piece to that number.
- **FYI:** Students may subitize the amount shown on the card and express this by saying, "I knew the number."
- **Supporting Learners:** Provide students with counters and ten frames to build each card's number.
- **Whiteboards:** Write the numbers from the cards in a different way.

Closure

- "How else can you show the numbers?" draw pictures; write the number; model with counters

Number Land

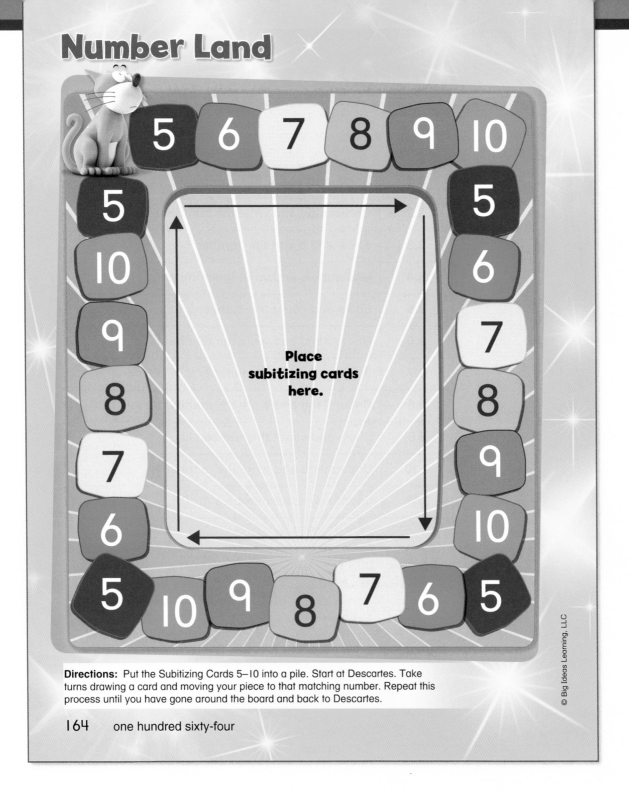

Place subitizing cards here.

Directions: Put the Subitizing Cards 5–10 into a pile. Start at Descartes. Take turns drawing a card and moving your piece to that matching number. Repeat this process until you have gone around the board and back to Descartes.

164   one hundred sixty-four

Learning Target Correlation

Lesson	Learning Target	Exercises
3.1	Show and count the number 6.	1
3.2	Understand and write the number 6.	2
3.3	Show and count the number 7.	3
3.4	Understand and write the number 7.	4
3.5	Show and count the number 8.	5
3.6	Understand and write the number 8.	6
3.7	Show and count the number 9.	7
3.8	Understand and write the number 9.	8
3.9	Show and count the number 10.	9
3.10	Understand and write the number 10.	10
3.11	Count and order numbers to 10.	11

3.1 Model and Count 6

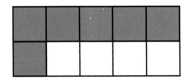

3.2 Understand and Write 6

6

3.3 Model and Count 7

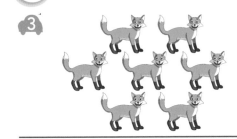

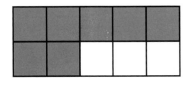

© Big Ideas Learning, LLC

Directions: ❶ Count the train engines. Color the boxes to show how many.
❷ Count the music notes. Say the number. Write the number. ❸ Count the foxes.
Color the boxes to show how many.

Chapter 3   one hundred sixty-five **165**

Chapter Resources

Surface Level	Deep Level	Transfer Level
Resources by Chapter • Extra Practice • Reteach Differentiating the Lesson Skills Review Handbook Skills Trainer Game Library Math Musicals	Resources by Chapter • Enrichment and Extension Graphic Organizers Game Library Math Musicals	Dynamic Assessment System • Chapter Test Assessment Book • Chapter Tests A and B

(3.4) Understand and Write 7

7

(3.5) Model and Count 8

(3.6) Understand and Write 8

8

Directions: 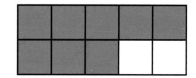 Count the lightning bolts. Say the number. Write the number.

Count the grapes. Color the boxes to show how many.

Count the grasshoppers. Say the number. Write the number.

3.7 Model and Count 9

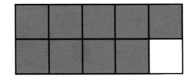

3.8 Understand and Write 9

3.9 Model and Count 10

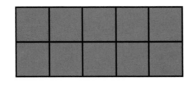

Directions: ♥ Count the shovels. Color the boxes to show how many.
8 Count the softballs. Say the number. Write the number.
9 Count the potatoes. Color the boxes to show how many.

© Big Ideas Learning, LLC

Chapter 3

one hundred sixty-seven   167

3.10 Understand and Write 10

10

3.11 Count and Order Numbers to 10

8   7   10   9

7   8   9   10

Directions: Count the shells. Say the number. Write the number. Count the dots on each domino. Say the number. Write the number. Then write the numbers in order.

168   one hundred sixty-eight

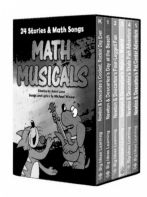

Math Musicals can be used with current topics, to review previous topics, or to preview upcoming topics.

Centers

Center 1: Number Land

Materials: Student Edition page 164, 1 manipulative per student to use as a playing piece, and 1 copy of Subitizing Cards 5–10* per student

Have students complete the Number Land activity. See page T-164 for the directions.

Center 2: Skills Trainer

Materials: computers or devices with Internet access

Have students go to *BigIdeasMath.com* to access the Skills Trainer.

Center 3: Flip and Find

Materials: Number Cards 5–10*, Subitizing Cards 5–10*

Students take turns flipping over two cards at a time. When students flip two cards with the same value, they keep the match. Students continue to play until all cards have been matched.

Center 4: Caterpillar Prints

Materials: Caterpillar Prints*, a small amount of green paint

Have students use green paint to make thumbprint caterpillar bodies. The number of thumbprints should match the number next to the caterpillar's head. Prepare an example for students to reference in advance.

Center 5: Missing Numbers

Materials: Missing Number Strips*, Missing Numbers*, glue stick, scissors

Have students cut out the Missing Numbers and place them in the correct order on the Missing Number Strips. Have them check with a partner before gluing them on the strips.

Found in the Instructional Resources

Chapter Assessment Guide

Chapter tests are available in the Assessment Book.
An alternative assessment option is listed below.

Bodily-Kinesthetic

Present number cards for 6 to 10 and have students build each number using linking cubes. Students place the number cards and cubes in order.

Task	Points
Students can identify the numbers 6, 7, 8, 9, and 10.	1 point per number; 5 points total
Students can correctly identify the quantity for the numbers 6, 7, 8, 9, and 10 with cubes or verbally.	1 point per number; 5 points total
Students can order the numbers 6, 7, 8, 9, and 10.	1 point per number; 5 points total
Total	15 points

My Thoughts on the Chapter

What worked...

Teacher Tip

Not allowed to write in your teaching edition? Use sticky notes to record your thoughts.

What did not work...

What I would do differently...

4 Compare Numbers to 10

Chapter Overview

Lesson	Learning Target	Success Criteria
4.1 Compare Groups to 10 by Matching	Use matching to compare the numbers of objects in two groups.	• Match objects from two groups. • Compare the numbers of objects in two groups using *greater than*, *less than*, or *equal to.*
4.2 Compare Groups to 10 by Counting	Use counting to compare the numbers of objects in two groups.	• Compare the numbers of objects in two groups using *greater than*, *less than*, or *equal to.* • Explain how to compare two groups by counting.
4.3 Compare Numbers to 10	Compare two numbers.	• Tell whether two numbers are the same. • Use *greater than* and *less than* to describe two numbers that are not the same. • Draw to show how one number compares to another.
4.4 Classify Objects into Categories	Tell whether objects belong or do not belong in a category.	• Describe what is the same about a group of objects. • Classify objects into a category. • Identify objects that are not in a category.
4.5 Classify and Compare by Counting	Compare the numbers of objects in two categories.	• Use marks to show each object in a category. • Count how many in each category. • Compare the numbers of objects in two categories using *greater than*, *less than*, or *equal to.*

Progressions

Chapter Learning Target:
Understand categories.

Chapter Success Criteria:
▪ Match objects.
▪ Explain how to compare numbers of objects.
▪ Classify objects into categories.
▪ Tell how many objects are in a category.

Through the Grades

Kindergarten	Grade 1
• Use matching and counting to tell whether the number of objects in a group is greater than, less than, or equal to the number of objects in another group. • Count objects in different arrangements. • Compare two written numerals between 1 and 10. • Classify objects into categories and sort by count.	• Compare 2 two-digit numbers based on the meanings of the tens and ones digits. • Use the >, =, and < symbols. • Answer questions about the number of objects in a category, and how many more or less are in one category than another. • Relate counting to addition and subtraction. • Understand the meaning of the equal sign, and determine if equations involving addition and subtraction are true or false.

Through the Chapter

Standard	4.1	4.2	4.3	4.4	4.5
Identify whether the number of objects in one group is greater than, less than, or equal to the number of objects in another group, e.g., by using matching or counting strategies.	●	●	●		●
Count to answer "how many?" questions about as many as 20 things arranged in a line, a rectangular array, or a circle, or as many as 10 things in a scattered configuration; given a number from 1–20, count out that many objects.		●	●		●
Compare two numbers between 1 and 10 presented as written numerals.		●	●		★
Classify objects into given categories; count the numbers of objects in each category and sort the categories by count.				●	★

Key: ▲ = Preparing   ● = Learning   ★ = Complete

Laurie's Overview

About the Math

Students are familiar with comparing numbers to 5, and now extend their comparison strategies to numbers within 10. These strategies include comparing by matching and comparing by counting.

In preparing to teach this chapter, consider the skills that students have developed that you will build upon. Students should now be more confident with cardinality and know the counting sequence to 10. Knowing the counting sequence, however, does not mean that students understand how one number relates to another. Think about how the numbers 6 and 7 are related. Students know that 7 comes after 6 when counting, just as L comes after K in the alphabet. The quantitative relationships we want to develop are six is *one less than* seven, and seven is *one more than* six. Knowing the relationships of *one* and *two more*, and *one* and *two less* are important to develop. These relationships are integrated into the chapter as students extend their understanding of comparing numbers.

The vocabulary needed for comparing numbers was introduced in Chapter 2: equal (same), greater than (more), and less than (fewer). The numbers being compared in this chapter are greater numbers, and for that reason will be more difficult for students to visually compare. The larger arrangements will also influence a student's ability to compare the numbers. Representing quantities in a ten frame can help students build a mental benchmark. Students may also be able to subitize a smaller group and count on to determine the number of objects in a group. Given the complexity of the visual comparisons, other comparison strategies are necessary. This is particularly true when two groups of objects are not noticeably different in quantity.

Comparing by matching and comparing by counting are two strategies that students use to compare numbers within 10. Consider a group of six stars and five suns arranged so that a segment can be drawn to match the objects in each set. Students are able to see that one star doesn't have a match. To compare these two groups you would say, "Six is more than five, and five is less than six."

If the same objects were scattered, students would need to count the objects in each group. They would also need to keep track of which objects have been counted. Placing small counters or drawing a line through the objects as they are counted are two techniques. When all of the stars are counted, students record their count and write 6. The second group of objects are counted using the same method. In the counting sequence, 5 comes before 6. Students may also know that five is one less than six, and six is one more than five.

Compare the numbers 5 and 6.

As the chapter progresses, students are asked to compare written numerals. A numeral is a symbol or name for a number. A number is an idea. To keep the language easier for students to understand, we say "compare the numbers" when the numerals are given. Students are expected to draw a model to show why 5 is less than 6.

The last two lessons of the chapter focus on categorical data and comparing the quantities in two categories. Students must be able to tell whether an object belongs or does not belong to a category before comparing. Given four green, two blue, and three red cubes, students must classify the cubes into two categories. Students should say, "There are four green cubes and five not green cubes. There are less green cubes than not green cubes."

Models

- Students are familiar with using fingers to show numbers. Students can use their fingers to show a number that is more than or less than a given number. For example, write the number 7 on the board, and have them use their fingers to show a number that is less than 7.

- A number path, a linear row of ten boxes, can be used to compare two numbers. Where are the two numbers located in the counting sequence? Which number is before (less) the other (greater) number?

- Students can use linking cubes that are arranged in towers or trains to determine whether two quantities are equal or not equal. Because it is often more difficult to determine when a number is less than another, linking cubes continue to be a great visual and tactile way for students to learn.

- A rekenrek can be used to compare numbers. Build the first number on the top row. Then, match and compare the number built on the second row. The structure of a rekenrek supports an understanding of the benchmark of five with the red and white beads.

- If you created an anchor chart for the comparison terms in chapter 2, it may be helpful to revisit and review the chart. Another idea is to have students give examples and make another anchor chart. Students will hear a concept explained in student-friendly terms along with having a visual reference that they can use for support.

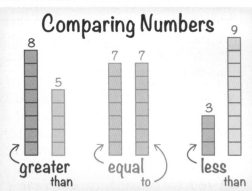

Comparing Numbers

greater than • equal to • less than

Chapter Materials and Resources

The primary materials and resources needed for this chapter are listed below. Other materials may be needed for the additional support ideas provided throughout the chapter.

Check out the virtual manipulatives.
BigIdeasMath.com

Classroom Materials	Chapter Opener	4.1	4.2	4.3	4.4	4.5	Connect and Grow
scissors	•						
echo ball	+						
linking cubes		•	•	•			
two bags or two socks			+				
two-color counters				•	•		•
whiteboards and markers				*		+	•
collections of objects					•	•	
10 paper clips							*
20 bear counters							*
2 clothes pins							*

Instructional Resources	Chapter Opener	4.1	4.2	4.3	4.4	4.5	Connect and Grow
Vocabulary Cards	•				+	+	
Toss and Compare Numbers from 0–10 Recording Sheet							*
Number Paths 1–10							*
Number Cards 0–5							*
Number Cards 5–10							*
Lion Cards 5–10							*
Lion Cards Recording Sheet							•

• class set   + teacher only   * per pair/group

Suggested Pacing

Day 1	Chapter Opener	Performance Task Preview		Vocabulary				
Day 2	Lesson 4.1	Warm-Up	Dig In	Explore	Think		Apply: Practice	Think: Modeling Real Life
Day 3	Lesson 4.2	Warm-Up	Dig In	Explore	Think		Apply: Practice	Think: Modeling Real Life
Day 4	Lesson 4.3	Warm-Up	Dig In	Explore	Think		Apply: Practice	Think: Modeling Real Life
Day 5	Lesson 4.4	Warm-Up	Dig In	Explore	Think		Apply: Practice	Think: Modeling Real Life
Day 6	Lesson 4.5	Warm-Up	Dig In	Explore	Think		Apply: Practice	Think: Modeling Real Life
Day 7	Connect and Grow	Performance Task		Activity			Chapter Practice	
Day 8		Centers						
Day 9	Chapter Assessment	Chapter Assessment						

Year-to-Date: 45 Days

Laurie's Notes

Performance Task Review

- Preview the page. Before asking the questions, give students time to look at the picture. Listen for students to make personal connections to the objects pictured.
- ? "Have you ever played with one of these toys?" Students will be excited to share their experiences. "What colors do you see in the picture?"
- "Describe a toy in our classroom to your partners. Use colors, shapes, and numbers when you talk."
- In the Performance Task at the end of the chapter, students will compare the numbers of toys in a picture by category.

4 Compare Numbers to 10

- Have you ever played with one of these toys?
- What colors do you see in the picture?

© Big Ideas Learning, LLC

one hundred sixty-nine 169

Laurie's Notes

Vocabulary Review

? "What do you notice about the picture?" Say, "Many pets have toys of their own. What kinds of toys do dogs play with?"

? Direct students to count and write the number of toys in front of each dog. Ask, "Do the dogs have the same numbers of toys? How do you know?" Have students circle the greater number. Listen to how they know which dog has more.

- **Extension:** Have students draw more toys so that each dog has the same number. Model how to draw simple toys using a thick line.

Chapter 4 Vocabulary

- Tell students that to sort objects into a group they must decide how they are alike in some way. Show the vocabulary card for the word *classify* and use it as the first word in the activity.

Activity

- **Echo:** Find a ball that can be easily and safely passed around by students. Designate this as the echo ball. Say a vocabulary word and then pass the echo ball to a student. The student echoes, or repeats the word, and then passes the echo ball back to you. Students need to listen carefully to repeat the word correctly. Consider challenging the students by having them define the words after they echo them.

- **Teaching Tip:** Before the game begins, decide how you are going to have your students pass the ball. Silent and gentle hand passes are recommended.

MATH MUSICALS

Math Musicals can be used with current topics, to review previous topics, or to preview upcoming topics. There are many *Math Musicals* to choose from!

Use your hand puppets to act out new stories and have students sing the songs several times to take full advantage of the power of music to learn math!

4

Vocabulary

③   2

Directions: Count the number of dog toys in front of each dog. Write each number. Circle the number that is greater than the other number.

category

chart

classify

mark

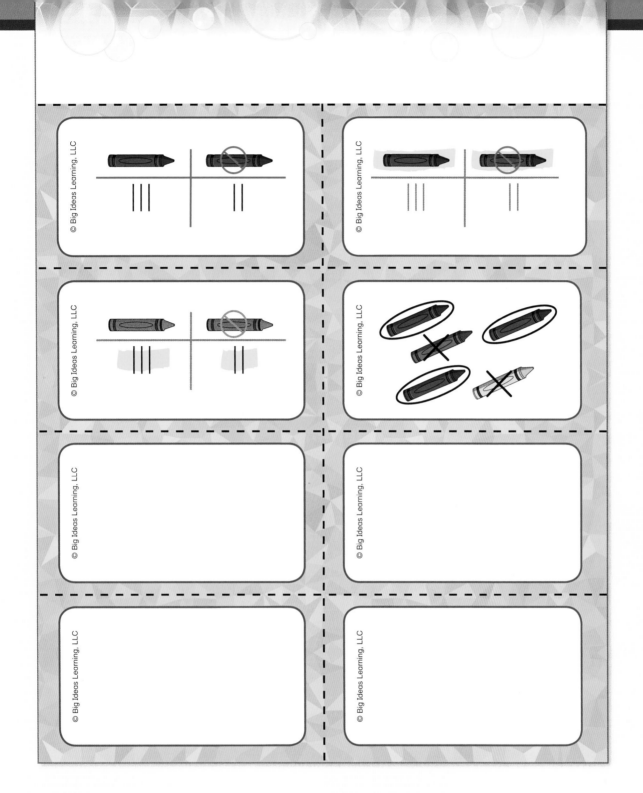

4.1

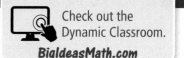
Laurie's Notes

Learning Target

Use matching to compare the numbers of objects in two groups.

Success Criteria

- Match objects from two groups.
- Compare the numbers of objects in two groups using *greater than*, *less than*, or *equal to*.

Warm-Up

Practice opportunities for the following are available in the Resources by Chapter or at *BigIdeasMath.com*.

- Daily skills
- Vocabulary
- Prerequisite skills

ELL Support

Remind students that the word *equal* means *the same as* and that the cognates *igual* in Spanish and *égal* in French sound similar. Explain that the word *match* may refer to an object that starts a fire, but can also mean to partner objects. In this chapter, students will match objects that are similar in number by choosing them and drawing a line from one to the other.

Preparing to Teach

Students are familiar with the counting sequence from 1 to 10 and have compared numbers 1 to 5. In this lesson, students use matching to compare numbers 1 to 10. Matching helps students compare groups of objects that may not be noticeably different. Using linear ten frames and drawing lines are the two strategies used in this lesson.

Remind students that *quantity* refers to *how many*. This will be helpful when presenting the learning target and success criteria. Tell students that when you compare two quantities, you must decide whether the quantities are equal, or whether one quantity is greater than or less than another.

Materials

- linking cubes

Dig In (Circle Time)

Today's circle time involves two comparing activities. The first is more hands-on and involves linking cubes while the second gets students up and moving.

? Place 10 blue linking cubes in a pile and five red linking cubes in another. Ask, "Which group has more?" Add a red cube. Ask, "Which group has more?" Continue until there are 10 red cubes. Discuss how the question became more difficult to answer as the amount of cubes in each group became closer in quantity.

- Repeat this process, however, begin with linking cubes in a tower. You want students to see that when the cubes are in a tower, or are linear, they are easier to compare. When the linking cubes are scattered, you must count them in order to compare.

? Have six students stand in one line and five students stand in another line directly across from them. Ask the seated students, "Which line has more students? How can you show that you are correct? Tell your neighbor." Solicit ideas. Do any students suggest a form of matching?

- Repeat several times with different numbers of students in each group. Make sure you have equal numbers in each line for at least one round.

- In today's Explore and Grow, the context is letters and mailboxes. You can talk about different types of mailboxes as students return to their seats.

? Teaching Prompt   ⊙ Learning Target

Learning Target: Use matching to compare the numbers of objects in two groups.

Explore and Grow

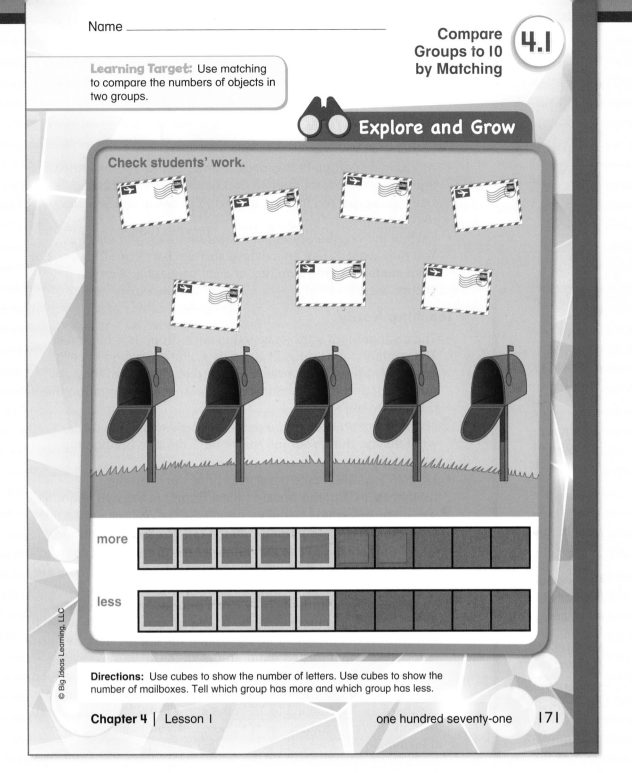

Check students' work.

more

less

Directions: Use cubes to show the number of letters. Use cubes to show the number of mailboxes. Tell which group has more and which group has less.

© Big Ideas Learning, LLC

Chapter 4 | Lesson 1

one hundred seventy-one 171

Explore and Grow

❓ "Look at the two groups. Do you think there is the same number in each group? Tell your neighbor." Listen to how students are deciding.

- Distribute linking cubes. Cover each letter with a cube and slide to the top grid. Repeat with the mailboxes. Use bottom grid.

- "Point to the frame with *more* cubes. How do you know?" Listen for thinking that suggests a matching process. Repeat with the word *less*.

- Show connected linking cubes as towers and then horizontally as trains. Quantities do not change because of the orientation!

Comparing Numbers

greater than · equal to · less than

Laurie's Notes

Think and Grow

Getting Started

- As students complete this page, remember to ask questions that show the logical relationship between *more* and *less*. Use a rekenrek, ten frames, or linking cubes to model each relationship.
- Review the vocabulary *equal to*, *greater than*, and *less than*. You may want to use an existing anchor chart from Chapter 2 or have students give examples of each concept and create a new anchor chart.

Teaching Notes

- The arrangement of objects within each group is intentional. The comparison is difficult to do by quickly glancing at each group. Matching is necessary. Remind students that they are not comparing the size of the objects. They are comparing the quantity of objects.
- ? "Look at the objects. If you used these objects every day, what do you think your job might be?" dentist; fire fighter; news reporter
- **Model:** Together, trace the dotted lines between the toothbrushes and toothpaste tubes. Compare the two quantities.
- ? **Attend to Precision:** "How do you know the groups are equal?" Listen for an understanding that the quantities are the same.
- **Note:** Students may use the length of the group or size of the objects to compare quantities. Quantity refers to *how many* are in the group, not the space it takes to display the group.
- **Common Error:** Students may circle or draw a line through individual objects instead of the whole group especially when it is a leftover object. Make sure students remember that they are comparing one group to another group.
- ◉ "Tell your neighbor what it means to compare numbers." Pause. Say, "You already learned to compare numbers 1 to 5. Can you compare the numbers 1 to 10 in the same way?" Solicit several responses. You want students to be comfortable sharing their thinking aloud.
- **Extension:** There are five cameras. This is a benchmark number. Refer the students to the cameras and say, "Use your fingers to show a number that is less than the number of cameras." Repeat this for a number that is equal to 5, and a number that is greater than 5.
- **Supporting Learners:** Using different colored linking cubes for each group is helpful for students who need to manipulate objects. Students can line up and match the different colors to make the comparison easier to see.
- **Supporting Learners:** Students can show two numbers on different rows of a rekenrek. Students can match the beads to compare.

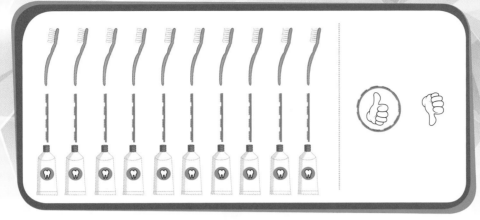

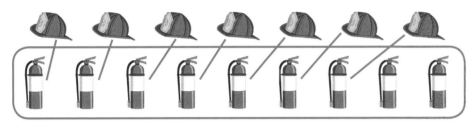

Sample answer:

Sample answer:

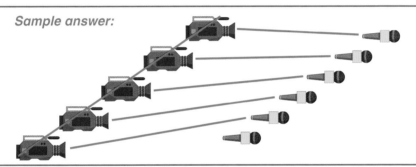

Directions: Draw lines between the objects in each group.

• Is the number of toothbrushes equal to the number of toothpaste tubes? Circle the thumbs up for *yes* or the thumbs down for *no*.

• Circle the group that is greater in number than the other group.

• Draw a line through the group that is less in number than the other group.

Apply and Grow: Practice

MAKING INSTRUCTIONAL DECISIONS

Students should make the connection that comparing numbers 1 to 10 uses the same strategies that they learned when comparing the numbers 1 to 5. Due to the size, or magnitude, of the numbers and their arrangement, it is unlikely that students will be able to visualize the quantity. Students may start to trace with their finger to match objects from each group or they may draw a line. Other students may count and remember the quantity in each group.

EMERGING students may have difficulty comparing quantities in two groups without using manipulatives or drawing lines as they match objects. They may also be confused with the vocabulary used to describe the relationship between the two quantities.

- Have students compare two numbers and complete the sentence "_____ is greater than _____." Offer more support by having them model and repeat after you or a peer.
- Give students 10 paper clips to lay on the paper as a way to show a match between two groups. Have students discuss why a picture may have a paper clip on it without a match.

PROFICIENT students are able to compare the quantities between two groups. They are confident in one or more strategies when comparing two quantities.

- Have students create their own practice pages by drawing two groups of objects in different arrangements. Students can trade pages with their partners.

Additional Support

- Have students make the quantities in each exercise using linking cubes. Give them 20 cubes; 10 of one color and 10 of another. Using two different colors will help distinguish the two quantities.

Extension: Adding Rigor

- Have students work with partners. Give each student 10 counters and number cards 5–10. Each student draws a card from the pile and builds that number with counters. Partners use comparison vocabulary to compare their numbers.

Meeting the needs of all learners.

Name _____

✓ Apply and Grow: Practice

1–3. Sample answers are given.

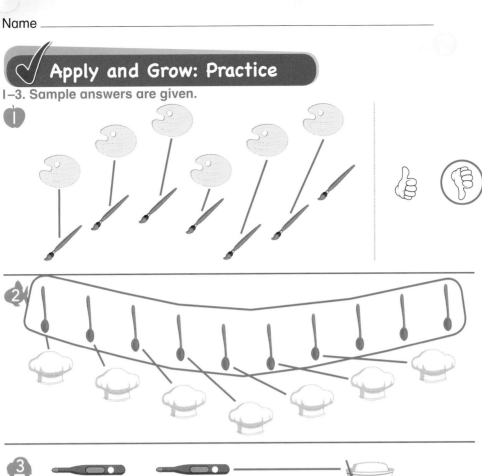

Directions: Draw lines between the objects in each group.
1 Is the number of paint palettes equal to the number of paintbrushes? Circle the thumbs up for *yes* or the thumbs down for *no*. 2 Circle the group that is greater in number than the other group. 3 Draw a line through the group that is less in number than the other group.

Chapter 4 | Lesson 1   one hundred seventy-three   173

Think and Grow: Modeling Real Life

This application allows students to show their understanding of the comparison terms *greater than* and *less than*. Students use matching to compare the quantities of two groups.

? Preview: "Have you ever used a hammer? What do you do with a hammer? Who might use a hammer every day?"

• In each exercise students are asked to draw a nail. It might be helpful to show a simple nail so that students are not hindered by the task of drawing. A vertical line with a short horizontal line at the top is close enough.

? Point to the top picture which has a board with hammers above it. Read the first direction line. Restate if necessary. "You want more nails than hammers." After, students draw the nails. "Draw lines to match objects. How do you know you are correct?" Listen for at least one extra nail that isn't matched to a hammer.

• **Supporting Learners:** If students are not organized in drawing their nails, it will be challenging to match them with the hammers. Have students use linking cubes to represent the hammers and paper clips to represent the nails.

• Before students begin the second exercise, explain that now there are hammers on both sides of the board. Project the picture and orally count so students know there are seven hammers total.

• Read the second direction line. Restate if necessary. "You want less nails than hammers." Again, listen for students to explain how they know they are correct.

• **Teaching Tip:** You should hear a stronger use of the terms *greater than* and *less than* during discussions. Listen to the vocabulary students use to monitor growth. Use these terms often so all students can hear how they are used.

• **Reason Abstractly and Quantitatively:** Have students show their pictures to each other. Make sure students notice that their neighbors may have different numbers of nails, and they are both correct.

⊙ Have students use their thumb signals to show how confident they are in comparing the numbers 1 to 10.

• **Supporting Learners:** Be sure the anchor chart is visible.

Closure

• Use finger models to show a number 1 to 10. Have students use their fingers to show a number that is greater than, less than, or equal to your number.

Sample answer:

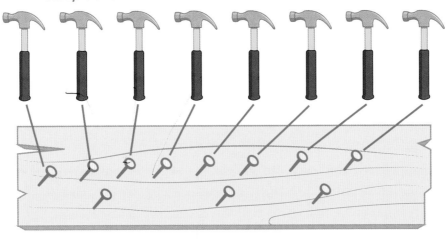

Sample answer:

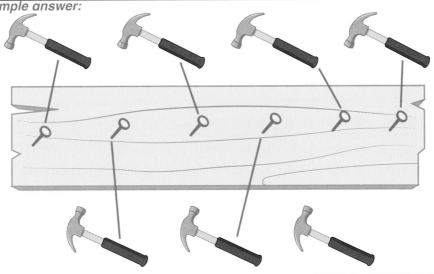

Directions:
- Draw nails on the board so that the number of nails is greater than the number of hammers. Draw lines between the objects in each group to show that you are correct.
- Draw nails on the board so that the number of nails is less than the number of hammers. Draw lines between the objects in each group to show that you are correct.

174   one hundred seventy-four

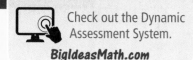
Connect and Extend Learning

Practice Notes

- Preview the pages. Ask students to identify the objects and the people that might use the objects.
- Remind students to draw a line to the closest partner for each picture.
- **Exercise 3:** Demonstrate how to draw a wand.

Cross-Curricular Connections

Language Arts

- *Ten Apples Up On Top* by Dr. Seuss, writing as Theo. LeSieg; Prepare 10 paper or felt circles for each student. Have students pretend the circles are apples to stack just like in the story. Have students see how many apples they can stack on a classroom object without them falling off. Students can then use matching to compare their numbers of stacked apples to a partners' numbers.

Social Studies

- As students learn or read about community helpers, have a discussion about the tools each helper uses. You can discuss how each person can do his or her job when the numbers of tools and helpers are the same. Have students think about what happens when the number of tools is greater than or less than the number of helpers.

Learning Target: Use matching to compare the numbers of objects in two groups.

Directions: Draw lines between the objects in each group. Is the number of police hats equal to the number of badges? Circle the thumbs up for *yes* or the thumbs down for *no*.

Sample answer:

1
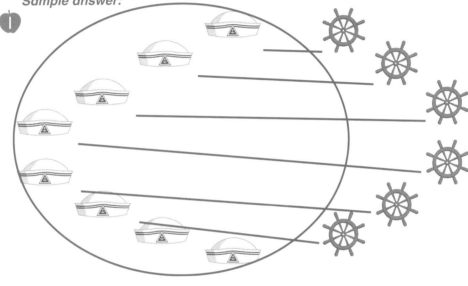

Directions: ① Draw lines between the objects in each group. Circle the group that is greater in number than the other group.

Chapter 4 | Lesson 1

one hundred seventy-five 175

Connect and Extend Learning

Extend Student Learning
Visual-Spatial

- Create puzzle pictures. Have students choose a number from 5 to 10. Assign half the class to draw that many letters on pieces of paper while the other half draws that many mailboxes. Once students' pictures are complete, have them tape their papers to a partner's so both pictures are visible. Students take turns drawing lines or using paper clips or pieces of string to match the letters to the mailboxes. Encourage students to use the correct vocabulary terms when comparing the number of letters to the number of mailboxes.

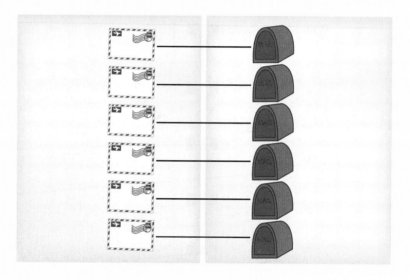

Lesson Resources	
Surface Level	**Deep Level**
Resources by Chapter • Extra Practice • Reteach Differentiating the Lesson Skills Review Handbook Skills Trainer	Resources by Chapter • Enrichment and Extension Graphic Organizers Dynamic Assessment System • Lesson Practice

Sample answer:

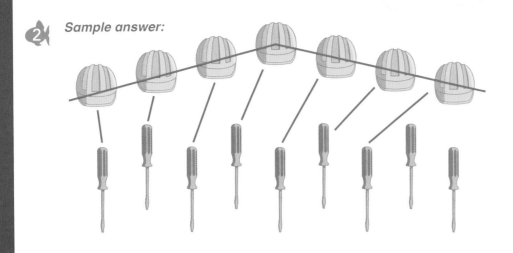

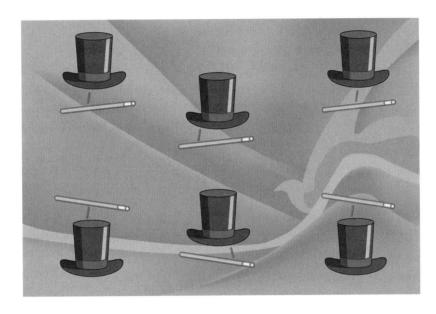

Directions: Draw lines between the objects in each group. Draw a line through the group that is less in number than the other group. **3** Draw wands on the cloth so that the number of wands is equal to the number of magician hats. Draw lines between the objects in each group to show that you are correct.

4.2

Learning Target

Use counting to compare the numbers of objects in two groups.

Success Criteria

- Compare the numbers of objects in two groups using *greater than*, *less than*, or *equal to*.
- Explain how to compare two groups by counting.

Warm-Up

Practice opportunities for the following are available in the Resources by Chapter or at *BigIdeasMath.com*.

- Daily skills
- Vocabulary
- Prerequisite skills

ELL Support

Students count two groups of objects separately and listen for the last numbers said for each group. Review the number sequence until students can locate the two given numbers on a number path.

Preparing to Teach

Students have compared numbers 1 to 5 by counting. In this lesson, they extend their understanding of this technique to numbers 1 to 10. The lesson should have a familiar feel as students decide whether the quantity of one group is more, less, or the same as another group. Students count and then record the amount for each group. When students compare, they are considering only the written numerals so understanding the counting sequence is important.

Materials

- linking cubes
- two bags or two socks

Dig In (Circle Time)

Big Ideas: If two groups of objects are not beside each other, the objects can't be matched. You need another strategy. Also, when you count groups of unequal quantities, the last numbers said for each group will be different.

- Allow students to observe you putting a collection of blue linking cubes in one bag and a collection of red linking cubes in another bag.
- "I wonder which color I have more of. Tell your partner how we can figure this out." Have students talk with each other and then have a group discussion.
- ? Some students will suggest counting. Ask for two volunteers to count the cubes aloud. Make sure students hear the last number said by each student. "Which color is there more of? less of?"
- Adding examples to an anchor chart for students to reference may be helpful.
- If time permits, give each pair of students two colors of linking cubes. Ask one student to make the number 6 and the other student to make a number greater than 6. "Count each amount to show you are correct." Reverse the students' roles, change the starting number, and change the comparison term each time.
- **Extension:** Students can discuss how to compare by matching and how to compare by counting.

? Teaching Prompt   ⊙ Learning Target

Learning Target: Use counting to compare the numbers of objects in two groups.

Explore and Grow

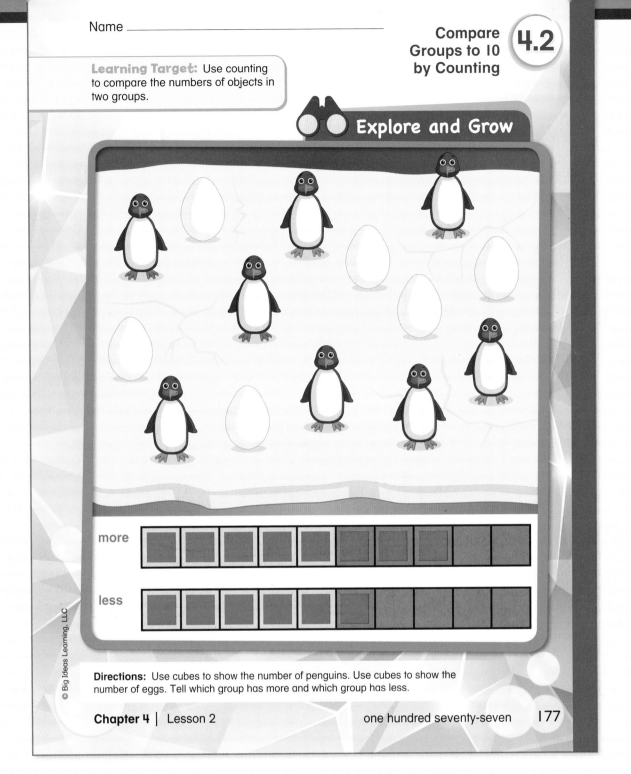

more										

less										

Directions: Use cubes to show the number of penguins. Use cubes to show the number of eggs. Tell which group has more and which group has less.

Chapter 4 | Lesson 2   one hundred seventy-seven   **177**

Explore and Grow

? "Look at the penguins and penguin eggs. Do you think there is the same number of each? Do you think there is more of one than the other?"

• Distribute linking cubes. Cover each penguin with a cube and slide to the top grid. Repeat with the eggs. Use the bottom grid.

? **Reason Abstractly and Quantitatively:** "How can you use your cubes to decide which group has more? has less?" Listen for understanding that the cubes tell *how many.*

? "Could you have used lines to match the penguins and eggs? Explain." Yes, it is possible, but the objects are not arranged in a line.

ELL Support

Teach the names of any unfamiliar objects. Students may not know the word blackberry. Explain that on the next two pages the animals are pictured with the foods that they typically eat. Have students practice language. One student asks the other, "Is the number of bears or the number of blackberries greater?" Then have them alternate roles to compare the bears and the fish. You may want them to continue with this type of practice on the next page.

Beginner students may only answer "blackberries."

Intermediate and **Advanced** students may answer with a sentence, such as, "The number of blackberries is greater than the number of bears."

Think and Grow

Getting Started

• Give students time to discuss the animals and what the animals like to eat.

• Refer to the anchor chart that should be visible. Remind students that when they compare two quantities, they are telling whether one quantity is greater than, less than, or equal to another quantity.

• Allow students to use the number path 1–10 in each exercise to compare the numerals.

Teaching Notes

• Students need to count and write the numbers of objects in each group to compare. Pause between each direction line.

? "Look at the green and purple dots. What strategy should you use to compare the groups of dots?" Listen for students to explain that the dots are difficult to match, and that they need to count to compare the groups of dots.

? Model: Chorally count the number of green dots. Write the number 9. Do the same for the purple dots. "Is the number of green dots equal to the number of purple dots?"

• Demonstrate how to use the number path and how to use the counting sequence to compare the two groups.

• Students may see a group of four bears without needing to count. They may also subitize a small portion of the berries and add on to find the total. Students may see the fish as six and one more. Have students share how they counted, or decided *how many*.

? Extension: "Are any of the groups equal in number? How can we make the number of fish and the number of blackberries equal?"

◉ Students may be able to count to compare two quantities but may not be able to explain what they are doing. Hearing other students explain how they count to compare will help all students. Ask about each success criterion separately.

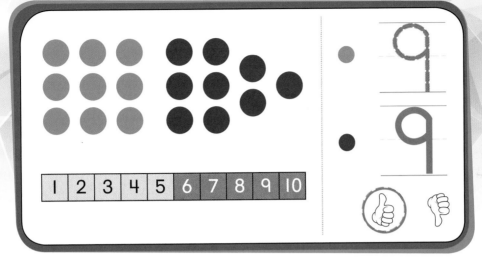

Directions: Count the objects in each group. Write each number.
- Is the number of green dots equal to the number of purple dots? Circle the thumbs up for *yes* or the thumbs down for *no*.
- Compare the numbers of blackberries and bears. Circle the number that is greater than the other number.
- Compare the numbers of bears and fish. Draw a line through the number that is less than the other number.

178 one hundred seventy-eight

Laurie's Notes

Meeting the needs of
all learners.

Apply and Grow: Practice

MAKING INSTRUCTIONAL DECISIONS

The way objects are arranged affects how easy or difficult it is for students to subitize or count. Some students may look for common patterns while other students still count or match objects one-by-one by tracking with their eyes. Remember to have students explain how they count each group. A good way to have students show you how they counted is to have them highlight any smaller quantity that they recognized or counted first.

EMERGING students may have difficulty counting the objects, and may even lose track of which objects have been counted. They may also lack fluency with the counting sequence.

- Provide more practice with seeing objects arranged in lines so that comparisons are easier to see.

PROFICIENT students are able to compare the quantities in two groups by counting. They may not be able to explain the different strategies related to how objects are clustered in the display, but can successfully compare two groups.

- Provide 10 bear counters, 10 linking cubes, and number cards 5–10 to each partner group. Each student draws a card from the pile and builds that number in a scattered arrangement using one type of manipulative. Have students use the vocabulary words to compare the groups of objects.

Additional Support

- Provide a cover sheet for students who are visually overwhelmed. Use small counters to focus their counting on one type of object at a time.
- Provide students with a number path and arrange objects in formations that are not as complicated. Students can explain how they identify the number and make their comparisons.

✓ Apply and Grow: Practice

1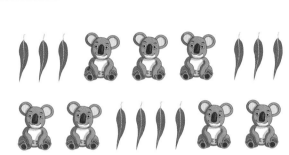

6

6
___

👍 👎

2

7

(10)

3

8

9
___

Directions: Count the objects in each group. Write each number. **1** Is the number of panda bears equal to the number of bamboo sticks? Circle the thumbs up for *yes* or the thumbs down for *no*. **2** Circle the number that is greater than the other number. **3** Draw a line through the number that is less than the other number.

© Big Ideas Learning, LLC

Chapter 4 | Lesson 2   one hundred seventy-nine   **179**

Laurie's Notes

Think and Grow: Modeling Real Life

This application allows students to show their understanding of *greater than* and *less than* using any strategy they have learned.

- **? Preview:** "What do you know about monkeys? What do you think monkeys like to eat? Have you ever climbed a tree or watched someone climb a tree?"
- In each exercise, students will draw bananas. Ask a volunteer to show how they would draw a banana. Assure students that a curved stroke with their crayon or pencil is fine, but an X or a dot would work just as well!
- Read the first set of directions. They know that the dotted lines mean that they will write the number of monkeys and bananas so focus on the comparison. "You want more bananas than monkeys."
- **Think-Pair-Share:** Give students time to think about the different strategies and choose an approach. Before they draw, have them share their thinking with their partners. Some students may count the monkeys, record 7, and draw seven bananas. Some may put a finger on a monkey as they draw a banana. Others may draw a banana and cross out a monkey. In the end, what matters is that they can explain how they know there are more bananas than monkeys.
- **Note:** Some students may draw more than 10 bananas. If students are able to write the number and explain how they know that it is greater, they have grasped the concept.
- **? Reason Abstractly and Quantitatively:** "How do you know that there is a greater number of bananas than monkeys?" Students may mention that every banana does not have a partner, or that the number of bananas comes after the number of monkeys when counting.
- Read the second set of directions. "Now you want less bananas than monkeys." Again, give students time to think versus offering them a strategy.
- ⊙ Ask several students who are showing a thumbs up to explain how they compare two groups by counting. Can students who are not showing a thumbs up ask questions or explain what is not clear?

Closure

- Review counting to 10. Show six linking cubes. Have students count the cubes. Have students use cubes to model a number that is greater than six. Allow students to share their answers. Repeat this process several times having students build numbers greater than, less than, or equal to the number modeled.

Sample answer:

Sample answer:

Directions:
- Draw bananas hanging from the tree so that the number of bananas is greater than the number of monkeys. Write the number of each object. Circle the number that is greater than the other number.
- Draw bananas hanging from the tree so that the number of bananas is less than the number of monkeys. Write the number of each object. Draw a line through the number that is less than the other number.

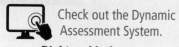
Connect and Extend Learning

Practice Notes

- **Exercise 1:** Students use a thumbs up or thumbs down response.
- **Exercises 2 and 3:** Students use a circle or line to indicate greater than or less than.
- **Exercise 3:** Demonstrate how to draw a simple rectangle to represent the bale of hay.

Cross-Curricular Connections

Language Arts

- *We All Went On Safari* by Laurie Krebs; Have students tell the numbers of each kind of animal in the story. Write these numbers on a chart. Include the name of each animal and a picture. Call on students to choose two animals. Then compare how many of each animal. Expect them to use vocabulary terms, such as *greater than*, *less than*, or *equal* when making their comparisons.

Science

- Give students the opportunity to design a tall structure by stacking objects. Use various manipulatives, such as cups, paper, straws, shells, bear counters, beads, buttons, and clay. Have students build independently at first and then partner up to build another structure. Have students compare the number of manipulatives used in their own building to the number of manipulatives used in the structure that they created together.

Name _____

Learning Target: Use counting to compare the numbers of objects in two groups.

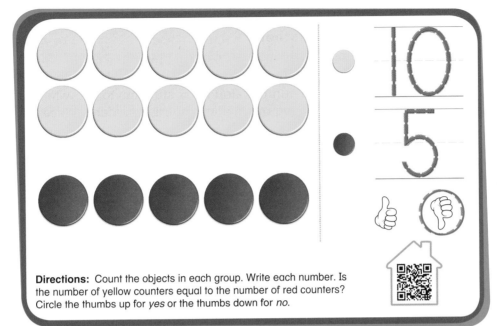

Directions: Count the objects in each group. Write each number. Is the number of yellow counters equal to the number of red counters? Circle the thumbs up for *yes* or the thumbs down for *no*.

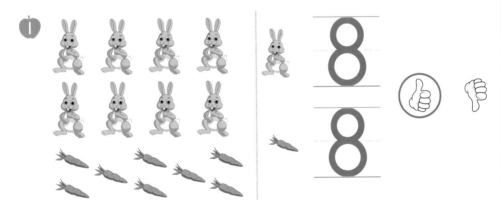

Directions: ❶ Count the objects in each group. Write each number. Is the number of rabbits equal to the number of carrots? Circle the thumbs up for *yes* or the thumbs down for *no*.

© Big Ideas Learning, LLC

Chapter 4 | Lesson 2   one hundred eighty-one   181

Connect and Extend Learning

Extend Student Learning

Bodily-Kinesthetic

- Provide number cards 5-10 and place the cards
  in a pile. Hold up a number card for students to see. Without
  saying the number aloud, ask students to show the number
  they see using manipulatives. Have students place their
  manipulatives on top of whiteboards. Hold up another card
  and ask them to show that number underneath their first group
  of manipulatives. Have students count the manipulatives and
  write each number next to its group. Ask, "How many do you
  have in each group?" Then have students compare the two
  numbers. "Compare your groups. Use the words *greater than*,
  less than, or *equal*."

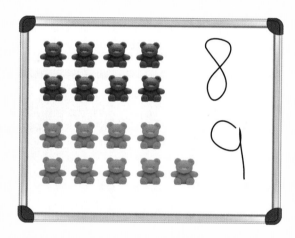

Lesson Resources	
Surface Level	**Deep Level**

Resources by Chapter
  • Extra Practice
  • Reteach
Differentiating the Lesson
Skills Review Handbook
Skills Trainer
	Resources by Chapter
	  • Enrichment and Extension
	Graphic Organizers
	Dynamic Assessment System
	  • Lesson Practice

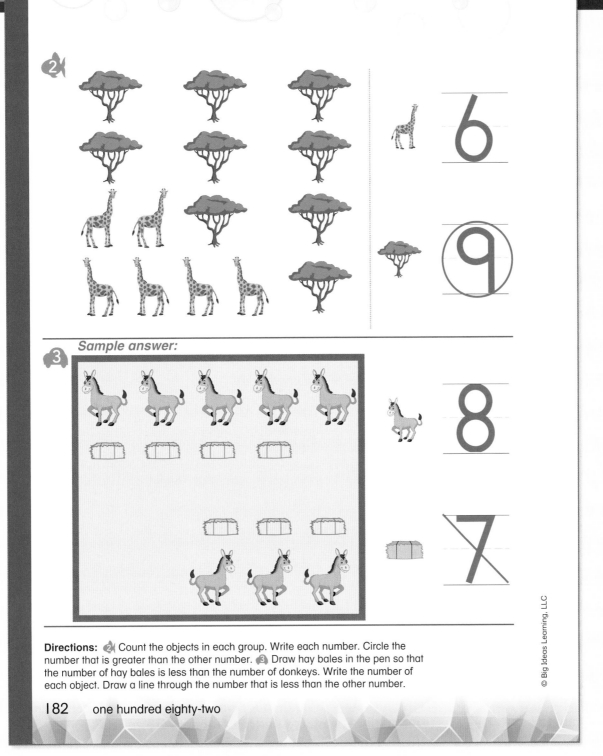

2 6

9 (circled)

Sample answer:

3 8

7 (line through)

Directions: **2** Count the objects in each group. Write each number. Circle the number that is greater than the other number. **3** Draw hay bales in the pen so that the number of hay bales is less than the number of donkeys. Write the number of each object. Draw a line through the number that is less than the other number.

182   one hundred eighty-two

4.3

Learning Target
Compare two numbers.

Success Criteria
- Tell whether two numbers are the same.
- Use *greater than* and *less than* to describe two numbers that are not the same.
- Draw to show how one number compares to another.

Warm-Up
Practice opportunities for the following are available in the Resources by Chapter or at *BigIdeasMath.com*.
- Daily skills
- Vocabulary
- Prerequisite skills

ELL Support
You may want to review numbers less than 10 that have homophones; such as one and won; two, to, and too; four and for; and eight and ate.

Laurie's Notes

Preparing to Teach
This lesson is similar to when students compared the numerals 1 to 5. Now they compare numerals 1 to 10. If students know and understand the counting sequence, they will be able to compare two numerals without drawing or matching the objects. Listen for students to say the counting sequence "6, 7, 8" in order to know that 6 comes first and is less than 8.

Materials
- linking cubes
- whiteboards and markers
- two-color counters

Dig In (Circle Time)
Give partners a whiteboard and 10 linking cubes.

- Write a number from 6 to 10 on your whiteboard. Do not reveal it to students. Have one partner also write a number from 6 to 10, and have their partner build a model of it.
- **?** "What does it mean to compare two numbers?" Listen for comparative vocabulary, such as greater than, less than, and equal to.
- Reveal your whiteboard. "Talk with your partner. How does your number compare to my number?" Give time for students to talk.
- "If you think your number is less than my number, hold up your whiteboard." Select a few students to explain how they know their number is less. What reasons are students giving? Do they talk about counting or number order? Do they mention a visual model?
- Ask students to hold up their whiteboard if they thought their number was greater than your number. Again, have them explain.
- **?** "Did everyone hold up their whiteboard yet? Why not?" Listen for an understanding that the numbers are equal.
- Repeat this several times and include 10 as one of your number choices.
- **Extension:** You could also designate three different areas of the room as greater than, less than, or equal to. Have students stand in the appropriate place to compare. Use the range of numbers 4 to 9.
- ⊙ Summarize the different ways students compared numbers. Discuss the first success criterion. If two numbers are not the same, one has to be greater than the other. Did students use the linking cube model when they explained how they compared their number to your number?

? Teaching Prompt   ⊙ Learning Target

Learning Target: Compare two numbers.

Explore and Grow

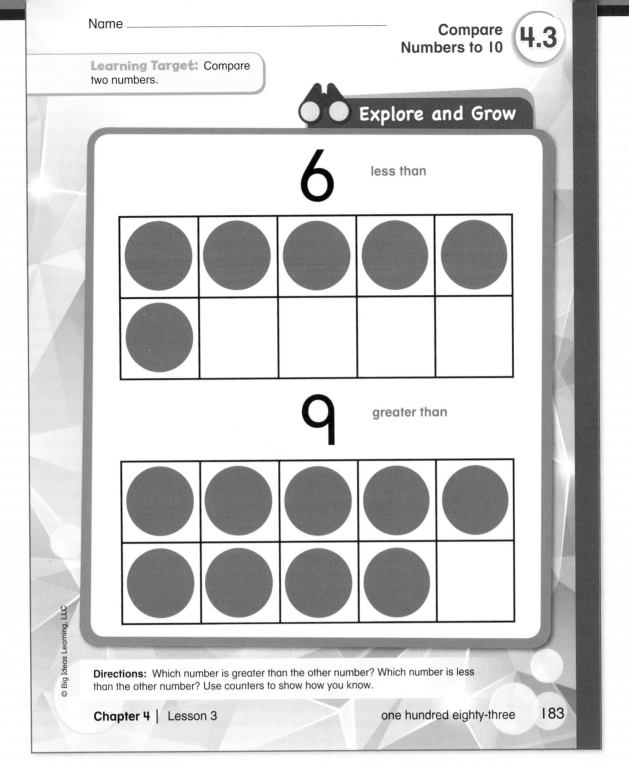

6   less than

9   greater than

Directions: Which number is greater than the other number? Which number is less than the other number? Use counters to show how you know.

© Big Ideas Learning, LLC

Chapter 4 | Lesson 3   one hundred eighty-three   183

Explore and Grow

- **Model with Mathematics:** Have students use counters to model the numbers 6 and 9 in the ten frames.
- **? Turn and Talk:** "Tell your partner which number is greater, 6 or 9. How do you know?" Select a few students to share their reasoning with the class. Some students will talk about the counting sequence. Others may point to the ten frame models.
- Change the comparison term to less than and repeat.

Think and Grow

Getting Started

- **Supporting Learners:** If students have trouble with drawing circular models, they could use manipulatives or draw an X to model the number. They can still draw the matching line.
- Some students will not want to draw at all, saying that they *just know* which number is greater or less. Refer to the second success criterion. Drawing the model shows that you know your answer is correct.

Teaching Notes

- There are three problems and three comparison statements. Pause between each direction line.
- The directions ask students to compare first, then draw a supporting model. Watch for students who need to draw first. You want students to understand the quantity and then draw to show their thinking.
- **? Model:** "We want to compare the numbers 8 and 5. Are they equal? Can you draw to show how you know?" Students should explain that the number of circles is not the same. Circle the thumbs down.
- **? Look for and Express Regularity in Repeated Reasoning:** "How did you compare 10 and 7?" I know 10 comes after 7, so 10 is greater. "How did you compare 1 and 6?" I know 6 comes after 1, so 6 is greater. If 6 is greater, then 1 is less.
- **Teaching Tip:** Students often have a harder time determining the number that is less than another number. Support these students by telling them to find the number that is greater, and then determine the number that is less.
- ⊙ Focus on the third success criterion. Talk about the models drawn on this page and other models they have used such as five and ten frames, fingers, dot models, and rekenreks. As students are still learning and understanding the counting sequence, the models provide a visual way to compare two quantities. "Signal with your thumb to show that you know how to use models to compare numbers."
- **? Extension:** Write the number 8 on the board. "What is a number greater than 8? less than 8? equal to 8?" Have students write or say each answer.
- **Supporting Learners:** Some students may have difficulty understanding that when they count, each successive number is one greater. Provide a visual of linking cube towers built from 1 to 10 to help students relate the counting sequence to the quantity of each number.

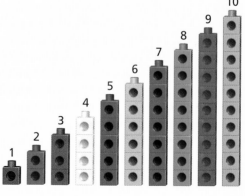

ELL Support

Have students continue to practice verbal language. One student asks the other, "Are the numbers equal?" Then have them switch roles for the other exercise.

Beginner students may only answer "yes" or "no."

Intermediate students may answer with a simple sentence, such as, "They are not equal."

Advanced students may answer with a sentence, such as, "No, 10 is greater than 7."

8 ◯◯◯◯◯◯◯◯
5 ◯◯◯◯◯

👍 👎

Sample answer:

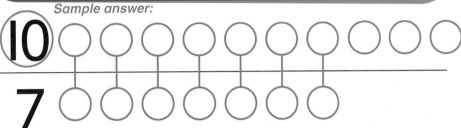

⑩ ◯◯◯◯◯◯◯◯◯◯
7 ◯◯◯◯◯◯◯

Sample answer:

1 ◯
6 ◯◯◯◯◯◯

Directions: Compare the numbers.
- Are the numbers equal? Circle the thumbs up for *yes* or the thumbs down for *no*. Draw to show how you know.
- Circle the number that is greater than the other number. Draw to show how you know.
- Draw a line through the number that is less than the other number. Draw to show how you know.

184   one hundred eighty-four

© Big Ideas Learning, LLC

MATH MUSICALS

Remember, you can use the song
Fish Crackers
to review counting to 10!

Fish Crackers

Meeting the needs of all learners.

Laurie's Notes

Apply and Grow: Practice

MAKING INSTRUCTIONAL DECISIONS

In this lesson, students are showing how they know that their comparisons of numerals are true. Check for students' understanding as you listen to their explanations. Encourage students to use vocabulary terms in their answers by modeling this for them. As you teach, use the terms and numbers in complete sentences. For example, ask, "Are the numbers 9 and 10 equal?" Then model the answer, "No, 9 and 10 are not equal."

EMERGING students may be successful in recognizing numbers that are equal but have difficulty when two numbers are not equal. They may not recognize all of the numerals, or they may not know the counting sequence well enough to know 7 is less than 8 without reciting the counting sequence 5, 6, 7, 8.

- Provide materials such as linking cubes or two-color counters to compare the numbers.
- Provide ten frames that have the numbers printed on them.
- Have students move counters forward or backward on the number path to help compare the numbers.

PROFICIENT students are able to explain how they are comparing two numbers. They can state the relationship between two numbers using correct comparative language.

- Pair these students with students who need extra support.

Additional Support

- Put two sets of number cards 1–10 in a box or bag. Have students work in pairs. Each student should pull out one number card from the bag. They will flip over their two cards and use a number path to determine the comparison.

Extension: Adding Rigor

- Provide students with 10 blue and 10 red linking cubes. Have students use the linking cubes to make their own comparison problems for their partners to solve. The partners use whiteboards to write the numbers, circle the number that is greater, or cross out the number that is less.

Name _____

1–3. Sample answers are given.

 5 ◯◯◯◯◯
9 ◯◯◯◯◯◯◯◯◯

👍 (👎)

 (8) ◯◯◯◯◯◯◯◯
6 ◯◯◯◯◯◯

 9 ◯◯◯◯◯◯◯◯◯
8̸ ◯◯◯◯◯◯◯◯

Directions: Compare the numbers. ① Are the numbers equal? Circle the thumbs up for *yes* or the thumbs down for *no*. Draw to show how you know. ② Circle the number that is greater than the other number. Draw to show how you know. ③ Draw a line through the number that is less than the other number. Draw to show how you know.

Chapter 4 | Lesson 3   one hundred eighty-five   (185)

© Big Ideas Learning, LLC

Laurie's Notes

Think and Grow: Modeling Real Life

This application allows students to show their understanding of comparing written numerals. It also involves quantitative reasoning each time the students decide what number satisfies a condition.

- **Note:** The directions ask students to think of numbers that are *one more* or *one less* than another number. You can alter the directions and ask students to think of numbers that are *more* or *less* than another number. This more open-ended direction line will result in students having different answers.

- **Preview:** Show a picture of a bouquet of flowers. Talk about the types of flowers that they are familiar with or may have picked.

- **? Make Sense of Problems and Persevere in Solving Them:** Introduce the first set of directions. Say, "I want you to think of some numbers greater than 6." 7, 8, 9, 10 "Which of those numbers is less than 8? 7 How many flowers should you draw?" 7 Have students write the number and draw the flowers. "You have seven flowers."

- **? Attend to Precision:** "What number is one more than 5?" 6 Have students write the number and draw the flowers. Circle the greater number.

- **Note:** If you altered the directions and said, "Draw any number greater than 5," students' work will differ. They may show 6, 7, 8, 9, or 10.

- **Look for and Make Use of Structure:** In the second exercise, you want students to make the connection between 10 being one more than 9, and 9 being one less than 10. Probe with questions that address this relationship.

- **? Extension:** "What is a number that is greater than 5 but less than 9?" Have partners *Turn and Talk* to discuss. You want students to realize that there could be multiple answers.

- ⊙ Have students talk about what they learned today. Listen for students to use the correct vocabulary and for them to talk about how models can show you are correct.

Closure

- Write the number 7 on the board. Show number cards 5–10 randomly. Have students stand when the number is greater than 7, sit when the number is less than 7, and jump when the number is equal to 7. To allow think time for all students, give a signal when they are to answer.

 Who has more?

You

Friend

 Who has less?

You

Friend

Directions:
- You have a number of flowers that is greater than 6 and less than 8. Your friend has a number of flowers that is one more than 5. Write and draw how many flowers you each have. Circle the number that is greater than the other number.
- You have a number of flowers that is one more than 9. Your friend has a number of flowers that is one less than 10. Write and draw how many flowers you each have. Draw a line through the number that is less than the other number.

© Big Ideas Learning, LLC

186   one hundred eighty-six

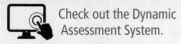
Connect and Extend Learning

Practice Notes

- Remind students to compare the numbers in each exercise first, then have them draw to show how they know. Encourage students to draw the dots in a row instead of a scattered configuration.
- **Exercises 1 and 2:** Students need to be clear about what comparison term they are using.
- **Exercise 3:** Read the direction lines one at a time to make sure students write the correct number on each writing line. Students draw a circle to indicate the number greater than the other number.

Cross-Curricular Connections

Language Arts

- *Count The Monkeys* by Mac Barnett and Kevin Cornell; Hide two or three sets of number cards 0–10 in the classroom. Tell students that the cards are hiding like the monkeys did in the story. Call on two students at a time to find one number card each. These students then compare the numbers on their cards using the vocabulary terms *greater than*, *less than*, or *equal*. Students then draw dots for each number on a whiteboard to show how they know they compared correctly.

Science

- When using Venn Diagrams, count and compare the number of objects that are in each region of the diagram. Write the numbers below each region to aid in the comparisons.

Name _____

Learning Target: Compare two numbers.

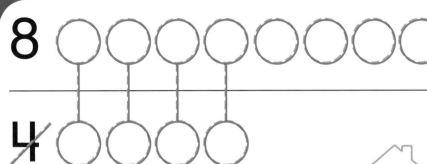

8

4

Directions: Compare the numbers. Draw a line through the number that is less than the other number. Draw to show how you know.

Sample answer:

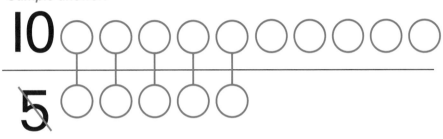

10

5

Directions: Compare the numbers. Draw a line through the number that is less than the other number. Draw to show how you know.

Chapter 4 | Lesson 3   one hundred eighty-seven   187

© Big Ideas Learning, LLC

Connect and Extend Learning

Extend Student Learning

Bodily-Kinesthetic

- Play "Number Freeze." Give each student a number card from 0 to 10. Have students hold their cards and walk around the room until you say, "Freeze!" Students stop and partner with a student standing near them. Have partners compare their number cards using the words *greater than*, *less than*, or *equal*. Have students switch cards with their partners and begin walking around the room again to play a new round.
- Teaching Tip: You can be a partner when there is an odd number of students.

7	3

Lesson Resources	
Surface Level	**Deep Level**
Resources by Chapter • Extra Practice • Reteach Differentiating the Lesson Skills Review Handbook Skills Trainer Math Musicals	Resources by Chapter • Enrichment and Extension Graphic Organizers Math Musicals Dynamic Assessment System • Lesson Practice

Sample answer:

 9 ○○○○○○○○○

7 ○○○○○○○

 Who has more?

 You

 Friend

(6) You

5 Friend

Directions: ② Compare the numbers. Are the numbers equal? Circle the thumbs up for *yes* or the thumbs down for *no*. Draw to show how you know. ❸ You have a number of marbles that is greater than 5 and less than 7. Your friend has a number of marbles that is one more than 4. Write and draw how many marbles you each have. Circle the number that is greater than the other number.

188   one hundred eighty-eight

Learning Target

Tell whether objects
belong or do not belong
in a category.

Success Criteria

• Describe what is the
same about a group
of objects.
• Classify objects into
a category.
• Identify objects that
are not in a category.

Warm-Up

Practice opportunities
for the following
are available in the
Resources by Chapter or
at *BigIdeasMath.com.*

• Daily skills
• Vocabulary
• Prerequisite skills

ELL Support

Explain the word
classify in simple
terms. "To classify
things is to group
things in ways that
show their similarities.
For example, out
of all the students
in the school, you
can be classified as
kindergarteners."

Laurie's Notes

Preparing to Teach

Students apply their counting and comparing skills to categorical
data in the next two sections. In this section, students are
presented with a group of objects that are the same (dogs, toys,
trees) but differ by one attribute such as color. You want students
to classify or identify the objects that belong to a category, say
red trees, and those that do not belong, meaning all other colors
of trees.

Materials

• collections of objects
• two-color counters

Dig In (Circle Time)

Introduce the vocabulary words **category** and **classify** as you
display different collections of objects such as crayons, blocks, and
buttons. Display one collection at a time.

? **Example:** Show the crayons. "Talk with your partner about
this collection of objects." Students should describe crayons,
mentioning various colors and lengths. Add one block to the
group and ask, "Does the block belong in this group?" No, it is
not a crayon. Introduce crayons as the category of objects.

⊙ Make a connection between the first success criterion and
students knowing that all of the objects were crayons. Now
have them classify the crayons into two categories, such as
broken and not broken, or red and not red.

? Sort all of the red crayons into one pile with all of the remaining
colors together in another pile. "How would you describe these
two groups of crayons?" Students will name the red crayons,
but may find it difficult to give a name to the second group. Tell
them that these are 'not red crayons.'

⊙ Explain that they are classifying objects into two categories.

• Repeat similar questioning with a collection of blocks
or buttons.

? Teaching Prompt   ⊙ Learning Target

Learning Target: Tell whether objects belong or do not belong in a category.

Explore and Grow

Directions: Place a yellow counter on each tree that is yellow. Place a red counter on each tree that is *not* yellow.

© Big Ideas Learning, LLC

Explore and Grow

- Have students discuss the page using the vocabulary word *category*.
- Distribute counters. "Let's classify the trees into two categories." Read the directions.
- **Common Misconception:** 'Not yellow' is more than one color. It means any color that is not yellow. Example: "Who is wearing a shirt that is not yellow?" a blue shirt is not yellow; a red shirt is not yellow
- Use the page to explore other classifications: red and not red trees, or orange and not orange trees.

ELL Support

Read the directions aloud and demonstrate the actions needed to have students complete the first exercise. Then have students practice language in pairs as they did before. One student asks the other, "How many animals are brown? Which animals are brown?" Provide them with the needed vocabulary, such as goat, mouse, beaver, monkey, and bear. Then have them switch roles for the exercise showing animals with wings. They should answer "seven, all six birds and the butterfly."

Beginner students may answer using a number and naming the animals.

Intermediate and **Advanced** students may answer using sentences, such as, "Five animals are brown. They are the goat, mouse, beaver, monkey, and bear."

Think and Grow

Getting Started

- Students have already used the vocabulary words **category** and **classify**. If you have not shown the vocabulary cards yet, display and discuss them now.
- Identifying a group of objects as a category, and then taking the same objects and classifying them into two categories may confuse students. The first step is naming the initial category. We named the category trees in the Explore and Grow. The next step is to classify, or sort, the trees into two groups. We separated them into yellow and not yellow trees. This requires a deeper level of reasoning for students.

Teaching Notes

- Throughout the Think and Grow, students need to identify a category of objects, such as classroom materials or animals. Students then classify the objects into two categories by some attribute. Pause between each direction line.
- **?** **Model:** "What do all of these objects have in common?" You find them in a classroom. "Circle the classroom objects that are green. Cross out the classroom objects that are not green."
- ⊙ In the next two exercises, the initial category is animals. Students that are unfamiliar with the name of each animal should still be able to tell whether the animals belong to a given category or not. This is the learning target today. Refer to the language of the learning target as students complete the exercises.
- **Note:** Students may not know whether turkeys have wings or not.
- **Connection:** Ask students how many objects they circled and how many they crossed out. Compare these two numbers.
- **Extension:** Have students brainstorm other ways to classify the objects into two categories, such as animals that live in water and animals that do not live in water, or those that have a tail and those that do not have a tail.
- ⊙ Discuss how each step in the problem demonstrates their learning of each success criterion. "You described is something that was the same about the group of objects when you gave them a category name." This was the first success criterion. Use similar statements that explicitly state when students demonstrated the second and third success criteria. Explaining this makes the learning visible to students.
- **Supporting Learners:** The page may be visually overwhelming for students because of the different colors and animals. Have students use a cover sheet to help them focus on one exercise at a time.

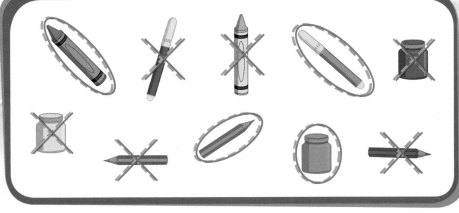

Directions:
- Circle the objects that are green. Cross out the objects that are *not* green.
- Circle the animals that are brown. Cross out the animals that are *not* brown.
- Circle the animals that have wings. Cross out the animals that do *not* have wings.

190   one hundred ninety

Laurie's Notes

Meeting the needs of all learners.

Apply and Grow: Practice

MAKING INSTRUCTIONAL DECISIONS

Students were introduced to vocabulary in this lesson they may not have heard before. Students may be familiar with the words *groups* and *sorting*, but need to become comfortable with using *category* and *classify*. Look for students' understanding of the learning target. Are they able to tell when an object belongs or does not belong in a category? Students will provide clear evidence of their learning as they complete the exercises.

EMERGING students may have difficulty with language in describing what is the same about a collection of objects. If there are more than two common characteristics, emerging students may have difficulty classifying them into only two groups.

- Provide additional experiences for students with classifying objects into two categories. Repeat activities similar to the Dig In. When students sort all of the green crayons into a pile, point to the remaining crayons and say, "All of these are not green crayons."

PROFICIENT students are able to name a category of objects and then classify them into two separate categories, those that have a particular attribute and those that do not.

- Can students classify all of the students in the classroom into two categories? For example, students who are wearing sneakers and students who are not wearing sneakers.

Additional Support

- Provide students with a handful of different colored cubes and a piece of paper. Have students fold the paper in half so there is a crease in the center. Scatter the cubes on the paper. Have students put all of the reds cubes on one side and the remaining cubes on the other. Practice naming the two collections, "These are red cubes. These are not red cubes." This could be done with partners. One student sorts the cubes and the other student names the two collections.

Name _____

1

2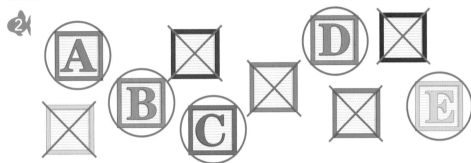

3

Directions: **1** Circle the pigs that have spots. Cross out the pigs that do *not* have spots. **2** Circle the blocks that have letters. Cross out the blocks that do *not* have letters. **3** Circle the animals that have tails. Cross out the animals that do *not* have tails.

© Big Ideas Learning, LLC

Chapter 4 | Lesson 4   one hundred ninety-one   191

Think and Grow: Modeling Real Life

This application allows students to show their ability to tell whether objects belong or do not belong to a given category.

- **Preview:** "Point to the top half of the page. Tell your partner what you know about all of these objects." Share as a class.
- Read the first set of directions.
- **?** "How many dogs did you circle?" 4 "How many dogs did you cross out?" 5 "Were there any dogs that you didn't circle *or* cross out?" If a student says yes, have them explain their reasoning.
- **Common Misconception:** Beginning anew with the nine dogs is confusing. Some students think they need to classify the black dogs into two groups, and the not black dogs into two groups. Cover the top half of the page and explain that you want to start again and try to classify them in a different way.
- **Reason Abstractly and Quantitatively:** "Think about other ways you could classify these same dogs into two categories." Give sufficient wait time and then have students share their thinking with neighbors. Students may focus on dogs that are standing and not standing, dogs with their tongues showing or not showing, and so on.
- ⊙ Display a picture of the nine dogs. Ask several students to describe how they classified the dogs into two categories. The rest of the class then tells which dogs belong in each category. This provides additional practice demonstrating the learning target. It also helps students see that there is more than one way to answer the question.
- **Extension:** Pair students. One student shows his or her work for the bottom half of the page. The other student describes how the dogs were classified.

Closure

- Use a collection of objects from the Dig In. "What do all of these objects have in common?" Then describe how you want the students to classify the objects. As you hold up each object, students signal a thumbs up when the object belongs to the group and a thumbs down when it does not belong to the group.

Think and Grow: Modeling Real Life

Sample answer:

Directions:
- Circle the dogs that are black. Cross out the dogs that are *not* black.
- Classify the dogs another way. Circle the dogs that belong in the new category. Cross out the dogs that do *not* belong in the new category. Tell how you classified the dogs. **sitting or standing**

192   one hundred ninety-two

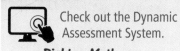

Check out the Dynamic
Assessment System.

BigIdeasMath.com

Connect and Extend Learning

Practice Notes

- **Exercises 1–5:** Students may need the direction lines for each exercise read more than once and one direction at a time.
- **Exercises 1–5:** Many of the objects in each picture share more than one attribute. Students need to listen cearfully to know how they are sorting the objects.
- **Exercise 5:** Students may classify the objects in more then one way. Have students share their pictures and let the class reason about how the sort was done.

Cross-Curricular Connections

Language Arts

- *One Frog Sang* by Shirley Parenteau; After the story, put number cards 0–10 in a pile. Have one student choose a number card and show it to the class. This student will say, "A number less than this number is _____" and call on another student to fill in the blank. Have the student who answers choose another number card from the pile and repeat the process. Replace *less than* with *greater than* and *equal to*.

Science

- Have students bring in different kinds of rocks for a class rock museum. Discuss the characteristics of each rock. Choose a number card from 5 to 10 and count that number of rocks out loud. Call on a student to be the rock collector and show a number of rocks less than the number you counted. Repeat this process with a different number card. You can also have the students create two categories, count, and compare the rocks.

Practice **4.4**

> **Learning Target:** Tell whether objects belong or do not belong in a category.

Directions: Circle the cars that are blue. Cross out the cars that are *not* blue.

1

2

Directions: **1** Circle the scooters that are red. Cross out the scooters that are *not* red. **2** Circle the toys that are balls. Cross out the toys that are *not* balls.

Extend Student Learning

Bodily-Kinesthetic

• Play "Erase a Number." Write the numbers 0 to 10 on the board in a scattered arrangement. Choose a number card 0 to 10 and call out, "Name a number that is greater than the number on this card." The student will then name and erase a number from the board that is greater than the number card. Replace *greater than* with *less than* and *equal to*. Make sure to use *greater than* or *equal to* for the number 0 and *less than* or *equal to* for the number 10.

Lesson Resources	
Surface Level	**Deep Level**
Resources by Chapter • Extra Practice • Reteach Differentiating the Lesson Skills Review Handbook Skills Trainer	Resources by Chapter • Enrichment and Extension Graphic Organizers Dynamic Assessment System • Lesson Practice

③

④

Sample answer:

⑤

Directions: ③ Circle the animals that have stripes. Cross out the animals that do *not* have stripes. ④ Circle the animals that have 2 legs. Cross out the animals that do *not* have 2 legs. ⑤ Classify the books into 2 categories. Circle the books in one category. Cross out the books in the other category. Tell how you classified the books. **closed or open**

4.5

Learning Target

Compare the numbers of objects in two categories.

Success Criteria

- Use marks to show each object in a category.
- Count how many in each category.
- Compare the numbers of objects in two categories using *greater than*, *less than*, or *equal to*.

Warm-Up

Practice opportunities for the following are available in the Resources by Chapter or at *BigIdeasMath.com*.

- Daily skills
- Vocabulary
- Prerequisite skills

ELL Support

Explain that a vehicle is something that moves people or things from one place to another. A car or a bus is a vehicle. There are vehicles that work on the ground, in the water, and in the air. Show the students simple pictures on the board or pictures cut from a magazine and ask them to identify whether the object is a vehicle or not using a thumbs up or thumbs down signal.

Preparing to Teach

Now that students can tell what objects belong or do not belong in a category, they learn to record this information in a chart by making a mark. Perhaps you already have charts in the room in which you have made tally marks to track something, such as a lost tooth or the number of books that have been read. Refer to these charts as you introduce this lesson. More work will be done with data throughout the year.

Materials

- collections of objects
- whiteboards and markers

Dig In (Circle Time)

Use the same materials that you prepared in the last lesson when students classified objects into two categories. Familiarity with how the objects were sorted into two categories allows students to focus on the new skill of recording the information in a chart.

- ⊙ Explain that today they are going to continue classifying objects into two categories, *and* that they are also going to do some counting. Introduce the learning target and success criteria.
- **Example:** Show 10 or fewer crayons. Ask a volunteer to classify the crayons into two piles, such as red and not red crayons. "Show a thumbs up when you agree."
- Use a whiteboard or chart paper. Explain that you want to record how many objects are in each pile. As you pick up each crayon say the name of the category, red or not red, and make a tally mark.

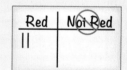

- **Note:** A tally mark to show a group of 5 is introduced in Grade 2. For now, have students make a single mark as they count each object.
- ? "What do you think each mark stands for?" Listen for an understanding that each mark represents one crayon.
- ? Explain the heading above each column, including the ⊘ symbol. "How many red crayons are there? How many crayons are not red? Which category has more? less?"
- Practice making a chart with another collection of objects, such as blocks or buttons. Keep the total count less than 10. Ask students for ideas of how to classify the objects into two categories.

? Teaching Prompt   ⊙ Learning Target

Name _____

Learning Target: Compare the numbers of objects in two categories.

Explore and Grow

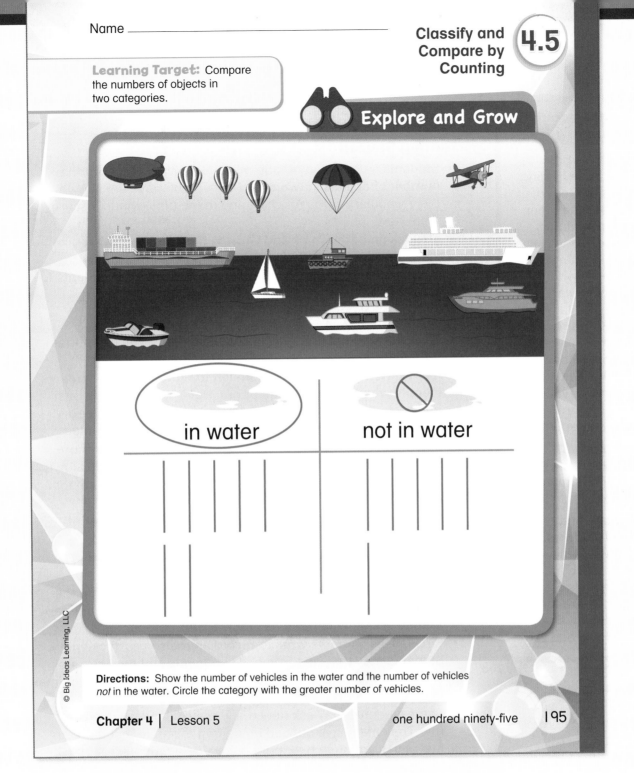

in water | not in water

Directions: Show the number of vehicles in the water and the number of vehicles *not* in the water. Circle the category with the greater number of vehicles.

Chapter 4 | Lesson 5 one hundred ninety-five 195

Explore and Grow

- Discuss the different types of vehicles. "We want to show the number of vehicles in the water and the number of vehicles not in the water."
- Count the vehicles in the water first. Suggest covering each vehicle with a small counter or crossing out as students count and make a mark for each object. Notice the *not* symbol.
- **? Turn and Talk:** "Which category has more and how do you know?" Solicit responses and listen to students' strategies.
- Use this example to point out that students have practiced each skill described in the success criteria.

ELL Support

Have students practice language by reviewing the example. One student asks the other, "How many animals are orange? Which animals are orange?" Provide them with the needed vocabulary, such as snake, ladybug, tiger, frog, bird, fox, and cat. Then have them switch roles for the exercise with animals that have four legs. Provide similar vocabulary support.

Beginner students may answer using a number and naming the animals.

Intermediate and **Advanced** students may answer using sentences, such as, "Seven animals are orange. They are the snake, ladybug, tiger, frog, bird, fox, and cat."

Laurie's Notes

Think and Grow

Getting Started

- Students have already made *marks* on a *chart* to record the number of objects in two categories. If you have not shown the vocabulary cards for **chart** and **mark**, display and discuss them now.
- The design of the Think and Grow is different from what students are used to. The pictures at the top are used twice, once for the example done as a class, and once for students to work with on their own.

Teaching Notes

- Work through the first example with students. The categories are orange and not orange.
- **Model:** Name each animal from left to right and have students identify whether it is orange or not. Have students trace over one dashed mark for each animal under the correct category. Make sure not to cross out the animals as they are counted.
- Completing the chart and deciding which category has more objects involves multiple steps. Work through each step slowly.
- ? "How many animals are orange? How many animals are not orange?" Have students trace the numbers shown.
- Students decide which category has the greater number of animals and circle that number.
- ? **Reason Abstractly and Quantitatively:** "How else could you classify the animals into two categories?"
- **Supporting Learners:** Because this is the final time using the animals, students may find it helpful to cross out each animal, as they decide whether it has four legs or not four legs.
- Circulate as students work to record animals in each category. Students may think the frog has two hands and two legs. Ask students to talk aloud as they decide what category each animal belongs in.
- Some students may ask how many marks they can make in a row. They may have noticed in the first example that there are five marks and then two more below. Fine motor skills may be a problem. How students place their marks and what size they make them will vary by student.
- ⊙ "Explain to your partner how we compared the number of objects in two categories." As you solicit responses from students, connect their responses to each success criteria.

orange | not orange

4 legs | not 4 legs

7 | 8 | 9 | 6

Directions: Classify the animals into the categories shown. Write the marks in the chart. Count the marks and write the numbers to tell how many animals are in each category. Circle the number that is greater than the other number.

196   one hundred ninety-six

Meeting the needs of
all learners.

Laurie's Notes

Apply and Grow: Practice

MAKING INSTRUCTIONAL DECISIONS

Students may need guidance in completing all of the steps involved in comparing the number of objects in two categories. If the collection involved 6 crayons, 4 red and 2 that were not, the comparison would be easy. We are working with categorical data and trying to build an understanding of (1) how to classify the data into two categories, (2) identifying what objects belong in each category, (3) making a mark for each object counted, (4) counting how many are in each category, and (5) comparing the quantity in each category. Assessing where in the process students might be having difficulty takes time. Students working in groups benefit by helping one another.

EMERGING students may have difficulty classifying objects into categories, identifying the number of objects in each category, or comparing those numbers.

- Pair students, and work through one picture at a time. Describe what the object is and explain why it belongs in a certain category.
- Have students draw the ⊘ symbol on objects that cannot be classified into a specific category.
- Work with a smaller set of pictures.

PROFICIENT students are able to classify objects into categories and compare the number of objects in each category.

- Have students draw 10 objects that can be classified into two categories. Students can create a chart with categories that correspond to their objects. Have students trade papers with partners and complete.

Additional Support

- See page T-191 for a description of additional support. This time students draw a mark for each linking cube.

Name _____

1

4 legs	not 4 legs
5	**8**

2

beak	no beak
7	**6**

Directions: **1** and **2** Classify the animals into the categories shown. Write the marks in the chart. Count the marks and write the numbers to tell how many animals are in each category. Draw a line through the number that is less than the other number.

Chapter 4 | Lesson 5   one hundred ninety-seven   197

Think and Grow: Modeling Real Life

This application allows students to show that they can compare the number of objects in two categories. The second exercise extends this skill to three categories.

? Preview: Point to the side of the page. "What are all of these objects? How are they the same? How are they different?" You want students to observe that all of the objects are buttons. Some have two holes and some have four. There are three different colors of buttons.

? "I'm curious. Do you think there are more buttons with two holes or with four holes? How can we decide?" Listen for a student to say, "Make a chart."

? Construct Viable Arguments and Critique the Reasoning of Others: "Does it matter what color the buttons are when we classify them by the number of holes they have? Explain how you know." Give think time. Solicit explanations and ask others whether the explanations make sense.

- Teaching Tip: Display the page, if possible. Model how to keep track of which buttons have been counted. Cover each button with a small counter or make a mark through each button as they are counted.

- Remind or probe students for the steps as they use marks to show each button in a category, count how many are in a category, and compare the numbers to decide whether there are more buttons with two holes or four holes.

- Now read the directions for classifying by color. If students made a mark through the buttons when classifying by the number of holes, they can turn it into an X now.

- Some students will be able to count each color while other students may want to make a chart with marks.

- ⊙ Refer to the first button exercise and ask students to use their thumb signals to show how well they could decide whether the button had two or four holes, make a mark for each button, count how many were in each category, and decide which category had more. Repeating the steps helps all students become more comfortable with the multi-step process.

Closure

- Display a chart with marks in two categories, such as the number of days in two weeks that are sunny or not sunny, rainy or not rainy, or hot or not hot. Discuss the two categories. "Compare the two categories. Which one has less?"

 2 holes

 4 holes

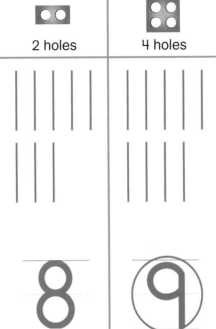

Directions:
- Classify the buttons into the categories shown. Write the marks in the chart. Count the marks and write the numbers to tell how many buttons are in each category. Circle the number that is greater than the other number.
- Classify the buttons by color. Count the number of buttons in each category. Write each number. Circle the numbers that are equal.

198   one hundred ninety-eight

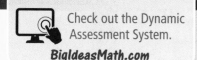

Connect and Extend Learning

Practice Notes

- Students may become distracted by the animals in the pictures so it is best to discuss the animals and categories before students begin working.
- **Exercise 1:** Students may tell you that sheep have horns. Acknowledge that some do have horns, but that they are to compare the sheep in the picture.
- **Exercises 2 and 3:** The frogs are classified in two different ways. First they are classified by spots and then by color. Remind students that they can cross out each animal as they write a mark in the chart.

Cross-Curricular Connections

Language Arts

- Write 5 to 10 common consonant-vowel-consonant words on the wall. Make sure some of the words begin with the same letter. Have students categorize the words in a chart. For example, if the words are cat, can, cup, cap, hat, and fan, then you make a chart with words that start with C on one side and words that do not start with C on the other side. Have students read and classify the words according to the chart. Then have them compare the numbers of objects in each category.

C words	C words
can	hat
cat	fan
cap	
cup	

Learning Target: Compare the numbers of objects in two categories.

blue	not blue
||||	||
4	2

Directions: Classify the animals into the categories shown. Write the marks in the chart. Count the marks and write the numbers to tell how many animals are in each category. Draw a line through the number that is less than the other number.

①

horns	no horns
|||	||||
3	4

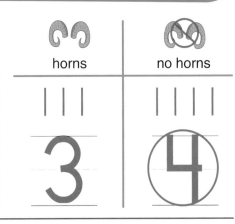

Directions: ① Classify the animals into the categories shown. Write the marks in the chart. Count the marks and write the numbers to tell how many animals are in each category. Circle the number that is greater than the other number.

© Big Ideas Learning, LLC

Chapter 4 | Lesson 5   one hundred ninety-nine   199

Connect and Extend Learning

Extend Student Learning

Logical-Mathematical

- Choose 6 to 10 students to come to the front of the classroom. Ask them yes or no questions about themselves such as "Is your favorite color pink?" Categorize the answers in a chart using marks. Count the marks and write the numbers. Call on students to compare the numbers of marks. Repeat this process with a new question and group of students.

Pink	Not Pink
3	5

Lesson Resources	
Surface Level	**Deep Level**
Resources by Chapter • Extra Practice • Reteach Differentiating the Lesson Skills Review Handbook Skills Trainer	Resources by Chapter • Enrichment and Extension Graphic Organizers Dynamic Assessment System • Lesson Practice

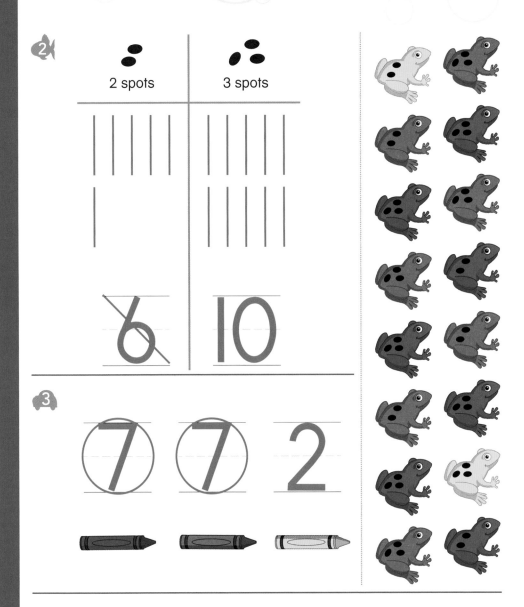

2 spots	3 spots
⑥	10

⑦ ⑦ 2

Directions: ② Classify the frogs into the categories shown. Write the marks in the chart. Count the marks and write the numbers to tell how many frogs are in each category. Draw a line through the number that is less than the other number.
③ Classify the frogs by color. Count the number of frogs in each category. Write each number. Circle the numbers that are equal.

Performance Task

In this task, students demonstrate their understanding of the comparison words.

- Decide ahead of time whether students will be working independently, in pairs, or in groups.
- Pause between direction lines for students to complete each step.
- Have students share their work and thinking with others. Discuss as a class.

Exercise	Answers and Notes	Points
1	7; 7; circle the thumbs up	3
2	nine tally marks; eight tally marks; circle around the green toys category	3
3	a number less than 7; include work (drawings) to show the number	2
	Total	8

Performance Task 4

①  7 • 7 👍 👎

②
green	not green
‖‖‖ ‖|	‖‖‖ ‖|‖

⑨ 8

③ *Sample answer:*

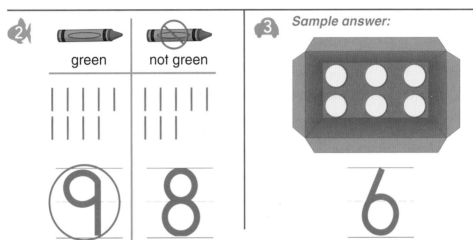

6

Directions: ① Count the toys in each group. Write each number. Is the number of spring toys equal to the number of balls? Circle the thumbs up for *yes* or the thumbs down for *no.* ② Classify the toys into the categories shown. Write the marks in the chart. Count the marks and write the numbers to tell how many toys are in each category. Circle the number that is greater than the other number. ③ More balls are delivered in a box. The number of balls in the box is less than the number of balls in the picture. Draw the balls in the box. Write the number of balls in the box.

Chapter 4   two hundred one 201

Laurie's Notes

Toss and Compare

Materials

- 1 two-color counter per student
- 1 Toss and Compare Numbers from 0-10 Recording Sheet* per pair of students

* Found in the Instructional Resources

Students can work in pairs or small groups.

? "What do you see on the Toss and Compare game board?" numbers and dot patterns showing the numbers 0 to 10

- Hand out a two-color counter and a Toss and Compare Numbers from 0–10 Recording Sheet to each pair or group.
- Read the directions at the bottom of the page. Model how to gently toss a counter to keep it from rolling off the game board. Let students know that when their counter rolls off of the page, they can toss it again.
- When game play concludes, focus the discussion on the students' reasoning about which number was greater.

? **Attend to Precision:** "How did you know which number was greater?" use the number path; count to the greater number; compare the written numbers

? "What number did you choose when your counter landed on Newton or Descartes?" 10 "Why did you choose 10?" It is the greatest number.

- **Supporting Learners:** Give students manipulatives to build each number.
- **Supporting Learners:** Allow students to draw dots on the Toss and Compare Numbers from 0–10 Recording Sheet to help them determine which number is greater.

Closure

- "How did you compare two numbers when one was written and one was drawn as a dot pattern?" I counted the dots and wrote that number. Then I used the number path to compare the two numbers; I drew dots for the written number. Then I matched the dots to find which number was greater.

Toss and Compare

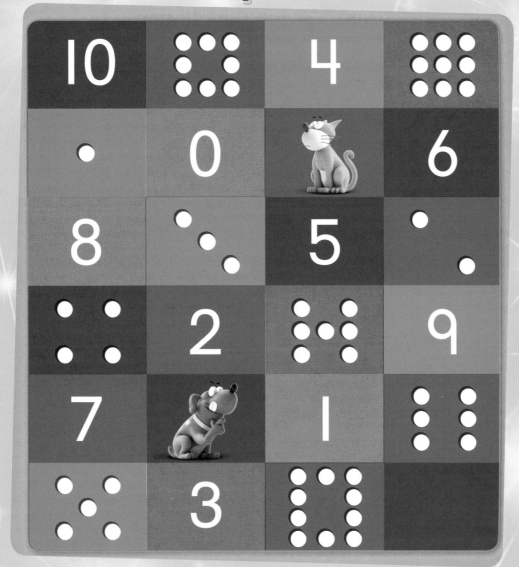

Directions: Take turns tossing a counter onto the board. If the counter lands on Newton or Descartes, choose any number from 0 to 10. Write the numbers on your Toss and Compare Numbers from 0 to 10 Recording Sheet. Circle the number that is greater than the other number. Circle both numbers if they are equal. Repeat this process until you fill your sheet.

© Big Ideas Learning, LLC

Learning Target Correlation

Lesson	Learning Target	Exercises
4.1	Use matching to compare the numbers of objects in two groups.	1–3
4.2	Use counting to compare the numbers of objects in two groups.	4–6
4.3	Compare two numbers	7–9
4.4	Tell whether objects belong or do not belong in a category.	10
4.5	Compare the numbers of objects in two categories.	11

Name _____

4.1 Compare Groups to 10 by Matching

I–3. Sample answers are given.

1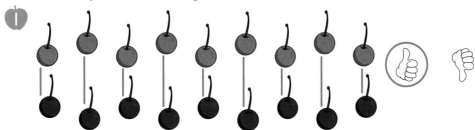

2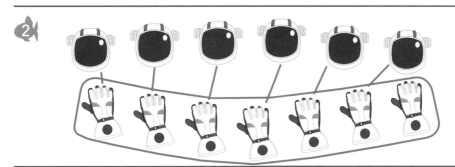

3

Directions: Draw lines between the objects in each group.
1 Is the number of red cherries equal to the number of black cherries? Circle the thumbs up for *yes* or the thumbs down for *no.* **2** Circle the group that is greater in number than the other group. **3** Draw a line through the group that is less in number than the other group.

Chapter 4 two hundred three 203

© Big Ideas Learning, LLC

Chapter Resources

Surface Level	Deep Level	Transfer Level
Resources by Chapter • Extra Practice • Reteach Differentiating the Lesson Skills Review Handbook Skills Trainer Game Library Math Musicals	Resources by Chapter • Enrichment and Extension Graphic Organizers Game Library Math Musicals	Dynamic Assessment System • Chapter Test Assessment Book • Chapter Tests A and B

(4.2) Compare Groups to 10 by Counting

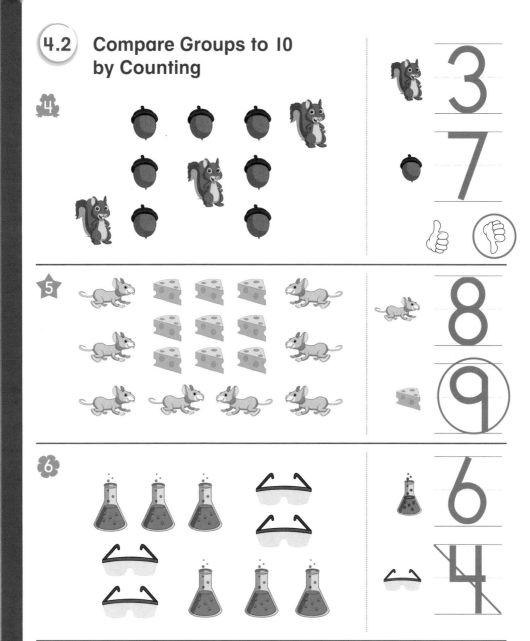

4

3

7

👍 (👎)

5

8

(9)

6

6

~~4~~

Directions: Count the objects in each group. Write each number.
4 Is the number of squirrels equal to the number of acorns? Circle the thumbs up for *yes* or the thumbs down for *no*. **5** Circle the number that is greater than the other number. **6** Draw a line through the number that is less than the other number.

4.3 Compare Numbers to 10

7 7

7

(thumbs up, circled) (thumbs down)

8 *Sample answer:*

2 ○○

(10) ○○○○○○○○○

Sample answer:

9 6 ○○○○○○

9 ○○○○○○○○

Directions: Compare the numbers. **7** Are the numbers equal? Circle the thumbs up for *yes* or the thumbs down for *no*. **8** Circle the number that is greater than the other number. Draw to show how you know. **9** Draw a line through the number that is less than the other number. Draw to show how you know.

Chapter 4

two hundred five **205**

4.4 Classify Objects into Categories

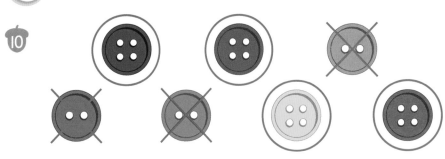

4.5 Classify and Compare by Counting

Directions: 🔟 Circle the buttons that have 4 holes. Cross out the buttons that do *not* have 4 holes. 🏛 Classify the animals into the categories shown. Write the marks in the chart. Count the marks and write the numbers to tell how many animals are in each category. Circle the number that is greater than the other number.

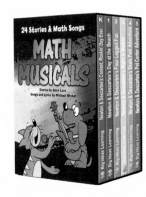

Math Musicals can be used with current topics, to review previous topics, or to preview upcoming topics.

Centers

Center 1: Toss and Compare

Materials: Student Edition page 202, Toss and Compare Numbers from 0–10 Recording Sheet per pair*, 1 two-color counter per student

Have students complete the Toss and Compare activity. See page T-202 for the directions.

Center 2: Skills Trainer

Materials: computers or devices with Internet access

Have students go to *BigIdeasMath.com* to access the Skills Trainer.

Center 3: Bear Match-Up

Materials per pair: Number Paths 1–10*, Number Cards 0–10*, 10 paper clips, 20 bear counters, 1 whiteboard, and 1 dry-erase marker

Each student chooses a number card and puts that number of bears on a number path. Student A places a paper clip between each match. Student B writes both numbers on the whiteboard. Students can use the terms *greater than*, *less than*, or *equal* to describe the numbers.

Center 4: Number Path Clip

Materials per pair: Number Paths 1–10*, Number Cards 0–10*, 2 clothespins, 2 whiteboards, and 2 dry-erase markers

Students take turns choosing a number card and placing a clothespin on that number on the number path. Each student writes both numbers on a whiteboard. Have students circle the number that is greater and draw a line through the number that is less. Have students clap when numbers are equal.

Center 5: Compare Lion Cards

Materials: Lion Cards 5–10* per pair, Lion Cards Recording Sheet* per student

Each student chooses a lion card and both students write the numbers on their recording sheets. Have students use their thumb signals to tell whether the numbers are equal. Students can circle the number that is greater or draw a line through the number that is less.

*Found in the Instructional Resources

Chapter Assessment Guide

Chapter tests are available in the Assessment Book.
An alternative assessment option is listed below.

Logical-Mathematical

Call students over individually or in small groups. Put paper
clips, one blue bear, three yellow bears, and five red bears in
front of each student. Students will classify the bears into two
color categories. Give wait time for students to identify the color
categories before telling them to classify them as red or not red.
Use a whiteboard with a line down the middle as a sorting area
and chart.

Ask students, "What strategy can you use to compare the bears?"
Listen for students to say they used the paper clips or paired the
bears. Students may also count and write the number to explain
how to compare the bears. Be sure to watch for students to model
these strategies. Some students may have trouble explaining.

"Tell me how the two numbers of bears in each group compare."
Listen for students to compare each group of bears using the
terms *equal*, *greater than*, or *less than*.

Give students another grouping of bears to compare using a
different strategy.

Task	Points
Students compare the numbers of objects using the terms *equal*, *greater than*, and *less than*.	1 point per term; 3 points total
Students can compare the numbers of objects by classifying objects into categories, matching groups of objects, and counting and comparing numerals.	1 point per strategy; 3 points total
Total	6 points

My Thoughts on the Chapter

What worked...

What did not work...

What I would do differently...

Teacher Tip

Not allowed to write in your teaching edition? Use sticky notes to record your thoughts.

Learning Target Correlation

Exercise	Lesson	Learning Target
1	1.3	Show and count the numbers 3 and 4.
2	1.7	Understand, name, and write the number 0.
3	4.3	Compare two numbers.
4	4.4	Tell whether objects belong or do not belong in a category.
5	1.8	Count and order numbers to 5.
6	3.3	Show and count the number 7.
7	3.7	Show and count the number 9.
8	3.2	Understand and write the number 6.
9	4.1	Use matching to compare the numbers of objects in two groups.
10	2.4	Use counting to compare the numbers of objects in two groups.
11	2.3	Show and tell whether one group has a lesser number of objects than another group.
12	2.1	Show and tell whether two groups are equal in number.

Name _____

1

○
○
●
○

2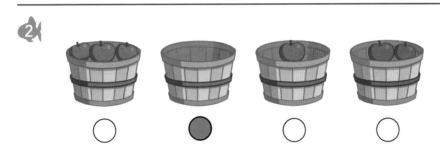

○ ● ○ ○

3

8

● 9
○ 8
○ 0
○ 6

Directions: Shade the circle next to the answer. **1** Which five frame shows the number of puzzle pieces? **2** Which basket has 0 apples? **3** Which number is greater than 8?

© Big Ideas Learning, LLC

Chapter 4

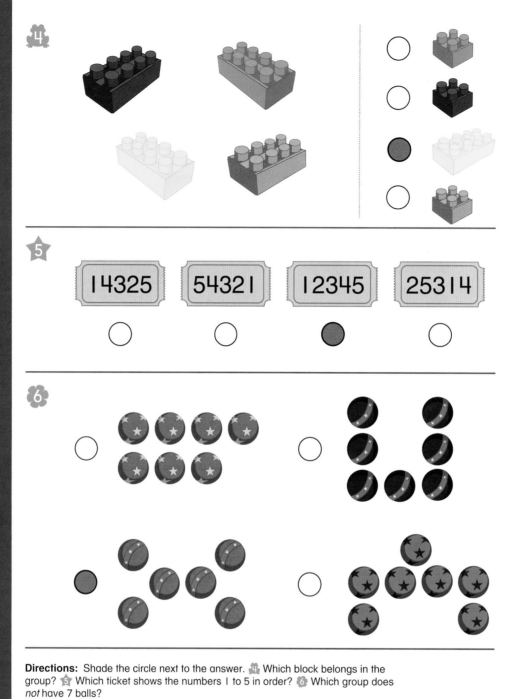

Directions: Shade the circle next to the answer. 🐸 Which block belongs in the group? ⭐ Which ticket shows the numbers 1 to 5 in order? 🌼 Which group does *not* have 7 balls?

208   two hundred eight

© Big Ideas Learning, LLC

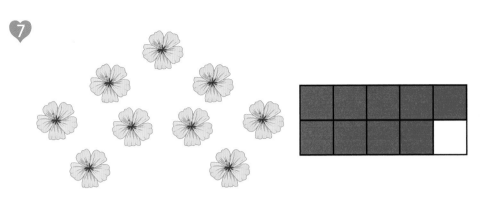

Sample answer:

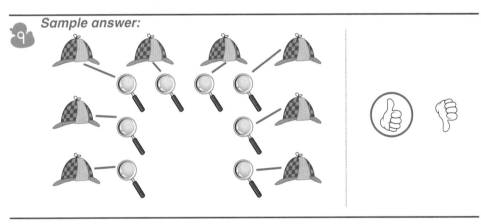

Directions: ⑦ Count the flowers. Color the boxes to show how many. ⑧ Count the salamanders. Say the number. Write the number. ⑨ Draw lines between the objects in each group. Is the number of detective hats equal to the number of magnifying glasses? Circle the thumbs up for *yes* or the thumbs down for *no*.

© Big Ideas Learning, LLC

Chapter 4

two hundred nine   209

Sample answer:

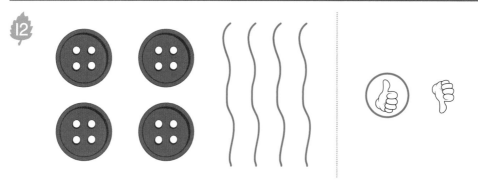

Directions: 🐿 Count the objects in each group. Write each number. Circle the number that is greater than the other number. 🏠 Draw lines between the objects in each group. Draw a line through the group that is less in number than the other group. 🍂 Draw 4 pieces of string. Is the number of pieces of string equal to the number of buttons? Circle the thumbs up for *yes* or the thumbs down for *no*.

5 Compose and Decompose Numbers to 10

Chapter Overview

Lesson	Learning Target	Success Criteria
5.1 Partner Numbers to 5	Use partner numbers to show numbers to 5.	• Name each part. • Name the whole. • Name the partner numbers for a whole.
5.2 Use Number Bonds to Represent Numbers to 5	Use number bonds to show the parts and the whole for numbers to 5.	• Model putting together the parts to show the whole. • Model taking apart the whole to show the parts. • Use a number bond to show the parts and the whole.
5.3 Compose and Decompose 6	Use partner numbers to make and take apart the number 6.	• Name the parts and the whole. • Use a number bond to show the parts and the whole.
5.4 Compose and Decompose 7	Use partner numbers to make and take apart the number 7.	• Name the parts and the whole. • Use a number bond to show the parts and the whole.
5.5 Compose and Decompose 8	Use partner numbers to make and take apart the number 8.	• Name the parts and the whole. • Use a number bond to show the parts and the whole.
5.6 Compose and Decompose 9	Use partner numbers to make and take apart the number 9.	• Name the parts and the whole. • Use a number bond to show the parts and the whole.
5.7 Compose and Decompose 10	Use partner numbers to make and take apart the number 10.	• Name the parts and whole. • Use a number bond to show the parts and the whole.
5.8 Compose and Decompose Using a Group of 5	Use a group of 5 to put together and take apart numbers to 10.	• Name the whole. • Find a group of 5. • Name the partner numbers when one part is 5.

Chapter Learning Target:
Understand partner numbers.
Chapter Success Criteria:
▢ Identify the parts and the whole.
▢ Name partner numbers.
▨ Compare parts of numbers.
▨ Model taking apart numbers.

Progressions

Through the Grades	
Kindergarten	**Grade 1**
• Represent addition and subtraction with various models and strategies. • Decompose numbers less than or equal to 10 into pairs in more than one way.	• Represent, write, and solve "Add To" and "Put Together" problems with unknowns. • Write and solve addition number sentences. • Solve addition word problems. • Represent, write, and solve "Take From" and "Take Apart" problems with unknowns. • Write and solve subtraction number sentences. • Solve subtraction word problems. • Solve addition and subtraction comparison problems.

Standard	Through the Chapter							
	5.1	**5.2**	**5.3**	**5.4**	**5.5**	**5.6**	**5.7**	**5.8**
Represent addition and subtraction with objects, fingers, mental images, drawings, sounds, acting out situations, verbal explanations, expressions, or equations.	●	●	●	●	●	●	●	●
Decompose numbers less than or equal to 10 into pairs in more than one way, e.g., by using objects or drawings, and record each decomposition by a drawing or equation.	●	●	●	●	●	●	●	●

Key: ▲ = Preparing   ● = Learning   ★ = Complete

Laurie's Overview

About the Math

Students developed their number sense by counting and comparing numbers to 10. In this chapter, students deepen their number sense by identifying pairs of numbers that are embedded or "hidden" within a number. Understanding how numbers can be put together and taken apart is the beginning of thinking about addition and subtraction. These operations are *not* the focus of this chapter, and hence the vocabulary we use needs to be precise. We want the learning in this chapter to help students think of putting together two groups of objects (composing) and taking apart a group of objects (decomposing).

Arrangements of 3:

The concept of embedded or hidden numbers is introduced in the first section along with partner numbers and the part-part-whole relationship.

Embedded Numbers in 3:

2 and 1 Parts

3 Whole

Students should be familiar with two different arrangements for the number 3; the triangular pattern and a linear array. When we use a vertical line to separate 3 into two groups, or we use two colors of counters or linking cubes, students may see the number 3 as being composed by two numbers, 2 and 1. This is when we introduce partner numbers. Three has no two pairs of distinct partner numbers, 0 and 3, and 1 and 2. Sometimes a set of partner numbers is "hidden" within the whole. Other times the parts can be easily identified as two separate groups. Students need an understanding of embedded numbers and partner numbers before they formally learn to add and subtract. Remember, we want students to develop fluency with addition and subtraction to 5 by the end of the year so pay special attention to the partner numbers for numbers to 5.

To support student learning and to facilitate discussion of patterns, consider using an anchor chart to record the partner numbers for each number within 10. Add the partner numbers to the chart each time a different number is introduced. If wall space allows,

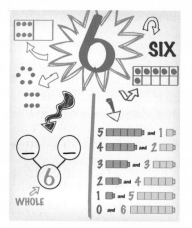

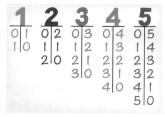

have an anchor chart for each number and include different arrangements and subitizing images along with a list of partner numbers. Alternately, list only the partner numbers. The anchor chart can be referred to during the lesson and viewed by students at any time.

Models

- A Number Bond is an important organizer that shows the relationship between a whole and its parts. The lines connecting the parts to the whole signify the composing relationship of putting together and the decomposing relationship of taking apart. The number bond is shown in four orientations throughout the chapter. Students learn to identify the parts and the whole regardless of how the number bond is shown. A part-part-whole mat can also be used to show this relationship.

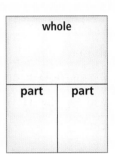

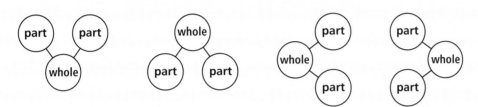

- Linking cubes are used often throughout this chapter to show the parts and the whole. You can use linking cube towers to show embedded partner numbers or show two smaller towers put together to make a whole.

- A dot and stick model is used to show various partner numbers by moving a stick between different dots. Students can make this model on a whiteboard and move their pencil to see all of the partner numbers for the whole.

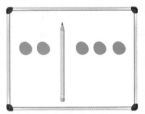

- Five and ten frames are used when working with the benchmarks of five and ten. Frames provide students with a visual of the different ways to make each number. Developing a mental benchmark and fluency with making five and ten helps students when they learn addition and subtraction strategies in later grades.

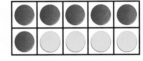

- A rekenrek is another model that can be used to show two parts that make a whole. Students see groups of five on a rekenrek because of the different colors of the beads. In this chapter, students recognize a group of five in a number 6 to 10 and identify the other partner number. This is known as the 5 + *n* pattern.

- Students also see a group of 5 on a number path.

  Students learn they can count on from 5 to the whole in order to find the missing partner number.

Chapter Materials and Resources

The primary materials and resources needed for this chapter are listed below. Other materials may be needed for the additional support ideas provided throughout the chapter.

Check out the virtual manipulatives.
BigIdeasMath.com

Classroom Materials	Chapter Opener	5.1	5.2	5.3	5.4	5.5	5.6	5.7	5.8	Connect and Grow
scissors	•									
two-color counters		•	•	•	•	•	•	•	•	*
linking cubes			•	•	+		+			•
paper clips										*
dominoes										•
dry-erase marker and eraser										*
glue sticks										•
crayons										•

Instructional Resources	Chapter Opener	5.1	5.2	5.3	5.4	5.5	5.6	5.7	5.8	Connect and Grow
Vocabulary Cards	•	+	+							
Number Bond					•					•
Number Bond Draw and Write					•					
Number Cards 0–5										*
Number Cards 5–10										*
Fishy Number Bonds										•
Fishy Number Bond Cards										•

• class set   + teacher only   * per pair/group

Suggested Pacing

Day 1	Chapter Opener	Performance Task Preview		Vocabulary			
Day 2	Lesson 5.1	Warm-Up	Dig In	Explore	Think	Apply: Practice	Think: Modeling Real Life
Day 3	Lesson 5.2	Warm-Up	Dig In	Explore	Think	Apply: Practice	Think: Modeling Real Life
Day 4	Lesson 5.3	Warm-Up	Dig In	Explore	Think	Apply: Practice	Think: Modeling Real Life
Day 5	Lesson 5.4	Warm-Up	Dig In	Explore	Think	Apply: Practice	Think: Modeling Real Life
Day 6	Lesson 5.5	Warm-Up	Dig In	Explore	Think	Apply: Practice	Think: Modeling Real Life
Day 7	Lesson 5.6	Warm-Up	Dig In	Explore	Think	Apply: Practice	Think: Modeling Real Life
Day 8	Lesson 5.7	Warm-Up	Dig In	Explore	Think	Apply: Practice	Think: Modeling Real Life
Day 9	Lesson 5.8	Warm-Up	Dig In	Explore	Think	Apply: Practice	Think: Modeling Real Life
Day 10	Connect And Grow	Performance Task		Activity		Chapter Practice	
Day 11		Centers					
Day 12	Chapter Assessment	Chapter Assessment					

Year-to-Date: 57 Days

Performance Task Preview

- Get students ready and excited about the chapter by discussing any prior knowledge they may have about butterflies. Give students time to look carefully at the picture and share their experiences with the class.

? "What type of insect do you see? Raise your hand if you have ever seen a butterfly. What colors are the butterflies?" These colors should be a review for students and color is an attribute that will be used to classify objects in this chapter.

? "How many butterflies are in the picture? How many butterflies are on the flower? How many are flying?" Listen for students to say that one butterfly plus one more butterfly makes two butterflies.

- In the Performance Task at the end of the chapter, students will use number bonds to classify insects in different ways.

5 Compose and Decompose Numbers to 10

- **How many butterflies are in the picture?** 2
- **How many butterflies are on the flower?** 1
  How many are flying?

Chapter Learning Target:
Understand partner numbers.

Chapter Success Criteria:
- I can identify the parts and the whole.
- I can name partner numbers.
- I can compare parts of numbers.
- I can model taking apart numbers.

© Big Ideas Learning, LLC

two hundred eleven   211

Laurie's Notes

Vocabulary Review

? **Preview:** "What do you see in the picture? Have you ever seen more than one squirrel at a time?" Repeat this question for the pigeons. "Where are the animals in the picture?"

- **Teaching Tip:** Have students trace the edge of the picture with their finger to remind them not to count the pigeon and squirrel next to the writing lines.

- Read each direction line one at a time. Have students count the animals in each group and write the numbers. Next, draw a line through the number that is less than the other number.

- **Extension:** Have students draw to make the number of squirrels greater than the number of pigeons.

Chapter 5 Vocabulary

Activity

- **Show and Tell:** Students lay their vocabulary cards in front of them with the picture side facing up. Show students a vocabulary card, say the word, and describe the picture definition. Students should find the corresponding card and then take turns showing the card and telling a partner about the word and its picture definition.

- **Supporting Learners:** Limit the number of cards the students lay out in front of them.

MATH MUSICALS

Math Musicals can be used with current topics, to review previous topics, or to preview upcoming topics. There are many *Math Musicals* to choose from!

Use your hand puppets to act out new stories and have students sing the songs several times to take full advantage of the power of music to learn math!

5 Vocabulary

 5   **3**

Directions: Count the animals in each group. Write each number.
Draw a line through the number that is less than the other number.

number bond	part
partner numbers	put together
take apart	whole

© Big Ideas Learning, LLC

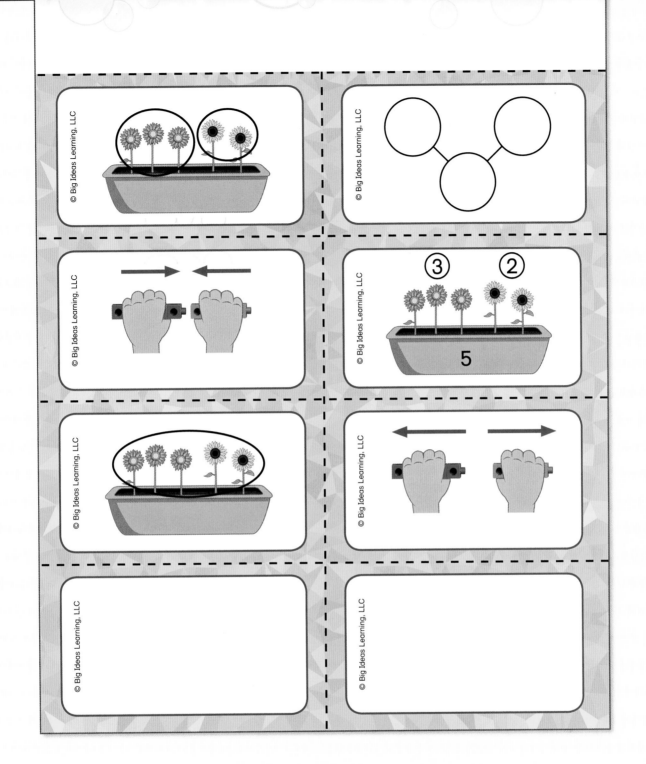

Learning Target

Use partner numbers to show numbers to 5.

Success Criteria

- Name each part.
- Name the whole.
- Name the partner numbers for a whole.

Warm-Up

Practice opportunities for the following are available in the Resources by Chapter or at *BigIdeasMath.com*.

- Daily skills
- Vocabulary
- Prerequisite skills

ELL Support

Explain that the word whole means "all of the group" when referring to groups that are being counted. Students may be familiar with the word hole, which sounds the same, but means something different— an empty space. The word part refers to only some of the things in the group, not the whole group. Students may be familiar with car parts or toy parts. Point out that these parts, together with all of the others, make up the whole car or toy.

Laurie's Notes

Preparing to Teach

Students may be able to count a group of six objects and understand the counting sequence, but that does not mean they know that six can be thought of as having two or more parts. The part-part-whole relationship is very important in developing number sense and beginning addition concepts. In this section, students identify the whole and the parts that make up the whole for numbers to 5. Students conceptually subitize when they see two smaller groups within a group. Once students can visualize the parts and the whole, they can identify all the partner numbers that are embedded within a number.

Materials

- two-color counters

Dig In (Circle Time)

Draw a row of three dots on a chart or the board. Have students tell how many dots they see.

- Place a pencil or popsicle stick between the first and second dots. Have students identify the number of dots on each side of the stick.
- "The numbers 1 and 2 were hidden inside the number 3!" Relate the terms *parts* and *whole* to the demonstration. "One and two are parts, and three is the whole."
- Continue moving the stick between different dots as students identify the parts as you add the partner numbers for 3 to the anchor chart. Be sure to include combinations with 0.
- Repeat the steps for the number 2.
- You can have students use their fingers to show the different sets of partner numbers.
- ◉ In this short activity students have been introduced to the three success criteria.

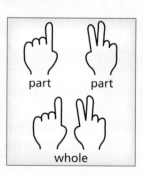

❓ Teaching Prompt   ◉ Learning Target

Learning Target: Use partner numbers to show numbers to 5.

Explore and Grow

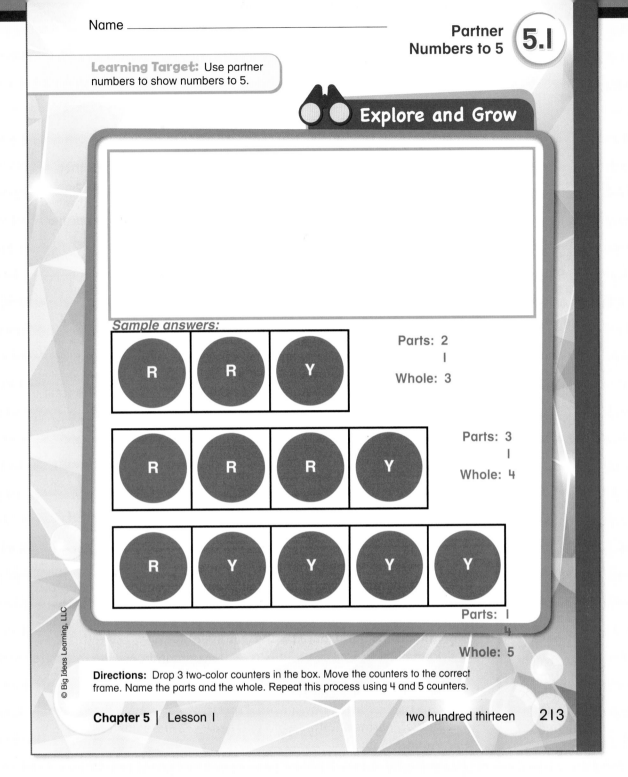

Sample answers:

R	R	Y

Parts: 2
1
Whole: 3

R	R	R	Y

Parts: 3
1
Whole: 4

R	Y	Y	Y	Y

Parts: 1
4
Whole: 5

Directions: Drop 3 two-color counters in the box. Move the counters to the correct frame. Name the parts and the whole. Repeat this process using 4 and 5 counters.

Chapter 5 | Lesson 1

two hundred thirteen 213

Explore and Grow

- Pass out two-color counters. Have students put three counters in their hands, shake, and then drop the counters in the box.
- "Move your counters to the frame with three boxes."
- Discuss how many counters show red, how many show yellow, and how many counters they dropped. Listen to conversations to gauge students' understanding of parts and whole. These are partner numbers for 3.
- Repeat the process for four and five counters. Ask several students to share their partner numbers for the wholes, 4 and 5.

Laurie's Notes

Think and Grow

Getting Started

- Introduce the vocabulary cards for whole, part, and partner numbers. Students may think of parts of a bicycle, orange, or toy set. Refer to the model of 3 (the whole) that had the numbers 1 and 2 (parts) hidden in it. One and two are partner numbers for the whole three.
- Remind students that you want to hear them use these words as they work with their partners today.

Teaching Notes

- Students count and write the numbers for the parts and the whole.
- Model: "Tell your partner what you notice about the counters." Listen for four counters, three are red and one is yellow. Students record the number of each color (parts) and the total (whole).
- Reason Abstractly and Quantitatively: You want students to recognize that there are other partner numbers for 4. The two-color counters suggest partner numbers 3 and 1. Return to the number 4 later. Do students understand that 2 and 2 are also partner numbers for 4?
- Extension: Expect some students to recognize the order of 3 and 1 or 4 and 0 can be reversed in terms of color. Although it is not taught in Kindergarten, some students may make the connection to the Commutative Property.
- ◉ As students are working on the exercises, continue to refer to the success criteria. "There are three cats. The *whole* is 3. There is one yellow cat and there are two black cats. The *parts* are 1 and 2, and 1 and 2 are partner numbers for 3."
- In the last exercise students may be confused because there are no brown rabbits to count. Explain that zero can be a partner number.
- ? Extension: "Imagine you see a group of five red counters. What hidden partner numbers do you see?" *Sample answer*: 1 and 4, 2 and 3, 0 and 5
- Supporting Learners: Students may try to compare the quantities of each part. Make sure students understand they are identifying the parts and the whole.
- Supporting Learners: Students prepare for fluency with addition and subtraction by developing conceptual subitizing with numbers to 5.

ELL Support

Teach the names of animals shown on the page if necessary. Have students work in pairs to practice verbal language. Have one ask the other "How many yellow cats/black cats are there? How many total cats are there?" Then have them switch roles, using the words grey rabbits and brown rabbits. Have them use the words total rabbits for the total. Remind them that when they talk about one animal, they should say "there is" and when they talk about zero or more than one they should say, "there are."

Beginner students may only state the answer using numbers alone.
Intermediate students may answer with a number and the object counted, such as, "one yellow cat."
Advanced students may answer with a complete sentence, such as, "There is one yellow cat."

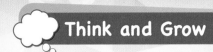
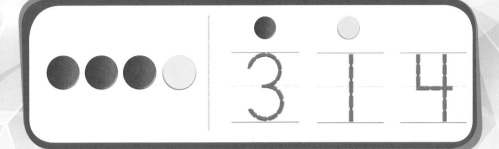

3 1 4

1 2 3

5 0 5

Directions: Count each type of object. Write each number. Count all of the objects. Write the number for the whole.

214 two hundred fourteen

MATH MUSICALS

Use the story *Cool Cats & Rockin' Dogs* from the book *Newton & Descartes's Coolest, Rockin' Day Ever* to reinforce partner numbers! In this story, Newton and Descartes invite the Cool Cats and Rockin' Dogs over to play some music. Using partner numbers, they realize there are 5 Cool Cats and 5 Rockin' Dogs! Turn to Appendix A for the music and lyrics to the songs *Cool Cats* and *Rockin' Dogs and Cool Cats*.

Cool Cats   *Rockin' Dogs and Cool Cats*

Meeting the needs of
all learners.

Laurie's Notes

Apply and Grow: Practice
SCAFFOLDING INSTRUCTION

This section of Laurie's Notes changes in this chapter to reflect students' increased number sense development. It also responds to needed scaffolding for students as they interact with the content. Support and extensions are now offered for targeted exercises.

EMERGING students may have difficulty with identifying part-part-whole relationships or understanding that there are different partner numbers for a given number.

- **Exercises 1–3:** "What hidden partner numbers are easy to see on the page? The hidden numbers are the *parts* of the *whole* collection of objects."
- **Exercises 1–3:** Review how to find each part that makes up the whole by using two-color counters to place over the animals. Use the red side of the counters for one kind of animal and the yellow side of the counters for the other.

PROFICIENT students are able to use partner numbers to identify part-part-whole relationships for numbers to 5.

- The exercises on this page model the problems on the previous page.
- **Exercises 1–3:** "How can you group the objects to show a different set of partner numbers?"

Additional Support

- Provide each student with the Part-Part-Whole Mat Instructional Resource to use with counters as they work on each exercise.
- Have students work with five frames and two-color counters to find the partner numbers that make 5.

Extension: Adding Rigor

- Play "Counter Drop." Have partners lay a sheet of paper on the floor. Have one student turn around while the other student drops five counters above the paper. This student announces the number of counters dropped and the number of counters that land on the paper. The other student must name the number of counters that did not land on the paper. Then have students look at the counters and say, "_____ and _____ are partner numbers for five. Five is the whole."

Name _____

 ❶

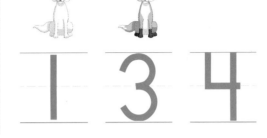

1   3   4

❷

3   2   5

❸

3   0   3

Directions: ❶ – ❸ Count each type of animal. Write each number. Count all of the animals. Write the number for the whole.

Chapter 5 │ Lesson 1   two hundred fifteen   215

Laurie's Notes

Think and Grow: Modeling Real Life

This application allows students to show their understanding of partner numbers to 5. Students use their understanding of part and whole to show different sets of partner numbers.

- **Preview:** "Have you ever seen a ladybug before?" Allow students to share their experiences with the class. Listen for knowledge of spots on a ladybug.
- **Think Time:** "How can you draw four spots on the two wings of a ladybug?" Once students have thought about their response, they should draw the spots.
- **Common Error:** Watch for students who draw four spots on each wing. Remind them the ladybug has only four dots. Four is the whole. What are partner numbers for four?
- **Turn and Talk:** Have partners use their ladybugs to name the parts and the whole. Listen for the language of partner numbers.
- ◉ Choose several students to share their partner numbers. Refer to the anchor chart to review the different sets of partner numbers for 4. Also have students use their thumb signals to show how confident they are in knowing what parts, whole, and partner numbers are.
- Students now draw and write two different sets of partner numbers for five.
- ❓ **Look for and Make Use of Structure:** "Is there more than one way to make the number 5? How do you know?"
- ❓ **Extension:** "What are two sets of partner numbers for 2?" 1 and 1; 2 and 0
- **Supporting Learners:** Students can use counters to practice the different partner numbers for numbers to 5.
- **Supporting Learners:** Some students may be able to visualize the different partner numbers for a whole. Have students verbalize their method of finding partner numbers, as others may benefit from hearing alternative methods.

Closure

- Choose one student to name a number from 1 to 5. Have the remaining students use their fingers to show a set of partner numbers that makes the whole. Students can show and discuss the various partner numbers for each whole.

Sample answer:

2  2

Sample answer:

2  3

4  1

© Big Ideas Learning, LLC

Directions:
- Show one way to draw 4 spots on the ladybug. Write the number of spots on each wing.
- Show two ways to draw 5 spots on the ladybug. Write the number of spots on each wing.

216   two hundred sixteen

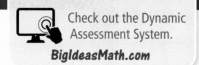
Connect and Extend Learning

Practice Notes

- **Exercise 4:** Students may have difficulty with the number zero. Monitor them as they work on the exercise that involve zero.

Cross-Curricular Connections

Language Arts

- *Fish Eyes: A Book You Can Count On* by Lois Ehlert; Read the book to the students up to the page that says: "4 striped fish plus me makes 5." (We will finish the book when we get to number 10 later in the chapter.) Students can now create their own "Fish Number Book." Give each student 2 pieces of paper. Students should draw partner numbers for 2, 3, 4, and 5, one pair on each side of the papers. If desired, have students create a cover for their "Fish Number Book."

Name _____

Learning Target: Use partner numbers to show numbers to 5.

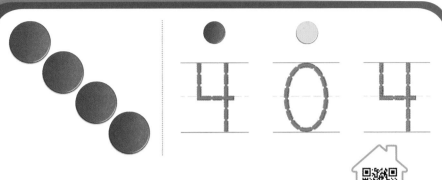

4   0   4

Directions: Count each type of object. Write each number. Count all of the objects. Write the number for the whole.

1   1   2

2   2   4

Directions: ① and ② Count each type of object. Write each number. Count all of the objects. Write the number for the whole.

Chapter 5 | Lesson 1   two hundred seventeen   217

Connect and Extend Learning

Extend Student Learning

Interpersonal

- Make 5 Matching Game;
  Each pair of students needs a set of matching cards. (Create a card that has 1 object, such as 1 star. Create another card that has 4 stars. That makes one pair of matching cards. Make several of these pairs of cards that equal 5 objects.) Shuffle and place the cards face down in two equal rows. Partner A turns over two cards. If the total of the objects on both cards is 5, Partner A collects both cards. If not, Partner A turns them back over. Repeat for Partner B.

  Variation: Provide each partner with 5 counters to help them determine the missing part.

Lesson Resources	
Surface Level	**Deep Level**
Resources by Chapter • Extra Practice • Reteach Differentiating the Lesson Skills Review Handbook Skills Trainer Math Musicals	Resources by Chapter • Enrichment and Extension Graphic Organizers Math Musicals Dynamic Assessment System • Lesson Practice

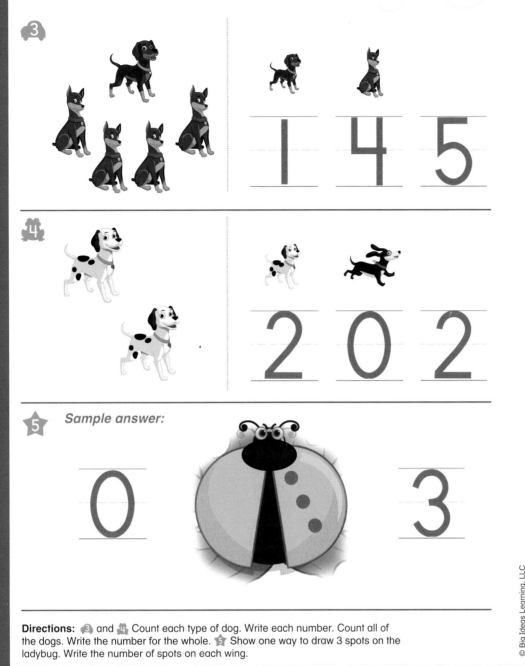

3

1 4 5

4

2 0 2

5 *Sample answer:*

0 3

Directions: **3** and **4** Count each type of dog. Write each number. Count all of the dogs. Write the number for the whole. **5** Show one way to draw 3 spots on the ladybug. Write the number of spots on each wing.

218   two hundred eighteen

© Big Ideas Learning, LLC

5.2

Learning Target
Use number bonds to show the parts and the whole for numbers to 5.

Success Criteria
- Model putting together the parts to show the whole.
- Model taking apart the whole to show the parts.
- Use a number bond to show the parts and the whole.

Warm-Up
Practice opportunities for the following are available in the Resources by Chapter or at *BigIdeasMath.com.*
- Daily skills
- Vocabulary
- Prerequisite skills

ELL Support
Explain that *to bond* means "to connect more than one thing." A bond is a type of connection that links things. A line is used for a number bond. Number bonds connect the numbers that represent parts of a group to the numbers that represent their whole group.

Laurie's Notes

Preparing to Teach
We introduce students to a number bond to show how to put together and take apart the parts and the whole. A number bond is an organizational tool that shows the relationship between the whole and its parts and corresponds to the additive relationship of composing.

The number bonds in this lesson will be oriented with two circles at the top (parts) and one circle below (whole). New orientations for the number bond are introduced in later lessons.

Materials
- two-color counters
- linking cubes

Dig In (Circle Time)
The circle time today models identifying partner numbers and the whole. You want to *put together* (compose) the partner numbers to make the whole, and *take apart* (decompose) the whole into the partner numbers. As you model with linking cubes, students can use their fingers.

? Show a group of 1 and a group of 3 linking cubes. "If I *put together* these parts, what is the whole?" 4 "Use your fingers to put 3 and 1 together."

? "If I *take apart* the number 4, what partner numbers could be hidden?" Have volunteers model their thinking with the linking cubes. When the parts 3 and 1 are demonstrated, say "So we can put together the parts 3 and 1 to make the whole 4, and we can take apart the whole 4 to make the parts 3 and 1." You are drawing attention to the inverse relationship of putting together and taking apart.

- Use an anchor chart to review the different sets of partner numbers for numbers within 5 as students model each set using their fingers.
- **Supporting Learners:** Students develop their conceptual subitizing skills by using counters to show each set of partner numbers for 5 on a five frame.
- **Supporting Learners:** Students draw a linear array of dots up to 5 on their whiteboard. Use a pencil to review the different sets of partner numbers.
- ? **Supporting Learners:** Show students the two linking cube towers. "How are the towers similar? How are they different?"

? Teaching Prompt   ◉ Learning Target

Learning Target: Use number bonds to show the parts and the whole for numbers to 5.

Explore and Grow

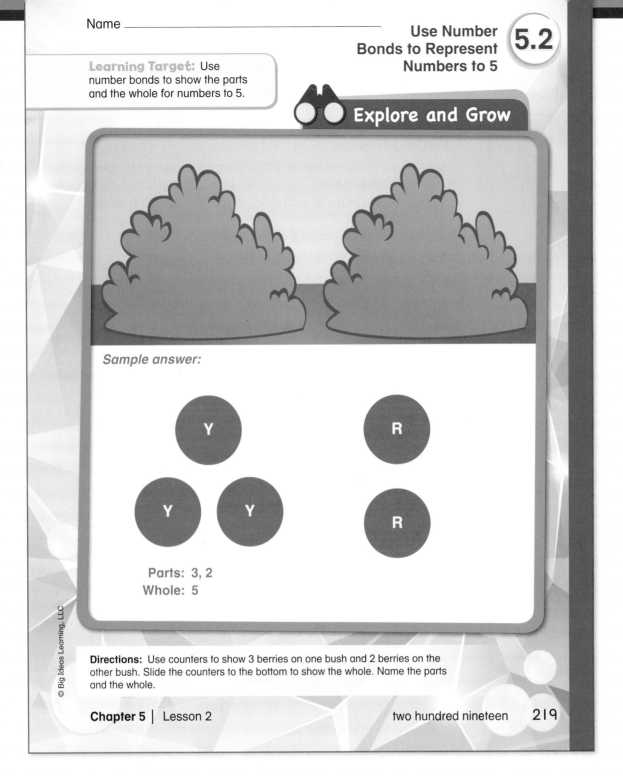

Sample answer:

Parts: 3, 2
Whole: 5

Directions: Use counters to show 3 berries on one bush and 2 berries on the other bush. Slide the counters to the bottom to show the whole. Name the parts and the whole.

Explore and Grow

- Pass out counters. "There are three berries on one bush and two berries on the other. Use counters to show the berries on each bush." Pause and check student work. "Use your fingers to show the number partners."
- ⊙ When students slide the counters to the bottom box, they can model putting together the parts to make the whole and taking apart the whole to show the parts. Students are demonstrating the first two success criteria.
- **Extension:** "Use your counters to show other partner numbers for 5."

Have students work in groups to complete the page after they do the first example as a class. Give them leading questions to work with, such as, "There are how many purple/green/total grapes?" Have students write the numbers in their own books after coming to an agreement with their group. Expect student discussion to be similar to the following descriptions.

Beginner students may only state the number that represents each group.
Intermediate students may answer with phrases, such as, "two purple grapes."
Advanced students may answer with a sentence, such as, "There are two purple grapes."

Think and Grow

Getting Started

- Introduce the vocabulary cards for **put together**, **take apart**, and **number bond**.
- Use the Number Bond Instructional Resource or sketch a number bond. Relate the terms *part, whole,* and *partner numbers* to the circles of the bond.
- Refer to an anchor chart as you fill in the bond for a number within 5. Choose a student to point to a circle on the bond as the class tells whether the circle shows a part or the whole.

Teaching Notes

- Students name the parts and whole and record in the number bond.
- **Model:** "Tell your partner what you notice about the counters." Listen for three counters, two are red and one is yellow. Students trace the numbers 2 and 1 (parts) and the number 3 (whole). Point out to students that there is a small symbol next to each circle to represent which part they are recording.
- **Attend to Precision:** Have students point to each circle of the number bond and describe what it shows.
- ⊙ Recording the parts and whole in a number bond is the third success criterion. As students work on the next two examples, use the vocabulary of the success criteria to describe the work they are doing.
- **?** **Make Sense of Problems:** "How do you know how many grapes are in the parts and how many grapes are in the whole?" Count each color of grape as the parts and all the grapes as the whole.
- **Supporting Learners:** Students may write the numbers in the wrong circles. Clarify what each circle on the number bond represents.
- **Supporting Learners:** Use the extension question to develop students' conceptual subitizing skills. This prepares them for fluently adding and subtracting within 5.
- **Extension:** "Imagine you see a group of four yellow counters. What hidden partner numbers do you see?" Students can tell the partner numbers, hold up fingers, or draw their answers.

Directions: Name the parts and the whole for the group. Then complete the number bond.

220   two hundred twenty

Laurie's Notes

Meeting the needs of
all learners.

Apply and Grow: Practice

SCAFFOLDING INSTRUCTION

A very big moment for students' number sense is to understand the embeddedness of numbers. This sets a foundation for the concepts of addition and subtraction and how numbers can be 'broken' apart.

EMERGING students may not recognize two distinct groups of objects, such as difference in color (red and black berries) or condition (whole and peeled bananas) of the objects. They may also not understand the part-part-whole concept.

Note: The questions and extensions below are used throughout Sections 5.2–5.7 due to the similar content of the lessons. There are slight modifications based on the change of number and orientation of the number bonds.

? **Exercises 1–3:** "What partner numbers are easy to see on the page?"

? **Exercise 1:** "Do you notice a difference in the colors of some of the berries?"

• **Exercises 1–3:** Walk students through how to complete the exercises. Ask specific questions that address the two different kinds of objects and where to write the quantity on the number bond.

• **Exercises 1–3:** Model with your two hands. Using both index fingers, point to the parts of the number bond and slide them together to make the whole.

PROFICIENT students are comfortable with the part-part-whole concept and can represent this concept correctly in a number bond.

• **Exercises 1–3:** Fill in the sentences, "___ and ___ are partner numbers for ___. _____ is the whole." 4, 1, 5, and five

? **Exercises 1–3:** "How can you group the objects to show a different set of partner numbers?"

Additional Support

• Create a number bond bracelet with five beads, string, and a piece of colored tape. String five beads together and tie a knot. Attach the colored tape like a tag and label with the number 5. Have students move the beads from side to side to show partner numbers for 5.

Extension: Adding Rigor

• Play *Flash Five.* Write the number 5 on the board. Tell students that 5 is the whole and that they will guess one of the partner numbers. Flash a subitizing card to the students. Say this number out loud and have students decide what partner number is missing to make 5.

Name _____

1

part: 4   part: 1
whole: 5

2

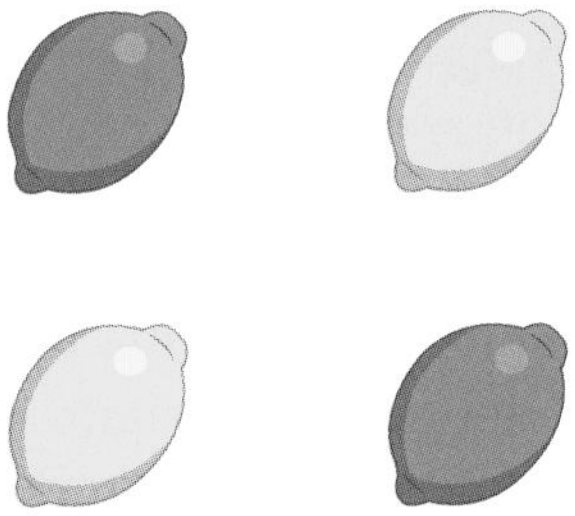

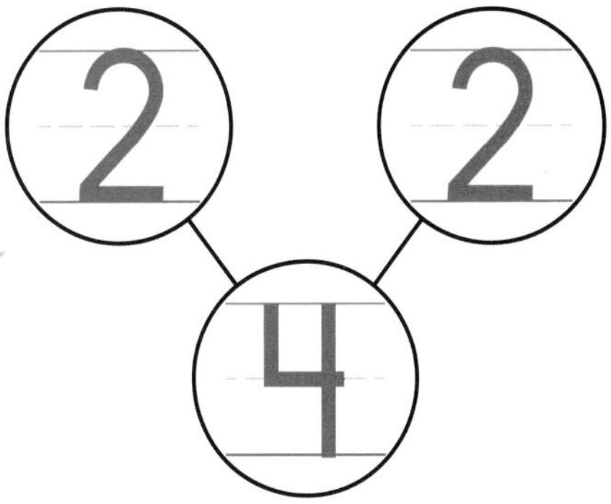

part: 2   part: 2
whole: 4

3

part: 1   part: 2
whole: 3

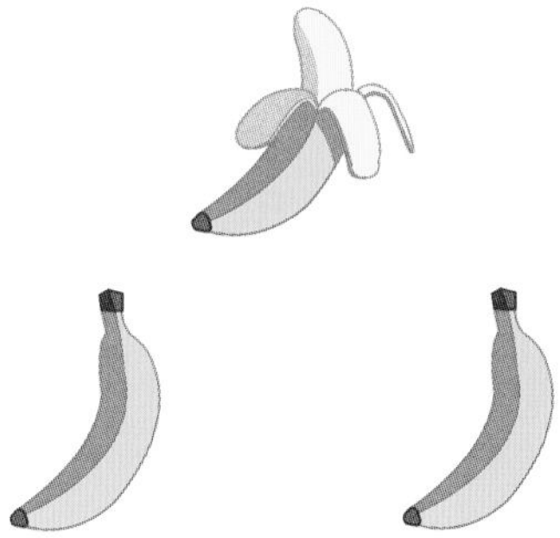

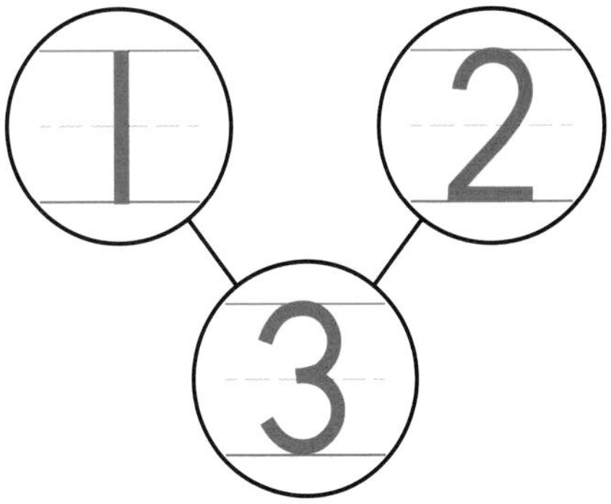

Directions: **1**–**3** Name the parts and the whole for the group. Then complete the number bond.

© Big Ideas Learning, LLC

Laurie's Notes

Think and Grow: Modeling Real Life

This application allows students to show the parts and the whole on a number bond. Encourage students to discuss the meaning and relationship of the numbers on each number bond.

- **Preview:** Have students discuss what they think they will show on each number bond. They may not think of a context for the problem but you should hear discussion of parts and whole.
- **?** "What might you see in a tree? Tell your partner." *Sample answers:* birds, leaves, bugs, branches, apples, cherries, fruit
- ◉ "Use your fingers to show three. This is the whole. How can you take apart three? What are partner numbers for three?"
- Observe as students share their different partner numbers for 3 with a neighbor. Refer to the anchor chart.
- Observe whether any student used 0 and 3 for the parts. Because the directions say there are *some* cherries in the tree, students will draw at least one cherry in the tree.
- ◉ In the second exercise, students may hesitate because the question has more than one correct answer. Pose the question back to students. "When you have 4, what are different ways you can take it apart?" Offer counters to students as a way to model the problem.
- **?** **Extension:** "Look at the first picture. What would the parts be if one of the cherries fell to the ground?"
- **?** **Look for and Express Regularity in Repeated Reasoning:** "Does the whole change if a cherry fails to the ground? Explain." The whole does not change. The parts will change.
- **Supporting Learners:** Name one part and the whole. Then ask students to identify the other partner number. This lays the foundation for addition and subtraction fluency within 5.
- **FYI:** Although students are not required to identify a missing addend in Kindergarten, they can use their understanding of partner numbers and their ability to subitize within 5 to determine a missing partner number.

Closure

- Have partners take turns saying a number to 5. Partners can use their fingers to show a set of partner numbers for the whole.

Sample answer:

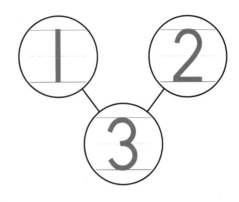

Sample answer:

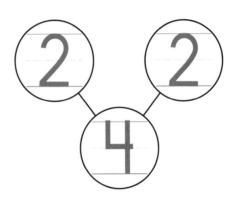

Directions:
- Draw 3 cherries on the picture. Draw some of the cherries in the tree and some of the cherries on the ground. Complete the number bond to match your picture.
- Draw 4 cherries on the picture. Draw some of the cherries in the tree and some of the cherries on the ground. Complete the number bond to match your picture.

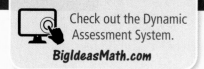
Connect and Extend Learning

Practice Notes

- Suggest that students think of the top two circles in each number bond as buckets, that each have one kind of thing in them. The bottom circle is like a third bucket that you pour the top two buckets into.
- Another way for students to think of the numbers in the top two circles in each number bond is as *partner numbers*, which they *put together* to find the number in the bottom circle.

Cross-Curricular Connections

Language Arts

- *Doggies* by Sandra Boynton; Read the book up to the page where 5 dogs are barking. (We will finish the book when we get to number 10 later in the chapter.) After you read a page, students can make number bonds for that number of dogs on that page.

Art

- Create "Rainbow Number Bonds." Give each student a plain white paper plate. Across the bottom of the paper plate write the numbers 0 through 5, evenly spaced out. Students should make a rainbow that goes from 0 to 5; a rainbow that goes from 1 to 4; and a rainbow that goes from 2 to 3 using different colors of paint. This activity is a great way to introduce the Commutative Property.

Name _____

Learning Target: Use number bonds to show the parts and the whole for numbers to 5.

Directions: Name the parts and the whole for the group. Then complete the number bond.

Directions: ① Name the parts and the whole for the group. Then complete the number bond.

Chapter 5 | Lesson 2

two hundred twenty-three 223

© Big Ideas Learning, LLC

Connect and Extend Learning

Extend Student Learning

Musical

- Sing songs with the class: 5 Green and Speckled Frogs, 5 Little Monkeys Jumping on the Bed, and 5 Little Ducks

Bodily-Kinesthetic

- Play a game called "Snap" with the students. Show the students 5 linking cubes stacked together. Put the linking cube stack behind your back and ask the students to say, "Snap!" Quickly break your linking cube stack into two. Show the students one part of the stack and ask whether they can tell you the part that is still behind your back. If students can't answer, then show them the stack is still behind your back and count the stack together. Try this activity again, still using the 5 stacked linking cubes but, choose a different combination of partner numbers.

Lesson Resources	
Surface Level	**Deep Level**
Resources by Chapter • Extra Practice • Reteach Differentiating the Lesson Skills Review Handbook Skills Trainer	Resources by Chapter • Enrichment and Extension Graphic Organizers Dynamic Assessment System • Lesson Practice

2–4. Sample answers are given.

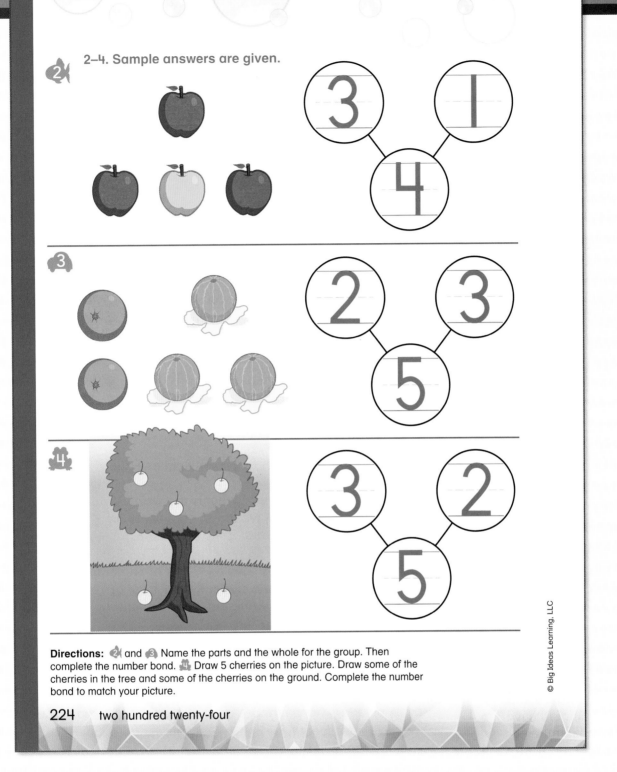

2 3 1 4

3 2 3 5

4 3 2 5

Directions: 2 and 3 Name the parts and the whole for the group. Then complete the number bond. 4 Draw 5 cherries on the picture. Draw some of the cherries in the tree and some of the cherries on the ground. Complete the number bond to match your picture.

5.3

Learning Target

Use partner numbers to make and take apart the number 6.

Success Criteria

- Name the parts and the whole.
- Use a number bond to show the parts and the whole.

Warm-Up

Practice opportunities for the following are available in the Resources by Chapter or at *BigIdeasMath.com.*

- Daily skills
- Vocabulary
- Prerequisite skills

ELL Support

Explain the verb phrase *to take apart*. Students should understand the word *take*. Explain that the word *apart* is made from two words, *a* and *part*. They should have a good understanding of the word *part* from earlier sections. Point out that when someone takes apart something, they end up with its different parts. Use building blocks to make a small object using several parts and then take it apart in front of the class to demonstrate the meaning of the phrase.

Laurie's Notes

Preparing to Teach

Students have been introduced to partner numbers and how to represent them in a number bond with the whole. Understanding the language and concept of part-part-whole is very important at this stage. The next five lessons focus on composing (put together) and decomposing (take apart) the numbers 6 to 10. Keep an anchor chart visible and use similar models to show composing and decomposing numbers to help students build fluency and subitizing skills.

Linking cubes are used so students can make trains to show the two partner number. They put them together to show the whole. The focus is *not* the color of the cubes, only *how many* are in each train.

Materials

- two-color counters
- linking cubes

Dig In (Circle Time)

- Show students a tower of five linking cubes and one single cube.
- ? "If I put together these *parts*, what is the *whole*?" 6
  "If I take apart the whole, what numbers could be the parts?" *Sample answers:* 2 and 4, 3 and 3, 6 and 0
- **Model with Mathematics:** Give each pair of students six linking cubes. Have one student show a set of partner numbers for six, while the other student names the partner numbers.
- "Hold up your partner numbers if you had 5 and 1." Pause. "Are there other partner numbers for 6?" Repeat until all pairs are mentioned.
- Now it is time to record student thinking about partner numbers for six on an anchor chart. See page T-211C for anchor chart ideas.
- ⊙ You have now spent time on the first success criterion. Have students use their fingers to show a set of partner numbers for 6.
- Call on several students to describe the parts and whole they are modeling with their fingers. Expect students to use the vocabulary, parts and whole.

? Teaching Prompt   ⊙ Learning Target

Learning Target: Use partner numbers to make and take apart the number 6.

Explore and Grow

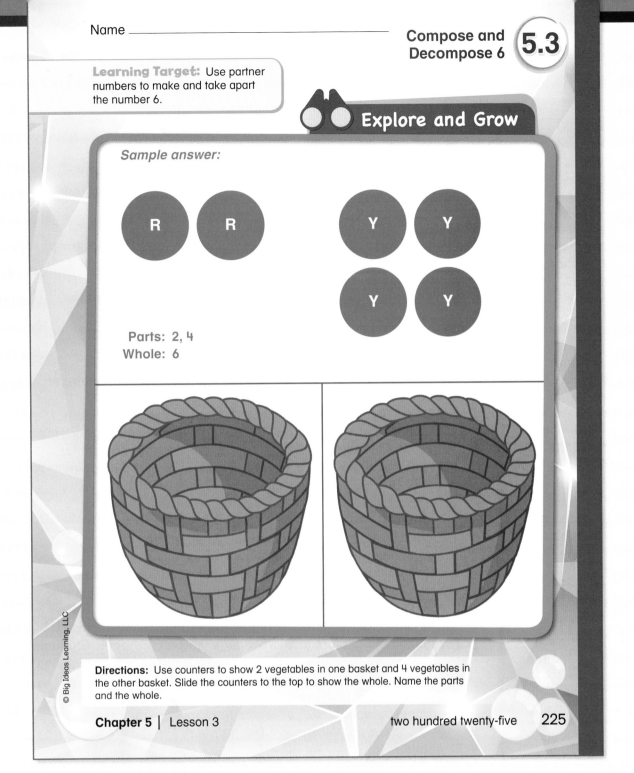

Sample answer:

Parts: 2, 4
Whole: 6

Directions: Use counters to show 2 vegetables in one basket and 4 vegetables in the other basket. Slide the counters to the top to show the whole. Name the parts and the whole.

© Big Ideas Learning, LLC

Chapter 5 | Lesson 3   two hundred twenty-five **225**

Explore and Grow

- Pass out counters. "I put vegetables from my garden into baskets. I put two vegetables in one basket, and four vegetables in the other. Use counters to show the vegetables." Pause and check student work. "Use your fingers to show the number partners."

⊙ When students slide the counters to the top box, they can model putting together the parts to make the whole and taking apart the whole to show the parts. Students are demonstrating the first success criterion.

- **Turn and Talk:** "Use counters to tell a partner your own story about a set of partner numbers for 6." Solicit stories from several students.

ELL Support

Teach the words peppers, broccoli, and cauliflower if necessary. Explain that all are vegetables. Have students work in pairs to practice verbal language. Have one ask the other "How many yellow/green peppers are there? How many *total peppers* are there?" Then have them switch roles, using the phrases pieces of broccoli or cauliflower. Have them use the word *vegetables* for the total.

Beginner students may only the answer using numbers alone.
Intermediate students may answer with a number and the object counted, such as, "three yellow peppers."
Advanced students may answer with a complete sentence, such as, "There are three yellow peppers."

Think and Grow

Getting Started

- The number bonds on this page have been oriented with the whole at the top and the parts below. This is how the counters were placed on the Explore and Grow page.
- Display a number bond under a document camera with parts 2 and 4 at the top and a whole of 6 at the bottom. Alternately, draw on a whiteboard. Have partners discuss the meaning of the circles and lines.
- Now rotate the number bond 180° to show the parts on the bottom. Have students discuss what is the same and what is different about the two ways the number bond was displayed.

Teaching Notes

- Students name the parts and whole and record in the number bond.
- **Model:** "Tell your partner what you notice about the counters." Listen for six counters, one is red and five are yellow. Students trace the numbers 1 and 5 (parts) and the number 6 (whole).
- **FYI:** Recall that this is a different orientation of the number bond. Objects are not shown in a number bond, but a visual is provided so students know where to write the number for each part.
- Note that the arrangements of the small groups of objects (parts) on this page should allow students to identify *how many* without counting. Many students will see a group of three yellow peppers and three green peppers. As you circulate ask students how they know how many are in each part.
- ⊙ Remind students of the work they have done today at circle time, on the Explore and Grow page, and on this page. Students share where their learning is with each success criteria by using their thumb signals.
- ❓ **Extension:** Write the numbers 1, 6, and 5 on the board. "Which number is the whole?" 6 "Which numbers are the parts?" 1 and 5 "How do you know?" The numbers 1 and 5 are partner numbers for 6.
- **Supporting Learners:** Students can use counters and a number bond or part-part-whole mat to practice putting together and taking apart the number 6.
- **Extension:** Have students work with a partner to practice conceptual subitizing. Have one partner turn six counters to red. Have the other partner say the hidden partner numbers they see. Students can show the embedded numbers by separating the groups or using their finger to circle each group. Have students switch roles and repeat the process several times until students have a good understanding of partner numbers for 6.

Directions: Name the parts and the whole for the group. Then complete the number bond.

Meeting the needs of all learners.

Laurie's Notes

Apply and Grow: Practice

SCAFFOLDING INSTRUCTION

The page shows two different orientations of number bonds. Have students explain how they will know where to write the parts and where to write the whole. Many students will focus on the two line segments. The segments connect the parts to the whole. Only one circle has the two segments drawn to it, making it the whole. You might want to use a white board to practice identifying the circles in a number bond before having students begin this page.

EMERGING students may not recognize the two distinct groups, or identify these groups as being the parts. They may also be unsure of where to write which numbers in the number bond.

Note: Pay attention to the order in which students are counting. Are they counting each part, recording, and then going back to count the whole? Do they count the whole first and record? You may need to suggest an explicit strategy, particularly if they are unsure of where to record each number in the number bond.

? **Exercises 1–3:** "What partner numbers are easy to see on the page? Can you explain how you were able to notice them?" Students may be influenced by color, arrangement or position.

• **Exercises 1–3:** You might suggest they count the parts first. Look for the circles that represent the parts and record the numbers there. "How will you know what the whole is?" Listening to student responses will give insights about where they are in knowing partner numbers for 6, or even the concept of part-part-whole.

PROFICIENT students are able to use a number bond to make or take apart the number 6.

? **Exercise 1:** "If all of the chile peppers were red, what would the partner numbers be?"

• **Exercises 1–3:** Use the words "put together" and "take apart" to describe the numbers on your number bond.

Additional Support

• Offer two-color counters to place on the groups of objects.
• Teaching Tip: Laminate a copy of the Number Bond Instructional Resource. Students use dry-erase markers to write on it and old cloth as erasers.

Extension: Adding Rigor

• Make Six: Have students roll a die and place that many counters in a part on a number bond. They will determine how many the other part needs to be to make the whole be 6. Have students write the corresponding numbers on the number bond.

Name _____

1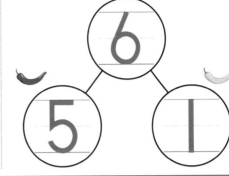

2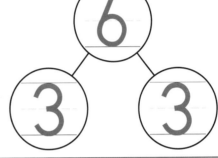

3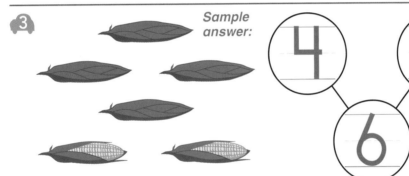

Sample answer:

Directions: **1** – **3** Name the parts and the whole for the group. Then complete the number bond.

Chapter 5 | Lesson 3   two hundred twenty-seven   227

© Big Ideas Learning, LLC

Think and Grow: Modeling Real Life

This application allows students to show different sets of partner numbers for 6. In addition to knowing the whole, a relationship between the parts is also known, one part is less than (fewer) than the other.

- **Preview:** Explain what a farm stand is and ask, "What are some different fruits or vegetables you might buy at the stand?"
- ? "What do you see for sale at the farm stand?" listen for 6 tomatoes
- You want students to recognize the group of tomatoes as the whole and visualize different ways they can take apart the number 6.
- ? **Make Sense of Problems and Persevere in Solving Them:** Read the first part of the directions and ask, "What is the whole in the first exercise?" six "Can we use any of the partner numbers?" No "Why?" Newton buys less tomatoes than Descartes.
- **Model with Mathematics:** Once students have decided how many to have Newton and Descartes buy, they draw the tomatoes and fill in the number bond.
- Students think of a different way to take apart (decompose) six.
- ? **Extension:** "Can Newton buy four tomatoes? How do you know?" no; that would mean Descartes only had 2 tomatoes and 2 is less than 4. Descartes is supposed to have more tomatoes than Newton.
- ? **Extension:** Use puppets or two students to model different ways that the six tomatoes can be bought so that Descartes has more tomatoes than Newton.
- ⊙ "We have put together (composed) numbers to make 6 and we have taken apart (decomposed) 6 to make two partner numbers. Use your thumb signal to show how well you understand putting together and taking apart." Ask a similar question about recording their work in a number bond.
- **Supporting Learners:** Some students may still benefit from using counters or linking cubes as a concrete way to see the different combinations of 6.
- **Supporting Learners:** Encourage students to explain what each circle on the number bond means. Students should locate the circles that show the parts and the circle that shows the whole before they fill in each number bond.

Closure

- Have one partner roll a die. The second student uses their fingers to show the partner number for 6.

Sample answer:

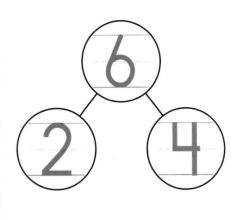

Sample answer:

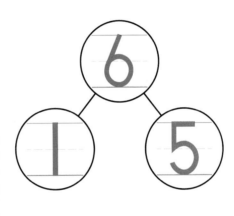

Directions: There are 6 tomatoes at a farm stand. Newton and Descartes buy all of them. Newton buys fewer tomatoes than Descartes.
- Draw tomatoes in the wagons to show how many tomatoes Newton and Descartes could buy. Then complete the number bond to match your picture.
- Draw another way to show how many tomatoes Newton and Descartes could buy. Then complete the number bond to match your picture.

228   two hundred twenty-eight

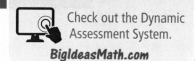
Connect and Extend Learning

Practice Notes

- Discuss with students how in the previous section, they *put together* two *partner numbers* to form a *whole*, but in this section they are *taking apart* a *whole* in two separate *partner numbers*. Point out that this is the same idea, only backwards.
- Let students know that one way to begin is to count all the pictures in a group and put the number in the *whole* circle.

Cross-Curricular Connections

Language Arts

- Show the students a completed number bond. The students turn to their partner and tell a story about the numbers in the number bond. Example: (Numbers 2, 4, 6 are in the number bond.) 2 cats and 4 dogs went into the house. Now there are 6 animals in the house.
- Continue to show students other completed number bonds that have a sum of 6 and have them tell their partner a story.

Art

- Give each pair of students several construction paper strips in two different colors. Students make a paper chain using both colors but no more than 6 rings in a chain. Next, they draw a number bond on a piece of paper to match their paper chain. If time allows, students can make additional paper chains for the number 6 and then complete the number bond.

Learning Target: Use partner numbers to make and take apart the number 6.

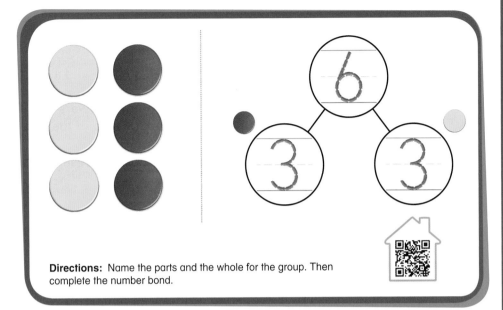

Directions: Name the parts and the whole for the group. Then complete the number bond.

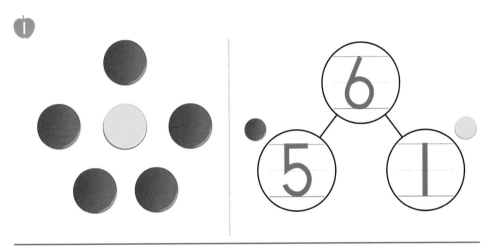

Directions: ❶ Name the parts and the whole for the group. Then complete the number bond.

Chapter 5 | Lesson 3

Connect and Extend Learning

Extend Student Learning

Bodily-Kinesthetic

- Each pair of students need 12 linking cubes and a die. Partners take turns rolling the die and then make a tower according to the number on the die. Partners compare towers and decide how many more cubes are needed for each of their towers to make 6.
- Students can also make a number bond representing their tower problems.

Lesson Resources	
Surface Level	**Deep Level**
Resources by Chapter • Extra Practice • Reteach Differentiating the Lesson Skills Review Handbook Skills Trainer	Resources by Chapter • Enrichment and Extension Graphic Organizers Dynamic Assessment System • Lesson Practice

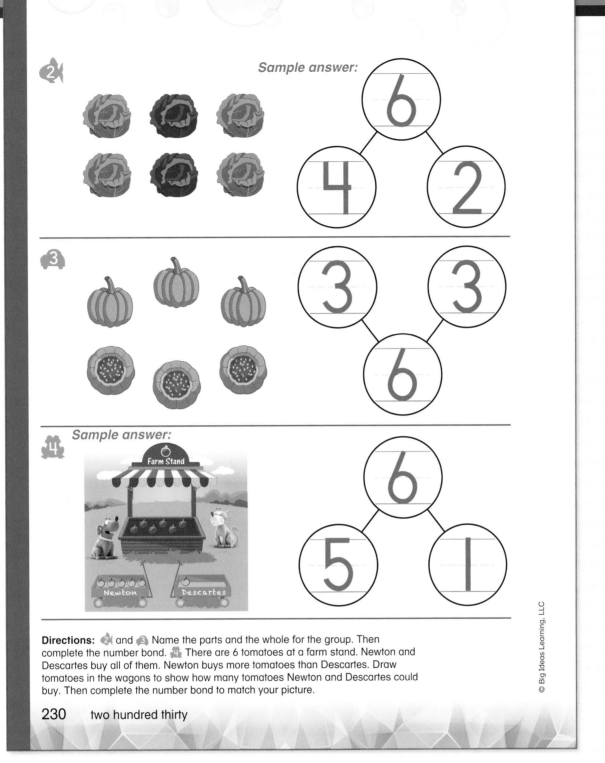

2 Sample answer:

6
4   2

3

3   3
6

4 Sample answer:

Farm Stand

Newton   Descartes

6
5   1

Directions: **2** and **3** Name the parts and the whole for the group. Then complete the number bond. **4** There are 6 tomatoes at a farm stand. Newton and Descartes buy all of them. Newton buys more tomatoes than Descartes. Draw tomatoes in the wagons to show how many tomatoes Newton and Descartes could buy. Then complete the number bond to match your picture.

230   two hundred thirty

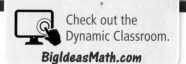
5.4

Laurie's Notes

Preparing to Teach

Students work with composing (put together) and decomposing (take apart) 7. You still want to use the put together and take apart vocabulary, making the connection of partner numbers and the whole. As an odd number there are no equal partner numbers, which some students may observe and comment on. No new number bond orientation is introduced, hence students have the opportunity to become comfortable with these two vertical orientations.

Materials

- two-color counters
- linking cubes
- Number Bond*
- Number Bond Draw and Write*

Found in the Instructional Resources

Dig In (Circle Time)

- Show students a linking cube tower of 7.
- **?** "What hidden partner numbers can be found in 7?" *Sample answers:* 3 and 4, 2 and 5, 1 and 6
- Pass the 7-tower around the circle. The first student says, "The whole is 7. I can *take apart* 7 to make ___ and ___." 3, 4 The next student says, "___ and ___ are the parts. I can *put them together* to make 7." 3, 4 Repeat this several times for different partner numbers.
- Ask students to help you make an anchor chart of the partner numbers for 7. See page T-211C for ideas. You may have students that want to share observations of patterns they are noticing in the anchor chart, particularly if they can see partner numbers for 6 and 7. You may want to have one or two students share, or ask if their pattern still works when they work with 8 as the whole.
- **Teaching Tip:** Because partner numbers were introduced with three dots in a linear arrangement, you can always model the whole in a linear arrangement and use a pencil to show the two hidden numbers. Students can draw this on a whiteboard as well.
- **?** **Model with Mathematics:** Have students place seven counters or objects in one hand. "What partner numbers do you have for 7?" 0 and 7 Have students transfer one object at a time to the other hand as they say the new set of partner numbers. Have students continue until all seven objects are in the other hand.

? Teaching Prompt   ⊙ Learning Target

Compose and
Decompose 7 **5.4**

Learning Target: Use partner numbers to make and take apart the number 7.

Explore and Grow

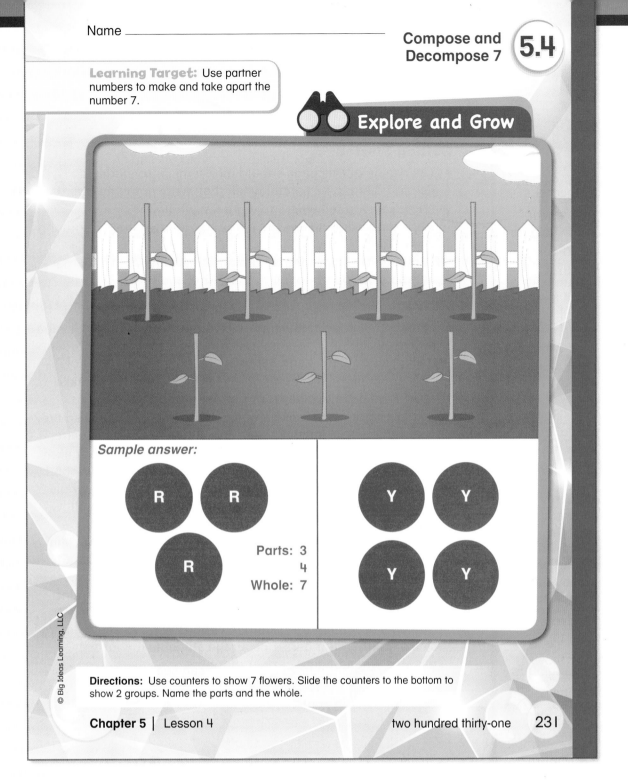

Sample answer:

R   R

R   Parts: 3
              4
         Whole: 7

Y   Y

Y   Y

Directions: Use counters to show 7 flowers. Slide the counters to the bottom to show 2 groups. Name the parts and the whole.

Chapter 5 | Lesson 4   two hundred thirty-one   231

© Big Ideas Learning, LLC

Explore and Grow

- Pass out counters. "There are seven flowers growing in a garden. Some are red and some are yellow. Use counters to show the flowers." Pause to look at where students place the counters and if there are 7.
- Have students slide all of the red counters to the bottom on one side and all of the yellow counters to the bottom on the other side.
- ? "What is the whole?" 7 "What are the parts?" Answers should include a set of partner numbers for 7
- ⊙ "This is part of our learning today. We can take apart our whole, 7."

ELL Support

Point to the flowers and shovels as you say the name of each and have students repeat. Explain that the flowers are a special type of flower known as a daffodil or jonquil. An ELL may not be familiar with this type of flower, so explain that it is associated with spring. Have students practice language in pairs. One student asks the other "How many yellow daffodils are there? How many white daffodils? How many total?" Then have students alternate roles for the other exercise. Remind them they must use *is* with only one daffodil, and *are* when saying any other number.

Beginner students may only state the correct numbers.
Intermediate students may answer using simple sentences, such as, "There is one yellow daffodil."
Advanced students may answer using compound sentences, such as, "There is one yellow daffodil and there are six white ones."

Laurie's Notes

Think and Grow

Getting Started

- The design of this page should look familiar to students. Remind them to be careful when they write in the number bond.
- ? "How can you tell where to write the whole?" listen for students describing the circle that has the two lines (segments) drawn to it
- ? "What do the lines on the number bond mean?" The partner numbers are *put together* to make the whole.

Teaching Notes

- **Model:** "Tell your partner about the counters at the top." Listen for seven counters, four are red and three are yellow. Students trace the numbers 4 and 3 (parts) and the number 7 (whole).
- ◉ "We are finding partner numbers for 7 today. When we take apart 7 we have two parts, or partner numbers for 7."
- Remind students to look carefully at the number bonds so they know where to write the whole and where to write the parts.
- **Teaching Tip:** If students do not mention it, point out that each whole is 7. You want students to recognize each number bond shows a different set of partner numbers for the same whole.
- ? **Extension:** "If you change one of the white flowers to yellow, what partner numbers will you see?" 2 and 5 "How did the number of yellow flowers change?" It is one more. "How did the number of white objects change?" It is one less. "Did the whole change?" No, the whole is still 7.
- **Supporting Learners:** Students can make linking cube trains to practice finding the partner numbers embedded within 7. Students take apart the 7 train in various ways to show different sets of partner numbers. Encourage students to look for patterns when finding partner numbers.

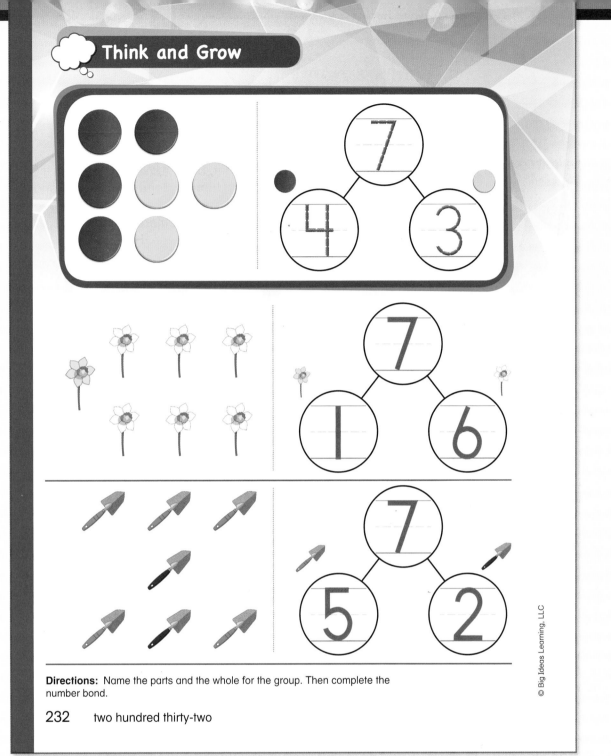

Directions: Name the parts and the whole for the group. Then complete the number bond.

232   two hundred thirty-two

Meeting the needs of
all learners.

Apply and Grow: Practice

SCAFFOLDING INSTRUCTION

Have students practice the "Build it, Draw it, Write it, and Say it" method. Provide students with a Number Bond, a Number Bond Draw and Write, and 7 two-color counters. Students use the two-color counters to place over the two different kinds of objects shown on the Apply and Grow: Practice page. Have students transfer the counters to the Number Bond to show the correct parts and whole. Then have students draw and write their findings on the Number Bond Draw and Write. Finally, have students "say it" or tell what the partner numbers are and identify the whole.

Teaching Tip: Allow students to work with partners. One student builds the number bond. The other student draws and writes on the Number Bond Draw and Write. Both students "say it" or tell each other what they found.

EMERGING students may find it difficult to use a number bond to name the parts and the whole.

- Cover the bottom two exercises so that students only focus on the first exercise. Are they better able to focus on the objects?
- **? Exercises 1–3:** Ask specific questions that address the two different kinds of objects and write the quantity on the number bond. An example of this for exercise 1 is to ask, "How many yellow roses are there? How do you know what circle to write 2 in?"

PROFICIENT students are able to use a number bond to make or take apart the number 7.

- "You have 7 pencils. Draw a picture of partner numbers 0 and 7."
- **Exercises 1–3:** Use the words "put together" and "take apart" to describe the numbers on your number bond.

Additional Support

- Create a number bond hanger. Use number cards 5 to 7 and place one on the hook part of the hanger. Attach five of the same color clothespins on one side of the hanger. Then attach the corresponding amount of clothespins needed to create the number card.

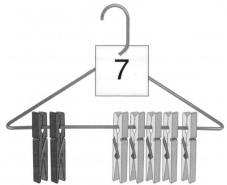

- **Teaching Tip:** Use five of the same color clothespins so that the benchmark of five is easily recognized.

✓ Apply and Grow: Practice

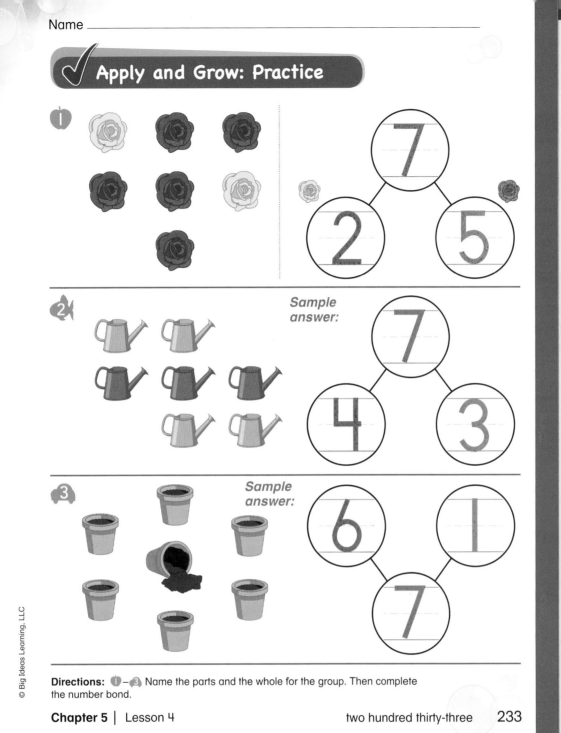

1

2 Sample answer:

3 Sample answer:

Directions: **1** – **3** Name the parts and the whole for the group. Then complete the number bond.

Chapter 5 | Lesson 4   two hundred thirty-three   233

Think and Grow: Modeling Real Life

This application allows students to show different sets of partner numbers for 7. Students show their understanding of the part-part-whole relationship by filling in a number bond.

- **Preview:** "Have you ever planted a seed or a bulb and watched it grow?" "What color flowers have you seen?" Choose several students to share their experiences.
- **FYI:** The planter suggests the whole. There are 7 flowers. As students color, they may group their colors together, meaning 3 of one color followed by 4 of another. Other students may not group by color. Displaying student work under a document camera will allow for good discussion of parts and whole.
- Both exercises allow students to demonstrate their understanding of decomposing 7. Make sure students are clear about the word *some*. You are not to tell them a specific amount.
- In the second exercise, students should color the flowers to show different partner numbers than the first exercise.
- **?** **Look for and Make Use of Structure:** "What do you notice about the flowers in the planter?" Listen for seven flowers.
- **?** **Construct Viable Arguments and Critique the Reasoning of Others:** "Some students had 1 and 6 as partner numbers and other students had 4 and 3 as partner numbers. Are both sets of partner numbers correct?" Yes "How do you know?" Both sets of partner numbers show the same whole. The picture shows different ways to take apart 7.
- Check to see that each number bond agrees with how students colored their flowers.
- ◉ Display the coloring work of several students. Each time, ask students to identify how the number bond should be filled in.
- **Extension:** "If I take apart 7 into the partner numbers of 3 and 4, what will the whole be when I put the parts together?" 7

Closure

- One partner says a number within 7. The second partner uses their fingers to show the other partner number.
- **Note:** The closure allows students to practice counting on from a number to find the other part. Students can use counting on as a strategy to solve addition and subtraction problems in later chapters.

Sample answer:

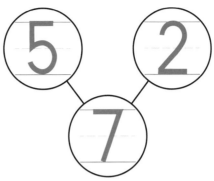

Sample answer:

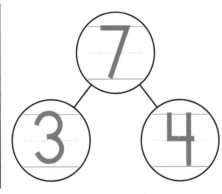

Directions:
- Color some of the flowers purple and some of the flowers yellow. Complete the number bond to match your picture.
- Color to show another way. Complete the number bond to match your picture.

234 two hundred thirty-four

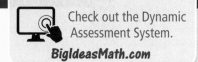
Connect and Extend Learning

Practice Notes

- **Exercise 4:** Students are asked to color some flowers yellow and some flowers purple. Remind them to make sure all the flowers are colored before they complete the number bond.

Cross-Curricular Connections

Language Arts and Social Studies

- *Johnny Appleseed* by Patricia Brennan Demuth; Read the book to the students and talk about Johnny Appleseed's journey. Discuss his different stops in the book. When you get to the end of the book, provide each student with a laminated cutout of a red apple with 2 green leaves at the top. Give each student 14 seeds, beans, or other counters. Students will take 7 seeds and put some on one leaf and the others on the other leaf. They will put the other 7 seeds on the red apple. Using a dry erase marker, students write the number of seeds on each leaf and the total number of seeds on the apple.
- They can continue by making other combinations of a sum of 7.

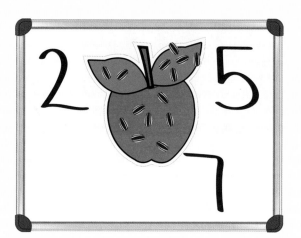

Name _____

Learning Target: Use partner numbers to make and take apart the number 7.

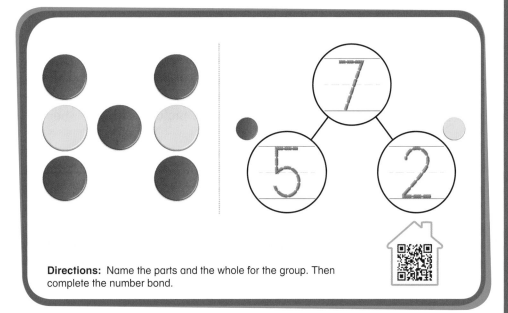

Directions: Name the parts and the whole for the group. Then complete the number bond.

Directions: ❶ Name the parts and the whole for the group. Then complete the number bond.

Chapter 5 | Lesson 4

two hundred thirty-five **235**

Connect and Extend Learning

Extend Student Learning

Interpersonal

- Students write a story called "The Story of 7." Give each student 3 sheets of paper. On each page, students draw pictures to show 2 numbers whose sum is 7. Encourage students to write the number bond under the picture. Students then share their stories with their partner.

  Extension: Give students 3 more sheets of paper and see whether they understand the Commutative Property.

  Example: 4 girls and 3 boys is the same as 3 boys and 4 girls.

Lesson Resources	
Surface Level	**Deep Level**
Resources by Chapter • Extra Practice • Reteach Differentiating the Lesson Skills Review Handbook Skills Trainer	Resources by Chapter • Enrichment and Extension Graphic Organizers Dynamic Assessment System • Lesson Practice

2–4. Sample answers are given.

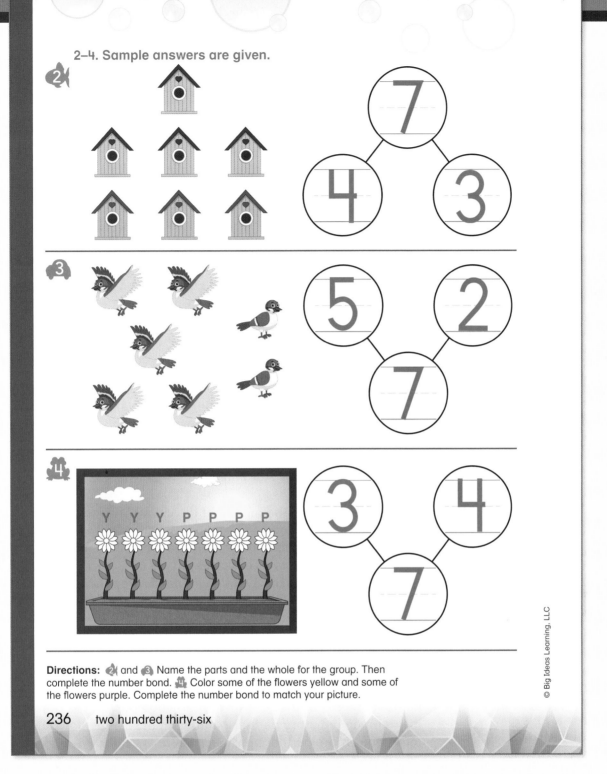

Directions: 🐟 and 🚗 Name the parts and the whole for the group. Then complete the number bond. 🐸 Color some of the flowers yellow and some of the flowers purple. Complete the number bond to match your picture.

236   two hundred thirty-six

Learning Target

Use partner numbers to make and take apart the number 8.

Success Criteria

- Name the parts and the whole.
- Use a number bond to show the parts and the whole.

Warm-Up

Practice opportunities for the following are available in the Resources by Chapter or at *BigIdeasMath.com*.

- Daily skills
- Vocabulary
- Prerequisite skills

ELL Support

Remind students that the word *eight* has the homophone *ate.* Ask them to show each meaning by acting each out. First ask for the number. Then ask what the other word means. This could involve tracing an 8 in the air with their fingers and mimicking eating. Making a drawing to represent each is also a good way to check meaning.

Preparing to Teach

This is the third lesson on composing and decomposing numbers. Students put together partner numbers for 8 and take apart the number 8 to show the numbers embedded within. A new orientation of the number bond is introduced. The circles are aligned vertically with the circle for the whole to the right. Remember, we are building understanding about the relationship of composing the parts to make the whole and decomposing the whole to make the parts. We are *not* talking about the operations of addition and subtraction yet!

Materials

- two-color counters

Dig In (Circle Time)

- Count aloud as you place eight counters, one at a time, in your hand. You want students to know the quantity is 8.
- Have students make a guess (predict) how many counters will land on red and how many will land on yellow when you drop them. You should hear students mention partner numbers for eight.
- Drop the counters in the middle of the circle. Choose a student to point to each red counter as you count aloud with the class. Follow the same procedure for the yellow counters. Discuss students' predictions with the class.
- **Popsicle Sticks:** Choose several students to drop the counters in the middle of the circle. Have the class identify the partner numbers shown for 8.
- Add all of the partner numbers for 8 to an anchor chart. See page T-211C for ideas. Ask a student to use linking cubes to model each set of partner numbers.
- **?** **Reason Abstractly and Quantitatively:** "Look at all of the partner numbers on the anchor chart. What do you notice?" The greater the number, the more partner numbers it has. "Why do you think 8 has more partner number?" There are more ways to take it apart.
- **Supporting Learners:** Challenge students to cover up some of their counters with their hand and then guess the number of counters that are hidden. Students can use their fingers to count on from the amount they see, or use the anchor chart to identify the missing partner number.

? Teaching Prompt   ⊙ Learning Target

Learning Target: Use partner numbers to make and take apart the number 8.

Explore and Grow

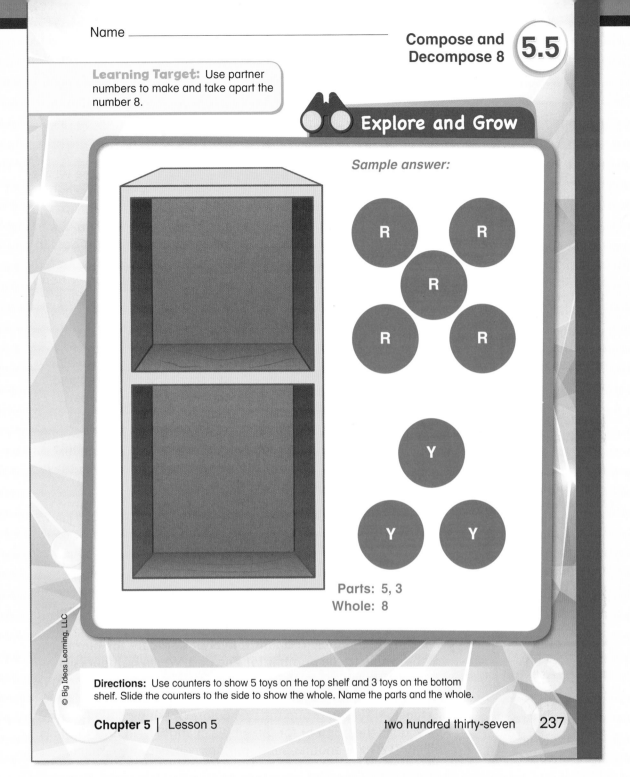

Sample answer:

R R
R
R R

Y

Y Y

Parts: 5, 3
Whole: 8

Directions: Use counters to show 5 toys on the top shelf and 3 toys on the bottom shelf. Slide the counters to the side to show the whole. Name the parts and the whole.

© Big Ideas Learning, LLC

Chapter 5 | Lesson 5   two hundred thirty-seven   237

Explore and Grow

- Pass out counters. "There are five toys on the top shelf and three toys on the bottom shelf. Use counters to show the toys on each shelf." Pause to see whether students are using different colors on each shelf. Ask why this would be a good idea.

- "What numbers are the parts?" 5 and 3 "Slide the counters on each shelf to the side. What is the whole?" 8 Note whether students keep the counters grouped by color on the right side. Ask why this would be a good idea.

- "Use the counters to tell a story about another set of partner numbers for 8."

Think and Grow

Getting Started

- Hold up a number bond with the parts on the left and the whole on the right. Have partners *Turn and Talk* to discuss the meaning of the circles and lines.
- Ask a student to share their thinking. If the number bond has been drawn on a whiteboard, the student can write numbers in the circles to explain their thinking.
- FYI: This is the first time students see a horizontal number bond where the numbers are written as they will be in an addition sentence, left to right.

Teaching Notes

- **Model:** "Talk with your partner about the counters you see at the top of the page." Listen for eight counters, one is red and seven are yellow. Students trace the numbers 1 and 7 (parts) and the number 8 (whole).
- Are students counting to find out how many? Are they visualizing any smaller groups of numbers and counting on? As you circulate, ask students how they know how many they have of each color of counter (yo-yo, puppet).
- Discuss with students that the number bond has been turned. "Which circles show the parts? Which circle is the whole? How do you know?" Point out the lines on the number bonds and how that helps us know where to write the parts and whole.
- **Make Sense of Problems:** Have students look at the yo-yo's and think how they will show the parts and the whole on the number bond. Do students see the small yo-yo icons to identify the parts?
- **? Reason Abstractly and Quantitatively:** "Compare the number of the whole to the number for one part. Which number is greater?" the whole "Why do you think it is greater?" The whole is made from the parts.
- **? Extension:** "If you group the two colors of puppets a different way, does the number for the whole change?" No, the whole is still 8. "What is another set of partner numbers for 8 that is not shown?"
- **Supporting Learners:** Students can use the Number Bond Draw and Write Instructional Resource to practice drawing and writing partner numbers for 8. Challenge students to write the numbers first and then draw to check their answer.
- ◉ Have students use their thumb signals to indicate how they are feeling about using the number bond. Note the new orientation.

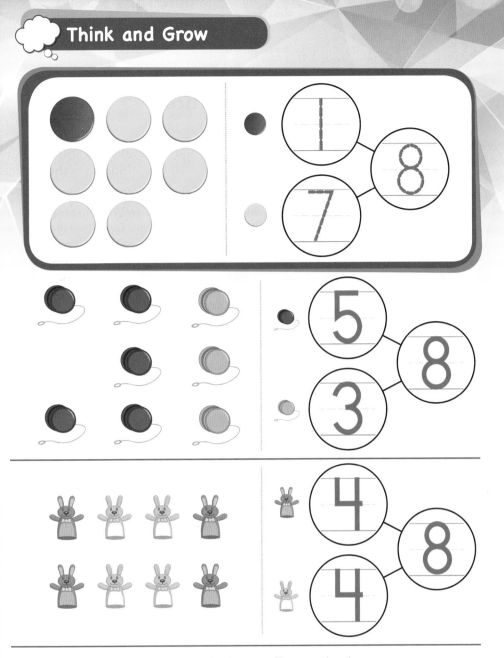

Directions: Name the parts and the whole for the group. Then complete the number bond.

238   two hundred thirty-eight

© Big Ideas Learning, LLC

Meeting the needs of all learners.

Apply and Grow: Practice

SCAFFOLDING INSTRUCTION

The page shows the new horizontal orientation of the number bond along with the last exercise which brings back the vertical, top-bottom orientation.

You do not want the orientation to interfere with students demonstrating their understanding of part-part-whole. It is most effective to use a document camera with counters or draw a number bond on a whiteboard. You want to be able to show a set of partner numbers for 8 and be able to rotate or turn the image. The parts do not change. The whole does not change. As student's cognitive and developmental stages progress, the change in orientation will be understood. Not all students will be at this stage.

EMERGING students may have difficulty in identifying the two parts, or groups of objects. The new orientation of the number bond may be confusing and students may write the parts and whole in the wrong circles.

? **Exercises 1–3:** Ask specific questions, such as "What do you notice about the jacks? How many of each color are there? Five and three are partner numbers for what whole?"

• **Exercises 1–3:** Use physical objects to model each exercise: counters, linking cubes, or counting bears.

PROFICIENT students are able to use a number bond to make or take apart the number 8.

• **Exercises 1–3:** What are the other partner numbers for the whole that are not shown?

? "Are there any partner numbers for 8 where the numbers are the same? Explain."

Additional Support

• Have students make different combinations of eight by putting together linking cubes to make a train. Make each train with two colors and keep the colors together.

Extension: Adding Rigor

• Play "Make 8." Provide students with a copy of Number Bond and write the number 8 in the whole. Direct students to roll a die and place that many counters in a part on the number bond. Have students determine the other part to make the whole. Have students write the corresponding numbers on the bond.

Name _____

①

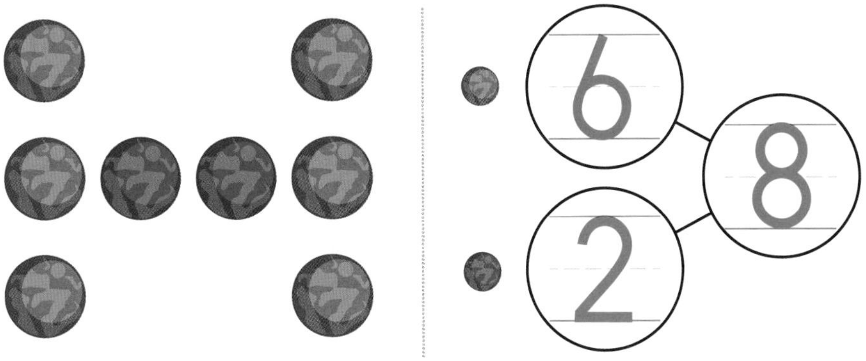

6   8

2

② *Sample answer:*

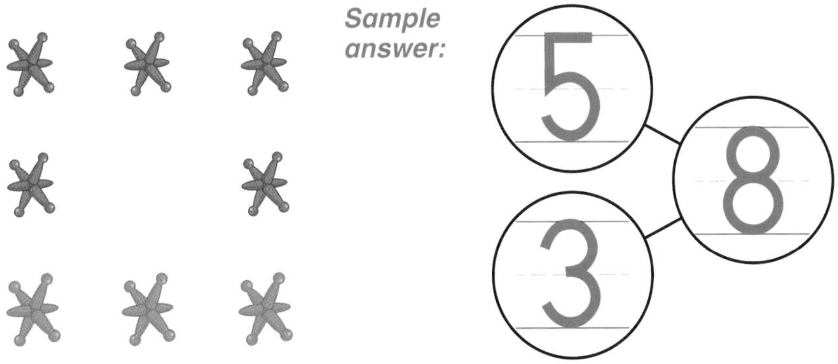

5   8

3

③ *Sample answer:*

6   2

8

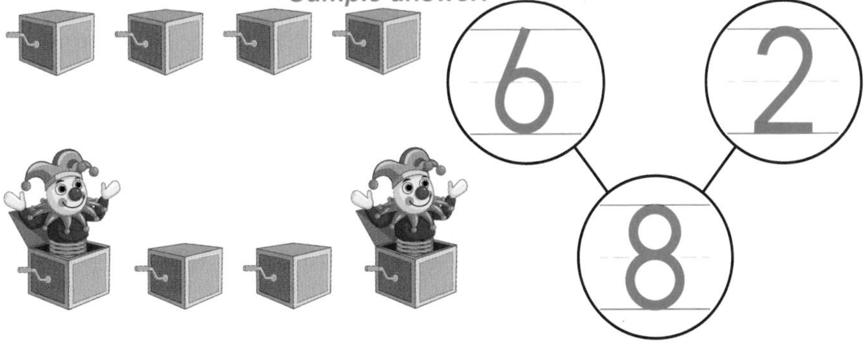

Directions: ① – ③ Name the parts and the whole for the group. Then complete the number bond.

© Big Ideas Learning, LLC

Think and Grow: Modeling Real Life

This application allows students to show different sets of partner numbers for 8. Notice that the arrangement for each whole is the same. The array may first appear to be nine for some students, three rows of three. Be sure students correctly count the whole as 8 for each exercise.

- **Preview:** "Have you ever played a game with marbles?" Have students talk about their experiences in small groups.
- Students see eight marbles in each number bond. The marbles are all one color instead of being shown as two distinct groups. Students develop their conceptual subitizing skills when they show different ways to decompose 8.
- **Look for and Make Use of Structure:** Have students discuss what the number bond shows. You want students to recognize they need to take apart the whole into two smaller groups.
- **Turn and Talk:** "Think about how you can draw the marbles in two groups." Have students draw and fill in the number bond.
- Students again decompose the number eight into two groups. Students may find it challenging to show a different set of partner numbers each time. They may even circle three different marbles and repeat the partner numbers 3 and 5.
- ◉ Revisit the learning target. Have students signal their ability to use partner numbers to make and take apart the number 8.
- **?** **Extension:** "Explain how you decided which partner numbers to draw and how you knew they were partner numbers for eight?" *Sample Answers:* I saw two groups and drew the groups I saw; I drew some marbles and then counted on to eight.
- **Supporting Learners:** Some students may want to model a set of partner numbers before they draw. Allow students to use manipulatives as needed.

Closure

- Have one partner draw a line of eight dots on their whiteboard and then move their pencil between the dots to show two groups. The other partner says the partner numbers and the whole. Have students switch roles.

Think and Grow: Modeling Real Life

Sample answer:

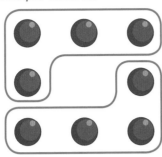

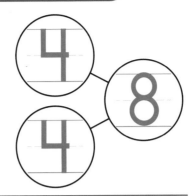

Sample answer:

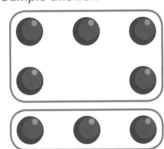

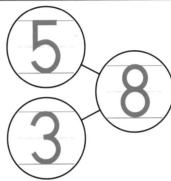

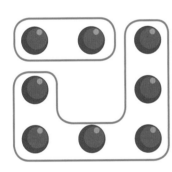

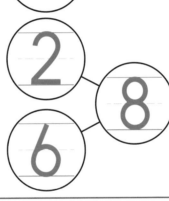

Directions:
- Put the marbles into 2 groups. Circle the groups. Then complete the number bond to match your picture.
- Show 2 other ways you can put the marbles into 2 groups. Then complete the number bonds to match your pictures.

240   two hundred forty

Connect and Extend Learning

Practice Notes

- Point out to students that the circles in a number bond diagram can be horizontal instead of vertical. Ask them to discuss which circle is the *whole*. It is the circle that is connected to both the other circles.

Cross-Curricular Connections

Language Arts

- Draw a completed number bond with a sum of 8 on the board. Ask a student to tell a story about the numbers in the number bond. Ask for one more story using the same number bond. Draw another completed number bond on the board and ask students to tell their partners a story.
- Students create a completed number bond with a sum of 8 and have their partners tell a story.
- Students create a number bond book for the number 8. Give the students number bonds in different orientations. Students illustrate the number bonds they have made.

Learning Target: Use partner numbers to make and take apart the number 8.

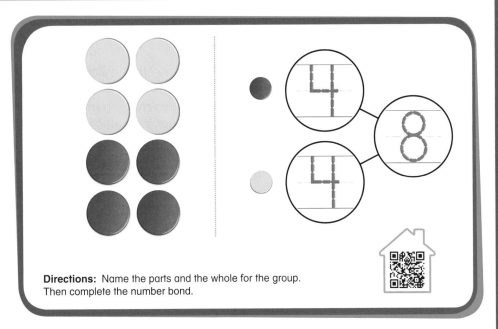

Directions: Name the parts and the whole for the group. Then complete the number bond.

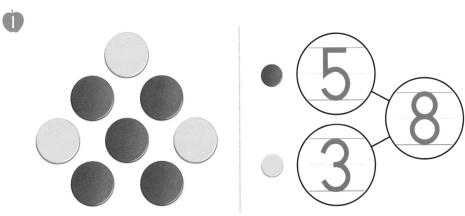

Directions: ① Name the parts and the whole for the group. Then complete the number bond.

Connect and Extend Learning

Extend Student Learning

Interpersonal

- In pairs, students play the game "In the Cave." Give each pair of students 8 bears or other counters. Make sure the students understand there are 8 bears when the game starts. One student hides some bears under a small container while the other student hides their eyes. The other student now opens their eyes and tries to figure out how many are hidden under the container. Student then completes a number bond and then checks by looking under the container. Partners change roles.
- This game can be played many different times as long as the students show interest.

Lesson Resources	
Surface Level	**Deep Level**

Resources by Chapter
  • Extra Practice
  • Reteach
Differentiating the Lesson
Skills Review Handbook
Skills Trainer
	Resources by Chapter
	  • Enrichment and Extension
	Graphic Organizers
	Dynamic Assessment System
	  • Lesson Practice

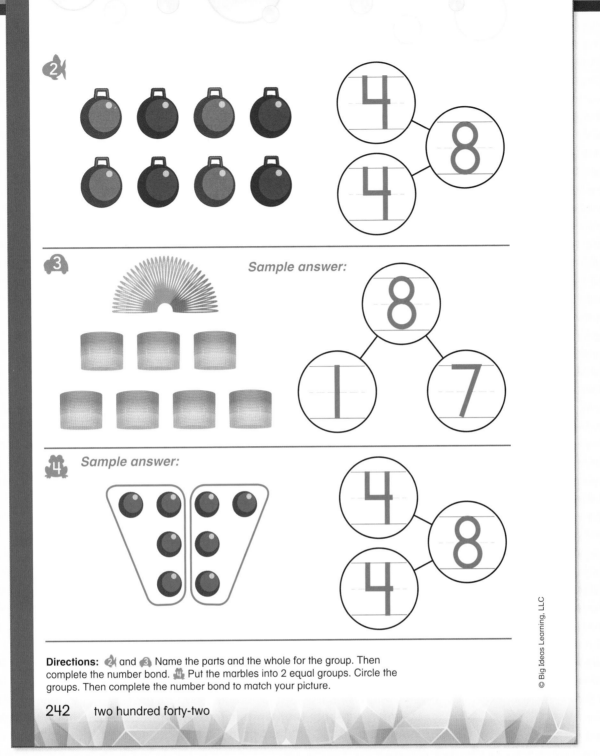

2

4
4
8

3 *Sample answer:*

8
1 7

4 *Sample answer:*

4
4
8

Directions: **2** and **3** Name the parts and the whole for the group. Then complete the number bond. **4** Put the marbles into 2 equal groups. Circle the groups. Then complete the number bond to match your picture.

5.6

Laurie's Notes

Learning Target

Use partner numbers to make and take apart the number 9.

Success Criteria

• Name the parts and the whole.
• Use a number bond to show the parts and the whole.

Warm-Up

Practice opportunities for the following are available in the Resources by Chapter or at *BigIdeasMath.com*.

• Daily skills
• Vocabulary
• Prerequisite skills

ELL Support

Preview the word vegetation by pointing to the visuals and explaining. Many students may be unfamiliar with an underwater scene. Explain that fish swim among the vegetation in a reef. If you have a photograph of one, display it. Some may know of shows or movies about fish living in underwater reefs.

Preparing to Teach

Students again see horizontal orientations of the number bond. Encourage students to use the terms *put together* and *take apart* when describing the relationship between the parts and the whole. The number 9 has many sets of partner numbers. Students need to understand each set of partner numbers is embedded within 9. Otherwise, students may count the parts and the whole without developing a true understanding of their relationship.

Materials

• two-color counters
• linking cubes

Dig In (Circle Time)

• Show students two linking cube towers (i.e. 3 and 6) that make 9.
• **?** "If I put together the parts, what is the whole? If I take the whole apart, what numbers can the parts be?" Listen for students to recognize the inverse relationship of composing and decomposing.
• Explain that they are going to clap their hands and tap their knees to show the partner numbers for 9. Example: Hold up the linking cube towers of 3 and 6. Point to the 3-tower and say, "Let's clap three times – clap, clap, clap." Point to the 6-tower and say, "Let's tap our knee six times – tap, tap, tap, tap, tap, tap."
• Clap and tap for all of the partner numbers for 9. By showing the partner numbers in order (0 and 9, 1 and 8, 2 and 7, and so on) students should recognize two patterns. They are clapping more each time and tapping their knees less each time. They will also see the lengths of the towers changing each time.
• Record the partner numbers on the anchor chart. See page T-211C for ideas.
• **Supporting Learners:** Students can practice finding partner numbers for 9 by holding up nine fingers and mentally drawing a line to separate their fingers into two groups. Have them name the parts and the whole.
• Have students turn all of their counters to red. Call out a number within 9 and have students flip that many counters to yellow. Students can count the number of counters that are still red to find the other partner number for 9.

? Teaching Prompt   ◉ Learning Target

Learning Target: Use partner numbers to make and take apart the number 9.

👓 **Explore and Grow**

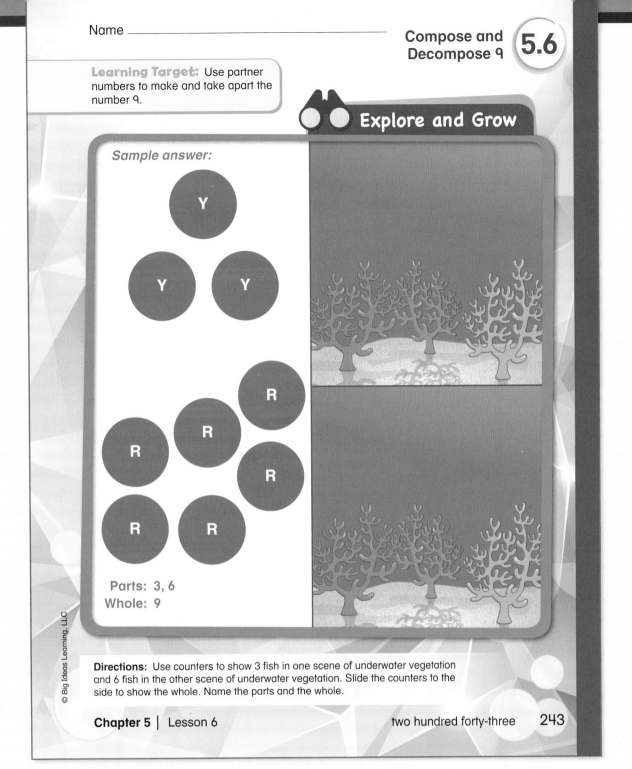

Sample answer:

Parts: 3, 6
Whole: 9

© Big Ideas Learning, LLC

Directions: Use counters to show 3 fish in one scene of underwater vegetation and 6 fish in the other scene of underwater vegetation. Slide the counters to the side to show the whole. Name the parts and the whole.

Chapter 5 | Lesson 6   two hundred forty-three   243

Explore and Grow

- Pass out counters. "There are three fish swimming in one coral and six fish swimming in the other coral. Use counters to show the fish in each coral." Pause to see if students are using different colors for the fish in each coral. This helps students subitize the numbers.
- "Slide the counters on each piece of coral to the side." Have students identify the parts and whole. Keeping the colors group together will help.
- "Use the counters to tell a story about another set of partner numbers for 9."

Point to the submarines and lobsters as you say the name of each. Have students repeat. Explain that they both can be found under the sea. Have students practice language in pairs. One student asks the other "How many total submarines are there? How many black ones? How many yellow ones?" Then have students alternate roles for the exercise with lobsters.

Beginner students may only state the appropriate numbers. **Intermediate** students may answer using the number and name of each item, such as, "nine total submarines." **Advanced** students may answer using sentences, such as, "There are nine total submarines."

Think and Grow

Getting Started

- Hold up a number bond with the parts on the right. This is a new orientation. Discuss how to tell where the whole and the parts are written.

Teaching Notes

- Students should be very familiar with these types of problems. The challenge they may have is in recognizing which circles show the parts and which circle shows the whole.

- **Model:** "How many counters do you see?" 9 "The whole is 9. Trace the number 9." Pause while students trace. "Tell your partner how many yellow counters and how many red counters you see." Students count and then trace the numbers 3 and 6.

- As you circulate make note of how students are counting how many there are in each group. Are students counting or are they subitizing smaller quantities?

- **Extension:** Write the numbers 9, 2, and 7 on the board. "Which number is the whole?" 9 "Which numbers are the parts?" 2 and 7 "How do you know?" The numbers 2 and 7 are partner numbers for 9.

- **Supporting Learners:** Students may find it helpful to circle the two groups before they start to count. This is more challenging for the blue lobsters. Perhaps they could cross the blue lobsters off as they count them.

- Students should be confident in naming the parts and the whole when they are shown two groups of objects that are partner numbers for nine. Are they confused by the orientation of the number bond? If this is the case, use the Number Bond Draw and Write Instructional Resource to have students record their thinking.

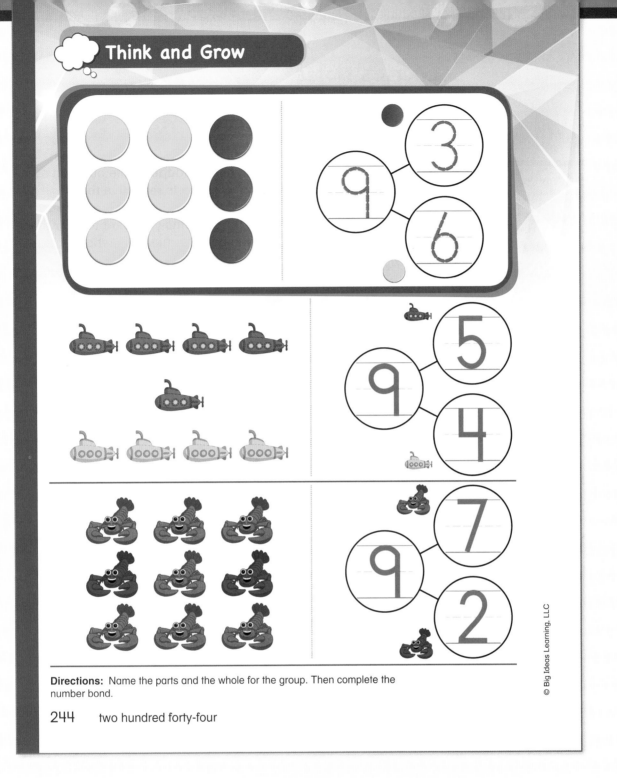

Directions: Name the parts and the whole for the group. Then complete the number bond.

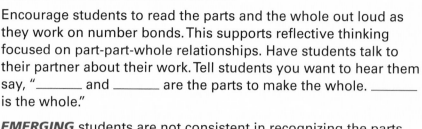

Laurie's Notes

Meeting the needs of
all learners.

Apply and Grow: Practice

SCAFFOLDING INSTRUCTION

Encourage students to read the parts and the whole out loud as they work on number bonds. This supports reflective thinking focused on part-part-whole relationships. Have students talk to their partner about their work. Tell students you want to hear them say, "_____ and _____ are the parts to make the whole. _____ is the whole."

EMERGING students are not consistent in recognizing the parts that are put together to make the whole. They may confuse which circles to represent the parts and whole in.

- **Exercises 1–3:** Have students describe the groups of objects before they begin to count.
- **Exercises 1–3:** Have students point to each object as they are counting, beginning with counting the whole. Now ask, "How many yellow seahorses are there? Cross out each yellow seahorse as you count. Write the number for the part."
- **Exercise 3:** Point out that the number bond in this exercise has been *turned around* and is different than the other two number bonds.

PROFICIENT students are able to use a number bond to make or take apart the number 9.

- **Exercises 1–3:** What are the other partner numbers for the whole that are not shown?
- **Exercises 1–3:** Use the words "put together" and "take apart" to describe the numbers on your number bond.

Additional Support

- Create missing-part strips on paper. Each strip has a numeral for the whole and two dot sets. The last dot set is covered by a flap. Have students find the missing part, say it out loud, and check their answers by opening the flap.

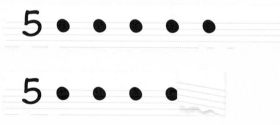

Extension: Adding Rigor

- Play "*You Pick Two.*" Have students write down a list of three numbers, two that are partner numbers for the number 9. The other number can be considered a distraction. Have students trade their lists with a partner. Tell them to find and circle the partner numbers for 9.

Name _____

Apply and Grow: Practice

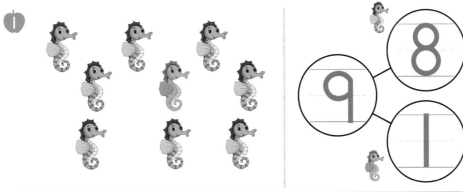

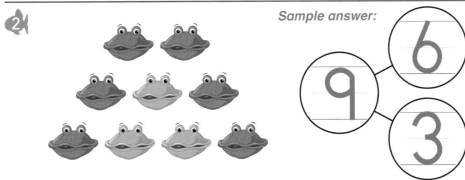

Sample answer:

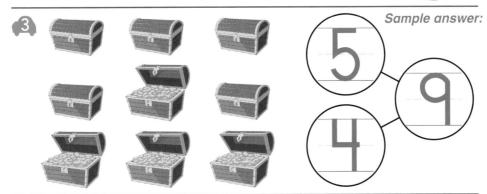

Sample answer:

Directions: ❶–❸ Name the parts and the whole for the group. Then complete the number bond.

© Big Ideas Learning, LLC

Laurie's Notes

Think and Grow: Modeling Real Life

This application allows students to show different sets of partner numbers for 9. It is similar to the last lesson in that students see the same arrangement of fish in each problem and none of the fish are colored. Student choice of partner numbers determines how the fish are colored.

- **Preview:** Have partners discuss their experiences with fish. Students may remember seeing fish at an aquarium, in a movie, at a pet store, or in a body of water.
- **? Make Sense of Problems:** "Can you choose any way to color the fish?" no "Why?" There is a greater number of orange fish than yellow fish.
- Remind students to plan what they will color for partner numbers before they begin. Remind them, "You purchase more orange fish than yellow fish."
- **Attend to Precision:** Have students discuss how they colored their fish and how they know their answer is correct. Students should mention the number of orange fish is greater than the number of yellow fish.
- Solicit volunteers to show their drawings at the document camera. Ask other students to identify the parts and the whole.
- **Turn and Talk:** "Tell your partner what each number on the number bond means."
- **? Extension:** "If 8 fish are orange, how many are yellow?" 1
- ◉ Revisit the learning target. Have students signal their ability to use partner numbers to make and take apart the number 9.
- **Supporting Learners:** Some students may want to use linking cubes or counters to show a set of partner numbers for nine before they draw. Allow students to use manipulatives as needed.
- **Supporting Learners:** Encourage students to explain how they know they colored nine fish. Some students may still count each object individually, some may count on from the first group, and others may be able to conceptually subitize the parts and the whole. Continue to build upon students' understanding.

Closure

- Pass out nine counters to each student. Have students put some of the counters in one hand and some in the other, then say the parts and the whole. Have students repeat the activity to show different partner numbers for 9.

Sample answer:

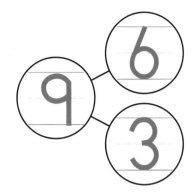

Sample answer:

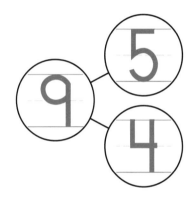

Directions: You buy 9 fish for your fish tank. You buy more orange fish than yellow fish.

• Color to show how many orange fish and yellow fish you could buy. Then complete the number bond to match your picture.

• Color to show another way. Then complete the number bond to match your picture.

246   two hundred forty-six

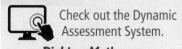
Connect and Extend Learning

Practice Notes

- **Exercise 4**: Remind students that there are a variety of combinations that represent a given number. Make sure they understand the words "more" and "fewer."

Cross-Curricular Connections

Language Arts and Science

- *The Very Hungry Caterpillar* by Eric Carle; Read the book to the students. Talk about the butterfly cycle. Students can now make number 9 caterpillars. Have students draw a caterpillar head or provide them with a picture of a caterpillar head. Give students two colors of dot stickers. Students add dot stickers to the caterpillar head to make 9. Example: 6 red dots and 3 yellow dots. Students should then make the number bond that represents their caterpillar.
- Students continue creating other combinations to make a sum of nine using additional caterpillar heads.

Name _____

Learning Target: Use partner numbers to make and take apart the number 9.

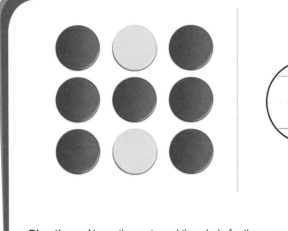

Directions: Name the parts and the whole for the group. Then complete the number bond.

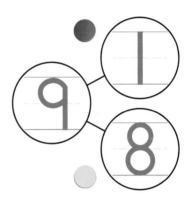

Directions: ❶ Name the parts and the whole for the group. Then complete the number bond.

© Big Ideas Learning, LLC

Chapter 5 | Lesson 6   two hundred forty-seven   **247**

Connect and Extend Learning

Extend Student Learning

Interpersonal

- Students can play "Puddle Jump" in the gymnasium or outside. Make 9 blue puddles and 9 brown puddles out of construction paper. Make them big enough for students to step on. Number each group of puddles from 1–9, one number on each puddle. Divide the students into 2 teams. Spread the blue puddles in front of one team and the brown puddles in front of the other team. Each student in each team needs a partner. When the whistle is blown or you say "GO", a pair of students from each team steps on two puddles to make a sum of 9. If a pair of students is correct, they step to the side. If a pair of students is incorrect, they must go to the end of the line for their team. The game continues until one of the teams has no one left.

Lesson Resources	
Surface Level	**Deep Level**
Resources by Chapter • Extra Practice • Reteach Differentiating the Lesson Skills Review Handbook Skills Trainer	Resources by Chapter • Enrichment and Extension Graphic Organizers Dynamic Assessment System • Lesson Practice

2–4. Sample answers are given.

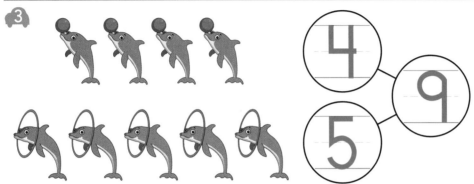

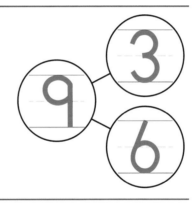

Directions: 2 and 3 Name the parts and the whole for the group. Then complete the number bond. 4 You buy 9 fish for your fish tank. You buy fewer red fish than purple fish. Color to show how many red fish and purple fish you could buy. Then complete the number bond to match your picture.

© Big Ideas Learning, LLC

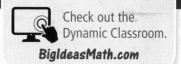

5.7

Learning Target
Use partner numbers to make and take apart the number 10.

Success Criteria
- Name the parts and the whole.
- Use a number bond to show the parts and the whole.

Warm-Up

Practice opportunities for the following are available in the Resources by Chapter or at *BigIdeasMath.com*.

- Daily skills
- Vocabulary
- Prerequisite skills

ELL Support

Because students will be working with familiar concepts and vocabulary, you may want to review the numbers from one to ten, pointing out any confusion that may arise with homophones, such as *one/won, two/to/too, four/for*, and *eight/ate*. Have students count chorally or sequentially from one to ten to check their knowledge of counting these numbers.

Laurie's Notes

Preparing to Teach

Students are familiar with the counting sequence and know that today is a really special day. Knowing the partner numbers for the benchmark 10 is extremely important so extra energy today is great. Students will use their knowledge of partner numbers for 10 as a strategy to solve addition and subtraction problems in later grades. Share that all of their good work in this chapter has led to this special lesson!

Number bonds are shown in all four orientations. Remind students to identify the circles that show the parts and the circle that shows the whole before filling in each bond.

Materials
- two-color counters

Dig In (Circle Time)

Students will use their fingers today to investigate partner numbers for 10. If there are three fingers up, there are seven fingers down.

- Begin by asking students to hold up both hands and show you 4 fingers, 7 fingers, 0 fingers, and so on. Each time comment that you see "4 fingers up" or "7 fingers up."
- ❓ Ask one student to use both hands and show 3 fingers up. "I wonder how many fingers they have down?" Give think time before having several students share their thinking. Listen for the concept of partner numbers and the knowledge that we have 10 fingers.
- Repeat this several times with different numbers.
- Record the partner numbers on an anchor chart. See page T-211C for ideas.
- Go back to asking the whole class to show 4 fingers and follow it up with students saying how many fingers are down, or not showing.
- ❓ Extension: "You have 2 fingers down. How many are up?"
- **Supporting Learners:** Students can show each set of partner numbers for 10 on a ten frame using two-color counters. Students develop their conceptual subitizing skills by seeing the parts and the whole on a ten frame.
- **Supporting Learners:** Give partner groups ten counters. One partner uses his or her hands to cover some of the counters. The other partner guesses how many counters are hidden. The first partner lifts their hands to show whether the answer is correct. Have partners switch roles to practice other ways to make 10.

❓ Teaching Prompt   ◉ Learning Target

Name _____

Learning Target: Use partner numbers to make and take apart the number 10.

Explore and Grow

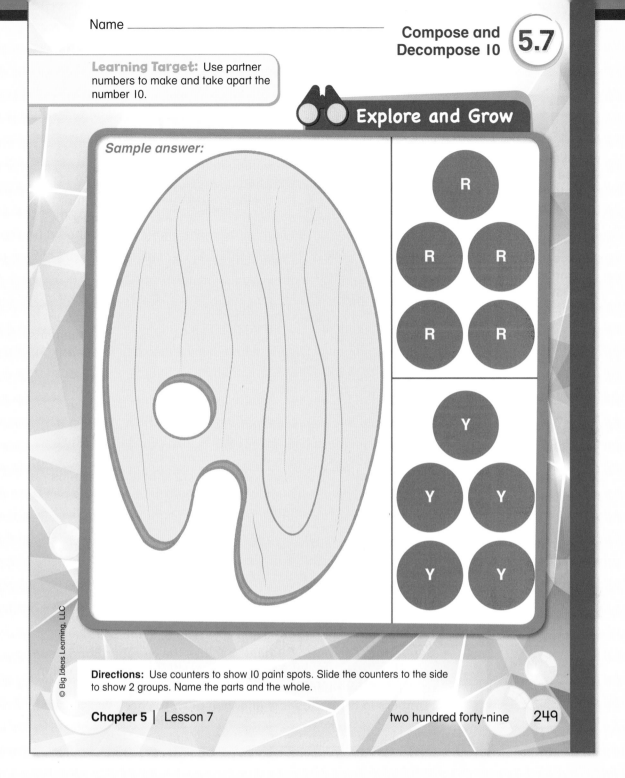

Sample answer:

Directions: Use counters to show 10 paint spots. Slide the counters to the side to show 2 groups. Name the parts and the whole.

© Big Ideas Learning, LLC

Chapter 5 | Lesson 7

two hundred forty-nine   249

Explore and Grow

- Pass out counters. "There are ten paint spots on my painting palette. Some are red and some are yellow. Use counters to show the paint spots."
- Students slide all of the red counters to one section and all of the yellow counters to the other. Counters should not overlap. They need to be visible to students who may arrange them in rows to help in the counting process.
- Ask different students to share: My parts are _____ and _____. My whole is _____.
- ⊙ "How good are you at naming the two parts when the whole is 10?"
- **Extension:** "I want more red spots than yellow. Show me what this looks like."

ELL Support

Students will likely be familiar with the words pencil and paintbrush. If not, teach them by pointing to each and stating its name. Have students practice language by working in groups to discuss each exercise and decide the answers.

Beginner students may count each item aloud.

Intermediate students may state the number and name of each item, such as, "one blue pencil."

Advanced students may use sentences to describe the parts and whole for each exercise. Remind them to change from using *is* to *are* as needed.

Think and Grow

Getting Started

- A discussion about models used in this chapter is on page T-211D. The ten frame and rekenrek have not been mentioned directly in the section notes. Two-color counters and linking cubes have been the primary models, along with fingers. The ten frames, subitizing cards, and rekenrek should be available to support student learning. If you feel students would benefit from their use in this lesson, use them.

Teaching Notes

- The layout of the page should be familiar to students. Be sure to remind students they need to know which circles show the parts and which circle shows the whole, as the orientation of each number bond is different.

- **?** **Model:** "How many counters do you see?" 10 "Which circle is the whole and how do you know?" There is a 10 to trace and the two lines show the parts make the whole. "Tell your partner how many yellow and how many red counters you see." Students count and then trace the numbers 3 and 7.

- **Connections:** The arrangement of objects should look familiar to students. The pencils are in a rectangular array and the paint brushes are the 10-pattern on a domino.

- ◉ Partners discuss how they filled in the number bond and knew which circles showed the parts and which circle showed the whole. Solicit several responses.

- **?** **Extension:** "If you group the paint brushes a different way, does the number for the whole change?" No, the whole is still 10. "What is another set of partner numbers for 10 that is not shown on the page?" 0 and 10; 2 and 8; 5 and 5

- **Supporting Learners:** Students can use the Number Bond Draw and Write Instructional Resource to practice drawing and writing the partner numbers for 10. Challenge students to write the numbers in the bonds first and then draw to check their answer.

Directions: Name the parts and the whole for the group. Then complete the number bond.

250   two hundred fifty

© Big Ideas Learning, LLC

Meeting the needs of
all learners.

Laurie's Notes

Apply and Grow: Practice

SCAFFOLDING INSTRUCTION

Students have been studying numbers within 10 for quite some time and you want them to build fluency with the partner numbers for 10. Show students *five* counters in your open hand. Have students count them and then close your hand around the counters. Put both hands behind your back and remove some counters into the other hand. Show one hand with some counters and ask the students, "How many are hidden?" Repeat this process with different amounts removed. Students are considered to have mastered a number when they answer quickly and accurately. They do not need to count one-by-one. Continue this process with higher numbers to 10 until students have difficulty.

EMERGING students may not have quick recall of the partner numbers and may need to have a visual model to know two parts for 10. They may still have difficulty identifying circles for the parts and the whole.

- **Exercises 1–3:** Walk students through how to complete the exercise. Ask specific questions that address the two different kinds of objects and where to put them on the number bond. An example of this for exercise 1 is to ask, "How many black aprons are there? Write the number for the part."
- **Exercise 2:** Have students use their fingers to model all of the paint tubes. The whole is 10. Now use fingers to model the purple paint tubes. How many fingers didn't they use?
- A ten frame and counters would be helpful for students who need to see the structure of the frame to help them visualize 10 objects.

PROFICIENT students are able to use a number bond to make or take apart the number 10.

- **Exercise 2:** "Compare the number of purple tubes and green tubes. Are there more or fewer purple tubes than green tubes?" fewer
- **Exercise 3:** "How many paint cans have spilled?" 2 "How many cans have not spilled?" 8 Note if students count to decide there are 8 or if they know 8 is the partner number for 2 to make 10.

Extension: Adding Rigor

- Play "Sandwich Bonds." Have students put their number cards 0–10 into a pile. Tell students a number 1–10 and have them find combinations of two cards that make that number. Repeat the process saying a different number.

Name _____

1

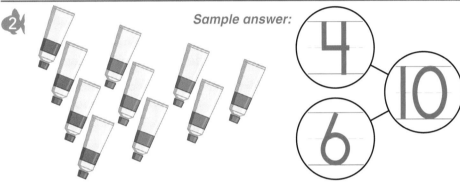

5   5

10

2   *Sample answer:*

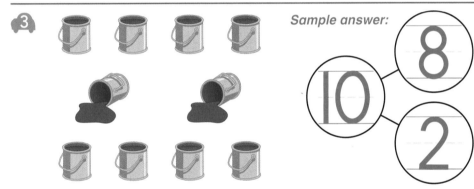

4

10

6

3   *Sample answer:*

8

10

2

Directions: **1**–**3** Name the parts and the whole for the group. Then complete the number bond.

© Big Ideas Learning, LLC

Chapter 5 | Lesson 7   **251**

Laurie's Notes

Think and Grow: Modeling Real Life

This application helps students identify different sets of partner numbers for 10. Students sort objects in different ways and show the parts and the whole on a number bond. Students need to recall the vocabulary word *category* and what it means.

- **Preview:** Begin with a discussion about buttons; how they are used, what they might look like. Students may notice the different buttons they have on their clothes. Students can share the color, size, and number of holes of any buttons they see. You can also use the story *Frog and Toad are Friends: The Lost Button* to introduce the topic of buttons.

- **Turn and Talk:** "Tell your partner different ways you can sort the buttons." Listen for students to mention the *color*, *shape*, and *size* of the buttons.

- Display the page under a document camera. Ask a volunteer to point to two buttons that are a different color; a different shape; a different size. These attributes need to be understood by students before they begin.

? "How many buttons are there altogether?" 10 "What will the whole be?" 10 "What will the parts be?" partner numbers for 10

- **Quiet Think Time:** Have students decide how they want to sort the buttons. "Has everyone decided how they will sort the buttons at the top?"

- **Teaching Tip:** You could suggest to students that they cross out the buttons as they count them. They could also try to circle buttons that belong to the same group.

- ◉ Students have spent five lessons on naming the part and the whole and recording the numbers in a number bond. Have students reflect back to when they first started using the number bonds. You want them to see their learning progress and be proud of their learning. How do they think they are doing now with seeing two groups that can be put together to make the whole? Can they take apart the whole and say the two parts? Can they use a number bond to show the parts and the whole?

- **Supporting Learners:** Have students draw a group of dots on their board and then say how many more they need to draw to make ten. Students can draw the remaining dots to check their answer.

Closure

- Have one partner say a number within 10. The second partner uses their fingers to show the other partner number.

Think and Grow: Modeling Real Life

Sample answer:
by size

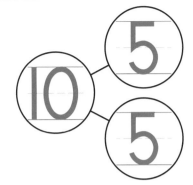

Sample answer:
by shape

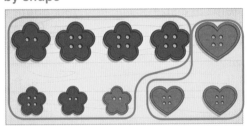

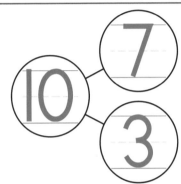

by color

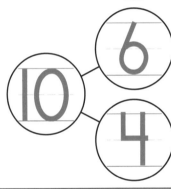

Directions:
- You have 10 buttons. Classify the buttons into 2 categories. Circle the groups. Then complete the number bond to match your picture.
- Show 2 other ways you can classify the buttons into 2 categories. Then complete the number bonds to match your pictures.

252   two hundred fifty-two

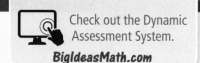
Connect and Extend Learning

Practice Notes

- **Exercise 4:** When students are asked to sort buttons, keep in mind there will be more than one way to sort (color, size, shape, number of holes).

Cross-Curricular Connections

Language Arts and Science

- *Fish Eyes: A Book You Can Count On* by Lois Ehlert; Now this time, you can read the whole book to the class. Take the opportunity to integrate a science lesson. Talk about the different kinds of fish you might find in the ocean. For math, students write a number bond for each page you read. When you are all finished with the book, call out a number of fish. Example: 6 fabulous fish. Ask them to write a number bond where the whole is 6. Talk about all the ways you can make 6. Continue this activity using other numbers up to 10.

Art

- Each student needs 1 pipe cleaner and 10 beads, preferably all of the same color. (Pony beads work best.) Students put all ten beads on the pipe cleaner. Students now slide the beads side to side to see the various ways of making 10. As they make a combination of ten, students write the number bond.

Practice (5.7)

Learning Target: Use partner numbers to make and take apart the number 10.

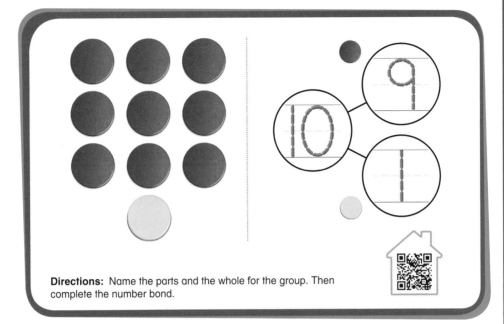

Directions: Name the parts and the whole for the group. Then complete the number bond.

Directions: Name the parts and the whole for the group. Then complete the number bond.

Chapter 5 | Lesson 7

two hundred fifty-three   253

Connect and Extend Learning

Extend Student Learning
Bodily-kinesthetic

- Each student gets a plastic three-divider plate and 20 counters. Students put some counters in the first small divider of the plate and the rest of the counters in the other small part of the plate. With a dry-erase marker, students can write the number of counters in each of the small dividers. The students now write the total number of counters in the large divider. Have them say the number bond out loud. *Example:* 5 and 2 are 7. Erase the numbers on the plastic plate and do more problems.

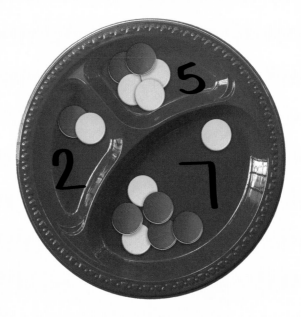

Lesson Resources	
Surface Level	**Deep Level**
Resources by Chapter • Extra Practice • Reteach Differentiating the Lesson Skills Review Handbook Skills Trainer	Resources by Chapter • Enrichment and Extension Graphic Organizers Dynamic Assessment System • Lesson Practice

2–4. Sample answers are given.

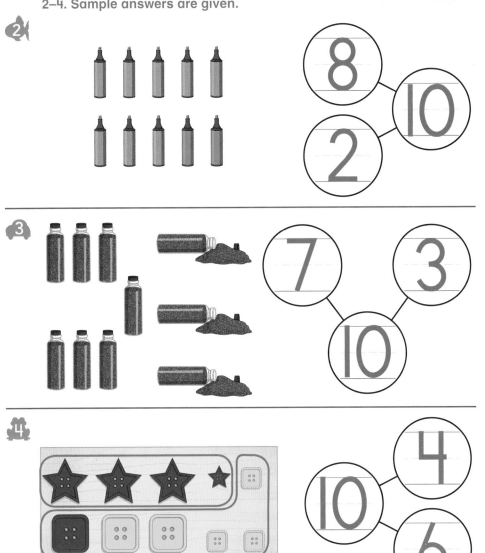

Directions: 🐟 and 🐢 Name the parts and the whole for the group. Then complete the number bond. 🐸 You have 10 buttons. Classify the buttons into 2 categories. Circle the groups. Then complete the number bond to match your picture.

254   two hundred fifty-four

5.8

Learning Target

Use a group of 5 to put together and take apart numbers to 10.

Success Criteria

- Name the whole.
- Find a group of 5.
- Name the partner numbers when one part is 5.

Warm-Up

Practice opportunities for the following are available in the Resources by Chapter or at *BigIdeasMath.com*.

- Daily skills
- Vocabulary
- Prerequisite skills

ELL Support

Explain that there are many action words (verbs) in English that are made of more than one part. Explain that the phrase *to put together* describes the opposite action of *to take apart*. Act out putting something on a shelf to demonstrate the word *put*. Gather several items in one group to demonstrate *together*. Use building blocks to put together a small object with several parts to demonstrate the meaning of the phrase.

Laurie's Notes

Preparing to Teach

Students know how to compose and decompose numbers to 10 and can show the relationship on a number bond. This lesson connects student's knowledge and use of the benchmark of 5 to compose and decompose numbers from 6 to 10. Students build their recognition of groups of five with fingers, ten frames, and a rekenrek. Review the ten frame and rekenrek as needed.

Materials

- two-color counters

Dig In (Circle Time)

? Hold up one hand and show five fingers to students. Hold your other hand behind your back with three fingers displayed. "I have eight fingers up, but some are hidden behind my back. How many fingers do I have up behind my back?"

- Solicit responses from several students. Then show students the three fingers you have displayed behind your back. "5 and 3 are partner numbers for 8."

- Hold up one hand again showing 5 fingers. "Help me count from 5 to 8 using your fingers."

- Slowly count from 5 to 8 as you hold up one more finger for each count. Have students determine the numbers of fingers they put up as you count from 5 to 8.

- Repeat this activity with other numbers from 6 to 10.

- Have one partner choose a number from 6 to 10 and use their fingers to show the number. Be sure they display all five fingers (one of the parts) on one of their hands. The other partner says the parts (5 and _____) and the whole.

◉ Explain they are still finding parts that are put together to make the whole. The difference today is that you want one of the parts to be 5. Discuss different models they know for 5: five frame, fingers, five beads on the rekenrek, subitizing cards, and so on. "We want to find a 5 as one of the parts today."

? Teaching Prompt   ◉ Learning Target

Compose and
Decompose Using
a Group of 5

5.8

Learning Target: Use a group of 5 to put together and take apart numbers to 10.

Explore and Grow

Sample answer:

Directions: How many frogs are on the log? Place a counter on each frog. **5** Use more counters to show 9 frogs. Slide the counters to the bottom to show the 2 groups. Name the parts and the whole.

Chapter 5 | Lesson 8   two hundred fifty-five **255**

© Big Ideas Learning, LLC

Explore and Grow

- Pass out counters. "There are nine frogs in the pond. Place a red counter on each frog on the top log. How many frogs do we have?" 5 "There are some frogs hiding behind the bottom log. I know there are 9 frogs altogether. Use yellow counters to show the hiding frogs on the bottom log."

- Encourage students to count on from 5 to find the missing part.

? Students slide all of the red counters to one section and all of the yellow counters to the other section. "What are the parts?" 5 and 4 "What is the whole?" 9

◉ Refer to the anchor chart for 9. There are many partner numbers for 9. Today we are looking at those that have 5 as a part.

| 1 | 2 | 3 | 4 | 5 | 6 | 7 | 8 | 9 | 10 |

ELL Support

Have students practice language by working in groups to discuss each exercise and decide the answers. Explain that the total number of dots is named in the top circle and that they must decide how many more dots to draw to make this total. They also must include the number of dots already drawn.

Beginner students may only state the number needed.
Intermediate/ Advanced students may use sentences to describe how many are needed, such as, "I need to draw one dot and the number 1."

Laurie's Notes

Think and Grow

Getting Started

- Take time to discuss and model how to use a number path and ten frame to find a missing part when the whole is 7 and one part is 5.
- Hold up a number path. Have students talk about how they could use the number path to find what number you put together with 5 to make a whole of 7. Model counting from 5 to 7 while students count the hops. Identify the number of hops as a partner number. This is the first time students are formally introduced to counting on using a number path.
- Model the same problem with the ten frame. Have students discuss how to find the partner number with 5 to make 7 altogether.

Teaching Notes

- Students see a number bond where one part is five and a ten frame with five dots. You want students to count on from the group of five to determine the other partner number to make the whole given on the number bond. Have students name the parts and the whole.
- ? Model: "What is the whole in the number bond?" 8 "We want two parts that are put together to make 8. One part is 5. What is the missing part?" 3 Students draw 3 more dots and trace the 3.
- Critique the Reasoning of Others: Point to the number path. Have students *Turn and Talk* about using a number path for finding the other partner number.
- Note the different orientations of the number bond on this page.
- ? Look for and Express Regularity in Repeated Reasoning: "What is the same about each number bond?" One part is 5.
- ◉ On this page students found a group of 5 and identified the other partner number. "Show me with your thumb signals how you are doing with your learning today."
- ? Extension: "If you have 5 dots, how many more dots do you need to make 6?" 1 "7?" 2 "8?" 3 "9?" 4 "10?" 5 "What do you notice each time the whole is one more?" The other partner number is one more.
- Supporting Learners: Relate the groups of five on a ten frame to using fingers from the Dig In activity. Remind students they can use their fingers to count on from 5 to find the other partner number.

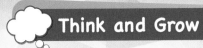
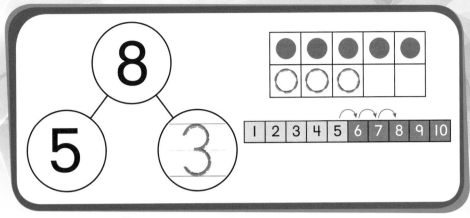

8

5   3

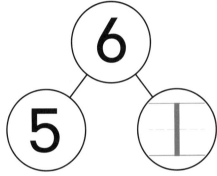

6

5   1

Sample answer:

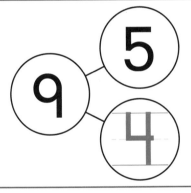

9   5

4

Sample answer:

Directions: Draw dots in the ten frame to make the whole. Use the ten frame to complete the number bond.

256   two hundred fifty-six

© Big Ideas Learning, LLC

Meeting the needs of all learners.

Laurie's Notes

Apply and Grow: Practice

SCAFFOLDING INSTRUCTION

The benchmarks of 5 and 10 are certainly integrated in this section. Before students begin this page you might want to gain further information about students' understanding of the $5 + n$ pattern. Have students explain their understanding of the $5 + n$ pattern by telling how they see the five and count on. Relate to student's own hands by modeling the embedded 5 in the $5 + n$ patterns with your hands.

FYI: Do not use the phrase "$5 + n$ pattern" with students. Use "group of 5" instead.

EMERGING students may find it difficult to use a group of 5 to put together and take apart numbers to 10.

- **Exercises 1–3:** Have students use a ten frame and counters to model each exercise.
- **Exercises 1–3:** Have students talk about what is the same in each exercise and what is different. Do they *see* five dots on the ten frame? Do they notice that 5 is one of the parts in the number bond?
- **? Exercises 1–3:** Walk students through how to complete the exercise. Have students point to the whole and then point to the partner number that is shown. Ask, "How can we make the whole if we start with a group of 5?" I can count on from five to see what the partner number is. I can draw to show it in the ten frame.

PROFICIENT students are able to use a group of 5 to put together and take apart numbers to 10.

- **Exercises 1–3:** Use the words "put together" and "take apart" to describe the numbers on your number bond.
- **?** "How many spaces are empty on the ten frame when you started the problem? How many spaces were empty when you finished?"

Extension: Adding Rigor

- Make a copy of the Draw Lines On Number Bonds Instructional Resource for each student. Have students draw the lines so the two parts make the whole.

Name _____

1

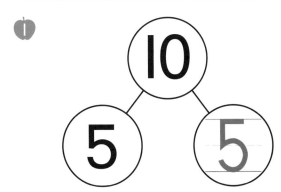

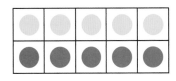

2

Sample answer:

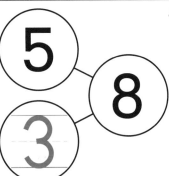

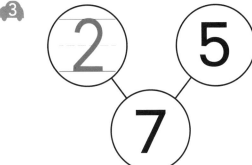

3

Sample answer:

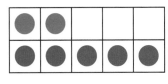

Directions: **1**–**3** Draw dots in the ten frame to make the whole. Use the ten frame to complete the number bond.

© Big Ideas Learning, LLC

Think and Grow: Modeling Real Life

This application has students draw the other partner number when one group is 5. Students need to know how to compare two quantities to draw the other partner number and fill in the number bond.

- **Preview:** "Do you see what Newton is holding? Why do you think he has balloons? Do you think Descartes would like a few balloons?"
- ◉ "How many balloons is Newton holding?" 5 This is the second success criterion.
- "Draw balloons for Descartes so he has *fewer* balloons than Newton." Have students talk with a partner about how many balloons they want to draw and why. Partners may help them remember numbers that are *less than* 5.
- After students draw their balloons and complete the number bond, choose several students to share how they found the number for the whole. Students benefit from hearing different strategies such as counting all the balloons, counting on from the group of 5, or recognizing a set of partner numbers on the anchor chart.
- Have students complete the second exercise. Observe and note whether students write the numbers in the correct circles.
- **Partner Speaks:** Have partners tell each other the meaning of each number on the number bond. Choose several students to share their partner's answer.
- ❓ **Extension:** "If Descartes has less balloons than Newton, what is the greatest number of balloons he can hold?" 4 "What would be the whole?" 9 "If Newton and Descartes had the same number of balloons, what would be the whole?" 10
- ◉ Revisit the learning target and ask students to show their thumb signal.
- Some students may want to show the partner numbers with linking cubes or counters on a ten frame. Have students use manipulatives as needed.

Closure

- Have one partner choose a number from 5 to 10. The second student identifies the other partner numbers when one group is 5. Have partners switch roles. Students can use their fingers or a number path to determine the missing partner number.

Sample answer:

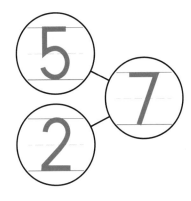

Sample answer:

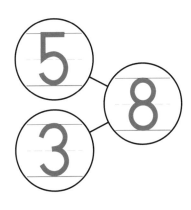

Directions: Newton has 5 balloons. Descartes has fewer balloons than Newton.
- Draw Descarte's balloons. Complete the number bond to match your picture.
- Draw to show another way. Then complete the number bond to match your picture.

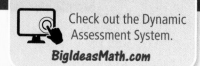

Connect and Extend Learning

Practice Notes

- Ask students whether they carry anything around with them all the time that can help them make whole groups where one partner number is five. The fingers on their hands.
- Have students call out what numbers they can make with their fingers using all of the fingers on one hand and some number of fingers on the other.

Cross-Curricular Connections

Language Arts

- *Doggies* by Sandra Boynton; Read the entire book to the students. This activity will start on the page "Six quiet dogs". For each of the next pages up through 10, students will write a number bond where one of the parts of the whole is 5. Then they will tell their partner a story that represents their number bond. Make sure the students use the dogs in the book for their story. Example: $5 + 2 = 7$, There are 5 big dogs and 2 small dogs.

Practice **5.8**

Learning Target: Use a group of 5 to put together and take apart numbers to 10.

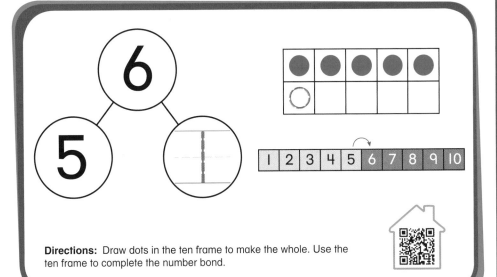

Directions: Draw dots in the ten frame to make the whole. Use the ten frame to complete the number bond.

❶

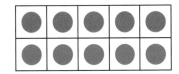

Directions: ❶ Draw dots in the ten frame to make the whole. Use the ten frame to complete the number bond.

Chapter 5 | Lesson 8

two hundred fifty-nine **259**

Connect and Extend Learning

Extend Student Learning

Musical

- Sing songs together such as "5 Little Monkeys Jumping on the Bed" and "5 Green and Speckled Frogs".

Bodily-Kinesthetic

- Make a few large number bonds on the playground using chalk. Students will play "Outdoor Number Bonds." Have 5 students stand in one of the part circles. Then ask 9 students to stand in the whole circle. Ask the students "How many students need to stand in the other part circle?" When there are 4 children in the other circle, ask a student to say the number bond. "5 and 4 are 9." You can continue playing this game, always having 5 students in one of the circles.

Lesson Resources	
Surface Level	**Deep Level**
Resources by Chapter • Extra Practice • Reteach Differentiating the Lesson Skills Review Handbook Skills Trainer	Resources by Chapter • Enrichment and Extension Graphic Organizers Dynamic Assessment System • Lesson Practice

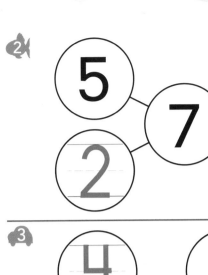

Sample answer:

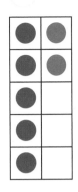

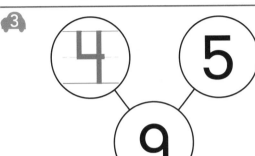

Sample answer:

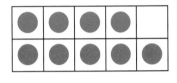

Directions: ② and ③ Draw dots in the ten frame to make the whole. Use the ten frame to complete the number bond. ④ Newton has 5 balloons. Descartes has the same number of balloons as Newton. Draw Descartes's balloons. Complete the number bond to match your picture.

Laurie's Notes

Performance Task

In this task, students will compose and decompose numbers and fill in number bonds to show the whole and its partner numbers. It may be challenging for students to classify butterflies another way. Use student responses to gauge their thinking about composing and decomposing numbers to 10.

- Decide ahead of time whether students will be working independently, in pairs, or in groups.
- Pause between direction lines for students to complete each step.
- Have students share their work and thinking with others. Discuss as a class.

Exercise	Answers and Notes	Points
1	Students color 1 red, 9 yellow; 2 red, 8 yellow; 3 red, 7 yellow; or 4 red, 6 yellow. 10 is the whole. Students write the corresponding numbers in the parts.	3
2	3 is one of the parts. 8 is the whole.	3
3	6 and 2 are the parts. 8 is the whole.	2
	Total	8

Sample answer:

①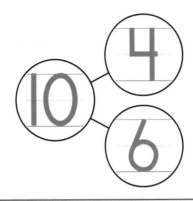

② by color

⑤ 3

8

③ **Sample answer:**
by size

2 8

6

Directions: ① Color to show fewer red ladybugs than yellow ladybugs. Then complete the number bond to match your picture. ② Use the number bond to classify the butterflies. Then complete the number bond. ③ Classify the butterflies another way. Then complete the number bond.

Number Bond Spin and Cover

Materials

- 1 paper clip and pencil per pair
- 16 two-color counters per pair

Students can work in pairs or small groups.

- **?** "What do you see on this page? Is there a partner number given in the number bond? What is different about this number bond?" There is more than one number in one of the parts.
- This is the first time that students are working with spinners using a paper clip and pencil. It is important to address the spinner and to have students practice before completing the activity.
- Read the directions at the bottom of the page.
- Model how to spin the spinner, name the part, and find the whole. Then cover the whole on the game board with a counter.
- **FYI:** Have students spin again if the numbers for the whole are all covered on the page.
- When game play concludes, the discussion should focus on students' reasoning for how they found the whole.
- **?** **Attend to Precision:** "How did you know what number to cover as you played the game?" I knew one partner number was 5. I used the spinner to find the other partner number. I counted on from 5 to find the whole.
- Provide students with counters, a ten frame, and a number path 1–10 to assist them in finding the partner numbers.
- **Whiteboards:** Have students make a visual by creating the filled in number bond on a whiteboard.
- **Teaching Tip:** Put a number bond in a plastic sheet. Have students take turns writing on the page and wiping it off once they are finished finding the whole.

Closure

- **?** "What is the greatest number you can make as the whole? Why?" 10, because 5 is the greatest number on the spinner. I know that 5 and 5 are partner numbers for 10.

Number Bond Spin and Cover

Directions: Take turns using the spinner to find your partner number with 5. Use your partner numbers to find the whole on the game board. Cover the whole with a counter. Repeat this process until you have covered all of the numbers.

Learning Target Correlation

Lesson	Learning Target	Exercises
5.1	Use partner numbers to show numbers to 5.	1, 2
5.2	Use number bonds to show the parts and the whole for numbers to 5.	3
5.3	Use partner numbers to make and take apart the number 6.	4
5.4	Use partner numbers to make and take apart the number 7.	5
5.5	Use partner numbers to make and take apart the number 8.	6
5.6	Use partner numbers to make and take apart the number 9.	7
5.7	Use partner numbers to make and take apart the number 10.	8, 9
5.8	Use a group of five to put together and take apart numbers to 10.	10–12

5.1 Partner Numbers to 5

$$2 \quad 2 \quad 4$$

$$3 \quad 0 \quad 3$$

5.2 Use Number Bonds to Represent Numbers to 5

 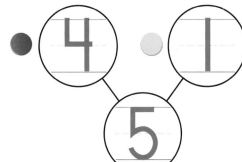

Directions: ① and ② Count each type of object. Write each number. Count all of the objects. Write the number for the whole. ③ Name the parts and the whole for the group. Then complete the number bond.

© Big Ideas Learning, LLC

Chapter Resources		
Surface Level	**Deep Level**	**Transfer Level**
Resources by Chapter • Extra Practice • Reteach Differentiating the Lesson Skills Review Handbook Skills Trainer Game Library Math Musicals	Resources by Chapter • Enrichment and Extension Graphic Organizers Game Library Math Musicals	Dynamic Assessment System • Chapter Test Assessment Book • Chapter Tests A and B

5.3 Compose and Decompose 6

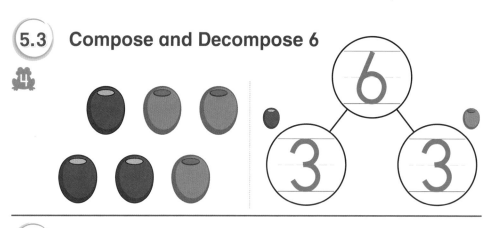

5.4 Compose and Decompose 7

Sample answer:

5.5 Compose and Decompose 8

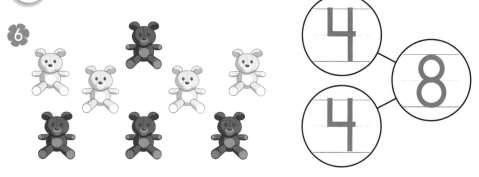

Directions: 4 – 6 Name the parts and the whole for the group. Then complete the number bond.

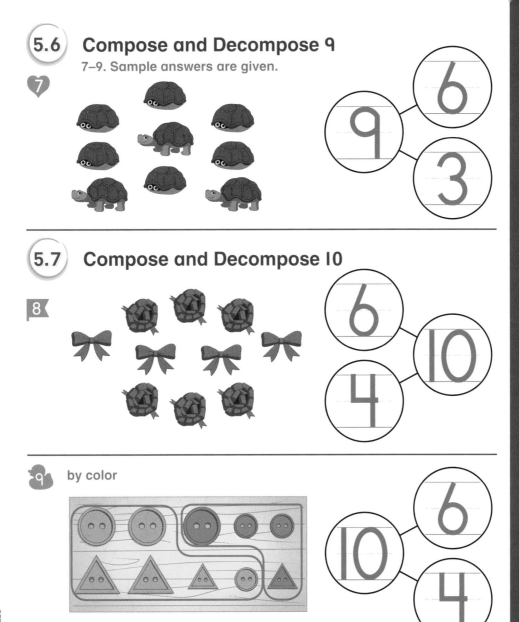

5.6 Compose and Decompose 9

7–9. Sample answers are given.

7

$$9 \quad 6 \\ 3$$

5.7 Compose and Decompose 10

8

$$6 \\ 4 \quad 10$$

9 by color

$$10 \quad 6 \\ 4$$

Directions: **7** and **8** Name the parts and the whole for the group. Then complete the number bond. **9** You have 10 buttons. Classify the buttons into 2 categories. Circle the groups. Then complete the number bond to match your picture.

(5.8) Compose and Decompose Using a Group of 5

10–12. Sample answers are given.

Directions: 🔟 and 🏠 Draw dots in the ten frame to make the whole. Use the ten frame to complete the number bond. 🍁 Newton has 5 balloons. Descartes has fewer balloons than Newton. Draw Descartes's balloons. Complete the number bond to match your picture.

Math Musicals can be used with current topics, to review previous topics, or to preview upcoming topics.

Centers

Center 1: Number Bond Spin and Cover

Materials per pair: Student Edition page 262, 1 paper clip and pencil, and
16 two-color counters

Have students complete the Number Bond Spin and Cover activity. See
page T-262 for the directions.

Center 2: Skills Trainer

Materials: computers or devices with Internet access

Have students go to *BigIdeasMath.com* to access the Skills Trainer.

Center 3: Fun with Dominoes

Materials per pair: Number Cards 1–10*, dominoes

Lay out number cards on the table, face up. Students work together to match
the dominoes that add up to each number.

Center 4: Write and Wipe Number Bonds

Materials per pair: Number Bond*, dry-erase marker, eraser, and a few cups
of two-color counters of various quantities (1 cup with 6 two-color counters,
another cup with 9 two-color counters)

A student pours the counters out of one cup. Together they count how many
red counters they have and write that number on their number bond. Then
they count how many yellow counters they have and write that number on the
number bond. Next, they count how many counters they have in total and then
write that number on the number bond. They can erase their work and use the
same cup of counters or they can pick another cup.

Center 5: Fishy Number Bond

Materials: Fishy Number Bonds*, 1 set of 10 Fishy Number Bond Cards*,
crayons, glue stick

Students color the fish red or blue and then cut out the fish cards. They now
glue some fish in one fish bowl and some in the other fish bowl. Next, students
use the Fishy Number Bond to write in their numbers.

Found in the Instructional Resources

Chapter Assessment Guide

Chapter tests are available in the Assessment Book.
An alternative assessment option is listed below.

Bodily-Kinesthetic

Materials: 10 linking cubes, laminated Number Bond, dry-erase marker, and eraser

Call students over individually. Play a game called "Snap" with the student. Show the student a linking cube tower. Put the tower behind your back and ask the student to say "Snap!" Quickly break your tower into two. Show the student one part of the tower and ask if he/she can tell you the part that is still behind your back. If the student can't answer, show the student the tower from behind your back and count the cubes in the tower together. Repeat 4 times with different combinations and different numbers of cubes.

Extension: For more points, have the student use a number bond to show the part-part-whole representation for the problem.

Task	Points
Student can answer how many linking cubes are behind your back.	1 point per; 5 points total
Student can complete a number bond to match the linking cubes.	1 point per; 5 points total
Total:	10 points

My Thoughts on the Chapter

What worked...

What did not work...

What I would do differently...

Teacher Tip

Not allowed to write in your teaching edition? Use sticky notes to record your thoughts.

6 Add Numbers Within 10

Lesson	Learning Target	Success Criteria
6.1 Understand Addition	Add to a group of objects and tell how many.	• Tell how many objects there are to start. • Tell how many objects are added to a group. • Tell how many objects there are in all.
6.2 Addition: Add To	Add to a group of objects and complete an addition sentence.	• Tell what the plus sign means. • Tell what the equal sign means. • Explain an addition sentence.
6.3 Addition: Put Together	Put two groups of objects together and complete an addition sentence.	• Show how to put together two groups of objects. • Tell how many there are in all. • Write an addition sentence.
6.4 Addition: Partner Numbers	Find partner numbers for a number and write an addition sentence.	• Show two partner numbers for a whole. • Write an addition sentence with partner numbers.
6.5 Addition Number Patterns	Explain addition patterns with 0 and 1.	• Describe a pattern. • Explain that I have the same number when I add 0. • Explain that I have the next number when I add 1.
6.6 Practice Addition	Add partner numbers to 5.	• Show and tell how to add numbers to 5. • Complete an addition sentence.
6.7 Use a Group of 5 to Add	Use a group of 5 to write an addition sentence.	• Use a ten frame to add on to 5. • Add on to 5 to make a whole. • Write an addition sentence.
6.8 Add to Make 10	Find partner numbers for 10 and write an addition sentence.	• Add on to a number to make 10. • Show partner numbers for 10. • Write an addition sentence for 10 when one group is given.

Chapter Learning Target:
Understand addition patterns.
Chapter Success Criteria:
- Identify a number sentence.
- Describe a pattern.
- Write an addition sentence.
- Explain addition sentences.

Progressions

Through the Grades	
Kindergarten	**Grade 1**
• Represent addition with various models and strategies. • Write an addition number sentence using symbols. • Represent, write, and solve "Add To" and "Put Together" problems with unknowns. • Break apart numbers to 10 in different ways. • Understand that the next number stated is one number greater. • Write the same number when 0 is added. • Solve addition word problems. • Fluently add within 5. • Find number patterns that make 10.	• Add in any order. • Understand the equal sign. • Answer true and false questions. • Represent and count on to find the change unknown. • Add using doubles 1–5. • Compare strategies for addition.

Standard	Through the Chapter							
	6.1	6.2	6.3	6.4	6.5	6.6	6.7	6.8
Represent addition and subtraction with objects, fingers, mental images, drawings, sounds, acting out situations, verbal explanations, expressions, or equations.	●	●	●	●	●	●	●	
Solve addition and subtraction word problems, and add and subtract within 10, e.g., by using objects or drawings to represent the problem.	●	●	●	●	●	●	●	
Decompose numbers less than or equal to 10 into pairs in more than one way, e.g., by using objects or drawings, and record each decomposition by a drawing or equation.				★				
Understand that each successive number name refers to a quantity that is one larger.					●			
Fluently add and subtract within 5.					●	●		
For any number from 1 to 9, find the number that makes 10 when added to the given number, e.g., by using objects or drawings, and record the answer with a drawing or equation.								●

Key: ▲ = Preparing   ● = Learning   ★ = Complete

Laurie's Overview

About the Math

All of the work students have done with composing and decomposing numbers in the last chapter has prepared them to begin work with the operations of addition (Chapter 6) and subtraction (Chapter 7). At this stage of learning we want students to use fingers, models, acting out, and drawings to explore and represent addition situations. In this chapter, we introduce the symbols associated with an addition equation, initially referring to it as an addition sentence.

This chapter presents the two types of addition situations expected in kindergarten: *Add To* with result unknown and *Put Together* with either total unknown or both addends unknown. The *Add To* problems are easiest for students to understand and model. The *Put Together* problems can be modeled but there is no physical action that brings the two addends together. In the addition situation, students must conceptually understand that pigs and cows are both animals.

Addition Situations

Change Problems	Result Unknown	
Add To	There are 3 pigs in the pen. Two more join them. How many pigs are there altogether? 3 + 2 = _____	
Part-Part-Whole Problems	**Total Unknown**	**Both Addends Unknown**
Put Together	There are 3 pigs in the pen and 2 cows in the pasture. How many animals are there in all? 3 + 2 = _____	There are 5 animals altogether. Some are pigs and some are cows. How many of each could there be? 5 = _____ + _____

The language of addition is introduced through the story problems where the contexts naturally use words such as *join*, *some more,* or *in all*. Two necessary symbols, the plus sign and equal sign, are introduced as a way to help students record what they are thinking when they tell a story. Be careful when talking about the equal sign. It represents a relationship between two quantities and we do not want students to believe it means "the answer." That leads students to seeing the equal sign as a rightward pointing arrow. Use language such as 'is the same amount as' or 'is the same as'.

Addition situations are presented in the early part of the chapter. The later part of the chapter makes connections to the partner numbers students worked with in Chapter 5. Now they can write addition sentences for partner numbers. Patterns with adding 0 and 1 are also explored.

The last two lessons provide a natural opportunity for deeper learning to occur. The surface level skills of understanding addition situations and writing addition sentences are necessary to use a group of 5 to write an addition sentence. The $5 + n$ pattern is an important benchmark that enables students to build fluency in addition.

Models

- Linking cubes are used often throughout this chapter to show the two parts or addends in a story problem. Consider the role of color and how it connects to the addition situation and the story.

- Acting out an addition story problem is a kinaesthetic approach to help students see the joining of two quantities to make the whole. Students can also hold a plus sign between the two groups of addends.

- Fingers are readily available to model two quantities whose sum is 10 or less. In thinking of partner numbers for 10, when 8 fingers are up, 2 are down. Students can see the partner numbers and begin to conceptually subitize the two quantities.

- Five and ten frames are used with two-colored counters to show the parts and whole. Frames provide students with a visual of the different ways to make each number. Developing a mental benchmark and fluency with making five and ten helps students when they learn addition and subtraction strategies in later grades.

- Dominos have two parts that represent the addends. We want students to conceptually subitize the number 8 when they see two groups of four dots.

Chapter Materials and Resources

The primary materials and resources needed for this chapter are listed below. Other materials may be needed for the additional support ideas provided throughout the chapter.

Check out the virtual manipulatives.
BigIdeasMath.com

Classroom Materials	Chapter Opener	6.1	6.2	6.3	6.4	6.5	6.6	6.7	6.8	Connect and Grow
scissors	•									
linking cubes		•	•	•	•				•	•
two-color counters		•	•				•	•		•
whiteboard			+	+						
collection of objects to put together				+						
crayons				•	•	•	•			
paper cups					+					
floor number path						+				
manipulative to use as a game piece										•
die										*
sticky notes										*
deck of cards										*

Instructional Resources	Chapter Opener	6.1	6.2	6.3	6.4	6.5	6.6	6.7	6.8	Connect and Grow
Vocabulary Cards	•	+	+			+				
Number Cards 0–5										*

• class set   + teacher only   * per pair/group

Suggested Pacing

Day 1	Chapter Opener	Performance Task Preview		Vocabulary			
Day 2	Lesson 6.1	Warm-Up	Dig In	Explore	Think	Apply: Practice	Think: Modeling Real Life
Day 3	Lesson 6.2	Warm-Up	Dig In	Explore	Think	Apply: Practice	Think: Modeling Real Life
Day 4	Lesson 6.3	Warm-Up	Dig In	Explore	Think	Apply: Practice	Think: Modeling Real Life
Day 5	Lesson 6.4	Warm-Up	Dig In	Explore	Think	Apply: Practice	Think: Modeling Real Life
Day 6	Lesson 6.5	Warm-Up	Dig In	Explore	Think	Apply: Practice	Think: Modeling Real Life
Day 7	Lesson 6.6	Warm-Up	Dig In	Explore	Think	Apply: Practice	Think: Modeling Real Life
Day 8	Lesson 6.7	Warm-Up	Dig In	Explore	Think	Apply: Practice	Think: Modeling Real Life
Day 9	Lesson 6.8	Warm-Up	Dig In	Explore	Think	Apply: Practice	Think: Modeling Real Life
Day 10	Connect And Grow	Performance Task		Activity		Chapter Practice	
Day 11		Centers					
Day 12	Chapter Assessment	Chapter Assessment					

Year-to-Date: 69 Days

Laurie's Notes

Performance Task Preview

- Have students *Turn and Talk* to discuss the picture and then share what they know.
- ? Ask, "Where are the animals? What are the animals doing?" Point out that the picture is an *underwater* scene and the animals are not on land.
- ? "What kinds of animals live in the ocean?" Discuss the characteristics of animals that live on land and in the ocean.
- ? "How many turtles are in the picture? If another turtle joins the group, how many turtles will there be in all?" Have a group of students act like swimming turtles and one more student joining the group. Use the word *whole* as you state how many students there are *in all*.
- In the Performance Task at the end of the chapter, students will join groups of fish to write an addition sentence.

6

Add Numbers within 10

- What kinds of animals live in the ocean?
- How many turtles are in the picture? If another turtle joins the group, how many turtles will there be in all?

Chapter Learning Target:
Understand addition patterns.

Chapter Success Criteria:
- I can identify a number sentence.
- I can describe a pattern.
- I can write an addition sentence.
- I can explain addition sentences.

two hundred sixty-seven   267

© Big Ideas Learning, LLC

ELL Support

Review the words *part, whole,* and *put together* by demonstrating them with a sheet of paper. Take a sheet of paper and draw perpendicular lines on it dividing the paper into four pieces. Hold up the paper and say, "This is the whole sheet of paper." Then cut it into pieces, using the lines. Hold up each piece and say, "This is part of the paper." Pantomime putting the pieces together as you say, "I put together the parts of the sheet of paper." Students may be familiar with the word *sheet* as it applies to linens on a bed. Point out that the same word can mean different things.

Vocabulary Review

❓ Activate prior knowledge by asking students, "What objects do you see in the picture? Have you seen these objects before?" Listen for students to name the number bond, the parts, and the whole.

• Some students will mention the water, sand, beach, and the starfish. Provide time for students to share their experiences.

• Discuss the starfish located near each part of the number bond.

• **Supporting Learners:** Give students counters to place on the starfish as they are counting. Provide a copy of Number Bond for students to place counters on as they count the starfish.

❓ **Extension:** Ask students, "If the starfish were not next to the parts, how would you know where to write the whole?" Listen for students to mention looking at the lines from each part to the whole.

Chapter 6 Vocabulary

Activity

• **Word/Picture Toss:** Lay out a set of vocabulary cards on the floor with the word side up. Students take turns gently tossing a counter onto a card. Read the word on the card that the counter lands on and have the student repeat the word. The student turns over the card to see the definition and shows it to the class. Repeat this process until all of the cards are definition-side up.

MATH MUSICALS

Math Musicals can be used with current topics, to review previous topics, or to preview upcoming topics. There are many *Math Musicals* to choose from!

Use your hand puppets to act out new stories and have students sing the songs several times to take full advantage of the power of music to learn math!

6

Vocabulary

Review Words
part
number bond
whole

5   2

7

Directions: Name the parts and the whole for the group.
Then complete the number bond.

Chapter 6 Vocabulary Cards

add

addition sentence

equal sign

in all

join

pattern

plus sign

© Big Ideas Learning, LLC

© Big Ideas Learning, LLC

$2 + 3 = 5$

© Big Ideas Learning, LLC

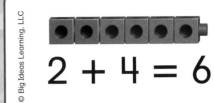

$2 + 4 = 6$

© Big Ideas Learning, LLC

© Big Ideas Learning, LLC

$3 + 4 = 7$

© Big Ideas Learning, LLC

$1 + 1 = 2$

$2 + 1 = 3$

$3 + 1 = 4$

© Big Ideas Learning, LLC

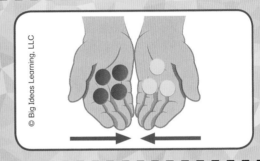

© Big Ideas Learning, LLC

© Big Ideas Learning, LLC

$2 + 1 = 3$

6.1

Learning Target
Add to a group of objects and tell how many.

Success Criteria
• Tell how many objects there are to start.
• Tell how many objects are added to a group.
• Tell how many objects there are in all.

Warm-Up

Practice opportunities for the following are available in the Resources by Chapter or at *BigIdeasMath.com.*

• Daily skills
• Vocabulary
• Prerequisite skills

ELL Support

Students may know the word *add* as it applies to an advertisment, or an *ad*. Explain that when you add to a group of objects, you put more objects with the group. In math when you add two numbers you put them together to get a larger number.

Laurie's Notes

Preparing to Teach

Students have named partner numbers and represented the part-part-whole relationship in number bonds. They are ready to think about the operation of addition. We will always use contextual problems to help students in their reasoning and to be able to explain their thinking. We use the words join and add to describe the *change* problem. (See page T-267C for discussion problem types.) We start with some objects, more are added (join) the group, and we want to know how many in all. The contexts will suggest physical movement which can be modeled with manipulatives, but let students act out the joining process first.

Materials
• linking cubes
• two-color counters

Dig In (Circle Time)

Students will act out two groups being joined together and also model this with linking cubes.

• Use the words *join*, *add*, and *in all* as you talk with students.
• **Example:** "I need some wigglers." Ask one student to stand in the middle. "We have one wiggler. I want two more wigglers to join." Select two students to join the first. "How many wigglers do we have in all?" Summarize, "We started with 1 wiggler (hold up 1 linking cube), we added 2 wigglers (join 2 linking cubes), and we had 3 wigglers in all." Students will want to wiggle now!
• Repeat for another combination with a sum within 5. Call them jumpers, kneelers, or whatever actions or poses your students will enjoy. Each time model with the linking cubes as you summarize.
• **?** "How can you tell how many there are in all? Tell your neighbor." Students should mention counting or just knowing partner numbers.
• **◉** Review the learning target. "We started with 1 wiggler, we added 2 wigglers, and we had 3 wigglers in all. Today we will add a group of objects and tell how many we have."

Name _____

Learning Target: Add to a group of objects and tell how many.

Explore and Grow

3 and 2

Directions: Use counters to act out the story.
- There are 3 students on the bus. Write the number.
- 2 more students get on the bus. Write the number.
- Tell how many students are on the bus now. 5

Chapter 6 | Lesson 1   two hundred sixty-nine   269

© Big Ideas Learning, LLC

Explore and Grow

- **Note:** Use this page multiple times without recording any numbers. You want students to become familiar with the language and concept of joining together. After several iterations, have students record the last example.
- **Example:** Use two-color counters. Read the directions using the numbers 3 and 2 as stated. Ask about the sight word *and* on the page.
- The bus windows should remind students of a five frame.
- **Supporting Learners:** Five frames and/or whiteboards can be used for additional practice. Students can also use their fingers to act it out.

Think and Grow

Getting Started

- Introduce the vocabulary cards for **join**, **add**, and **in all**. Connect these words to work with partner numbers and the acting out they did during circle time.
- Remind students that you want to hear them use these words as they work with their partner today.
- **Note:** The printed words shown (_____ and _____ is _____ in all) are to prepare students for the addition sentence in the next lesson.

Teaching Notes

- There are three parts to each problem on this page. The image suggests some physical movement or social encounter, the related number bond is given, and an addition statement is completed. We are not introducing addition sentences in this lesson. Refer to it as a sentence that tells about the math.
- **Model:** "Tell your partner what is happening in the picture. How many students are at the table to start? How many join? Then how many are there in all?" Ask questions about the parts in the number bond and about the whole. Students trace the numbers.
- Ask a student to tell the story of what happened in the picture and to use today's vocabulary.
- **?** **Reason Abstractly and Quantitatively:** "One more student joined the group. Do we have more or less now? How do you know?" Listen for different student reasoning.
- Discuss the context in the second problem to assure that all students understand the scenario.
- **Supporting Learners:** Each problem can be modeled using a five frame and counters.
- **Extension:** Display a number bond at the document camera or board. Write the first part followed by the second part. Give time for students to think of a story to tell about these two parts and about how many in all. A volunteer can fill in the whole as they tell their story to the class.
- ◉ Use one of the two contexts on this page to ask specific questions about the success criteria. Can they tell how many they start with, how many join, and how many there are in all?

2 and 1 is 3 in all.

1 and 3 is 4 in all.

Directions: Complete the sentence to tell how many students are in the group to start, how many join, and how many there are in all.

270   two hundred seventy

© Big Ideas Learning, LLC

Meeting the needs of all learners.

Laurie's Notes

Apply and Grow: Practice

SCAFFOLDING INSTRUCTION

An effective tool we have for helping students construct an understanding of addition is to use physical actions that suggest a context they can relate to. The contexts give meaning to their thinking. The exercises on this page suggest scenarios familiar to students. They are with a group and someone or some others join them. You might discuss each of the pictures first to be sure all students understand what the actions suggest.

EMERGING students may not understand the physical action of joining two groups together and how that connects to a number bond. They may not understand yet that we write the two parts first, (_____ and _____) and then we write the whole (_____ in all).

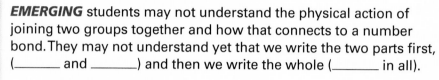

- **Exercises 1–3:** Students can use counters to place on each child in the pictures. These counters can be moved to a five frame or counted with their fingers.
- **Exercises 1–3:** Additional support may be needed as students learn to record the starting number first, how many are joining the group, and finally how many in all.

PROFICIENT students understand what it means to join two groups of objects together and can record their thinking.

- **Exercises 2 and 3:** Have students draw a number bond to represent the number situation

Additional Support

- Have students act out any of the exercises. Pause so that students can record how many they start with, how many join, and how many in all.
- Use linking cubes to model the story as you have students record.

Extensions: Adding Rigor

? "How many would there be in all if one more student joined the group?"
- Have students come up with their own problem using two given numbers. You could tell them the two numbers or they could draw two number cards or dot cards.

Name _____

Apply and Grow: Practice

1

4 and 1 is 5 in all.

2

2 and 3 is 5 in all.

3

4 and 3 is 7 in all.

Directions: 1–3 Complete the sentence to tell how many students are in the group to start, how many join, and how many there are in all.

© Big Ideas Learning, LLC

Laurie's Notes

Think and Grow: Modeling Real Life

This application allows students to show their understanding of joining two groups together to find out how many in all.

- **Preview:** Have students discuss what they think is happening in the picture. Do they think other students will join them on the basketball court? Some students might think students will leave the court!
- **?** "How many students are there to start? Where will we write this number?"
- "Five more students join them." Have students draw the students that join. Circulate and observe if all students are drawing five stick figures.
- **Model with Mathematics:** If a document camera is available, have different students show their model of "five more join the group."
- **?** "How many do we have in all? How do you know?" Listen for different student reasoning.
- **?** **Extension:** "What if zero students joined them? How many would there be in all?"
- ◉ Have students indicate with their thumb signals how well they can add to a group and tell how many.
- **Supporting Learners:** Display the problem and use counters to show the five students that joined. Have students identify the two parts. Record this in a number bond.
- **Supporting Learners:** Ask students to use their fingers to show how many students as you tell the story about children playing basketball.

Closure

- Hold up 2 fingers and say, "There are two children at the desk. Hold up 2 fingers." Wait as students show two fingers. "Three more students joined them. Show me three fingers on your other hand."
- "Show me how many in all." Wait as students move their two hands together.
- "Tell me how many in all."
- Repeat with other number pairs.

5 and 5 is 10 in all.

Directions: 5 students are playing basketball. 5 more students join them. Draw the students who join the group. Then complete the sentence to tell how many students are in the group to start, how many join, and how many there are in all.

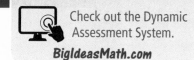
Connect and Extend Learning

Practice Notes

- Provide students with counters and ten frames for additional support.

Cross-Curricular Connections

Language Arts

- Have students draw their own story problem. Ask volunteers to share their stories with the class. Write "_____ and _____ is _____ in all" on the board and use number cards to fill in the blanks for each story.

Practice (6.1)

Learning Target: Add to a group of objects and tell how many.

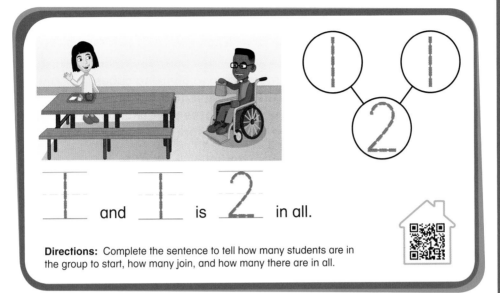

___|___ and ___|___ is ___2___ in all.

Directions: Complete the sentence to tell how many students are in the group to start, how many join, and how many there are in all.

①

___3___ and ___|___ is ___4___ in all.

Directions: ① Complete the sentence to tell how many students are in the group to start, how many join, and how many there are in all.

Chapter 6 | Lesson 1   two hundred seventy-three 273

Connect and Extend Learning

Extend Student Learning

Visual-Spatial

- Have students work with a partner. Provide each student with a random number of up to 5 linking cubes or counters. One student uses their counters to show how many are in a group to start, the other student uses their counters to show how many join the group. Partners work together to find how many there are in all.

Lesson Resources	
Surface Level	**Deep Level**
Resources by Chapter • Extra Practice • Reteach Differentiating the Lesson Skills Review Handbook Skills Trainer	Resources by Chapter • Enrichment and Extension Graphic Organizers Dynamic Assessment System • Lesson Practice

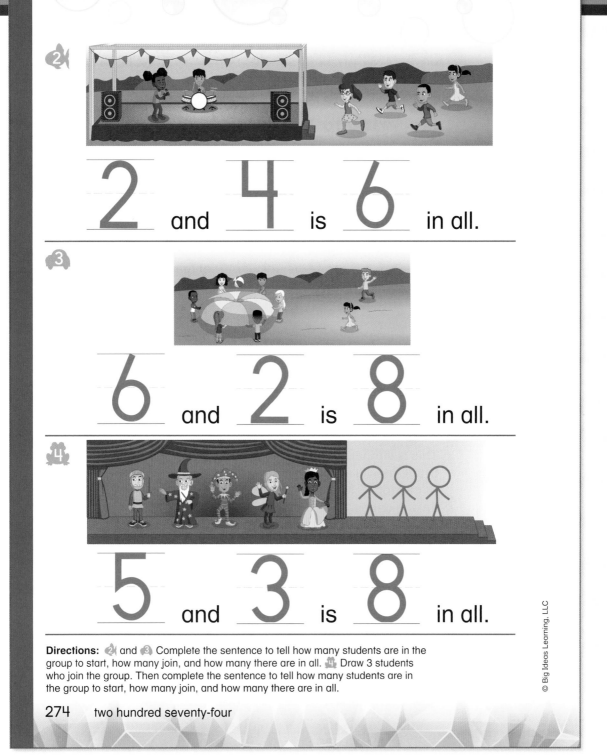

2 ___2___ and ___4___ is ___6___ in all.

3 ___6___ and ___2___ is ___8___ in all.

4 ___5___ and ___3___ is ___8___ in all.

Directions: **2** and **3** Complete the sentence to tell how many students are in the group to start, how many join, and how many there are in all. **4** Draw 3 students who join the group. Then complete the sentence to tell how many students are in the group to start, how many join, and how many there are in all.

© Big Ideas Learning, LLC

274   two hundred seventy-four

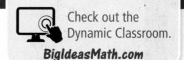
Laurie's Notes

Preparing to Teach

Two symbols are introduced today, the plus sign and equal sign. This is a natural way to help students record what they are thinking when they tell a story, such as the children getting on the bus in the last section. The parts are joined together and we show that by writing the plus sign and in all they equal the whole. Be careful when talking about the equal sign. It represents a relationship between two quantities and we don't want students to believe it means "the answer." That leads students to seeing the equal sign as a rightward pointing array. The addition sentence is also introduced.

Materials

- whiteboard
- linking cubes
- two-color counters

Dig In (Circle Time)

This is similar to the previous circle time. Students will act out two groups being joined together and also model this with linking cubes. The difference will be having a plus sign written on a whiteboard.

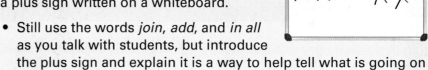

- Still use the words *join*, *add*, and *in all* as you talk with students, but introduce the plus sign and explain it is a way to help tell what is going on in the story.
- **Example:** "I need three twisters." Ask students to stand in middle. "We have three twisters. I want two *add* two more twisters." Select two students to join the three. "The first part was 3 and we added 2 more. I'm going to use this symbol to show that we joined the two parts. We call it the *plus sign.*" Summarize "We started with 3 twisters (hold up 3 linking cubes), we added 2 twisters (add 2 linking cubes), and we have 5 twisters in all." Students will want to twist now!
- Repeat for another combination with a sum within 5. Each time have the middle students hold the plus sign and also model with the linking cubes as you summarize.
- ❓ Hold up the whiteboard with the plus sign. "What do you think is happening when you see the plus sign? Tell your neighbor." Students should mention joining two groups together to make one.
- ◉ Review the first success criterion. "Can you tell what the plus sign means?"

Name _____

Learning Target: Add to a group of objects and complete an addition sentence.

Explore and Grow

$4 + 2$

Directions: Use counters to act out the story.
- There are 4 elephants in the water. Write the number.
- 2 more elephants join them. Write the number.
- Tell how many elephants are in the water now. 6

Chapter 6 | Lesson 2   two hundred seventy-five   275

© Big Ideas Learning, LLC

Explore and Grow

- **Note:** Use this page multiple times with various numbers. Students can use their fingers to make the plus sign. After several iterations, have students record the last example.
- **Example:** Use two-color counters. Read the directions using the numbers 4 and 2 as stated. Ask about the *plus sign* on the page. "How many elephants in all?"
- This is an *add to* problem. The parts are known and students tell the whole.
- **Supporting Learners:** Have students trace a plus sign with their fingers on their desk or other textured surface as you discuss what + means.

Have students read aloud chorally the example, "Two and three is five." Explain that the plus and equal signs show addition in math terms. Say, "Two plus three equals five." Have students work in pairs to practice verbal language as they complete pages 276–277. Have one student ask the other "How many toucans are in the tree? How many join? Describe the total." Have them provide answers using both types of sentences. Then have students alternate roles for the other exercises.

Beginner students may only state answers simply as numbers.

Intermediate students may answer with a simple sentence, such as, "There are five toucans." and will give both types of sentences for the total.

Advanced students may answer using a detailed sentence, such as, "There are five toucans in the tree." and will give both types of sentences for the total.

Think and Grow

Getting Started

- Refer to the elephants in the water story as you write the *addition sentence* for the story: $4 + 2 = 6$. You are using the *equal sign* to show that 6 is how many elephants there are in all. Relate the addition sentence to sentences in a book that tell a story. "What story does $4 + 2 = 6$ tell?"
- Introduce the vocabulary cards for **plus sign**, **equal sign**, and **addition sentence**. Add them to the anchor chart of vocabulary wall.
- **Attend to Precision:** When talking about the equal sign be sure to say "is the same as" instead of "makes" to help students understanding of the equal sign.

Teaching Notes

- Each problem shows the language from the previous lesson and the equivalent addition equation. Help students make meaning of the addition sentence by talking about the story suggested by the image.
- Note, the "in all" is not included in the word sentence.
- **? Model:** "Tell your partner what is happening in the picture. How many pigs are in the mud to start? How many join them? Then how many are there in all?"
- Refer to the two numbers being added as the parts. "Two and 3 are the parts. Two pigs plus 3 more pigs."
- Refer to the 5 as the whole. "There are 5 pigs in all. Two pigs plus 3 pigs is the same as 5 pigs."
- Discuss the context in the second problem to assure that all students understand the scenario.
- **Supporting Learners:** Each problem can be modeled using counters or linking cubes. Students should tell the story as they manipulate the counters or cubes.
- **Make Sense of Problems:** Display an addition sentence such as $1 + 3 = 4$ and hold up a group of four objects, such as markers. "This addition sentence tells a story about my markers. Can you tell your partner the story?" Share stories, looking for different contexts such as picking up markers, dropping markers on the floor, or placing markers in the tray.
- ⊙ Refer to the $1 + 3 = 4$ addition sentence. "Can you tell someone what the plus sign and equal sign mean? For instance, what would you tell your friend in another class?"

2 and 3 is 5 .

2 + 3 = 5

5 and 2 is 7 .

5 + 2 = 7

Directions: Complete the sentence to tell how many animals are in the group to start, how many join, and how many there are in all. Then complete the addition sentence to match.

© Big Ideas Learning, LLC

276   two hundred seventy-six

Meeting the needs of
all learners.

Laurie's Notes

Apply and Grow: Practice

SCAFFOLDING INSTRUCTION

Help students make meaning of the addition sentence by seeing or hearing a contextual scenario. The exercises on this page suggest a scene that allows students to tell a story. You might have groups of students look at the page and tell one another a story about the picture they see. Listen to the students' stories. Do they convey an understanding of addition, two groups being joined together?

EMERGING students may not be clear about the two groups that are being added together. They may see the picture and think of a total, meaning no operation or action has taken place.

- **Exercises 1–3:** Ask students to *read* the picture from left to right. Do they see a beginning quantity in a scene? As they look to the right, are there more of the same objects that can join the group?
- **Exercises 1–3:** Use a sticky note to cover the equal sign and blank. Have students fill in only the two parts that are being added. Draw that portion on a number bond.

PROFICIENT students are able to tell what an addition sentence means. They are comfortable using the plus sign and equal sign to record the actions in a story.

- **Exercises 1–3:** Have students tell what the start number is and what number is being added to it.
- **Reason Abstractly and Quantitatively:** In any of the exercises, probe students about the two parts. What if there were 5 fish and you add 1 more? How is this the same or different from starting with 1 fish and adding 5 more?

Additional Support

- Have students act out any of the exercises. Pause so that students can record the numbers in the addition sentence.
- Write the addition sentence template
  _____ + _____ = _____ on the board. Have students tell the story suggested by the picture. Stop as they mention each quantity and ask (or tell) where to write that number.

Extension: Adding Rigor

- Play "Drop Five." One partner drops five two-color counters on a desk. The counters represent students. Their partner sorts the counters into two groups, say 2 red and 3 yellow. Tell or write the addition sentence for this story. "There are 2 students plus 3 more students. This equals 5 students."

Apply and Grow: Practice

1

2 and 2 is 4.

$2 + 2 = 4$

2

$1 + 5 = 6$

3

$2 + 7 = 9$

Directions: **1** Complete the sentence to tell how many ducks are in the group to start, how many join, and how many there are in all. Then complete the addition sentence to match. **2** and **3** Complete the addition sentence to tell how many animals there are in all.

Chapter 6 | Lesson 2   two hundred seventy-seven   **277**

Think and Grow: Modeling Real Life

This application allows students to show their understanding of adding two groups and writing an addition sentence.

- **Preview:** Have students discuss what they think is happening in the picture. Do they know what animals burrow underground?

- ? "How many rabbits are there to start? Where will we write this number?" Pause. "Six more rabbits join them." Have students draw the rabbits that join. The rabbits can be drawn as simple circles.

- **Model with Mathematics:** If a document camera is available, have different students show their model of "six more join the group."

- ? "How many do we have in all? How do you know? Where do we write 9? How do you know?" Listen for understanding of the equal sign.

- ⊙ Display or write the addition sentence 3 + 6 = 9. "I want you to tell your partner what this plus sign means." After students have discussed, have a few share with the whole class. Do the same for the last two success criteria.

- **Supporting Learners:** Use a ten frame with two-color counters to model this exercise. As you tell the story of the rabbits, students place counters on the ten frame. When six more rabbits join they should alternate to the other color.

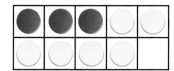

Closure

- Have the students that acted as your twisters at the beginning of class come to the front of the room. They act out the problem from the circle time. (Three twisters plus two more join them.)

- Ask the other students to write the addition sentence that shows how many twisters there all in all.

3 + 6 = 9

Directions: There are 3 rabbits in a burrow. 6 more rabbits join them. Draw the rabbits that join the group. Then complete the addition sentence to tell how many rabbits there are in all.

278   two hundred seventy-eight

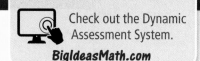
Connect and Extend Learning

Practice Notes

- Provide students with counters and ten frames for additional support.

Cross-Curricular Connections

Language Arts

- *Ten Black Dots* by Donald Crews; Provide each student with a number of black dots, up to 10. Read the book aloud to students. Have students hold up their dots when their number matches the number on the page. After finishing the book, choose two students to hold up their dots, and ask how many there are in all.

Learning Target: Add to a group of objects and complete an addition sentence.

1 and 2 is 3 .

1 + 2 = 3

Directions: Complete the sentence to tell how many otters are in the group to start, how many join, and how many there are in all. Then complete the addition sentence to match.

3 and 2 is 5 .

3 + 2 = 5

Directions: ❶ Complete the sentence to tell how many monkeys are in the group to start, how many join, and how many there are in all. Then complete the addition sentence to match.

Chapter 6 | Lesson 2   two hundred seventy-nine   279

Connect and Extend Learning

Extend Student Learning

Bodily-Kinesthetic

- Write +, =, and three numbers that form an addition sentence (for example, 3, 4, and 7) on different pieces of paper and give to five students. Have them line up to form an addition sentence.

Lesson Resources	
Surface Level	**Deep Level**
Resources by Chapter • Extra Practice • Reteach Differentiating the Lesson Skills Review Handbook Skills Trainer	Resources by Chapter • Enrichment and Extension Graphic Organizers Dynamic Assessment System • Lesson Practice

© Big Ideas Learning, LLC

$$3 + 1 = 4$$

$$4 + 5 = 9$$

$$3 + 4 = 7$$

Directions: ② and ③ Complete the addition sentence to tell how many animals there are in all. ④ Draw 4 mice that join the group. Then complete the addition sentence to tell how many mice there are in all.

Learning Target

Put two groups of objects together and complete an addition sentence.

Success Criteria

* Show how to put together two groups of objects.
* Tell how many there are in all.
* Write an addition sentence.

Warm-Up

Practice opportunities for the following are available in the Resources by Chapter or at *BigIdeasMath.com*.

* Daily skills
* Vocabulary
* Prerequisite skills

ELL Support

Prepare students to act out the story by reviewing the words case, pencil, and crayon. Point to the case shown on the page. Hold up a pencil and a crayon and state each one's name. Explain that they will use counters to represent pencils and crayons.

Preparing to Teach

In the previous two lessons, the objects being added together were the same type of objects, such as students, ducks, or rabbits. In this section the objects being *put together* are not identical. We want students to understand that we can still model this using the addition sentence.

Materials

* collection of objects to put together
* linking cubes
* crayons
* whiteboard

Dig In (Circle Time)

You will model putting together two groups of objects that are similar, but not identical. You could use pencils and markers, books and magazines, or spoons and bread knives. The language of addition is still used, referring to the total as, for instance, a "group of writing tools."

* **Example:** Place two markers in the circle and say, "I have two markers to write with." Show 3 pencils. "Now I add three pencils. Tell your partner how may objects I have altogether that I can write with." Use a whiteboard. Discuss how to write the addition sentence.
* Repeat for another combination of objects. Each time write the addition sentence. Ask volunteers to read and explain the sentence.
* For the last set of objects you add, simply place the two groups in the center of the circle. "Tell you partner a story about putting these two groups together." Listen to see that students are counting the number of objects in each group. Do you hear language of addition?
* Have a few volunteers share their thinking. Record an addition equation as they talk about putting the objects together.
* ? "How did you know how many objects were in each group?" Listen for students counting or subitizing to know the amount.
* ◉ Review the first two success criteria. Explain they are still putting two groups of objects together. The objects are not exactly the same but we can still find out how many objects in all.

? Teaching Prompt   ◉ Learning Target

Learning Target: Put two groups of objects together and complete an addition sentence.

Explore and Grow

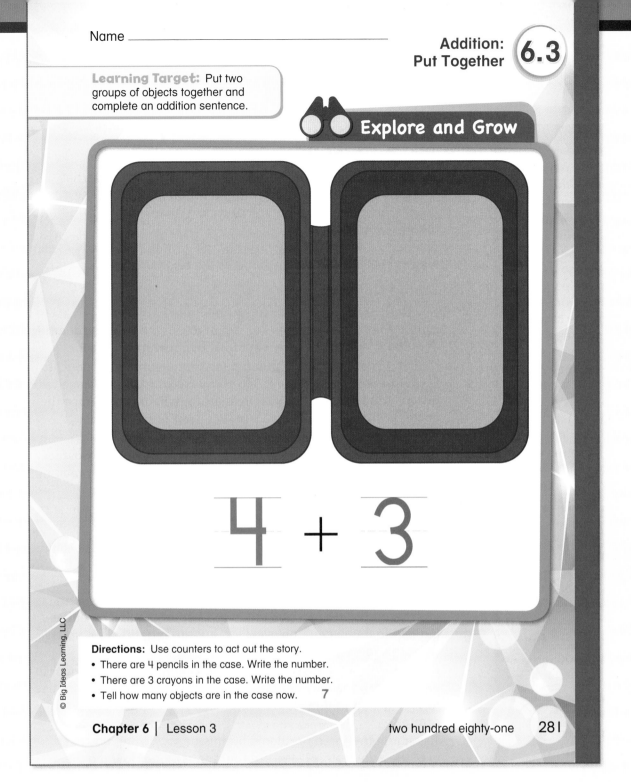

$$4 + 3$$

© Big Ideas Learning, LLC

Directions: Use counters to act out the story.
- There are 4 pencils in the case. Write the number.
- There are 3 crayons in the case. Write the number.
- Tell how many objects are in the case now.   **7**

Chapter 6 | Lesson 3   two hundred eighty-one   281

Explore and Grow

- **Teaching Tip:** Model this page using pencils and crayons. Display with a document camera and have a volunteer place the pencils and crayons as classmates use linking cubes to act out the story.
- ❓ "What does the plus sign mean? How do you know what to do?" The plus sign means I put the groups together. I have to join the two groups.
- ❓ "Can you use your fingers to find how many in all? Explain."

Have students read aloud chorally the example, "Two plus five is seven." Have students work in pairs to practice verbal language as they complete pages 282–283. Have one student ask the other, "How many green cubes are in the first picture? How many orange cubes? What is the total?" Have the second student answer using the addition sentence. Then have students alternate roles for the other exercises.

Beginner students may only state answers simply as numbers. **Intermediate/ Advanced** students may answer with simple sentences, such as, "There are five green cubes." and will state the addition sentence for the total.

Think and Grow

Getting Started

- There is no context for the addition problems. To show that two groups of objects are being put together, students will draw a circle around all of the objects. We are joining or putting together the groups.
- **Attend to Precision:** Remember, when writing how many in all, we say this number *is the same as* the two parts.

Teaching Notes

- ◉ Students need to count to know how many objects are in each group. The plus sign means we want to put the groups together. The equal sign means we want to know how many in all.
- **Model:** "There are some green pencils and some blue pencils." Point to the second picture. "To show we want to put these two groups together, we draw a circle around all of them. Trace the circle."
- Talk about the addition sentence as students trace.
- Students will recognize the linking cubes and counter, however there is no physical action of children or animals as in previous sections. Putting groups together may not be obvious.
- "Tell your partner what you see in the picture of the green and orange linking cubes."
- ? "How do you know to put the two groups together?" plus sign
- Remind students to circle the two groups and write the addition sentence.
- The last problem may confuse students. You may hear them say that a counter can't be put at the end of the linking cubes. Explain that you can't physically put them together, but you want to know how many math tools there are in all.
- **Supporting Learners:** How are students counting the number in each group? Are they subitizing? They can act out the quantities in each group or they could tap or clap for the quantity in each group.
- ◉ Talk about the three problems on this page. "What did we do with the two groups?" We put them together. "How did we show that we put them together?" We circled the two groups. "How did we know how many there were in all?" We counted.

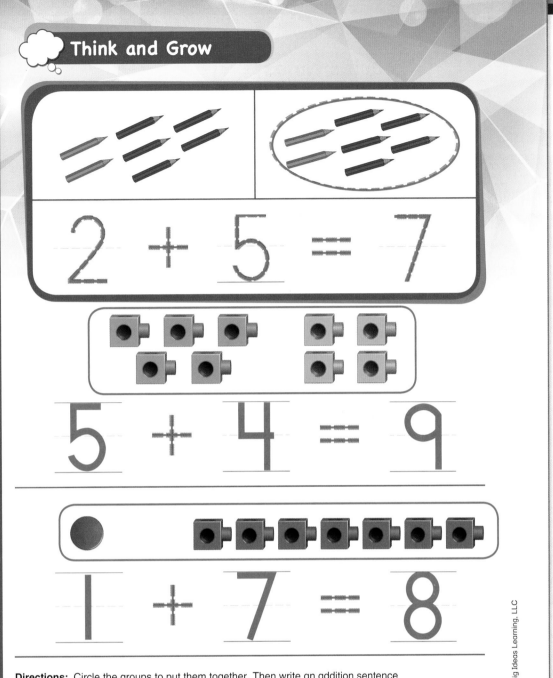

$$2 + 5 = 7$$

$$5 + 4 = 9$$

$$1 + 7 = 8$$

Directions: Circle the groups to put them together. Then write an addition sentence to tell how many objects there are in all.

Laurie's Notes

Apply and Grow: Practice
SCAFFOLDING INSTRUCTION

It is not always possible to physically put two groups together in order to find how many in all. For instance, there are three streetlights in front of the school and two behind the school. How many are there in all? We can model this problem but we cannot put the streetlights next to each other. We want students to understand that even when we can't put two groups together physically, we can still find how many in all. Counters and cubes cannot be put together physically, but we can find how many there are in all.

EMERGING students may not be ready to put together two groups of objects that are not exactly the same. They may need to hear the problem described in addition to seeing it.

- **Exercises 1–3:** Talk students through how to complete a exercise. Ask specific questions that address the two different kinds of objects and write the quantity on a number bond. "How many red counters are there? Where do we write 3 in the addition sentence? How many yellow cubes are there? Where do we write the number 5? How do we show we are putting them together?"

PROFICIENT students are able to tell what it means to put two groups of objects together and write the related addition sentence.

- **Exercises 1–3:** Do you observe students counting with their fingers? Probe to see if they are counting individual objects or seeing small collections that they know.

Additional Support
- The materials shown on this page are likely in your math center. Any of the problems could be acted out using the actual materials.

Extension: Adding Rigor
- Put two groups of objects in a bag, each group having 5 or fewer pieces. Example: use 5 triangles and 4 squares from a pattern block set. One partner pulls out a group of pieces. The other partner writes an addition sentence to show how many pattern block pieces in all.

Meeting the needs of all learners.

Name _____

1

$1 + 3 = 4$

2

$3 + 5 = 8$

3

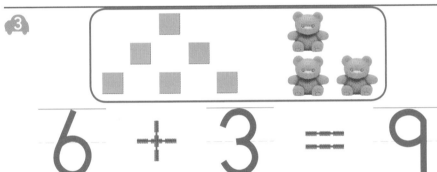

$6 + 3 = 9$

Directions: **1** – **3** Circle the groups to put them together. Then write an addition sentence to tell how many objects there are in all.

© Big Ideas Learning, LLC

Chapter 6 | Lesson 3   two hundred eighty-three **283**

ELL Support

After they have completed the page, have each student use the cards they have already made, and make new ones as needed. They should have cards with 1, 2, 5, 6 and 8 on them. Check for understanding of Section 6.3 by asking the following questions and having students answer by holding up the appropriate card.

1. How many balls of red clay do you have?
2. How many balls of blue clay do you have?
3. How many total balls of clay do you have?
4. How many balls of red clay does your friend have?
5. How many balls of blue clay does your friend have?
6. How many total balls of clay does your friend have?

Think and Grow: Modeling Real Life

This application allows students to show their understanding of putting two groups together and writing an addition sentence.

- **Preview:** Have students discuss what they see in the picture. What could we put on the tables? What would be fun to have on the tables?"
- Read, "You have 5 balls of red clay and 1 ball of blue clay." Remind students to draw the clay on the *top* table.
- Note, when you ask how many balls of clay in all, some students may say one. Ask them to explain. They pushed all the clay together and made one big ball! Clarify that you don't want to push the small balls into one large ball.
- **? Connection:** The bottom table is for your friend's clay. "What sound does the 'F' make?"
- ⊙ Hold up 3 markers and 2 crayons. "Turn and tell your partner how many of each object you have and how many in all." Have students share with the class. Review the success criteria, connecting each to the problem just modeled. Now state the learning target and ask students to use their thumb signals to show how well they can put two groups together and write an addition sentence.
- **Supporting Learners:** Use a ten frame with two-color counters to model this problem. As you tell the story of the clay, students place counters on the ten frame.

Closure

- Have students draw a picture of four counters (circles) and three blocks (squares). "Talk to your partner. How many shapes do you have in all? Write an addition sentence to show how many you have in all."

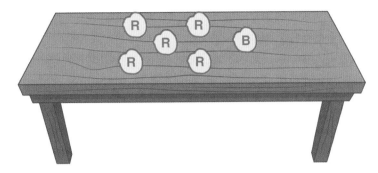

$$5 + 1 = 6$$

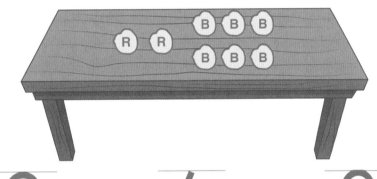

$$2 + 6 = 8$$

Directions:
- You have 5 balls of red clay and 1 ball of blue clay. Draw and color the balls of clay. Then write an addition sentence to tell how many balls of clay you have in all.
- Your friend has 2 balls of red clay and 6 balls of blue clay. Draw and color the balls of clay. Then write an addition sentence to tell how many balls of clay your friend has in all.

284   two hundred eighty-four

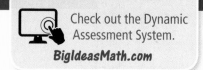
Connect and Extend Learning

Practice Notes

- For additional support, allow students to use linking cubes, centimeter cubes, or bear counters.

Cross-Curricular Connections

Physical Education

- Have students work with a partner to play the game "Beanbag Toss". Place a toy hoop some distance away from a starting point. Students will stand at the starting point and try to toss bean bags inside of the toy hoop. Partners will work together to write number sentences on scratch paper for the number of bean bags inside the hoop and those that landed outside. Students will add both numbers together to come up with the sum.

Learning Target: Put two groups of objects together and complete an addition sentence.

$$2 + 1 = 3$$

Directions: Circle the groups to put them together. Then complete the addition sentence to tell how many linking cubes there are in all.

1

$$1 + 1 = 2$$

2

$$4 + 2 = 6$$

Directions: **1** and **2** Circle the groups to put them together. Then write an addition sentence to tell how many objects there are in all.

Connect and Extend Learning

Extend Student Learning

Bodily-Kinesthetic

- Provide students with number cards from 1 to 5. Students choose two cards and say an addition number sentence for the cards aloud. For example, if they choose a 3 and a 5, students would say 3 + 5. Students will hop the number of times displayed on each card to find the sum. They will then repeat the number sentence: 3 + 5 = 8.

Lesson Resources	
Surface Level	**Deep Level**
Resources by Chapter • Extra Practice • Reteach Differentiating the Lesson Skills Review Handbook Skills Trainer	Resources by Chapter • Enrichment and Extension Graphic Organizers Dynamic Assessment System • Lesson Practice

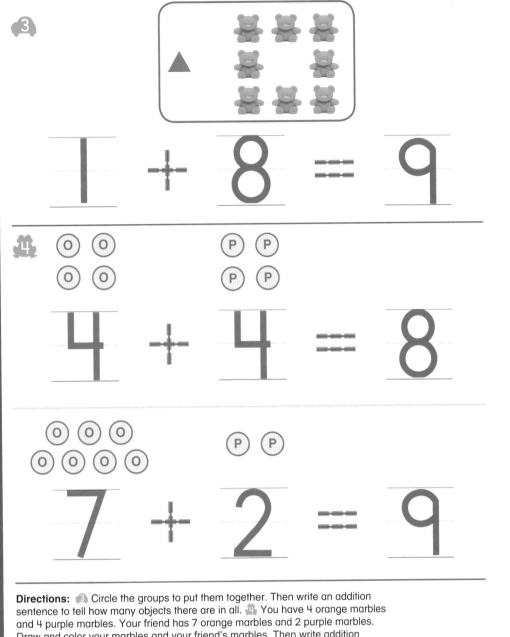

3 △

$$1 + 8 = 9$$

4

$$4 + 4 = 8$$

$$7 + 2 = 9$$

Directions: **3** Circle the groups to put them together. Then write an addition sentence to tell how many objects there are in all. **4** You have 4 orange marbles and 4 purple marbles. Your friend has 7 orange marbles and 2 purple marbles. Draw and color your marbles and your friend's marbles. Then write addition sentences to tell how many marbles you each have in all.

6.4

Learning Target

Find partner numbers
for a number and write
an addition sentence.

Success Criteria

- Show two partner
numbers for a whole.
- Write an addition
sentence with partner
numbers.

Warm-Up

Practice opportunities
for the following
are available in the
Resources by Chapter or
at *BigIdeasMath.com*.

- Daily skills
- Vocabulary
- Prerequisite skills

ELL Support

Remind students of
the relationship of the
words part and partner.
A partner number is
one part of the whole,
just like a part is also
one part of a whole
object. Explain how
the phrase partner
number is related to
working with a partner.
When you work on an
exercise with a partner
you are one part of the
whole group working
on the exercise.

Laurie's Notes

Preparing to Teach

Students have been introduced to the equal sign as a way of
describing one number is the same as two groups that have been
added together. Another way to think of the equal sign is as a
balance. The sum 2 + 3 *balances* with five. The two sides of an
equation balance. In this section, we want students to find the
partner numbers for a given number. Because we start with the
given number, the sum is written to the right of the equal sign
for example, _____ = _____ + _____. Connect this to how
number bonds would be written with the partner numbers on
the right.

Materials

- paper cups
- linking cubes
- crayons

Dig In (Circle Time)

You will use a set of six paper cups
that students can separate to show
partner numbers. Each time a volunteer
models two partner numbers, record
in a horizontal number bond. This will
be connected to writing an addition sentence in the Explore and
Grow.

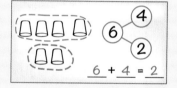

- **Example:** Place six cups in the circle and say, "I have six cups.
  Can someone show us how to make partner numbers for six by
  moving some of the cups?" Give think time before calling on a
  volunteer.
- ❓ "What are the partner numbers?" Answers vary. "Can you show
  the partner numbers in a number bond?" Be sure your number
  bonds are pre-drawn in the horizontal position with the whole
  to the left.
- Repeat for different partner numbers for six. Each time have the
  student record in a new number bond.
- **Make Sense of Problems and Persevere in Solving Them:**
  Continue until students are sure they have all of the possible
  partner number pairs for 6.
- **Note:** Students will want to record 4 and 2 as well as 2 and 4.
  We know from the Commutative Property that 4 + 2 = 2 + 4.
  For students to see the patterns from the anchor chart in the last
  chapter, it is necessary to list each order.
- ◉ Explain that in this lesson they will find the partner numbers
  for a number. Instead of writing partner numbers in a number
  bond, they are going to write an addition sentence!

❓ Teaching Prompt   ◉ Learning Target

Learning Target: Find partner numbers for a number and write an addition sentence.

Explore and Grow

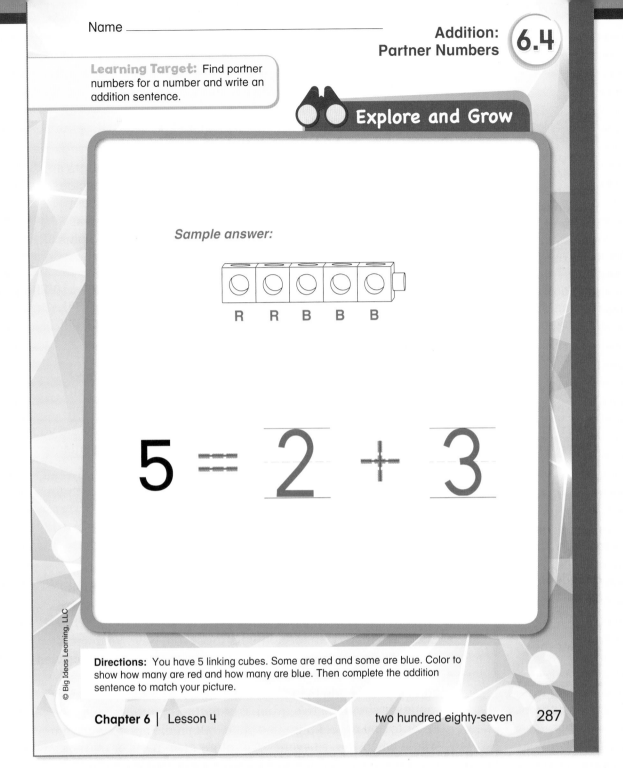

Sample answer:

R R B B B

$$5 = 2 + 3$$

Directions: You have 5 linking cubes. Some are red and some are blue. Color to show how many are red and how many are blue. Then complete the addition sentence to match your picture.

© Big Ideas Learning, LLC

Chapter 6 | Lesson 4

two hundred eighty-seven   287

Explore and Grow

- Provide two colors of linking cubes to each group, blue and red, if possible. Students also need two colors of crayons to match the linking cubes.
- ? "I have 5 linking cubes. Some are red and some are blue. Can you show me how many I have of each?" You may need to repeat the relationship. "Talk to your partner." After several iterations of the problem, students color the linking cubes.
- ? "What do you notice about the addition sentence?" Students recognize the total is given first. Use different language to talk about the equal sign.

ELL Support

Have students practice language in pairs as they complete the two exercises on the page. One student asks the other "What colors did you use to color the cubes? How many cubes did you color with (name of first color)? How many cubes did you color with (name of second color)?" Then have students alternate roles for the other exercise.

Beginner students may only state short answers, such as, "green and blue."

Intermediate students may answer using simple sentences, such as, "I used green and blue."

Advanced students may answer using longer sentences, such as, "I used green and blue to color the cubes."

Think and Grow

Getting Started

- Students use their knowledge of partner numbers to write an addition sentence. The whole is known and students decide, by coloring, how to write it as a sum of two partner numbers.
- **Attend to Precision:** Use the language, "six is the same as 3 plus 3," or "six equals 3 plus 3," or "six balances with 3 plus 3."

Teaching Notes

- **Model:** "There are six stars." Point to the second picture. "Three of them are colored red and three are colored yellow. What addition sentence can we write to show that 3 and 3 are partner numbers for six?"
- Talk about the addition sentence as students trace.
- **Extension:** "What other partner numbers are there for six? What would the addition sentence be for each pair?"
- Students use two colors to fill in the linking cubes.
- "How many linking cubes did you color?" 4 "How many did you color blue? Red?" Answers vary. "Does your addition sentence explain what you colored? Explain."
- **Critique the Reasoning of Others:** It is very possible that a student will produce the work shown. Some students will say this is wrong because the addition sentence should be $4 = 1 + 3$. Others will say it doesn't matter if you write $1 + 3$ or $3 + 1$. The point is not to introduce the Commutative Property, rather give students the opportunity to think about the relationship and critique the reasoning of others.

  $4 = 3 + 1$

- There are many partner numbers for seven. Have volunteers share their work to demonstrate there is more than one answer.
- **Supporting Learners:** Provide two colors of linking cubes so students can build the model. They can then take apart the model to show the two groups, or partner numbers.
- Refer to any problem on this page. "What did we do with the whole when it was seven?" We colored two parts or partner numbers for seven. "What did the addition sentence for this problem start with?" $7 =$ "How did you know what numbers to write next?" They were partner numbers for seven.

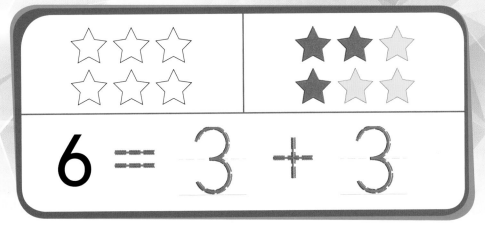

$$6 = 3 + 3$$

Sample answer:

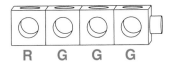

R G G G

$$4 = 1 + 3$$

Sample answer:

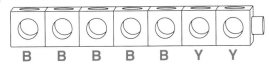

B B B B B Y Y

$$7 = 5 + 2$$

Directions: Use 2 colors to show partner numbers that make the whole. Then complete the addition sentence to match your picture.

288   two hundred eighty-eight

© Big Ideas Learning, LLC

MATH MUSICALS

Rockin' Dogs and Cool Cats

Remember, you can use the song *Rockin' Dogs and Cool Cats* to review partner numbers to 5!

Meeting the needs of
all learners.

Laurie's Notes

Apply and Grow: Practice
SCAFFOLDING INSTRUCTION

Students are asked to use two colors to show partner numbers for the whole. It is important to ask students about their work to be sure they are connecting the model to the addition sentence. You want to hear the language and understanding of partner numbers for a whole.

EMERGING students may not be confident in the part-part-whole relationship and hence have not connected the whole with the partner numbers.

- **Exercises 1–4:** Talk students through how to complete a problem. "How many linking cubes are there?" We have 3 in all. "How can we take apart 3 and make two groups?" Wait for student response. "Use two colors to show this." Wait while they color. "Can you write the number of [color 1] and [color 2] in the addition sentence?" Have student point to the cubes and say the numbers.

PROFICIENT students understand how to represent a quantity in two groups called partner numbers. They can write an addition sentence that corresponds to their model.

- **Exercises 1–4:** Students may want to make a pattern when coloring the counters, for instance alternating the colors. Ask them if the partner numbers are as easy to see when they make a pattern instead of grouping the same colors together.

Additional Support
- The anchor chart(s) created in Chapter 5 should be on display to help remind students of the partner numbers for a whole.
- Ask students to use their fingers on both hands to represent the whole. The fingers on each hand are the partner numbers for the whole.

$$5 = 3 + 2$$

Extension: Adding Rigor
- Have students find different number bond pairs for the number 10. Write the associated addition sentence for each pair.

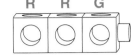 **Apply and Grow: Practice**

1–4. Sample answers are given.

1

$3 = 2 + 1$

2

R R R R G

$5 = 4 + 1$

3

R R R R G G G G G G

$10 = 4 + 6$

4

R G G G G G

$7 = 1 + 6$

Directions: ① – ④ Use 2 colors to show partner numbers that make the whole. Then complete the addition sentence to match your picture.

Think and Grow: Modeling Real Life

This application allows students to show their understanding of partner numbers for 8 and writing the associated addition sentence.

- **Preview:** Have students discuss what they see in the picture. "Have you written with sidewalk chalk? What games can you play on a sidewalk?" Students may mention sidewalk safety.
- Read, "You have 8 pieces of sidewalk chalk. Some are red and some are blue." Point to the top picture and ask students to color some chalk red and some chalk blue.
- **?** **Construct Viable Arguments:** "[name] colored 2 red. How many did [name] color blue? How do you know? Tell your neighbor." Call on several students to share their reasoning.
- **?** "What addition sentence did [name] write?" Solicit responses and then have [name] share their work.
- **?** **Connection:** "What would a number bond look like for [name's] addition sentence?"
- Students need to show another way to show how to make 8.
- ◉ Use a whiteboard to show 3 red counters and 4 yellow counters. "Tell your partner an addition sentence for this picture and how you know your addition sentence is correct."
- **Supporting Learners:** Some students may need additional work writing partner numbers in a number bond. Display the anchor charts from Chapter 5 and use the Number Bond Writing Instructional Resource.
- **Supporting Learners:** Use two colors of linking cubes to make a train of 8. Students point and count how many of each color and write this in the addition sentence. "How many in all?" If students need to start counting from 1, they do not understand partner numbers or counting on from the greater number. These students need additional work with counting and finding *how many in all.*

Closure

- Hold up 2 fingers on one hand and 4 fingers on the other. Ask students to tell how many fingers in all. Then they write the addition sentence _____ = _____ + _____.

Think and Grow: Modeling Real Life

Sample answer:

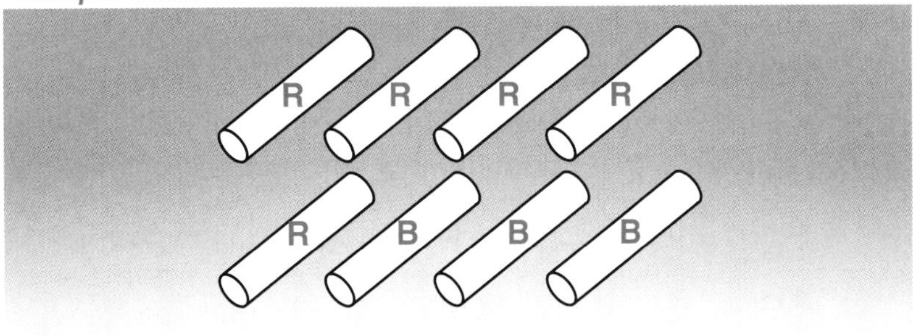

8 = 5 + 3

Sample answer:

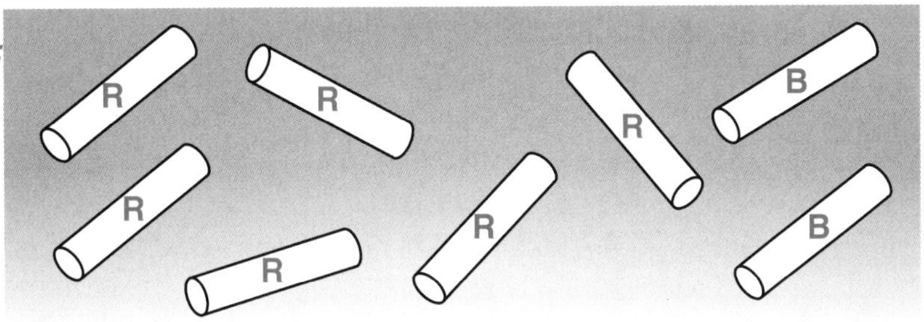

8 = 6 + 2

Directions: You have 8 pieces of sidewalk chalk. Some are red and some are blue.

- Color the pieces of chalk to show partner numbers that make 8. Then write an addition sentence to match your picture.
- Color to show another way to make 8. Then write an addition sentence to match your picture.

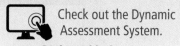

Connect and Extend Learning

Practice Notes

• Provide students with two different colored linking cubes to model the problem before coloring the items.

Cross-Curricular Connections

Art

• Have students choose a card from a deck (without face cards or aces) and draw that many circles, flowers, or other objects. Students trade drawings with a partner and color the objects using two colors, and write an addition sentence to match the picture.

Learning Target: Find partner numbers for a number and write an addition sentence.

$$3 = 2 + 1$$

Directions: Use 2 colors to show partner numbers that make the whole. Then complete the addition sentence to match your picture.

1 and 2. Sample answers are given.

1

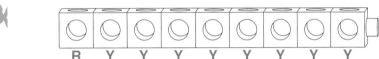

R   Y

$$2 = 1 + 1$$

2

R   Y   Y   Y   Y   Y   Y   Y   Y

$$9 = 1 + 8$$

Directions: **1** and **2** Use 2 colors to show partner numbers that make the whole. Then complete the addition sentence to match your picture.

Connect and Extend Learning

Extend Student Learning

Visual-Spatial

- Have a group of 2 to 10 students stand up in front of the class. Ask students to write an addition sentence for the group. Have students use categories to find numbers (for example, students wearing red and students not wearing red) or students can choose their own numbers. Repeat with different groups of students.

Lesson Resources	
Surface Level	**Deep Level**
Resources by Chapter • Extra Practice • Reteach Differentiating the Lesson Skills Review Handbook Skills Trainer Math Musicals	Resources by Chapter • Enrichment and Extension Graphic Organizers Math Musicals Dynamic Assessment System • Lesson Practice

3 and 4. Sample answers are given.

3️⃣

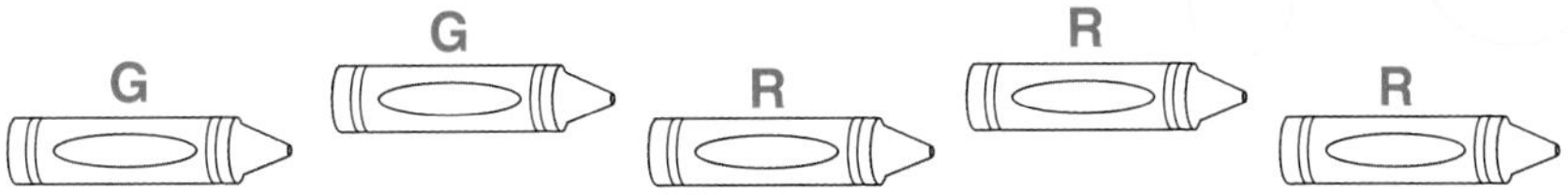

G   G   R   R   R

$$5 = 2 + 3$$

4️⃣

P P P
P P G

$$6 = 5 + 1$$

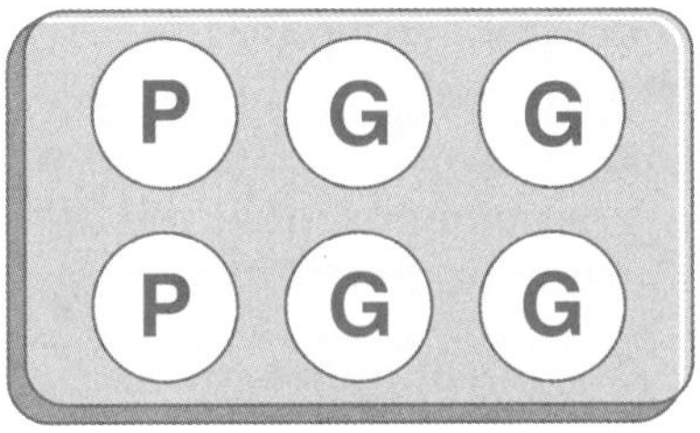

P G G
P G G

$$6 = 2 + 4$$

Directions: 3️⃣ Use 2 colors to show partner numbers that make the whole. Then complete the addition sentence to match your picture. 4️⃣ There are 6 paint spots on a paint tray. Some are purple and some are green. Color the paint spots to show partner numbers that make 6. Then color the paint spots to show another way to make 6. Write addition sentences to match your pictures.

© Big Ideas Learning, LLC

292   two hundred ninety-two

6.5

Learning Target
Explain addition patterns with 0 and 1.

Success Criteria
- Describe a pattern.
- Explain that I have the same number when I add 0.
- Explain that I have the next number when I add 1.

Warm-Up

Practice opportunities for the following are available in the Resources by Chapter or at *BigIdeasMath.com.*

- Daily skills
- Vocabulary
- Prerequisite skills

ELL Support

Draw a pattern of repeated shapes and lines on the board. Point and say, "This is a pattern of different shapes." Draw a second pattern. Say, "This is another pattern of shapes." Explain that patterns can be found in many things, such as art, language, and math. Say that we will now look at patterns in addition.

Laurie's Notes

Preparing to Teach
Students have written addition sentences where one of the addends (parts) was 0 or 1. Students may have comments that adding 0 is like not adding anything. Student language may not be precise but they are trying to communicate that they notice a pattern. The goal of this lesson is to help students explain clearly what the patterns are when you add 0 or 1 to a quantity. A double domino is used as a model with one side being 0 or 1.

Materials
- floor number path
- crayons

Dig In (Circle Time)
Use Appropriate Tools Strategically: Use a number path that can be placed on the floor. Laminated pages, each with a counting number, work just fine. You want the number path to be large enough so that it is clear what number the students' position represents. In the figure shown, the student is standing on 4.

- **Example:** Ask a volunteer to stand at the beginning of the number path. "Take four steps." Student moves to 4. "Take 2 more steps." Student moves to 6. Ask students to help you record the steps in an addition sentence. Write $4 + 2 = 6$. Repeat once or twice more.

- Now do a few trials where the number being added is 0. The first time you do this, students will think you made a mistake. "You can't take 0 steps." Let students talk about what *plus zero* means. Record each trial in an addition sentence. $4 + 0 = 4$.

- Finally, do a few trials where the number being added is 1. "Gee, you don't go very far do you?" Listen to students' observations. "It's just the next number."

- **Look for and Express Regularity in Repeated Reasoning:** Have students talk to their partners about what they noticed whenever they were told to take 0 steps. Listen for the concept of staying on the same space. Ask about taking 1 step—they ended on the very next number.

⊙ Explain that this lesson is about the patterns when you add 0 or 1 to a number.

❓ Teaching Prompt   ⊙ Learning Target

Learning Target: Explain addition patterns with 0 and 1.

👓 **Explore and Grow**

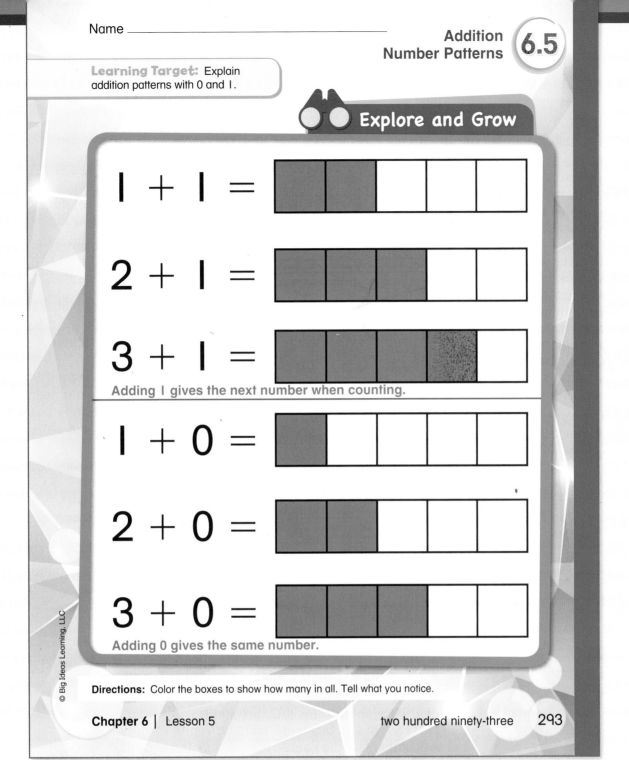

$1 + 1 =$

$2 + 1 =$

$3 + 1 =$

Adding 1 gives the next number when counting.

$1 + 0 =$

$2 + 0 =$

$3 + 0 =$

Adding 0 gives the same number.

© Big Ideas Learning, LLC

Directions: Color the boxes to show how many in all. Tell what you notice.

Chapter 6 | Lesson 5   two hundred ninety-three   **293**

Explore and Grow

- Explain there are two parts. You want observations for each portion.
- Students color boxes to show how many in all. Ask what they notice on the first part. Students may focus only on the length of the colored boxes getting longer. Draw attention to the addition sentence and how it is changing.
- **?** Repeat for the bottom portion, adding zero. "What do you notice when you add 0 to a number?" Students may not have precise language.

Think and Grow

Getting Started

- Introduce the vocabulary card for **pattern**. Give examples of when something is repeated. For instance, use a clapping pattern students hear, or an ABB pattern with colored counters students see.
- **Look for and Make Use of Structure:** Refer to partner numbers. Every number can be written using itself plus 0. ($4 + 0 = 4$)

Teaching Notes

- If students are not familiar with dominos, introduce the pieces. The models shown are all double dominos. Point out to students that we are reading two numbers, one on each half of the domino.
- **Model:** "Describe the domino piece to your partner." Listen for four dots and one dot and five dots all together. Ask a volunteer to describe the domino to the whole class. "Let's write an addition equation to show the two parts and how many in all." Trace.
- **?** "What number did we start with?" 4 "How many did we add?" 1 "How many in all?" 5 "When we add 1 to a number what do you notice?" Answers will vary; listen for understanding of *the next number when you count.* Point to Newton's thought bubble.
- **Common Misconception:** When students see a blank domino for 0 they will say there is no number there. "It's blank." Remind students of how to model or draw pictures of the number 0. Review the vocabulary cards.
- Repeat the same questioning for adding 0. Descartes summarizes the pattern.
- **Supporting Learners:** Students may need help interpreting the domino and writing the addition sentence. Tell a story to go with the domino. Repeat the directions. They are counting the number of dots and telling how many in all.
- ⊙ Let Newton and Descartes summarize the success criteria. Ask students if they agree by using their thumb signals.

Next number when counting

$4 + 1 = 5$

Same number

$4 + 0 = 4$

$6 + 0 = 6$ same number

$6 + 1 = 7$ next number when counting

Directions: Write an addition sentence to tell how many dots there are in all. Tell what you notice.

Apply and Grow: Practice

SCAFFOLDING INSTRUCTION

Students can add 0 and 1 to a number and correctly tell what the sum equals. They may not be able to describe a pattern as a result of repeating these two operations with different start numbers. Ask students to explain their thinking as they complete the exercises on this page. "How do you know 5 + 0 = 5?"

EMERGING students may not recognize a pattern when adding 0 or 1. They see each exercise as a new problem, not related to the previous exercise(s).

- **Exercises 1 and 2:** Ask students how many dots are on each half (side) of the domino. "These are the parts, or numbers that we are adding." Pause as students record the numbers. "How many in all?"
- **Exercises 3–6:** Have students say the addition sentence aloud. "I start with 5. I add 0. I have 5 in all."

PROFICIENT students understand the pattern when you add 0 or 1 to a number. They are developing precision in their language to describe the pattern.

- Have students talk to their partners about a problem and explain how they know their work is correct.

Additional Support

- Use linking cubes and number bonds for additional practice.
- Focus on only one pattern at a time. Start with adding 1. Explore each counting number to 9. (1 + 1, 2 + 1, 3 + 1, ..., 9 + 1). "Can you tell what is going to happen when we add one to a number?"

Extension: Adding Rigor

- Explore the pattern for 0 + _____ = _____. When we write 0 first, the number 0 is added to does not change.

Meeting the needs of all learners.

Name _____

1.
$$2 + 0 = 2$$
same number

2.
$$2 + 1 = 3$$
next number when counting

3.
$$5 + 0 = 5$$
same number

4.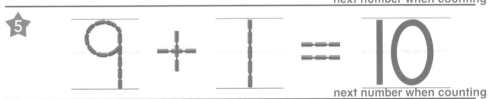
$$5 + 1 = 6$$
next number when counting

5.
$$9 + 1 = 10$$
next number when counting

6.
$$10 + 0 = 10$$
same number

Directions: ❶ and ❷ Write an addition sentence to tell how many dots there are in all. Tell what you notice. ❸–❻ Complete the addition sentence. Tell what you notice.

© Big Ideas Learning, LLC

Chapter 6 | Lesson 5   two hundred ninety-five   295

Explain that a common type of bank for saving coins is a piggy bank. Display examples of coins. Make sure they understand that a penny, nickel and dime are worth different amounts, but all are just one coin. After they have completed the page, have each student use the cards they have already made, and make new ones as needed. They should have cards with 0, 1, 7 and 8 on them. Check for understanding of 6.5 by asking the following questions and having students answer by holding up the appropriate card.

1. How many coins did you draw in the first picture?
2. What number did you write in the first space?
3. What number did you write in the next space?
4. What number did you write in the last space?
5. How many coins did you draw in the second picture?
6. What number did you write in the first space?
7. What number did you write in the next space?
8. What number did you write in the last space?

Think and Grow: Modeling Real Life

This application allows students to show their understanding of adding 0 and adding 1 to a start amount of 7.

- **Preview:** Have students discuss what they see in the picture. "Do you have a piggy bank? What do you keep in a piggy bank?" Perhaps students have other objects that they collect coins in.
- Read, "You have 7 coins that you put in your bank." Students draw the coins and write 7 as the starting number in the addition sentence.
- **?** "You cannot find any more coins. You have none to add. How do we show that in the addition sentence?" Write 0. "When you add 0 to a number does the amount change?" no
- **Note:** It is helpful to mention a period of time passes and your friend gives you a coin for your bank. "The next day, your friend…"
- "How many coins are in your bank?" Pause while students draw the seven coins and write 7 in the addition sentence. "Your friend gives you a coin for your bank. How do you show one more coin?" Pause while students draw another coin and write 1 in the addition sentence.
- **?** "You added one coin. When you add 1 to a number does the amount change?" yes "What does it equal when you add one to a number?" It equals the next number. Although this is not precise language, students know the next number as being the next *counting* number.
- ◉ Ask volunteers to share what they learned today about adding 0 and adding 1.

Closure

- Have students hold up four fingers. "Show me 4 + 0 fingers." Pause. "Show me 4 + 1 fingers."
- Repeat, using a different number of fingers to start with and add 1 first and then 0.

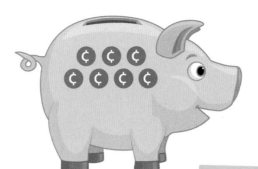

7 + 0 =

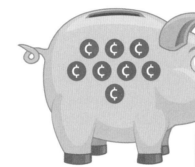

7 + 1 = 8

Start

Work on together as class.

Directions: You find 7 coins to put in your piggy bank.

- You cannot find any more coins. Draw and color all of your coins. Then write an addition sentence to tell how many coins you have in all.
- Your friend gives you a coin to put in your piggy bank. Draw and color all of your coins. Then write an addition sentence to tell how many coins you have in all.

296 two hundred ninety-six

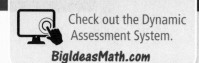
Connect and Extend Learning

Practice Notes

- Provide students with linking cubes and ten frames for support if needed.

Cross-Curricular Connections

Language Arts

- *Chicka Chicka 1, 2, 3* by Bill Martin Jr. and Michael Sampson; Read the book aloud to students. On the first page, stop and make the connection to how when you add the number one to two it equals three. Continue making this connection as you read through the book by asking, "If I add one more to four, what will I get?" Provide students with the number sentences on the board showing the pattern when adding one.

Name _____

Learning Target: Explain addition patterns with 0 and 1.

$$1 + 1 = 2$$

next number when counting

same number

$$1 + 0 = 1$$

Directions: Write an addition sentence to tell how many dots there are in all. Tell what you notice.

1

$$3 + 0 = 3$$

same number

2

$$3 + 1 = 4$$

next number when counting

Directions: **1** and **2** Write an addition sentence to tell how many dots there are in all. Tell what you notice.

Chapter 6 | Lesson 5

two hundred ninety-seven   297

© Big Ideas Learning, LLC

Connect and Extend Learning

Extend Student Learning

Interpersonal

- Give each pair of students a deck of cards (with the face cards removed) and counters labeled with "+0" and "+1." Have one student choose a card and the other student choose a counter. Students then work together to find the sum.

Lesson Resources	
Surface Level	**Deep Level**
Resources by Chapter • Extra Practice • Reteach Differentiating the Lesson Skills Review Handbook Skills Trainer	Resources by Chapter • Enrichment and Extension Graphic Organizers Dynamic Assessment System • Lesson Practice

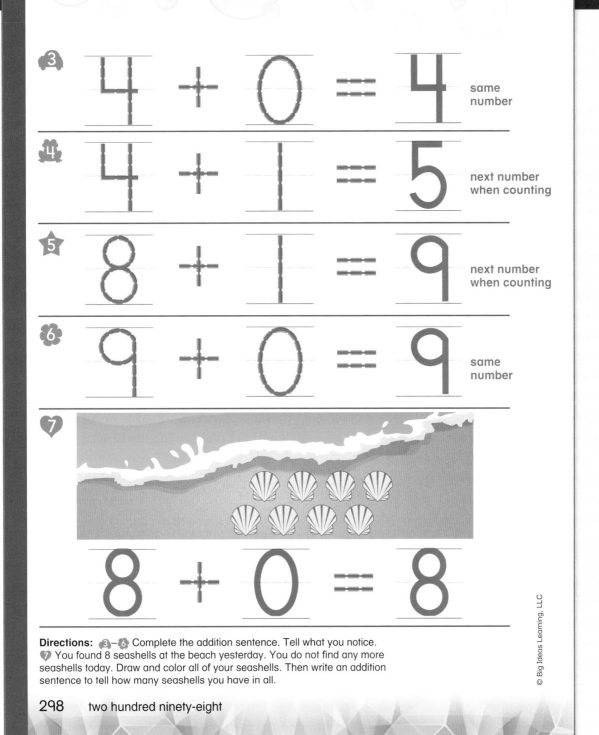

3 $4 + 0 = 4$ same number

4 $4 + 1 = 5$ next number when counting

5 $8 + 1 = 9$ next number when counting

6 $9 + 0 = 9$ same number

7 $8 + 0 = 8$

Directions: **3–6** Complete the addition sentence. Tell what you notice.
7 You found 8 seashells at the beach yesterday. You do not find any more seashells today. Draw and color all of your seashells. Then write an addition sentence to tell how many seashells you have in all.

298   two hundred ninety-eight

Laurie's Notes

Learning Target

Add partner numbers to 5.

Success Criteria

- Show and tell how to add numbers to 5.
- Complete an addition sentence.

Warm-Up

Practice opportunities for the following are available in the Resources by Chapter or at *BigIdeasMath.com.*

- Daily skills
- Vocabulary
- Prerequisite skills

ELL Support

Explain that this lesson focuses on practicing addition. Practice is used to improve a skill and it is common for musicians and sports teams to practice to improve their performance. Students have already practiced many math concepts in other lessons and will practice addition here to improve their ability to add.

Preparing to Teach

This is the first section in kindergarten where the focus is on **fluency**. Mathematics literature refers to procedural fluency as *the skill in carrying out procedures flexibly, accurately, efficiently and appropriately.* Students have learned to count, and have modeled and reasoned about addition. In this section you want to see evidence that students can accurately and efficiently add numbers within 5 and will know the sum without the use of counters or picture stories. The additional practice of this lesson will help students move towards fluency.

Materials

- two-color counters
- crayons

Dig In (Circle Time)

There is no new content presented today so it would be helpful to make an anchor chart of the many different ways to do addition. Include drawing a picture of the problem, using fingers to count, using a number path, counting on, using counters, and using knowledge of all the ways to make five (partner numbers). Ask, "Did anyone do it another way?" Include all answers that make sense in the list.

- ⊙ Share the learning target and success criteria for the day. Explain that you want them to show all of the ways they know to add numbers. "Tell your partner different ways you can show how to add two numbers."
- You may want to have manipulatives and whiteboards available for students to demonstrate their thinking.
- ⁇ **Critique the Reasoning of Others:** When students share their thinking with classmates, ask other students to comment on what they have heard. "Do you agree with how [name] explained using your fingers to count? Did their thinking make sense? Why?"
- Because all of their work today will be adding within 5, display and review earlier anchor charts that showed partner numbers to 5.

⁇ Teaching Prompt   ⊙ Learning Target

Learning Target: Add partner numbers to 5.

Explore and Grow

$$1 + 2 = 3$$

$$3 + 2 = 5$$

$$0 + 4 = 4$$

Directions: Use counters in the five frame to show how many there are in all. Complete the addition sentences.

© Big Ideas Learning, LLC

Explore and Grow

- Students use an empty five frame and two-color counters to demonstrate how to show (model) addition of two numbers. Students also tell their partner what the picture means so they are practicing the telling part.
- **?** "How did you complete the addition sentence? What do the different colors of the counters mean? How do you know your answer is correct?"
- **?** **Extension:** "How many ways can you make _____?"
- ⊙ Students work with a partner. You say a number (for example, 4). One partner says the start number (for example, 3). The other partner says "3 + 1 = 4."

Think and Grow

Getting Started

- The example at the top shows the addition sentence, a number path, fingers, and two-color counters. It can be used as a resource for students to refer back to as they work through the exercises on this page.
- Note that in the exercises, students only give the sum. They are no longer tracing or writing the entire addition sentence.

Teaching Notes

- **Model:** "Tell your partner how to show 2 + 3." Solicit ideas from volunteers. "So 2 + 3 is the same as what number?" Have the students trace the 5.
- Observe as students are working on the three exercises. Are they using models? their fingers? counting on?
- When students finish, have them tell their partner how they found the answer.
- **Supporting Learners:** Provide a five frame and counters as needed.
- **Extension:** Write each of the three problems in a different order (4 + 1, 3 + 0, 3 + 1). "Did the order we write the parts change the answer?"
- ⊙ Ask students to use their thumb signals to show how good they feel (confident) about adding numbers to 5.

$$2 + 3 = ?$$

| 1 | 2 | 3 | 4 | 5 |

✌ + 🖐 = 🖐

$$2 + 3 = 5$$

$$1 + 4 = 5$$

$$0 + 3 = 3$$

$$1 + 3 = 4$$

Directions: Complete the addition sentence. Tell how you found your answer.

Sample answer: **used counters**

© Big Ideas Learning, LLC

300   three hundred

Meeting the needs of
all learners.

Apply and Grow: Practice

SCAFFOLDING INSTRUCTION

Students are practicing their addition facts to five today. You could have small groups or learning centers specific to the support and extension needed by students. You might consider having students self-select where to work based upon their understanding of addition facts within 5. Explain that we each learn differently and at different rates. "What will be most helpful for your learning today?" See additional support and extension below.

EMERGING students are not fluent with their addition facts within 5. They need the support of models to find *how many in all*.

- **Exercises 1–4:** Have students say the addition sentence aloud. "I start with 1. I add 2. I have 3 in all." As they say the problem aloud they may use counters to model the problem.
- **Exercise 5:** Use a five frame and counters to model each part. Compare the two models. "How are they the same? How are they different?"

PROFICIENT students are efficient and accurate with their addition facts within 5.

- **Exercise 5:** Talk to your partner about the exercise. "What do you notice about the problem? Can you think of another pair of addition sentences for 5 that have this same pattern?"

Additional Support

- Provide dot and number cards 0–5 so that students can model the problem and use the number cards to tell their thinking.
- Pose questions where the sum is known and students need to think of possible partner numbers. On a whiteboard write _____ + _____ = 4. Students can use manipulatives as needed.

1 plus 2 is the same as 3.

• + •• = •ᵈᵒᵗˢ

| 1 | + | 2 | = | 3 |

Extension: Adding Rigor

- Put the 1, 2, or 3 Instructional Resource inside a plastic sleeve as shown, or laminate the sheet. Player 1 writes one number in any box on each addition sentence. Player 1 may only use the numbers 1, 2, or 3 and each number may only be used once. Player 2 fills in the other two boxes to make a correct addition sentence.

1, 2, or 3

☐ + ☐ = ☐

☐ + ☐ = ☐

☐ + ☐ = ☐

Name _____

1   $1 + 2 = 3$

1–4.
Sample answer:
used fingers

2   $0 + 5 = 5$

3   $2 + 2 = 4$

4   $0 + 0 = 0$

5   $2 + 3 = 5$

$3 + 2 = 5$

same answer

Directions: 1 – 4 Complete the addition sentence. Tell how you found your answer. 5 Complete the addition sentences. Tell what you notice.

Chapter 6 | Lesson 6

three hundred one   301

Think and Grow: Modeling Real Life

This application allows students to show their understanding of showing and telling about addition facts for 4 and 5.

- **Preview:** "What are some board games that you have played? Do any of the games have pieces that you move?" Have students share their experiences.
- In the first exercise there are 4 game pieces. "Some are green and some are yellow." Students make a decision about how many to color of each and write the corresponding addition sentence.
- **?** "How do you know your addition sentence is correct? Tell your partner."
- **Note:** Any two colors can be substituted for green and yellow.
- In the next two exercises, students demonstrate that they can write an addition sentence with a total of 5 and draw a picture to show what the addition sentence means. It is helpful to use the same context so students are thinking about five game pieces.
- ⊙ Review the learning target. Students have done many addition problems today with sums within 5. "Are you pretty good at knowing the partner numbers to 5?"
- **Supporting Learners:** Have students use a five frame and counters to model the problem first before they draw the picture.

Closure

- Use both hands to show an addition problem within 5. Students use their fingers to show the sum.

Think and Grow: Modeling Real Life

Sample answer:

$$4 = 3 + 1$$

G G G Y

$$1 + 2 = 3$$

$$3 + 2 = 5$$

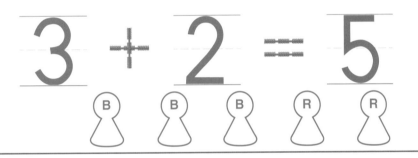

B B B R R

Directions:

- You have 4 game pieces. Some are green and some are yellow. Write an addition sentence to show partner numbers that make the whole. Color to show how you know.
- There is 1 game piece on a game board. You put 2 more game pieces on the board. Write an addition sentence to tell how many game pieces are on the game board. Draw to show how you know.
- You have 3 blue game pieces and 2 red game pieces. Write an addition sentence to show how many game pieces you have in all. Draw to show how you know.

302   three hundred two

© Big Ideas Learning, LLC

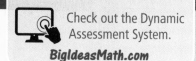

Connect and Extend Learning

Practice Notes

- Provide students with counters, linking cubes, or centimeter cubes for support if needed.

Cross-Curricular Connections

Science

- Gather a number of leaves or flowers that have between 1–5 district points or petals. Provide each student with a leaf or flower. Have students write an addition number sentence by decomposing the number of points or petals. Students should repeat this process multiple times with different leaves or flowers.

Learning Target: Add partner numbers to 5.

$$3 + 2 = 5$$

| 1 | 2 | 3 | 4 | 5 |

Directions: Complete the addition sentence. Tell how you found your answer.

1 $$0 + 2 = 2$$

2 $$1 + 3 = 4$$

3 $$1 + 2 = 3$$

Directions: **1**–**3** Complete the addition sentence. Tell how you found your answer.

Sample answer: **used counters**

Chapter 6 | Lesson 6

three hundred three   303

Connect and Extend Learning

Extend Student Learning

Interpersonal

- Have students work in pairs. Provide each pair with a cup of 5 craft sticks numbered 1–5. Each student takes 1 craft stick and writes an addition sentence, without the sum, using partner numbers for the number chosen. For example, if a student chooses 4, they could write 3 + 1 = _____. Students trade with their partner and complete the sentence.

Lesson Resources	
Surface Level	**Deep Level**
Resources by Chapter • Extra Practice • Reteach Differentiating the Lesson Skills Review Handbook Skills Trainer	Resources by Chapter • Enrichment and Extension Graphic Organizers Dynamic Assessment System • Lesson Practice

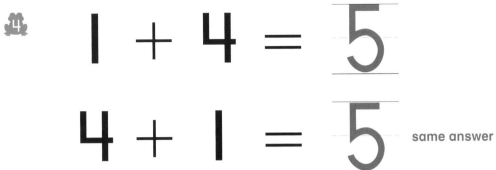

4 $1 + 4 = 5$

$4 + 1 = 5$ same answer

Sample answer:

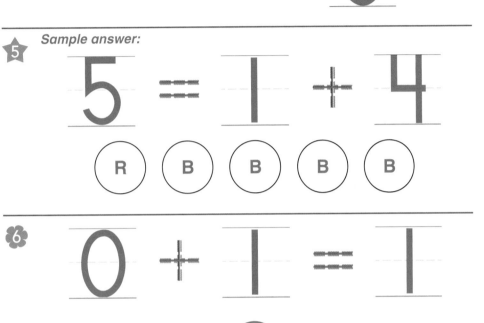

5 $5 = 1 + 4$

R B B B B

6 $0 + 1 = 1$

○

Directions: 4 Complete the addition sentences. Tell what you notice. 5 You have 5 game pieces. Some are red and some are black. Write an addition sentence to show partner numbers that make the whole. Color to show how you know. 6 There are no game pieces on a game board. You put 1 game piece on the board. Write an addition sentence to tell how many game pieces are on the game board. Draw to show how you know.

304   three hundred four

6.7

Laurie's Notes

Preparing to Teach

This section builds on students' work with using a group of 5 to put together and take apart numbers to 10. When students first worked with sums within 10 they recorded their work in a number bond. Now we want them to make the connection to an addition sentence. In addition, we want them to focus on partner numbers that include 5. The $5 + n$ pattern is an important benchmark that enables students to build fluency in addition.

Materials
• two-color counters

Dig In (Circle Time)

Fingers provide a great model for students to use, particularly in this lesson. Students use their fingers to show a number between 5 and 10. The challenge is that they must use all of the fingers on one hand, and some more fingers on the other hand.

• "Use your fingers to show me the number 6." Point out particular students so students see the different partner numbers for 6. For each model, ask a volunteer to write the associated addition sentence: $1 + 5 = 6$, $2 + 4 = 6$, $3 + 3 = 6$, $4 + 2 = 6$, and $5 + 1 = 6$.
• "Now I have a new rule before you show me your number. You must use all of the fingers on one hand, and then some more fingers on the other hand. Show me the number 6 again."
? "Look at everyone's fingers. What do you notice?" Listen for 5 fingers and 1 finger.
• **Reason Abstractly and Quantitatively:** There are several pairs of partner numbers for 6 and there is only one unique pair ($5 + 1$ and $1 + 5$) that involves 5. The $5 + n$ pair is one we want students to be very familiar with.
• Repeat this activity, using 5 fingers plus some more to model numbers from 7 to 10, each time asking a volunteer to write the addition sentence $5 + n =$ _____.
◉ Share the learning target and success criteria. Students have just demonstrated the second and third success criteria. "You used 5 fingers plus some more to make a whole. Then you wrote an addition sentence."

Learning Target
Use a group of 5 to write an addition sentence.

Success Criteria
• Use a ten frame to add on to 5.
• Add on to 5 to make a whole.
• Write an addition sentence.

Warm-Up

Practice opportunities for the following are available in the Resources by Chapter or at *BigIdeasMath.com.*
• Daily skills
• Vocabulary
• Prerequisite skills

ELL Support

Explain that students will use groups of five objects as they add. There will be one to five additional objects added to the group of five. Remind them that the words *and* and *plus* can both be used to describe the plus sign (+).

? Teaching Prompt   ◉ Learning Target

Learning Target: Use a group of 5 to write an addition sentence.

Explore and Grow

Sample answer:

$$5 + 3 = 8$$

Directions: Add more counters to make 8. Then complete the addition sentence.

Chapter 6 | Lesson 7   three hundred five   **305**

Explore and Grow

- The ten frame shows 5 and students use two-color counters to make 8. They have just done this with their fingers and now they use the ten frame.
- "Look at the addition sentence. Tell your partner what it says and what you need to do." Listen for a partner number for 5 to make 8.
- ? "Look at everyone's fingers. What do you notice?" Listen for 5 fingers and 3 fingers.
- "Add more counters to make 8." Ask a volunteer to explain their thinking.
- **Extension:** Have students explain their understanding of the $5 + n$ pattern. They start at 5 and add on to make a new number.
- ⊙ "You added on to 5 to make 8. The addition sentence is $5 + 3 = 8$."

Laurie's Notes

ELL Support

Have students work in groups to practice verbal language as they complete the page. Point out that the first number in each addition sentence will be five. They should work together to describe the number of items added in each exercise.

Beginner students may only state the number needed to complete the equation. **Intermediate** students may say the addition sentence, such as, "Five and two are seven." **Advanced** students may say the addition sentence two ways, such as, "Five and two are seven. Five plus two equals seven."

Think and Grow

Getting Started

- The example at the top shows a ten frame, a number path, and an addition sentence. The example is just like the Explore and Grow page and should feel familiar to students.
- Note that for any of these problems, students can use their fingers to show and explain the 5 + n pattern.

Teaching Notes

- **?** Model: "We want to make the number 7. What is the partner number for 5 so we can make 7?" Solicit an answer. "Draw two more counters so there are 7 in all." Trace the 5 + 2.
- Ask questions about the number path. The start is 5. When we add on 2, we end at 7. The partner numbers 5 and 2 make 7.
- ⊙ Have students try the next two problems. Remind them that they are going to write an addition sentence using a group of 5. Start by looking at the ten frame. Decide how many need to be added on in order to make the whole.
- **?** "How do you know what the whole is?" Look at the addition sentence.
- When students finish, have them compare their work with their partners. "Do they have the same work?"
- Extension: Ask students to think of a word problem to go with any of the addition sentences. You can give them counting bears or other small objects to act out their word problem.
- ⊙ "Can you use a ten frame to add on to 5? Explain how this is done and how to write the addition sentence." Have students use their thumb signals to show how well they are doing with the learning target.

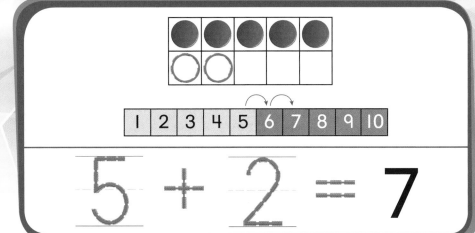

$$5 + 2 = 7$$

Sample answer:

$$5 + 1 = 6$$

Sample answer:

$$5 + 4 = 9$$

Directions: Draw more counters to show how many in all. Use the ten frame to complete the addition sentence.

306   three hundred six

Meeting the needs of
all learners.

Laurie's Notes

Apply and Grow: Practice

SCAFFOLDING INSTRUCTION

Students are working with the $5 + n$ pattern. Using fingers, ten frames, linking cubes, and a rekenrek are all visual ways for students to see this pattern. All of the sums are 10 or less, so having the model of 5 on a ten frame visible for students to see helps them make the connection to adding on from 5.

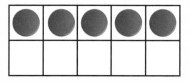

EMERGING students are not confident in showing part-part-whole relationship when one of the parts is 5. They may need support in writing an addition sentence when a model is given.

- **Exercises 1 and 2:** Have students say the addition sentence aloud. "I start with 5 and I want to have 8 in all." They can use their fingers to point to the bottom row of the ten frame as they count 6, 7, 8. This is the ending number. They need to draw 3 counters.

- **Exercise 3:** Use a ten frame and counters to model. "How do you show 5?" Place 5 red counters. "Is this like Exercise 1 and 2 now?"

PROFICIENT students are able to use their fingers to model 5 plus some more and write the addition sentence that shows this relationship.

- **Exercises 1–3:** Note if students are completing the addition sentence without, or before, drawing in the additional counters. Are they confident in the $5 + n$ pattern for numbers to 10?

Additional Support

- Provide a rekenrek for students to use as they complete the page. Slide 5 beads to the left to show the $5 + n$ pattern. Ask questions to help them understand that the white beads they are sliding is how many more are needed to make the whole.

Extension: Adding Rigor

- Give pairs of students a set of number cards 6 to 10. One partner picks a card. Their partners use their fingers to show the number using 5 fingers plus some more. Say, "five plus _____ equals _____."

Name _____

Sample answer:

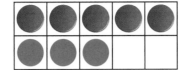

$$5 + 3 = 8$$

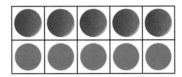

$$5 + 5 = 10$$

 Sample answer:

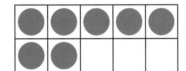

$$5 + 2 = 7$$

Directions: ❶ and ❷ Draw more counters to show how many in all. Use the ten frame to complete the addition sentence. ❸ Draw 5 counters. Draw more counters to show how many in all. Use the ten frame to complete the addition sentence.

© Big Ideas Learning, LLC

Chapter 6 | Lesson 7

three hundred seven   307

Think and Grow: Modeling Real Life

This application allows students to show their understanding of using their fingers to show the 5 + *n* pattern. They also write the related addition sentence.

4 fingers

? **Preview:** Draw a stick diagram similar to the one shown. "What do you think I'm trying to draw?" There will be different ideas. Tell students that you are just trying to draw four fingers! You might take time to ask about how other amounts of fingers could be drawn.

• Use your own fingers to model as you read the directions. Students need to draw a simple picture to show more fingers and then write the addition sentence that matches the picture.

? "How did you know how many fingers to draw? Tell your partner."

• **Note:** Remind students to make simple pictures to show more fingers, like your picture of 4 fingers.

• The second exercise may be more challenging for students. Some students may need to write 3 + _____ = 8 in order to think about it. Others may need to model it with manipulatives. Students may not see yet the commutative relationship of 5 + 3 and 3 + 5.

◉ Review the learning target. "Tell your partner how to use a group of 5 to write an addition sentence that equals 7." Write _____ + _____ = 7 to clarify your words. Ask several students to share.

• **Supporting Learners:** Have students use a ten frame and counters to model the problem first before they draw the picture of fingers.

Closure

• Have partners take turns using their fingers to show a number more than 5. They need to use all of the fingers on one hand plus some more fingers on the other hand. Say the addition sentence that matches their fingers.

ELL Support

Say that to tell your age, you say, "I am (X) years old." It is common in many languages to use the equivalent of the phrase, "I have (X) years." Have students state their age using the correct phrase. After they have completed the page, have each student use the cards they have already made, and make new ones as needed. They should have cards with 3, 4, 5, 8, and 9 on them. Check for understanding by asking the following questions and having students answer by holding up the appropriate card.

1. How many fingers did you draw in the top picture?
2. What number did you write in the first space?
3. What number did you write in the next space?
4. What number did you write in the last space?
5. How many fingers did you draw in the bottom picture?
6. What number did you write in the first space?
7. What number did you write in the next space?
8. What number did you write in the last space?

5 + 4 = 9

3 + 5 = 8

Directions:
- A boy holds up 5 fingers to tell his age. His sister is 9 years old. Draw more fingers to show his sister's age. Then write an addition sentence to match your picture.
- A girl holds up 3 fingers to tell her age. Her brother is 8 years old. Draw more fingers to show her brother's age. Then write an addition sentence to match your picture.

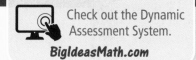

Connect and Extend Learning

Practice Notes

- Provide students with counters, linking cubes, or centimeter cubes for support if needed.

Cross-Curricular Connections

Physical Education

- Have the numbers 0–5 written on paper and lay them close together on the floor. Students throw a bean bag onto a number and add it to 5. Have students write the addition sentence on the board.

Learning Target: Use a group of 5 to write an addition sentence.

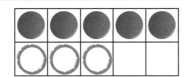

$$5 + 3 = 8$$

Directions: Draw more counters to show how many in all. Use the ten frame to complete the addition sentence.

Sample answer:

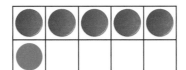

$$5 + 1 = 6$$

Sample answer:

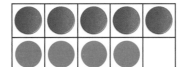

$$5 + 4 = 9$$

Directions: ❶ and ❷ Draw more counters to show how many in all. Use the ten frame to complete the addition sentence.

Chapter 6 | Lesson 7

three hundred nine **309**

Connect and Extend Learning

Extend Student Learning
Visual-Spatial

- Provide each student with 10 two-color counters. Have students place 5 counters on their desk and 5 counters in a cup. The counters on the desk should all have the same color showing. Have students shake the cup to mix up the counters and then dump them out onto their desk, separate from the other 5. Students write an addition sentence for the counters that show the same color. For example, if students start with 5 red counters and 3 red counters come out of the cup, students write $5 + 3 = 8$. Students should repeat this process several times.

Lesson Resources	
Surface Level	**Deep Level**
Resources by Chapter • Extra Practice • Reteach Differentiating the Lesson Skills Review Handbook Skills Trainer	Resources by Chapter • Enrichment and Extension Graphic Organizers Dynamic Assessment System • Lesson Practice

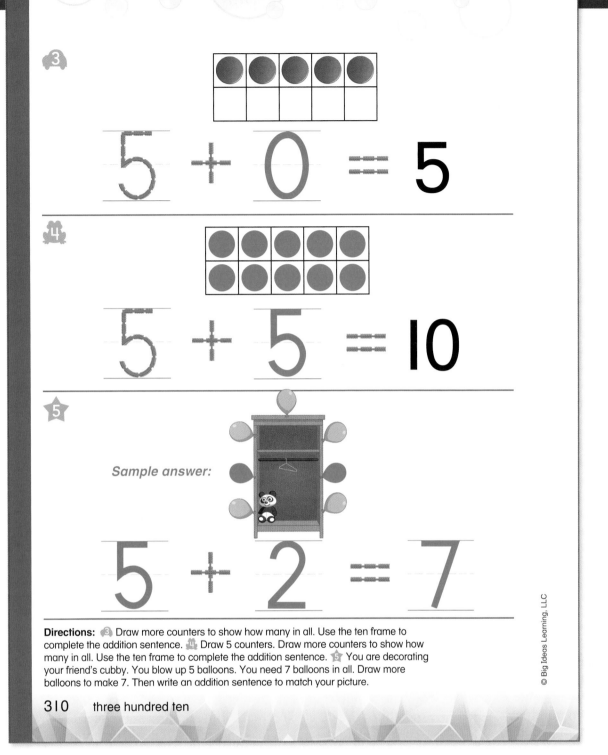

3 $5 + 0 = 5$

4 $5 + 5 = 10$

5 *Sample answer:*

$5 + 2 = 7$

Directions: **3** Draw more counters to show how many in all. Use the ten frame to complete the addition sentence. **4** Draw 5 counters. Draw more counters to show how many in all. Use the ten frame to complete the addition sentence. **5** You are decorating your friend's cubby. You blow up 5 balloons. You need 7 balloons in all. Draw more balloons to make 7. Then write an addition sentence to match your picture.

310   three hundred ten

Laurie's Notes

Preparing to Teach

In later work when students find sums greater than 10 they will first think of sums to 10. For example, to add $7 + 4$, students will think of 4 as $3 + 1$. So $7 + 4$ is the same as $7 + 3 + 1 = 10 + 1 = 11$. Knowing the partner numbers for 10 is a foundational concept. It is a strategy used in both addition and subtraction problems in later grades. Recall that students have also composed and decomposed the number 10 in Lesson 5.7 and in this section, they write number pairs for 10 in an addition sentence.

Materials

- linking cubes

Dig In (Circle Time)

Two colors of linking cubes can be used to model the number 10. Because the model can be turned 180°, it helps students think about the commutative relationship. The related number pairs for 10 can also be modeled with two colored counters and a ten frame. Adjust the activity for ten frames.

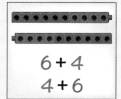

$6 + 4$
$4 + 6$

- Hold up 6 linking cubes in a train. "What number is this?" Pause while students count. "Tell you partner how many more we need to make 10."

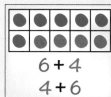

$6 + 4$
$4 + 6$

- **Construct Viable Arguments:** Solicit an answer and ask the volunteer how they know they are correct. Then have the volunteer use another color of linking cubes to finish the 10 train.

- ? **Critique the Reasoning of Others:** "Do you all agree with [name]?" If no one suggests the related pair ($4 + 6$ versus $6 + 4$), rotate the linking cube model 180°. You want students to see that [name] was correct *and* there is a second addition sentence that is also correct. *Both* addition sentences are correct. Hold the cubes in a vertical as well as horizontal direction so students see different orientations.

- Repeat this activity using a start number other than 6.

- ⊙ Share the learning target and success criteria. Students have been demonstrating the first and second success criteria. Point out how [name] was able to explain why $6 + 4$ equals 10. "You also used the linking cubes to show partner numbers for 10."

? Teaching Prompt   ⊙ Learning Target

Learning Target: Find partner numbers for 10 and write an addition sentence.

Explore and Grow

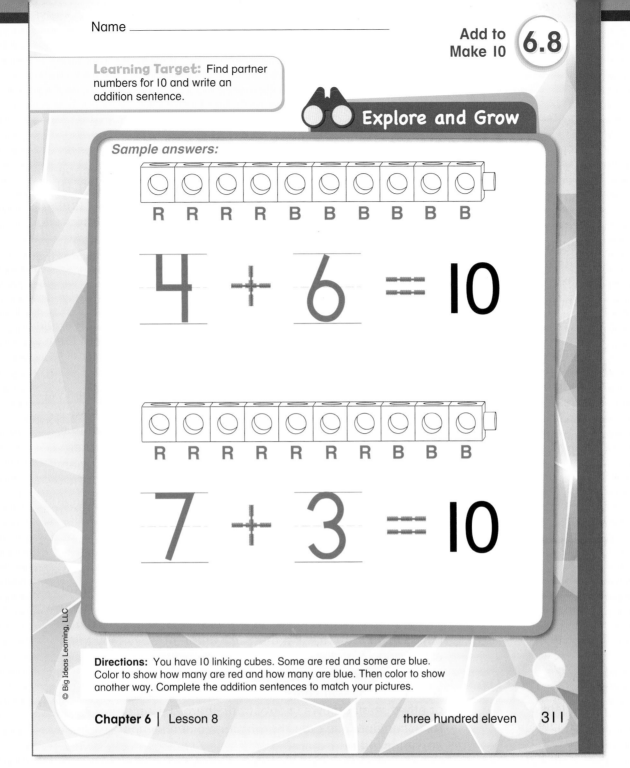

Sample answers:

R R R R B B B B B B

$$4 + 6 = 10$$

R R R R R R R B B B

$$7 + 3 = 10$$

Directions: You have 10 linking cubes. Some are red and some are blue. Color to show how many are red and how many are blue. Then color to show another way. Complete the addition sentences to match your pictures.

© Big Ideas Learning, LLC

Chapter 6 | Lesson 8   three hundred eleven **311**

Explore and Grow

- The directions specify red and blue. Students can use any two colors.
- "Use your two colors to show a pair of partner numbers for 10. Then write the addition sentence that matches." Pause. "Color a different pair of partner numbers for 10 and write the addition sentence that matches."
- ? "How did you know what numbers to write in the addition sentence?"
- **Extension:** Make a list of the different addition sentences for 10.

Laurie's Notes

Think and Grow

Getting Started

- The example at the top shows a ten frame and a number path that model a particular addition sentence for a sum of 10. The students have seen the linking cube model for partner numbers for 10. You want them to also be familiar with the ten frame model.
- Display the anchor chart made earlier that shows number pairs for 10.

Teaching Notes

? **Model:** "What number is shown in the ten frame? What number do you add on to 6 to make 10?" Have students talk with their partner. "Color four more counters to show you have 10. Complete the addition sentence."

- Ask questions about the number path. The start is 6. When we add on 4 we end at 10. The partner numbers 6 and 4 make 10.

⊙ Have students try the next two problems. Remind them that they are going to write an addition sentence about partner numbers for 10. Start by looking at the ten frame. How many more are needed to make 10?

- Circulate as students complete the two problems. Are students writing the missing part before they color the additional counters?

? "How do you know what you need to add on to make 10?" Listen for students to mention the boxes in the ten frame that are empty. Listen for students to say the partner number for 10. Watch for students who look at their fingers to decide how many more to make 10. All of these are responses you may hear so continue to ask if there are different ways they think about how to make 10.

- **Extension:** Ask students to think of a word problem to go with any of the addition sentences. You can give them counting bears or other small objects to act out their word problem.

⊙ Have students use their thumb signals to show how well they are doing with the learning target.

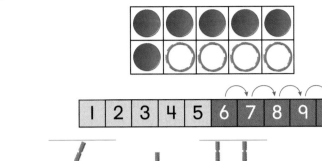

$$6 + 4 = 10$$

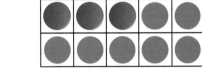

$$3 + 7 = 10$$

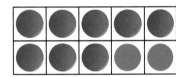

$$8 + 2 = 10$$

Directions: Draw more counters to make 10. Use the ten frame to complete the addition sentence.

312   three hundred twelve

© Big Ideas Learning, LLC

Meeting the needs of
all learners.

Laurie's Notes

Apply and Grow: Practice
SCAFFOLDING INSTRUCTION

Partner number combinations that make 10 are one of the most important strategies for students to know. Are students still counting each number to decide sums for 10? Do they know that the colored boxes plus the empty boxes in a ten frame are partner numbers for 10? Do students need to see a visual model for 6 to know that 4 is the missing part to make 10? These are questions to help you assess where students are in their learning of this important strategy.

EMERGING students are at the counting stage when finding partner numbers for 10. They may use their fingers or visual models to decide what amount is added to the start number to make 10.

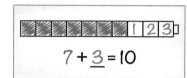

$7 + \underline{3} = 10$

- **Exercise 1:** Have students tell how many boxes are filled and how many are empty.
- **Exercises 2 and 3:** Instead of coloring, have students write the numbers they say as they count on to make 10.

PROFICIENT students are generally confident in giving the partner number that make 10. They may be more confident when the start number is greater than 5.

- **Exercises 1 and 2:** Students can color the boxes or linking cubes by shading with a pencil.
- **Exercise 3:** Instead of using crayons, put an X on 4 linking cubes. Shade more cubes to make 10.

Additional Support
- Provide two colors of linking cubes for students to use to complete the exercises.

Extension: Adding Rigor
- Make a book to show the different combinations of 10. Draw pictures and write the addition sentences for each picture.

Name _____

①

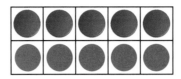

$$5 + 5 = 10$$

②

G G G G G G G

$$2 + 8 = 10$$

③

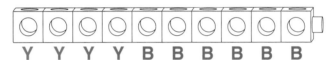

Y Y Y Y B B B B B B

$$4 + 6 = 10$$

Directions: **①** Draw more counters to make 10. Use the ten frame to complete the addition sentence. **②** Color more linking cubes to make 10. Use the linking cubes to complete the addition sentence. **③** Color 4 linking cubes yellow. Color more linking cubes blue to make 10. Use the linking cubes to complete the addition sentence.

© Big Ideas Learning, LLC

Chapter 6 | Lesson 8   three hundred thirteen   313

Think and Grow: Modeling Real Life

This application allows students to show their understanding of showing the partner numbers for 10 when one part is given. They also write the related addition sentence.

- **Preview:** "Have you gone to an arcade or fair?" Have students share their experiences. You want to see if students are familiar with winning tickets when you play games at an arcade. They may be familiar with tokens instead of tickets.

- **Note:** These two exercises have a start number less than 5. Students generally find problems more challenging when the lesser of the two partner numbers is known. It is easier for students to count on from 9 to make 10 than to count on from 1 to make 10.

- **?** "You need 10 tickets to win a prize." Point to the top picture and ask, "How many tickets do you have so far? 1 "Think, how many more do I need to have 10? Draw more tickets to make 10."

- Circulate as students draw more tickets and write the addition sentence. Do students organize their drawing to help them know when they have drawn nine more? Do they keep re-counting to see if they are at 9 yet?

- **?** Point to the bottom picture and ask, "How many tickets does your friend have?" 3 "How many more do they need to have 10? Draw more tickets to make 10."

- **? Construct Viable Arguments:** "Who needs more tickets? Tell your partner how you know."

- ◉ Show this figure under a document camera or on a whiteboard. "How did the ten frame and linking cubes help you learn today? Tell your partner."

$$7 + \underline{} = 10$$

- **Supporting Learners:** Have two students work together and use linking cubes to act out the problem. Students may benefit from seeing the problem modeled on a ten frame. Use counters to represent the tickets.

Closure

- Explain that you are going to say the start number. You want them to show the partner number to make 10. Students can use their whiteboards or fingers to show their answer.

Think and Grow: Modeling Real Life

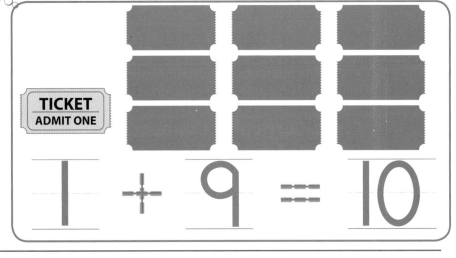

$1 + 9 = 10$

$3 + 7 = 10$

Directions: You need 10 tickets in all to win a prize.
- You win 1 ticket. Draw more tickets to make 10. Then write an addition sentence to match your picture.
- Your friend wins 3 tickets. Draw more tickets to make 10. Then write an addition sentence to match your picture.
- Who needs more tickets? Circle your answer.

314   three hundred fourteen

Connect and Extend Learning

Practice Notes

- Provide students with linking cubes, centimeter squares, and/or counters if needed for support.

Cross-Curricular Connections

Language Arts

- *Ten Apples Up On Top* by Dr. Seuss writing as Theo. LeSieg; Read the book aloud to students. Provide students with linking cubes or counters. As you read each page, have students begin with that number of apples presented using their manipulatives. Students will then count on to see how many more they need to make 10. Continue this process as you read through the book. Ask, "What are some ways we can make ten?" Write down student responses on the board.

Name _____

Learning Target: Find partner numbers for 10 and write an addition sentence.

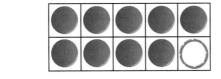

$$9 + 1 = 10$$

Directions: Draw more counters to make 10. Use the ten frame to complete the addition sentence.

1

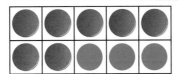

$$7 + 3 = 10$$

2

$$10 + 0 = 10$$

Directions: **1** Draw more counters to make 10. Use the ten frame to complete the addition sentence. **2** Color more linking cubes to make 10. Use the linking cubes to complete the addition sentence.

© Big Ideas Learning, LLC

Chapter 6 | Lesson 8

Connect and Extend Learning

Extend Student Learning

Visual-Spatial

- Provide students with a deck of cards (only cards with digits on them) and linking cubes or counters. Have students turn over one card. This is the first added in their addition number sentence. They will begin at this number and will count on using their manipulatives until they get to the sum of 10. Have students continue this process until they no longer have playing cards.

Lesson Resources	
Surface Level	**Deep Level**
Resources by Chapter • Extra Practice • Reteach Differentiating the Lesson Skills Review Handbook Skills Trainer	Resources by Chapter • Enrichment and Extension Graphic Organizers Dynamic Assessment System • Lesson Practice

3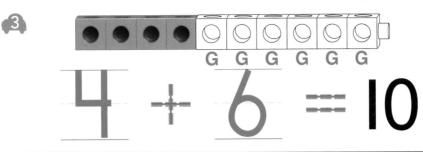
G G G G G G

$$4 + 6 = 10$$

4
Y Y Y Y Y Y B B B B

$$6 + 4 = 10$$

5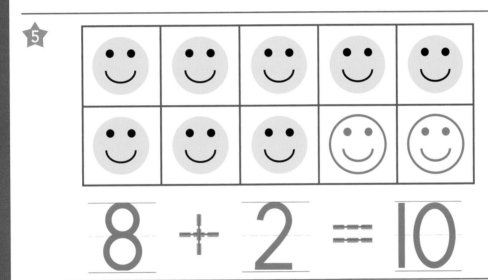

$$8 + 2 = 10$$

Directions: **3** Color more linking cubes to make 10. Use the linking cubes to complete the addition sentence. **4** Color 6 linking cubes yellow. Color more linking cubes blue to make 10. Use the linking cubes to complete the addition sentence.
5 You need 10 stickers in all to win a prize. You have 8 stickers. Draw more stickers to make 10. Write an addition sentence to match your picture.

Laurie's Notes

Performance Task

In this task, students will demonstrate how to use comparison words to show two groups of objects and then they will write a corresponding addition sentence. Use student responses to gauge their thinking about adding numbers within 10.

- Decide ahead of time whether students will be working independently, in pairs, or in groups.
- Pause between direction lines for students to complete each step.
- Have students share their work and thinking with others. Discuss as a class.

Exercise	Answers and Notes	Points
1	Students color the fish as 3 red and 2 blue; 4 red and 1 blue; or 5 red and 0 blue. Students write a corresponding addition sentence for the colored fish.	3
2	Students draw and color five fish as 0 red and 5 blue; 1 red and 4 blue; or 2 red and 3 blue. Students write a corresponding addition sentence for the colored fish.	3
3	Students draw 5 pellets, one for each fish. $5 + 5 = 10$	2
	Total	8

Name _____

 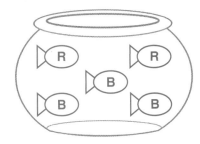
I and 2. Sample answers are given.

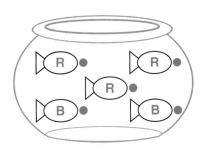 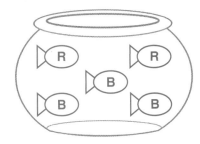

① $3 + 2 = 5$

② $2 + 3 = 5$

③ $5 + 5 = 10$

Directions: **①** You buy more red fish than blue fish at a pet store. Color to show the fish that you buy. Then write an addition sentence to match your picture. **②** Your friend buys 5 fish. Draw and color your friend's fish to show fewer red fish than blue fish. Then write an addition sentence to match your picture. **③** You put food pellets into your fishbowl to feed *your* fish. The number of food pellets is equal to the number of fish. Draw the food pellets. Then write an addition sentence to tell how many objects are in your fishbowl in all.

© Big Ideas Learning, LLC

Chapter 6   three hundred seventeen   317

Laurie's Notes

Add and Cover

Materials

- 1 manipulative per student to use as a playing piece
- 15 two-color counters per pair
- 1 die per pair

Students can work with partners or in groups. Provide whiteboards or scratch paper for students to show their work.

? "What do you see on this page that has to do with math?" *Sample answers:* numbers; plus signs; part of an addition sentence. This preview question helps students develop or strengthen number recognition as well as their vocabulary.

? "Do the numbers with a plus sign show complete addition sentences? What's missing?" the equal sign and how many in all This is the first time students are exposed to an expression. Students do not need to know this term.

- Read the directions at the bottom of the page. Model how to roll a die and move a manipulative clockwise that many spaces. Students solve the addition expression that they land on and cover the answer on the cloud with a counter.

- Have one student use the red side of the counters and the other student use the yellow side of the counters. If a number is already covered, then the student cannot place a counter. It is the next student's turn.

- When game play concludes, the discussion should focus on the students' reasoning about how they solved the addition expressions.

? **Attend to Precision:** "As you played the game, how did you know what cloud to cover?" I completed the addition sentence by counting on, remembering partner numbers, or by drawing objects.

- **Supporting Learners:** Provide students with counters and a ten frame or a number bond to use to solve each addition expression.

Closure

? "Did you notice any number patterns? What were they?" One is added to each number on the top row. I know that when I add one to a number it is one greater than that number; Zero is added to each number on the bottom row. I know when I add zero to a number the other number stays the same.

Add and Cover

| | 3 + 1 | 4 + 1 | 5 + 1 | ☀ | 6 + 1 | 7 + 1 |

2 + 4		7		5		10		2 + 3
5 + 5			5			8		2 + 2
7 + 2			6		6			4 + 5
☀				4		9		2 + 6
6 + 4		9		8		6		☀
3 + 2			7			5		2 + 7
		10					

| 8 + 0 | ☀ | 7 + 0 | 9 + 0 | 5 + 0 | 4 + 0 | 6 + 0 |

Directions: Start at Newton. Roll a die and move forward that number of spaces. Use the numbers on the space to find how many in all. Place a counter on a cloud with that number. If you land on a sun, cover a cloud of your choice. Repeat this process until you cover all of the clouds.

318   three hundred eighteen

Learning Target Correlation

Lesson	Learning Target	Exercises
6.1	Add to a group of objects and tell how many.	1
6.2	Add to a group of objects and complete an addition sentence.	2
6.3	Put two groups of objects together and complete an addition sentence.	3
6.4	Find partner numbers for a number and write an addition sentence.	4, 5, 6
6.5	Explain addition patterns with 0 and 1.	7, 8
6.6	Add partner numbers to 5.	9, 10, 11
6.7	Use a group of 5 to write an addition sentence.	12
6.8	Find partner numbers for 10 and write an addition sentence.	13, 14

Chapter Practice 6

6.1 Understand Addition

__3__ and __1__ is __4__ in all.

6.2 Addition: Add To

__2__ and __3__ is __5__ .

__2__ + __3__ = __5__

Directions: ❶ Complete the sentence to tell how many students are in the group to start, how many join, and how many there are in all. ❷ Complete the sentence to tell how many owls are in the group to start, how many join, and how many there are in all. Then complete the addition sentence to match.

Chapter 6   three hundred nineteen   319

Chapter Resources

Surface Level	Deep Level	Transfer Level
Resources by Chapter • Extra Practice • Reteach Differentiating the Lesson Skills Review Handbook Skills Trainer Game Library Math Musicals	Resources by Chapter • Enrichment and Extension Graphic Organizers Game Library Math Musicals	Dynamic Assessment System • Chapter Test Assessment Book • Chapter Tests A and B

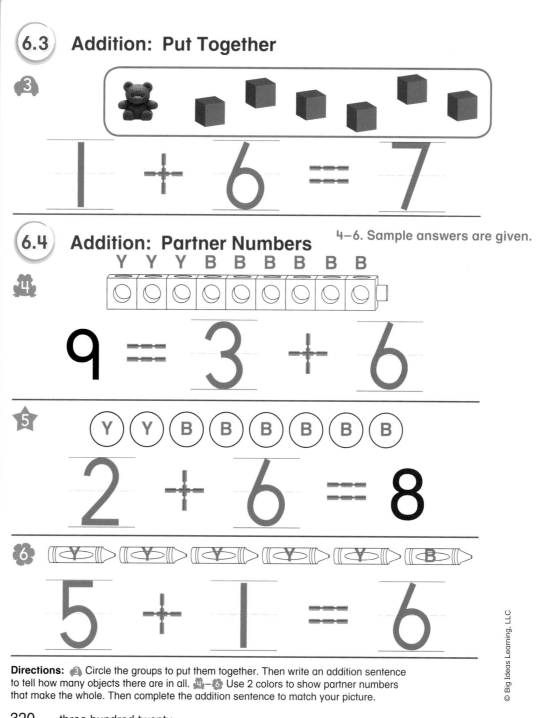

3

$$1 + 6 = 7$$

6.4 Addition: Partner Numbers

4–6. Sample answers are given.

Y Y Y B B B B B B

4

$$9 = 3 + 6$$

5

Y Y B B B B B B

$$2 + 6 = 8$$

6

$$5 + 1 = 6$$

Directions: 3 Circle the groups to put them together. Then write an addition sentence to tell how many objects there are in all. 4–6 Use 2 colors to show partner numbers that make the whole. Then complete the addition sentence to match your picture.

6.5 Addition Number Patterns
next number when counting

7 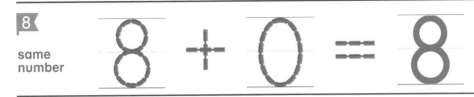 $5 + 1 = 6$

8
same
number

$8 + 0 = 8$

6.6 Practice Addition

9 $2 + 2 = 4$ *Sample answer:* used fingers

10 $0 + 0 = 0$ *Sample answer:* used fingers

11 $2 + 1 = 3$

$1 + 2 = 3$ same answer

Directions: **7** Write an addition sentence to tell how many dots there are in all.
Tell what you notice. **8** Complete the addition sentence. Tell what you notice.
9 and **10** Complete the addition sentence. Tell how you found your answer.
11 Complete the addition sentences. Tell what you notice.

© Big Ideas Learning, LLC

Chapter 6   three hundred twenty-one   321

6.7 Use a Group of 5 to Add

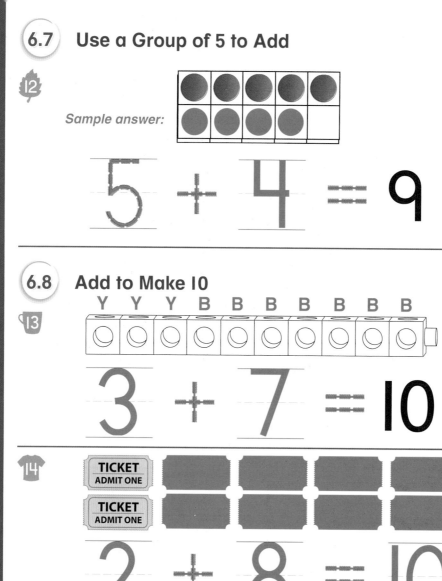

Sample answer:

$$5 + 4 = 9$$

6.8 Add to Make 10

Y Y Y B B B B B B B

$$3 + 7 = 10$$

TICKET ADMIT ONE

TICKET ADMIT ONE

$$2 + 8 = 10$$

Directions: 12 Draw more counters to show how many in all. Use the ten frame to complete the addition sentence. 13 Color 3 linking cubes yellow. Color more linking cubes blue to make 10. Use the linking cubes to complete the addition sentence. 14 You need 10 tickets in all to win a prize. You win 2 tickets. Draw more tickets to make 10. Then write an addition sentence to match your picture.

Math Musicals can be used with current topics, to review previous topics, or to preview upcoming topics.

Centers

Center 1: Add and Cover

Materials: Student Edition page 318, 1 die per pair, 15 two-color counters per pair, and 1 playing piece per student

Have students complete the Add and Cover activity. See page T-318 for the directions.

Center 2: Skills Trainer

Materials: computers or devices with Internet access

Have students go to *BigIdeasMath.com* to access the Skills Trainer.

Center 3: Number Flip

Materials per pair: Number Cards 0–5*, sticky notes, paper and pencil

Write a + symbol on one sticky note and an = symbol on the other sticky note. Place on the table face up, leaving room for the cards to sit in between the symbols. Have each student flip over one card from the pile and place it into the addition equation. Have the students write the addition sentence, including the answer, on their paper.

Center 4: Build It

Materials per pair: deck of cards (face cards and aces removed), linking cubes

Each student turns over one card at a time and uses linking cubes of two different colors to show partner numbers for the number of the card. Partners check each other's work. Students mix the cards back into the deck and choose again.

* Found in the Instructional Resources

Chapter Assessment Guide

Chapter tests are available in the Assessment Book.
An alternative assessment option is listed below.

Bodily Kinesthetic

Materials: linking cubes, Number Cards 0–5, Number Cards 5–10

Play a game called Match & Add with the student. Choose two number cards and show them to the student. Have the student use linking cubes to represent each number and then find the sum. Did the student answer correctly? If not, show the student.

Task	Points
Student used linking cubes to match the first number	1 point
Student used linking cubes to match the second number	1 point
Student can find the sum of the two numbers	1 point
Total	3 points

My Thoughts on the Chapter

What worked...

What did not work...

What I would do differently...

7 Subtract Numbers within 10

Chapter Overview

Lesson	Learning Target	Success Criteria
7.1 Understand Subtraction	Subtract a group of objects and tell how many are left.	• Tell how many objects there are in all. • Tell how many objects are taken away. • Tell how many objects are left.
7.2 Subtraction: Take From	Take from a group of objects and write a subtraction sentence.	• Tell what the minus sign means. • Tell how many objects are left. • Explain a subtraction sentence.
7.3 Subtraction: Take Apart	Take apart a group of objects and write a subtraction sentence.	• Show how to take apart a group of objects. • Take apart a group of objects to tell the partner numbers. • Write a subtraction sentence.
7.4 Subtraction Number Patterns	Find and explain subtraction patterns.	• Subtract 0, 1, or all of the objects from a group. • Explain the patterns of subtracting 0, 1, or all.
7.5 Practice Subtraction	Subtract within 5.	• Show and tell how to subtract numbers within 5. • Complete the subtraction sentence.
7.6 Use a Group of 5 to Subtract	Use a group of 5 to write a subtraction sentence.	• Use a ten frame to subtract 5. • Subtract 5 and tell how many are left. • Write a subtraction sentence.
7.7 Related Facts	Use related facts to add or subtract within 5.	• Write addition and subtraction sentences to show related facts. • Explain what is the same and different in these sentences.

Chapter Learning Target:
Understand subtraction.
Chapter Success Criteria:
▨ Identify a number sentence.
▨ Describe how objects can be taken away.
▨ Write a subtraction sentence.
▨ Explain subtraction sentences.

Progressions

Through the Grades	
Kindergarten	**Grade 1**
• Represent subtraction with various models and strategies. • Write a subtraction number sentence using symbols. • Represent, write, and solve "take from" problems with results unknown. • Represent, write, and solve "take apart" problems with one or two parts unknown. • Understand that taking away from a group will tell how many are left. • Understand that subtracting 0 doesn't change the number. • Fluently subtract within 5. • Explain the similarities and differences between addition and subtraction sentences.	• Solve addition and subtraction word problems with unknowns in all positions within 20. • Apply properties of operations as strategies to add and subtract. • Understand subtraction as an unknown addend problem. • Add and subtract within 20, demonstrating fluency within 10. • Use the equal sign to determine whether equations involving addition and subtraction are true or false. • Use the relationship between addition and subtraction to write related addition and subtraction equations. • Determine the unknown whole number that makes an equation true.

	Through the Chapter						
Standard	7.1	7.2	7.3	7.4	7.5	7.6	7.7
Represent addition and subtraction with objects, fingers, mental images, drawings, sounds, acting out situations, verbal explanations, expressions, or equations.	●	●	●	●	●	●	★
Solve addition and subtraction word problems, and add and subtract within 10, by using objects or drawings to represent the problem.	●	●	●	●	●	●	★
Fluently add and subtract within 5.				●	●		★

Key: ▲ = Preparing   ● = Learning   ★ = Complete

Laurie's Overview

About the Math

In earlier chapters, perceptual and conceptual subitizing were discussed as students were learning to count and understand numbers. Conceptual subitizing plays a role in developing ideas about addition and subtraction as well. Students are introduced to subtraction as an operation that takes one quantity from a greater quantity. Subtraction answers the question, *"How many are left?"* Several models are used throughout the chapter so that students can visualize this operation. Students who have subitized the number 3 in different arrangements are able to answer the question $5 - 3$ more quickly. For example, students know that when they hold up 5 fingers and then take away a group of 3 fingers, there are 2 fingers left. This is different than counting back 3, one number at time.

←2 dots
←3 dots
5 dots in all

5 takeaway 3

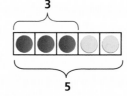

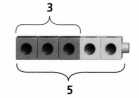

This chapter presents the two types of subtraction situations expected in kindergarten: *Take From* with result unknown and *Take Apart* with one part unknown or both parts unknown. In *Take Apart* situations there is no action or physically separating two quantities.

Subtraction Situations

Change Problems	Result Unknown	
Take From	There are 5 pigs in the pen. Two pigs leave. How many pigs are left? $5 - 2 = \rule{1cm}{0.4pt}$	
Part-Part-Whole Problems *Take Apart*	**One Part Unknown** $5 - \rule{0.8cm}{0.4pt} = 3$	**Both Parts Unknown** $5 - \rule{0.8cm}{0.4pt} = \rule{0.8cm}{0.4pt}$

The language of subtraction, *minus sign*, *subtract*, *take away*, and *separate* are introduced in the first few lessons. The equal sign is already known to students. All of these words should be added to the vocabulary wall or anchor chart. Point out when subtraction situations occur during the day:

"I have 5 grapes and I shared 2 with my friend. I have 3 grapes left."

"There were 5 pencils in the cup and now there are none left."

The last statement is an example of one of the subtraction patterns explored in this chapter. Students describe what they notice when you subtract 0, 1, and all.

Throughout the chapter expect some students to make observations about the inverse relationship between the operations of addition and subtraction, though they will not use these words. They may say, "Addition is when you put numbers together and then subtraction takes them apart," or " When you add 4 and 1 you get 5. Then you take 1 away from 5 and get back to 4." Their language is not precise, however they recognize the inverse relationship of these operations.

There is an expectation in kindergarten of fluency for addition and subtraction within five. Provide opportunities for students to continue practicing throughout the year.

Models

- Pictures are very useful in telling a story, especially when there is a physical action or scenario shown. Students can also draw pictures to show their understanding of subtraction. Drawing an X or line through an object suggests that the object is being subtracted.

- Number bonds show the relationship between a whole and its parts. This model is used when *take apart* problems are taught.

- Linking cubes are used often throughout the chapter to act out taking a group away from the whole, or separating a whole into two parts. A linking cube train represents the whole.

- Counters on a five and ten frame can be used to model subtraction. The crossed-out counters represent the amount removed.

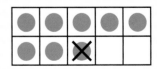

Chapter Materials and Resources

The primary materials and resources needed for this chapter are listed below. Other materials may be needed for the additional support ideas provided throughout the chapter.

Check out the virtual manipulatives.

BigIdeasMath.com

Classroom Materials	Chapter Opener	7.1	7.2	7.3	7.4	7.5	7.6	7.7	Connect and Grow
scissors	•								•
linking cubes		•	•	•				•	•
two-color counters		•	•	•		•	•		
whiteboards and markers			+					•	
paper cups								+	
floor number path					+				
transparent spinner or 1 pencil and 1 paper clip									•
piece of cardboard, elastic string, 40 beads									•
playing cards									•

Instructional Resources	Chapter Opener	7.1	7.2	7.3	7.4	7.5	7.6	7.7	Connect and Grow
Vocabulary Cards	•	+	+						
Ten Frames							•		
Five Frames					•				
Subtraction Recording Sheet									•

• class set   + teacher only   ∗ per pair/group

Suggested Pacing

Day 1	Chapter Opener	Performance Task Preview		Vocabulary			
Day 2	Lesson 7.1	Warm-Up	Dig In	Explore	Think	Apply: Practice	Think: Modeling Real Life
Day 3	Lesson 7.2	Warm-Up	Dig In	Explore	Think	Apply: Practice	Think: Modeling Real Life
Day 4	Lesson 7.3	Warm-Up	Dig In	Explore	Think	Apply: Practice	Think: Modeling Real Life
Day 5	Lesson 7.4	Warm-Up	Dig In	Explore	Think	Apply: Practice	Think: Modeling Real Life
Day 6	Lesson 7.5	Warm-Up	Dig In	Explore	Think	Apply: Practice	Think: Modeling Real Life
Day 7	Lesson 7.6	Warm-Up	Dig In	Explore	Think	Apply: Practice	Think: Modeling Real Life
Day 8	Lesson 7.7	Warm-Up	Dig In	Explore	Think	Apply: Practice	Think: Modeling Real Life
Day 9	Connect And Grow	Performance Task		Activity		Chapter Practice	
Day 10		Centers					
Day 11	Chapter Assessment	Chapter Assessment					

Year-to-Date: 80 Days

Laurie's Notes

Performance Task Preview

- Have students discuss the picture and then share what they know.
- ? Ask students, "What are the objects on the page? What do you do to make bubbles?" blow, add soap to the bath, wash yourself
- ? Read the questions on the page. "Where have you seen bubbles before?" Listen for students to mention the bathtub, in a sink, in hair or on skin, in a fish tank, or outside in the air.
- Note: Make sure that students do not count the bubbles in the design at the top of the page for the next set of questions.
- ? "How many bubbles are in the picture? If 5 bubbles pop, how many bubbles will be left?" You may want to provide counters for students to cover the five bubbles or cross out the five bubbles as they are counted.
- In the Performance Task at the end of the chapter, students will draw groups of big and small bubbles and will then write subtraction sentences to answer questions about the groups of bubbles.

7 Subtract Numbers within 10

- Where have you seen bubbles before?

- How many bubbles are in the picture? If 5 bubbles pop, how many bubbles will be left?

Chapter Learning Target:
Understand subtraction.

Chapter Success Criteria:
- I can identify a number sentence.
- I can describe how objects can be taken away.
- I can write a subtraction sentence.
- I can explain subtraction sentences.

© Big Ideas Learning, LLC

three hundred twenty-three 323

Laurie's Notes

Vocabulary Review

? **Preview:** "What do you see on the page?" a number bond,
rubber ducks, a bathtub "How can you tell how many rubber
ducks there are?" count

- "Name the whole and the parts for the group. Then complete
the number bond."
- Discuss what it means to *take apart* the number five. Have
students explain how the parts are related.
- **Supporting Learners:** Have students use two-color counters and
a copy of Number Bond to make and show each part.
- **Extension:** Have students take apart other numbers.

Chapter 7 Vocabulary

Activity

- **Echo:** Find a ball that can be easily and safely passed around by
students. Designate this as the echo ball. Say a vocabulary word
and then pass the echo ball to a student. The student echoes,
or repeats the word, and then passes the echo ball back to you.
Students need to listen carefully to repeat the word correctly.
Consider challenging the students by having them define the
words after they echo them.
- **Teaching Tip:** Before the game begins, decide how you are
going to have your students pass the ball. Silent and gentle
hand passes are recommended.

MATH MUSICALS

Math Musicals can be used with current
topics, to review previous topics, or to
preview upcoming topics. There are many
Math Musicals to choose from!

Use your hand puppets to act out new
stories and have students sing the songs
several times to take full advantage of the
power of music to learn math!

7

Vocabulary

> **Review Words**
> parts
> whole
> number bond

Directions: Name the parts and the whole for the group. Then complete the number bond.

Chapter 7 Vocabulary Cards

left	minus sign
separate	subtract
subtraction sentence	take away

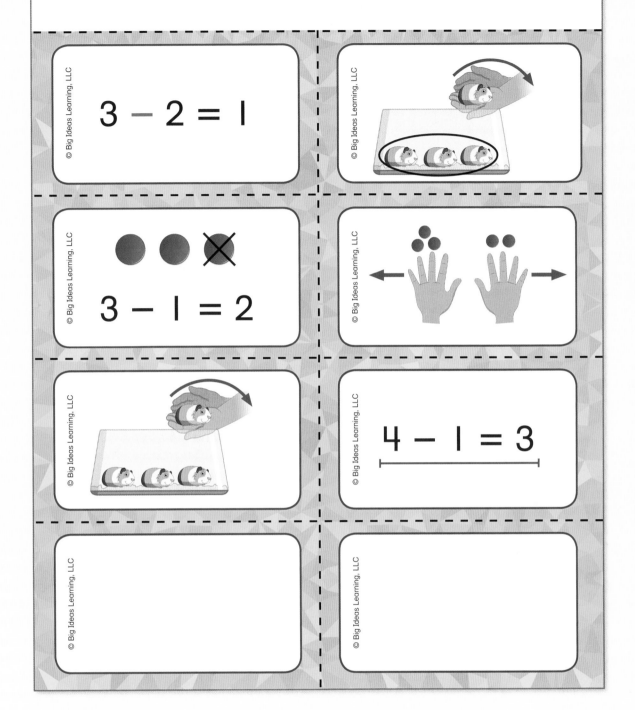

Learning Target

Subtract a group of objects and tell how many are left.

Success Criteria

- Tell how many objects there are in all.
- Tell how many objects are taken away.
- Tell how many objects are left.

Warm-Up

Practice opportunities for the following are available in the Resources by Chapter or at *BigIdeasMath.com*.

- Daily skills
- Vocabulary
- Prerequisite skills

ELL Support

Tell students that when they subtract, they take objects away from a group and tell how many are left. They may be familiar with the word left as a direction, as in right and left hands. Explain that left also refers to what stays behind.

Laurie's Notes

Preparing to Teach

Students have given away some of their toys or snack items and know that results in having less than what they began with. This is the operation of subtraction. Like addition, we will use contextual problems to help students in their reasoning and ability to explain their thinking. We use the words take away and subtract to describe the *change* problem. (See page T-323C for a discussion of problem types.) We start with a group of objects, some are taken away (subtracted) from the group, and we want to know how many are left. The contexts will suggest physical movements which can be modeled with manipulatives, but let students act out the taking away process first.

Materials

- linking cubes
- two-color counters

Dig In (Circle Time)

Students will do acting out of one group being taken away, or separated from a group. They also model this with linking cubes.

- Use the words *take away*, *subtract*, and *left* as you talk with students. Other words that suggest subtraction are remove or separate. This is similar to the Lesson 6.1 Dig In.
- **Example:** "I need some wigglers." Ask three students to stand in middle and wiggle. "We have three wigglers. I want take away two of the wigglers." Have two of the students move back to the circle. "How many wigglers are left?" Summarize. "We started with 3 wigglers (hold up 3 linking cubes), we took away 2 wigglers (remove 2 linking cubes), and we had 1 wigglers left."
- Repeat for another combination with a starting number of 5 or less. Call them jumpers, kneelers, or whatever actions or poses your students will enjoy. Each time model with the linking cubes as you summarize.
- ❓ "How can you tell how many are left? Tell your neighbor." Students should mention counting or just knowing partner numbers.
- ◉ Review the learning target. "We started with 3 wigglers, we took away 2 wigglers, and we had 1 wiggler left. Today we will subtract a group of objects and tell how many we have left."

❓ Teaching Prompt　　◉ Learning Target

Name _____

Learning Target: Subtract a group of objects and tell how many are left.

Explore and Grow

4 take away 3

Directions: Use counters to act out the story.
- There are 4 students in the school. Write the number.
- 3 students leave the school. Write the number.
- Tell how many students are left in the school. |

Chapter 7 | Lesson 1   three hundred twenty-five   **325**

© Big Ideas Learning, LLC

Explore and Grow

- **Note:** Use this page multiple times without recording any numbers. You want students to become familiar with the language and concept of taking away. After several iterations, have students record the last example.
- **Example:** Use counters. Read the directions using the numbers 4 and 3 as stated. Have students say "4 take away 3" and ask how many are left.
- Students move the counters off the page as they subtract 3 counters.
- **Supporting Learners:** Five frames and/or whiteboards can be used for additional practice. Students can also use their fingers to act it out.

Laurie's Notes

Think and Grow

Getting Started

- Introduce the vocabulary cards for take away, subtract, and left. Connect these words to work with partner numbers and the acting out they did during circle time.
- Remind students that you want to hear them use these words as they work with their partner today.
- Note: The printed words shown (___ take away ___ is ___) are to prepare students for the subtraction sentence in the next lesson.

Teaching Notes

- There are two parts to each problem. The image suggests some physical movement or social encounter and a subtraction statement is completed. We are not introducing *subtraction sentence* in this lesson. Refer to it as a sentence that tells about the math.
- Common Error: Students may interpret the picture as an addition story. The actions should suggest that children are leaving a group not joining a group.
- Model: "Tell your partner what is happening in the picture. How many children were on the rug to start? How many are leaving? Then how many are left?" Ask questions about the counters shown. How many to start, how many are being removed, and how many are left. Students trace the numbers.
- Ask a student to tell the story of what happened in the picture and to use today's vocabulary.
- ? Reason Abstractly and Quantitatively: "One student leaves the group. Do we have more or less now? How do you know?" Listen for different student reasoning.
- Discuss the context in the second problem to insure that all students understand the scenario.
- Supporting Learners: Each problem can be modeled using a five frame and counters, using fingers, or having students act it out.
- Contextual stories help students make sense of the operation of subtraction. The operation can be modeled or acted out, but it is most helpful to include a context.
- ⊙ Use one of the two contexts on this page to ask specific questions about the success criteria. Can they tell how many they start with, how many are taken away, and how many are left? The questions help students to be clear about their learning.

4 take away 1 is 3 .

5 take away 3 is 2 .

Directions: Complete the sentence to tell how many students there are in all, how many are leaving, and how many are left.

326 three hundred twenty-six

© Big Ideas Learning, LLC

Meeting the needs of
all learners.

Laurie's Notes

Apply and Grow: Practice
SCAFFOLDING INSTRUCTION

An effective tool we have for helping students construct an understanding of subtraction is to use physical actions that suggest a familiar context. The contexts give meaning to their thinking. The exercises on this page suggest scenarios familiar to students. They are with a group, and someone or some others leave them. You might discuss each of the pictures first to be sure all students understand what the actions suggest.

EMERGING students may not understand the physical action of a group becoming smaller when objects are removed. They may see two smaller groups and think they should join them together as they did with addition. It is important for students to understand the context.

- **Exercises 1–3:** Students can use counters and place them on each child in the pictures. These can be removed as they count how many are being subtracted.
- **Exercises 1–3:** Additional support may be needed as students learn to record the total first, how many are leaving the group, and finally how many are left.

PROFICIENT students understand what it means to take away a number of objects from a group and have a strategy for deciding how many are left.

- **Exercises 1–3:** Have students tell their partner how they decided how many were left.

Additional Support
- Have students act out any of the exercises. Pause so that students can record how many they began with, how many were taken away, and how many are left.
- Use linking cubes to model the story as you have students record.

Extensions: Adding Rigor
? "How many would be left if one more student decided to leave the group?"
- Have students come up with their own problem using two given numbers. You could tell them the two numbers or they could draw two numbers from the 1-5 number cards or dot cards.

 Apply and Grow: Practice

1

6 take away 2 is 4 .

2

8 take away 3 is 5 .

3

10 take away 3 is 7 .

Directions: **1** – **3** Complete the sentence to tell how many students there are in all, how many are leaving, and how many are left.

Chapter 7 | Lesson I three hundred twenty-seven **327**

Verify that students know what green beans and carrots are by pointing to each. Then have them complete the activity. Have each student use their existing number cards, including numbers from 1-8. Check for understanding of Lesson 7.1 by asking the following questions and having students answer by holding up the appropriate card.

1. How many green beans are not crossed out in the top picture?
2. How many carrots did you cross out?
3. If you crossed out one, how many are left?
4. If you crossed out two, how many are left?
5. If you crossed out three, how many are left?
6. If you crossed out four, how many are left?

You may want to check their subtraction sentences by having them write them on an individual white board and hold them up.

Think and Grow: Modeling Real Life

This application allows students to show their understanding of taking objects away from a group and finding out how many are left.

- **Preview:** Have students discuss what they think is happening in the picture. Do they think some of the vegetables are going to be eaten? Some students might think more vegetables will be put on the plate!
- ? "How many green beans are on the plate? That is how many we start with. Where do we write this number?"
- "You eat 6 green beans. How can we show that the beans are eaten?" Listen for reasonable ideas such as drawing an x or line through the 6 beans.
- **Model with Mathematics:** If a document camera is available, have different students share how they represented 6 beans being removed.
- ? "How many do we have left? How do you know?" Listen for different student reasoning.
- ? **Extension:** "What if you ate 8 beans? How many would be left?"
- ◉ Have students discuss how well they understand taking objects away from a group and telling how many are left.
- **Supporting Learners:** Display the problem and use counters to show the 8 green beans. Ask a student to demonstrate what it looks like to take away 6.
- **Supporting Learners:** Ask students to use their fingers to show how many beans remain if you begin with 8 and you eat 1; eat 2; continue until you eat 6.

Closure

- Hold up a linking cube train of 6. "How many cubes are there?"
- Wait as students count. "I want to take away 2 cubes. How many will be left? Show me with your fingers."
- Repeat with two other numbers.

Sample answer:

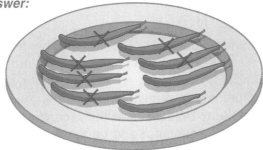

8 take away 6 is 2 .

Sample answer:

6 take away 2 is 4 .

Directions:
- You have 8 green beans on your plate. You eat 6 of them. Cross out the green beans you eat. Then complete the sentence to match your picture.
- You have 6 carrots on your plate. You eat some of them. Cross out the carrots you eat. Then complete the sentence to match your picture.

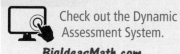
Connect and Extend Learning

Practice Notes

- Remind students that the first number in a subtraction sentence is the whole, so it will be the greatest number. The second number is how many are being taken away, and the third number is how many are left.
- Point out to students that the second and third numbers in the subtraction sentence add up to the whole (the first number) when you put them together.
- Extra support may be provided to students through the use of manipulatives. For example, a student may work with a group of blocks, counting them all to find the whole, and then taking away different numbers of the whole to find the number that remain.

Cross-Curricular Connections

Art

- Divide students into groups of three. In each group, give each of the three students a different color of crayon, plus a blank sheet of paper. Have each student draw up to 10 circles or other simple empty shapes on their sheet of paper. Then have each student pass their sheet to another student in the group. The second student should color in some, but not all, of the shapes on the sheet. Then have the students pass their sheets within the group once more, so that each student has a sheet in front of them that they have not seen yet. Have each student say aloud the subtraction sentence that describes what they see. (For example, if 6 shapes were drawn on the sheet and 4 were colored in, the student would say "Six take away four is two.")

Name _____

Learning Target: Subtract a group of objects and tell how many are left.

5 ___ take away 2 ___ is 3 ___ .

Directions: Complete the sentence to tell how many students there are in all, how many are leaving, and how many are left.

3 ___ take away 1 ___ is 2 ___ .

5 ___ take away 1 ___ is 4 ___ .

Directions: ❶ and ❷ Complete the sentence to tell how many students there are in all, how many are leaving, and how many are left.

Chapter 7 | Lesson 1   three hundred twenty-nine   329

© Big Ideas Learning, LLC

Connect and Extend Learning

Extend Student Learning
Bodily-Kinesthetic

- Bring a group of 6–10 students up to the front of the class, on one side of the room. Point to that group and ask the class to count how many students are in the group, and call out the number. Then, have some (but not all) of the students in the group cross to the other side of the room. Say, "How many students did I take away?" and point to the group of students who crossed. The class should call out the number of students in that group. Say, "That leaves how many?" and point to the students in front who remained in their original spots. The class should call out the number of students who remain. Review by saying, "How many students came up to the front of the room?" Then say the number sentence that was acted out (for example, "9 take away 3 leaves 6.") Have the students in the group sit down and call a new group of students numbering between 6 and 10 up to the front of the class, and repeat the activity.

Lesson Resources	
Surface Level	**Deep Level**
Resources by Chapter • Extra Practice • Reteach Differentiating the Lesson Skills Review Handbook Skills Trainer	Resources by Chapter • Enrichment and Extension Graphic Organizers Dynamic Assessment System • Lesson Practice

3

_7_ take away _3_ is _4_.

4

_10_ take away _4_ is _6_.

5 Sample answer:

_9_ take away _5_ is _4_.

Directions: **3** and **4** Complete the sentence to tell how many students there are in all, how many are leaving, and how many are left. **5** You have 9 blueberries on your plate. You eat some of them. Cross out the blueberries you eat. Then complete the sentence to tell how many blueberries there are in all, how many you eat, and how many are left.

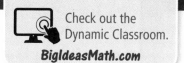

Check out the
Dynamic Classroom.

BigIdeasMath.com

Laurie's Notes

Preparing to Teach

Students may have expressed their thinking that subtraction is an undoing operation. Their language may not be precise, but they sense that instead of joining two groups to make a whole, they are taking the whole apart. Indeed, addition and subtraction are inverse operations.

The minus sign is introduced as students write subtraction sentences. Again, be careful when talking about the equal sign. It represents a relationship between two quantities and we don't want students to believe it means "the answer."

Materials

- whiteboards and markers
- linking cubes
- two-color counters

Dig In (Circle Time)

This is similar to the previous circle time. Students will do acting out of one group being taken away from another. You record the story as a subtraction sentence on a whiteboard. Use linking cubes to summarize.

- Use the words take away, subtract, and left as you talk with students, but introduce the minus sign and explain it is a way to help tell what is going on in the story.
- **Example:** "I need five twisters." Ask students to stand in middle. "We have five twisters." Let them twist a bit and record the 5. Ask two students leave (sit down). "We take away 2 students. How many are left?" Record the 2 and 3. Explain that instead of writing all the words, there are symbols that can tell the story. "I'm going to use this symbol to show that we subtracted a group. We call it the minus sign." Summarize. "We started with 5 twisters (hold up 5 linking cubes), we took away 2 twisters (remove 2 linking cubes), and we have 3 twisters left."
- Repeat for numbers where the whole is within 5. Write both subtraction sentences, words, and symbols.
- ⊙ Review the first success criterion. "Can you tell what the minus sign means?"

Learning Target

Take from a group of objects and write a subtraction sentence.

Success Criteria

- Tell what the minus sign means.
- Tell how many objects are left.
- Explain a subtraction sentence.

Practice opportunities for the following are available in the Resources by Chapter or at *BigIdeasMath.com*.

- Daily skills
- Vocabulary
- Prerequisite skills

ELL Support

The phrase *take from* signals subtraction. Students will see the subtraction symbol $(-)$ used. They can use the words *take away*, *take from*, *minus*, or *subtract* to describe what happens in place of the symbol. For example, "Five minus three is two."

? Teaching Prompt   ⊙ Learning Target

Name _____

Learning Target: Take from
a group of objects and write a
subtraction sentence.

Explore and Grow

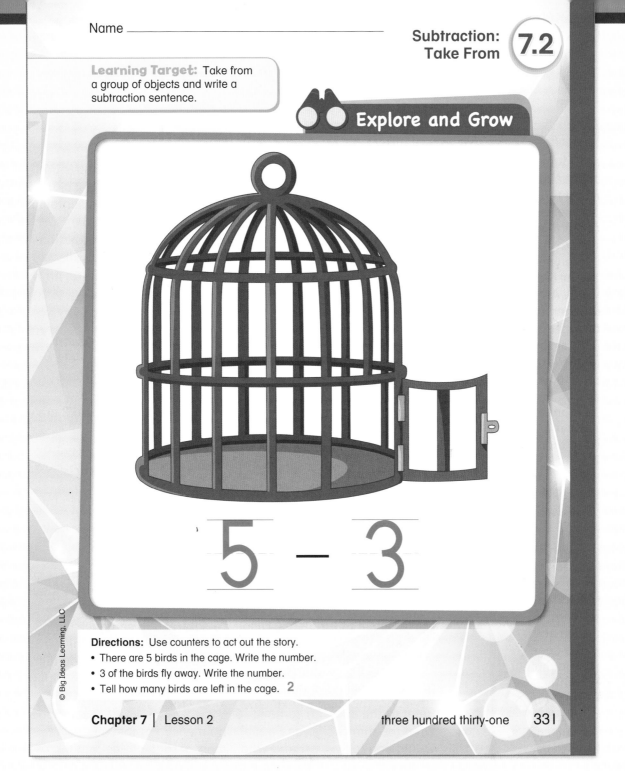

$$5 - 3$$

Directions: Use counters to act out the story.
- There are 5 birds in the cage. Write the number.
- 3 of the birds fly away. Write the number.
- Tell how many birds are left in the cage. **2**

© Big Ideas Learning, LLC

Chapter 7 | Lesson 2

three hundred thirty-one 331

Explore and Grow

- You can use this page multiple times with various numbers. Model the number of birds with linking cubes and practice taking some away. After several iterations, have students record the final example.
- **Example:** Use counters. Read the directions using the numbers 5 and 3 as stated. Ask about the minus sign on the page. "How many birds are left?"
- This is a *take from* problem. The whole and one part are known.
- **Supporting Learners:** Have students trace a minus sign with their fingers on their desk or other textured surface as you discuss what it means.

Think and Grow

Getting Started

- Refer to the birds in the cage story as you write the subtraction sentence for the story: $5 - 3 = 2$. You are using the equal sign to show that 2 is how many birds are left. The subtraction sentence tells a story. "What story does $5 - 3 = 2$ tell?"
- Introduce the vocabulary cards for **minus sign** and **subtraction sentence**. Add them to the anchor chart or vocabulary wall.
- To show subtraction when using models or on the picture, an X is used to indicate the objects that have been taken away.

Teaching Notes

- Each problem shows the language from the previous lesson and the equivalent subtraction sentence with symbols. Help students interpret the pictures so the context is understood.
- **Common Error:** Students may say there is 1 bird and 2 are leaving. They do not understand there were 3 to start and 2 are leaving. Interpreting the context correctly is essential.
- **Model:** "Tell your partner what is happening in the picture. How many birds are in the picture? How many are flying away? How many are left?"
- "Turn and tell your partner what the whole and parts are in this problem."
- Discuss the context in the second problem to ensure that all students understand the scenario.
- **Supporting Learners:** Each problem can be modeled using counters or linking cubes. Students should tell the story as they manipulate the counters or cubes.
- **Make Sense of Problems:** Display a subtraction sentence such as $5 - 2 = 3$ and hold up a group of five books. "This subtraction sentence tells a story about my books. Can you tell your partner the story?" Have students share their stories with the class.
- ⊙ Refer to the addition sentence $5 - 2 = 3$. "Can you tell someone what the minus sign and equal sign mean? For instance, what would you tell your friend who is absent today to help them understand?"

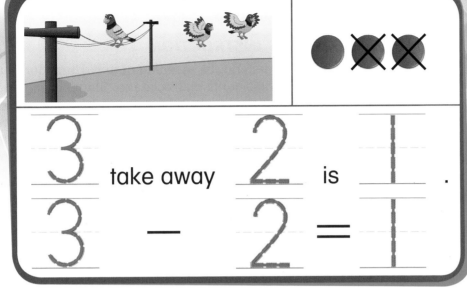

3 take away 2 is 1 .

3 − 2 = 1

5 take away 1 is 4 .

5 − 1 = 4

Directions: Complete the sentence to tell how many animals there are in all, how many are leaving, and how many are left. Then complete the subtraction sentence to match.

Meeting the needs of
all learners.

Laurie's Notes

Apply and Grow: Practice
SCAFFOLDING INSTRUCTION

Help students understand the meaning of the subtraction sentence
by seeing or hearing a contextual scenario. Students can practice
making sense of subtraction by telling a story about each picture
on this page. Have groups of students look at the page and tell one
another a story. Listen to the students' stories. Do they convey an
understanding of subtraction, one group being taken away from
another?

EMERGING students may not be clear about how to interpret a
contextual problem. They may see the picture and see two parts
that can be joined to make a whole. They may confuse addition
and subtraction.

- **Exercises 1–3:** Ask students to read the picture from left to right
  and notice that some in the group are leaving. This helps them
  connect the scenario to subtraction, not addition.
- **Exercise 2:** Students may be confused since both parts are two.
  Two leave and two are left.

PROFICIENT students are able to tell what a subtraction sentence
means. They are comfortable using the minus sign and equal sign
to record the actions in a story.

- **Reason Abstractly and Quantitatively:** In any problem probe
  students about the whole. How do you know what the whole is?
  How can you tell how many are being taken away?

Additional Support

- Have students act out any of the exercises. Pause so that
  students can record the numbers in the subtraction sentence.
- Write the subtraction sentence template ___ − ___ = ___ on the
  board. Have students tell the story suggested by a picture. Stop
  as they mention each quantity and ask (or tell) where to write
  that number.

Extension: Adding Rigor

- Play *Drop Five*. One partner drops five counters on a desk
  to represent five students. Their partner takes away the red
  counters. Tell or write the addition sentence for this story.
  "There are 5 students take away 3 students equals 2 students.

✓ Apply and Grow: Practice

1

$$5$$ take away $$4$$ is $$1$$.

$$5 - 4 = 1$$

2

$$4 - 2 = 2$$

3

$$9 - 3 = 6$$

Directions: **1** Complete the sentence to tell how many deer there are in all, how many are leaving, and how many are left. Then complete the subtraction sentence to match. **2** and **3** Complete the subtraction sentence to tell how many animals are left.

Think and Grow: Modeling Real Life

This application allows students to show their understanding of subtracting an amount from nine and writing a subtraction sentence.

- **Preview:** Have students discuss what they think is happening in the picture. Do they know what animal hangs from the roof of caves?

? "How many bats are hanging in the cave?"

- Explain that some of the bats fly away and they can decide how many! "How can you show that the bats fly away?" Listen for students to suggest drawing a line or X on the bats that leave.
- Students must decide how to write the subtraction problem that represents their picture.
- **Critique the Reasoning of Others:** If a document camera is available, have different students show their model and subtraction sentence. Ask others to explain why the sentence does or does not make sense.
- ⊙ Display or write the addition sentence $9 - 4 = 5$. "I want you to tell your partner what the minus sign means in this problem." After students have discussed, have a few share with the whole class. Do the same for last two success criteria.

Closure

- Write the subtraction problem $7 - 3 = \underline{}$ on the board. Ask students to show 7 fingers. "Now put 3 of your fingers down. How many are left?"

Think and Grow: Modeling Real Life

Sample answer:

$$9 - 8 = 1$$

Directions: Some of the bats in a cave fly away. Cross out the bats that fly away. Then complete the subtraction sentence to tell how many are left.

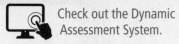
Connect and Extend Learning

Practice Notes

- Remind students that subtraction means "take away."
- Point out that in the exercises, the pictures above the subtraction sentences are not necessarily over the number they represent. The first number in the subtraction sentence should be the number students get by counting all the animals, the second number should be the number of animals that are running, jumping, or flying away, and the third number should be the number of animals that are staying behind.

Cross-Curricular Connections

Language Arts

- Ask the class to name different games that kids play. Say, "Here is a math story about kids playing tag and soccer. There were 6 kids playing tag and 8 kids playing soccer. Then, 2 kids left the group playing tag and went to go play soccer. How many kids were left in the group playing tag?" Then ask each student to tell a story about two groups of kids playing two different games. Have students tell how many kids were in each group; then they tell how many kids left one group; then they say how many kids were left in that group.

Learning Target: Take from a group of objects and write a subtraction sentence.

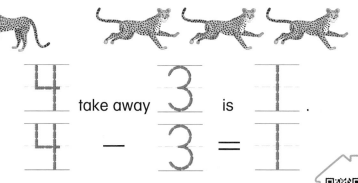

4 take away 3 is 1 .

4 — 3 = 1

Directions: Complete the sentence to tell how many cheetahs there are in all, how many are leaving, and how many are left. Then complete the subtraction sentence to match.

1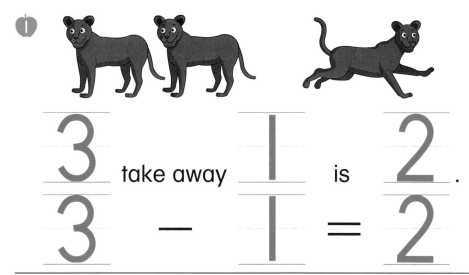

3 take away 1 is 2 .

3 — 1 = 2

Directions: **1** Complete the sentence to tell how many panthers there are in all, how many are leaving, and how many are left. Then complete the subtraction sentence to match.

© Big Ideas Learning, LLC

Chapter 7 | Lesson 2

three hundred thirty-five 335

Connect and Extend Learning

Extend Student Learning
Musical

- Teach students this song, to the tune of "Twinkle Twinkle Little Star":

    Twinkle, twinkle, _____ little stars
    _____ drive away in their cars
        Nobody knows where they go
        In their cars way down below
    Twinkle, twinkle, little stars
    _____ are left up there so far.

    Start the song with 10 little stars, 5 drive away, 5 are left. Hold up fingers to show the numbers as you sing. Have students hold up their fingers as well. Continue singing, using different combinations of numbers.

Lesson Resources	
Surface Level	**Deep Level**
Resources by Chapter • Extra Practice • Reteach Differentiating the Lesson Skills Review Handbook Skills Trainer	Resources by Chapter • Enrichment and Extension Graphic Organizers Dynamic Assessment System • Lesson Practice

2

$$4 - 1 = 3$$

3

$$7 - 4 = 3$$

4 *Sample answer:*

$$10 - 6 = 4$$

Directions: **2** and **3** Complete the subtraction sentence to tell how many animals are left. **4** Some of the wolves leave the group. Cross out the wolves that leave. Then complete the subtraction sentence to tell how many wolves are left.

7.3

Laurie's Notes

Learning Target

Take apart a group of objects and write a subtraction sentence.

Success Criteria

- Show how to take apart a group of objects.
- Take apart a group of objects to tell the partner numbers.
- Write a subtraction sentence.

Warm-Up

Practice opportunities for the following are available in the Resources by Chapter or at *BigIdeasMath.com*.

- Daily skills
- Vocabulary
- Prerequisite skills

ELL Support

Remind students that the phrase *put together* signals addition. Explain that the phrase *take apart* means the opposite. It signals subtraction. You may want to pantomime the actions of putting together and taking apart groups of objects as you say each phrase and have students repeat.

Preparing to Teach

In the last two lessons the subtraction situation was *take away*, meaning the whole and one part were known. In this lesson the situation is referred to as a *take apart* problem. The context is a about sharing, or taking the whole apart. Students generally find this situation more difficult to understand. Modeling the *take apart* situation with a linking cube train allows students to see the whole group and the two parts.

Materials

- linking cubes
- two-color counters

Dig In (Circle Time)

You will model taking apart a group of objects. This should remind students of decomposing a number into partner numbers. The language of subtraction is still used. The amount you take away and the amount left are the partner numbers.

- **Example:** Show five linking cubes in your hand and say, "I have five linking cubes. I am going to share some of the cubes with [name]." Model giving [name] some cubes. "How many do I have left?" Pause as students answer. "What if I share (new amount) with [name]? How many will I have left?" Repeat for several other combinations.
- Explain that in each problem you were taking apart a group of 5. You were giving away some cubes and you had some cubes left.
- Use a whiteboard. Discuss how to write a subtraction sentence for one of the problems, such as $5 - 2 = 3$.
- Repeat for a collection of six linking cubes. "Tell your partner how you could share the six linking cubes."
- Have a few volunteers share their thinking. Record a subtraction equation as they talk about taking apart a group of six linking cubes.
- ? "How did you know how many objects were left after you shared?" Listen for students counting or subitizing to know the amount.
- ⊙ Review the first two success criteria. "Did you remember partner numbers when you were taking apart a group of linking cubes?"

? Teaching Prompt   ⊙ Learning Target

Learning Target: Take apart a group of objects and write a subtraction sentence.

Explore and Grow

Sample answer:

7

R   Y

R   Y   Y

R   Y

3   4

Directions: There are 7 apples in the tree. Some are red and some are yellow. Use counters to show the apples in the tree. Write the number above the tree. Take apart the group of apples by placing the red apples in one group and the yellow apples in another group. Write the numbers.

Chapter 7 | Lesson 3   three hundred thirty-seven   **337**

Explore and Grow

• Model this page by dropping two-color counters. Display using a document camera. Have a volunteer show how to sort the counters into red and yellow. Count each. Record each trial.

? "What do you notice about the number of red apples and the number of yellow apples?" They are partner numbers for 7.

• We want students to make the connection to starting with 7 and taking it apart into two groups. The two groups are partner numbers for 7. Show this in a number bond.

Laurie's Notes

Think and Grow

Getting Started

- There is no context for the subtraction problems. To show that the linking cubes are being taken apart students will draw two circles. We are taking apart a group the group of 6 and then 5.
- The number bond tells what the partner numbers are. If there were no number bond, there would be several different subtraction sentences that would be correct.

Teaching Notes

- ◉ Students need to draw circles to show how they are taking apart a group of objects. The two groups of cubes circled need to be partner numbers for the amount of cubes shown.
- **Model:** "There are some red linking cubes." Point to the second picture. "What are the partner numbers in the number bond?" Pause. "Why do you think the four is crossed out?" Listen for subtraction.
- Talk about the subtraction sentence as students trace.
- Students will recognize the linking cubes and number bond, however there is no physical action of children or animals as in previous sections. Taking a group apart may not be obvious.
- "Tell you partner what you see in the pictures of the green linking cubes."
- ? "How do you know how to take the cubes apart?" look at the number bond
- Remind students to circle the two groups and write the subtraction sentence.
- **Make Sense of Problems:** The last problem may confuse students. You may hear them ask which part they are subtracting. Explain that you can take either part away from the whole.
- **Supporting Learners:** Provide linking cubes for students to manipulate and actually take apart.
- ◉ Refer to the two problems on this page. "How are you doing with your learning today? Can you show how to take apart a group of objects? Can you explain how to write a subtraction sentence to show how you take apart a number?"

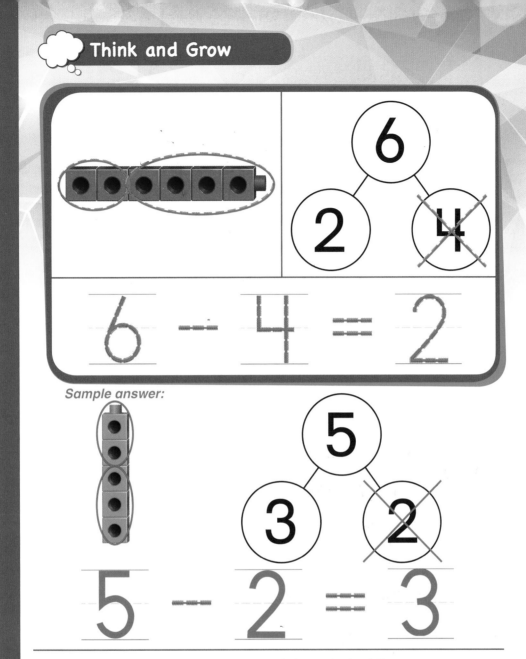

$$6 - 4 = 2$$

Sample answer:

$$5 - 2 = 3$$

Directions: Circle the linking cubes to show the parts in the number bond. Then write a subtraction sentence by taking one of the parts from the whole. Cross out the part on the number bond that you take away.

338   three hundred thirty-eight

MATH MUSICALS

Remember, you can use the song
Rockin' Dogs and Cool Cats
to review partner numbers to 5!

Rockin' Dogs and Cool Cats

Laurie's Notes

Apply and Grow: Practice

SCAFFOLDING INSTRUCTION

Refer to your anchor chart for partner numbers. Students will see that there are two related statements they made using partner numbers. Example: 2 and 5 are partner numbers for 7 and so are 5 and 2. When you take apart a group of 7 objects you can write two related subtraction sentences: $7 - 2 = 5$ and $7 - 5 = 2$.

EMERGING students may not be confident in understanding how to take apart a number of objects and how that relates to subtraction.

- **Exercises 1 and 2:** Talk students through how to complete an exercise. Ask specific questions. "How many blue counters are there? Where is that number in the number bond? Is it a part or the whole? Where do we write 8 in the subtraction sentence? Why?"

PROFICIENT students are able to show how to take apart a group of objects and explain how to write the related subtraction sentence.

- **Exercises 1 and 2:** Ask students to explain what the number bond means. "How does it help you write the subtraction sentence?"

Additional Support

- Provide linking cubes or other manipulatives for students to model the exercises with.

Extension: Adding Rigor

- "How could you show the subtraction without using manipulatives?" Listen for using fingers, drawing a picture, or seeing a picture in their mind.

Meeting the needs of all learners.

Name _____

1 and 2. Sample answers are given.

1

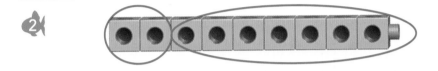

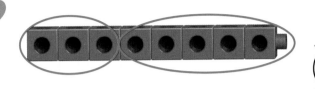

$$8 - 3 = 5$$

2

$$9 - 2 = 7$$

$$9 - 7 = 2$$

Directions: 1 Circle the linking cubes to show the parts in the number bond. Then write a subtraction sentence by taking one of the parts from the whole. Cross out the part on the number bond that you take away. 2 Take apart the linking cubes. Circle the parts. Write a subtraction sentence by taking one of the parts from the whole. Then write another subtraction sentence by taking the other part from the whole.

Think and Grow: Modeling Real Life

This application allows students to show their understanding of taking apart a group of balloons by sharing some with a friend.

- Have students discuss what they see in the picture. "What is your favorite color balloon? Why might you have a group of balloons?"
- Read the first part of the directions and circulate as students complete the problem. Observe to make sure that each balloon was either crossed out or is part of the group circled. The two groups should be partner numbers for 10.
- Students may ask how many balloons to cross out. Read the directions again saying, you give some balloons to your friend. "What does it mean when you give some?"
- Note the arrangement of balloons in each problem. Do students cross out an even number of balloons in the rectangular array? How are students counting the numbers in each group? Do you hear students using their number facts for 10?
- **Extension:** "Could you give 10 balloons to your friend? What would the subtraction sentence be if you did give 10 balloons away?"
- ◎ Hold up 6 linking cubes. "Turn and tell your partner how you could take apart this group of objects." Have students share with the class, listening for different partner numbers for 6. Review the success criteria, connecting each to the problem just modeled. Now state the learning target and ask students to use their thumb signals to show how well they can take apart a group of objects and write a subtraction sentence.
- **Supporting Learners:** Focus on *take apart* problems where the whole is within 5. Use counting bears or common objects (pencils, erasers, books) for students to use as they model problems. Use a story context of sharing the objects with a friend.

Closure

- Draw the number bond shown.
- Tell your partner a story that matches this number bond.

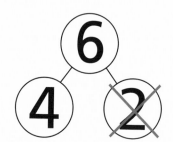

Sample answer:

$$10 - 4 = 6$$

Sample answer:

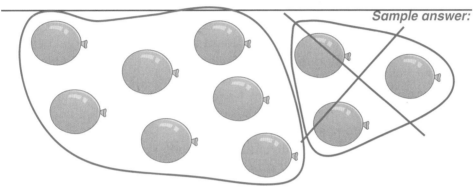

$$10 - 3 = 7$$

Directions: You have 10 balloons. You want to share some with your friend.

• Put the balloons into 2 groups. Circle the groups. Then cross out the group you give to your friend. Write a subtraction sentence to match your picture. Circle the number that shows how many balloons you have left.

• Show another way you can share the balloons. Then write a subtraction sentence to match your picture. Circle the number that shows how many balloons you have left.

340   three hundred forty

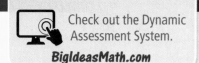
Connect and Extend Learning

Practice Notes

- Remind students that when you separate a whole into two parts, you can put the numbers of those parts in either order into the last two places in a subtraction sentence and it will still be right.
- Remind students that they've already learned about number bonds, so they already know almost everything they need to know to make subtraction sentences.

Cross-Curricular Connections

Science

- Use the Subtraction Animals Instructional Resource. To prepare, make one copy per student and cut out the animal cards.
- Have students (individually, in pairs, or small groups) put cards showing two different kinds of animals into one group. They should use between 1 and 5 of each kind of animal. Have them count the total number of animals in the group and say "Once there were _____ animals."
- Discuss with the students the differences between the two animals in their group.
- Have students take one kind of animal out of the group, and describe the leaving by using the difference that was discussed. For example, students might say "Then the 3 animals that could fly flew away."
- Have students count the animals that remain and say, for example, "4 animals that have fur were left."

Learning Target: Take apart a group of objects and write a subtraction sentence.

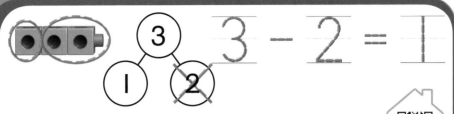

Directions: Circle the linking cubes to show the parts in the number bond. Then write a subtraction sentence by taking one of the parts from the whole. Cross out the part on the number bond that you take away.

I and 2. Sample answers are given.

 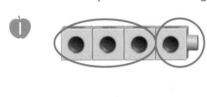 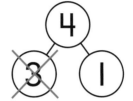

$$4 - 3 = 1$$

$$6 - 3 = 3$$

Directions: ❶ Circle the linking cubes to show the parts in the number bond. Then write a subtraction sentence by taking one of the parts from the whole. Cross out the part on the number bond that you take away. ❷ Take apart the linking cubes. Circle the parts. Then write a subtraction sentence by taking one of the parts from the whole.

Connect and Extend Learning

Extend Student Learning

Bodily-Kinesthetic

- Pair up students. Have one student in each pair hold up a number of fingers between 6 and 10 and say "I had _____ fingers." (Where _____ is the number of fingers they're holding up.) Then have the other student hold up a small number of fingers and say "And _____ went away" as they march their hand(s) away in the air. The first student should stop holding up however many fingers the second student marched away, and say "_____ were left on that fine day." (Where _____ is the number of fingers they are still holding up.) Have students switch roles and repeat the activity.

Lesson Resources	
Surface Level	**Deep Level**
Resources by Chapter • Extra Practice • Reteach Differentiating the Lesson Skills Review Handbook Skills Trainer Math Musicals	Resources by Chapter • Enrichment and Extension Graphic Organizers Math Musicals Dynamic Assessment System • Lesson Practice

3 and 4. Sample answers are given.

$$7 - 1 = 6$$

$$7 - 6 = 1$$

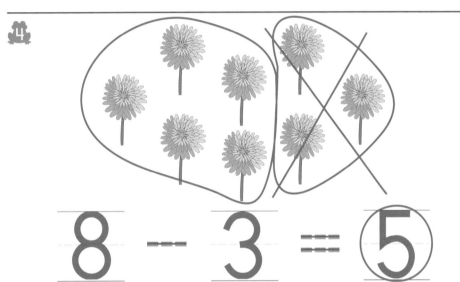

$$8 - 3 = \boxed{5}$$

Directions: ③ Take apart the linking cubes. Circle the parts. Write a subtraction sentence by taking one of the parts from the whole. Then write another subtraction sentence by taking the other part from the whole. ④ You pick 8 flowers. You want to give some to your friend. Put the flowers into 2 groups. Circle the groups. Then cross out the group you give to your friend. Write a subtraction sentence to match your picture. Circle the number that shows how many flowers you have left.

342   three hundred forty-two

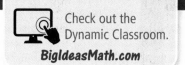

7.4

Laurie's Notes

Preparing to Teach

Students have written subtraction sentences where 0, 1, or all of the objects are subtracted. Students may have commented that subtracting 0 doesn't change anything, or subtracting all means you have none left. Student language may not be precise but they are trying to communicate that they notice a pattern. The goal of this lesson is to help students explain clearly what the patterns are when you subtract 0, 1, or all of the quantity. The subtraction is modelled in a ten frame. The whole is shown and the part to be subtracted is crossed out.

Materials

- floor number path

Dig In (Circle Time)

Use Appropriate Tools Strategically: Use a number path that can be placed on the floor that includes 0.

- **Example:** Ask a volunteer to stand at the number 4. "Which way should [name] step if we want to show subtraction and why? Tell your partner." Ask volunteers to share their thinking. They will say step backward. "[name], step back 2 steps." Ask students to help you record the steps in an subtraction sentence. Write $4 - 2 = 2$. Repeat once or twice more.
- Now do a few trials where the number being subtracted is 0. "You don't move," is what you will hear students say. Let students talk about what *subtract zero* means. Record each trial in a subtraction sentence. $4 - 0 = 4$.
- Do a few examples where the number being subtracted is 1. "Gee, you don't step back very far do you?" Listen to students' observations. "It's just the next number before."
- Finally, a few examples where you *subtract all*. "You don't have any left!" Listen to students' observations. "You always end at 0."
- **Look For and Express Regularity in Repeated Reasoning:** Have students talk to their partner about what they noticed whenever they were told to take 0 or all of the steps. Listen for the concept of staying on the same space or ending at 0. Ask about taking 1 step back—they ended on the number before.
- ⊙ Explain that this lesson is about the patterns when you subtract 0, 1, or all. Their language may not be precise, but their learning should be more visible after this activity.

Learning Target

Find and explain subtraction patterns.

Success Criteria

- Subtract 0, 1, or all of the objects from a group.
- Explain the patterns of subtracting 0, 1, or all.

ELL Support

Review with students the meaning of the word pattern. Draw a pattern of repeated shapes and lines on the board. Point and say, "This is a pattern of different shapes." Have students point out patterns they see or draw patterns. Explain this lesson is about subtraction patterns.

? Teaching Prompt   ⊙ Learning Target

Learning Target: Find and explain subtraction patterns.

Explore and Grow

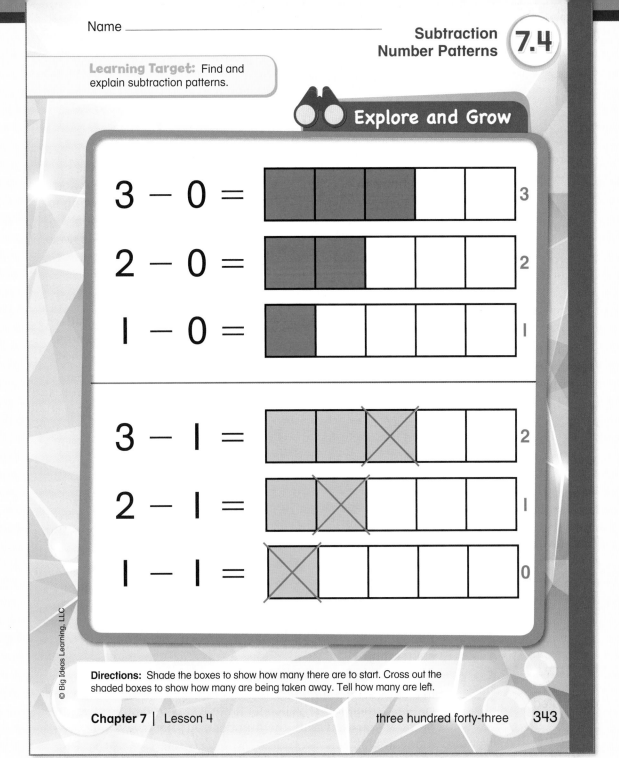

$3 - 0 =$ 3

$2 - 0 =$ 2

$1 - 0 =$ 1

$3 - 1 =$ 2

$2 - 1 =$ 1

$1 - 1 =$ 0

Directions: Shade the boxes to show how many there are to start. Cross out the shaded boxes to show how many are being taken away. Tell how many are left.

Chapter 7 | Lesson 4   three hundred forty-three   343

Explore and Grow

- "What do you notice on the top part?" Students should notice that no boxes were crossed out and, the number of shaded boxes is decreasing by 1. Both are patterns, and seeing no boxes crossed out is the pattern to focus on.
- "What do you notice when you take away 1?" Listen for understand of the previous number. Students may also mention one box is crossed out in each problem.
- Listen for subtraction vocabulary. "When I take away 0 I have 3 left."

Have students read aloud chorally each example, starting with "Five take away zero is five." Have students work in pairs to practice verbal language. Have one student ask the other, "What does the picture show?" Have the second respond. Then have them alternate roles for the other exercises.

Beginner students may state the subtraction sentence, such as , "Four take away four is zero."
Intermediate students may use alternate language to answer, such as, "Four less four is zero."
Advanced students may explain the picture and state the subtraction sentence.

Think and Grow

Getting Started

- Ask partners to talk about what a pattern is. They can give examples from math (adding 0 or 1), calendar time (ABA and ABB patterns), clapping hands to hear a pattern, or coloring to see a pattern.
- **Attend to Precision:** When students say "4 take away 4 is none," acknowledge their correct thinking and say, "The number for none is 0. So 4 take away 4 is 0."

Teaching Notes

- The five and ten frames are used to help students see patterns when you subtract 0, all, or 1. Remind students that we cross out the object (colored counter) to show that we are taking it away.
- There are three patterns in the example to discuss. Newton and Descartes puppets can be used to summarize the pattern.
- **Model:** "Describe the five frame to your partner." Listen for five dots are colored. "Are any dots crossed out?" no "Let's write a subtraction sentence to show how many are left when you take away 0." Trace the subtraction sentence.
- **?** "What number did we start with?" 5 "How many did we take away?" 0 "How many are left?" 5 "When we take away 0 from a number what do you notice?" Listen for understanding that the number doesn't change. Point to Newton's thought bubble.
- **Common Misconception:** Students are confused by subtracting 0 because they don't see any change. It is difficult for them to understand that an operation has been performed. It is an operation that does not change the number.
- Repeat the same questioning for subtracting all and subtracting 1.
- **Supporting Learners:** Use counters on a five or ten frame. Model the first number in red. To show subtraction the counter can be turned to the yellow side. That way you still know the number you start with, the number you take away, and how many are left.
- ◉ If the Newton and Descartes puppets are available, give them to students to explain what they learned today.

Same number

None left

Previous number when counting

$$5 - 0 = 5$$

$$5 - 5 = 0$$

$$5 - 1 = 4$$

$$4 - 4 = 0$$ none left

$$7 - 0 = 7$$ same number

© Big Ideas Learning, LLC

Directions: Complete the subtraction sentence to tell how many dots are left. Tell what you notice.

Meeting the needs of all learners.

Apply and Grow: Practice

SCAFFOLDING INSTRUCTION

Students have used models to show how to subtract 0, 1, or all from a group of objects. They have written the related subtraction sentence. Have they observed any patterns and are they able to explain the patterns? Ask students to explain their thinking as they complete the exercises on this page. "How do you know $5 - 0 = 5$?" Note that the first three exercises have a model to suggest the subtraction problem. In the last three exercises students need to find how many are left.

EMERGING students may not recognize a pattern when subtracting 0, 1, or all. They see each exercise as a new problem, not related to the previous.

- **Exercises 1–3:** Ask students how many dots are in the ten frame, meaning, what number do we start with? "How many dots are crossed out? What does it mean when we cross out dots?"
- **Exercises 4–6:** Have students say the subtraction sentence aloud. "I start with 6. I take away 6. I have 0 left."

PROFICIENT students can show how to subtract 0, 1, or all and recognize the patterns. They are developing precision in their language to describe the patterns.

- Have students talk to their partner about a problem. Explain how they know their work is correct.

Additional Support

- Use linking cubes and number bonds for additional practice.
- Focus on only one pattern at a time. Start with subtracting 0. Explore each counting number to 10. ($1 - 0, 2 - 0, 3 - 0, \ldots 10 - 0$). "Can you tell what is going to happen when we take away 0 from a number?"

Extension: Adding Rigor

- Explore the pattern for subtracting 2.

✓ Apply and Grow: Practice

1

$$8 - 0 = 8$$

same number

2

$$8 - 8 = 0$$

none left

3

$$8 - 1 = 7$$

previous number when counting

4

$$6 - 6 = 0$$

none left

5

$$9 - 1 = 8$$

previous number when counting

6

$$10 - 0 = 10$$

same number

Directions: **1**–**3** Complete the subtraction sentence to tell how many dots are left. Tell what you notice. **4**–**6** Complete the subtraction sentence. Tell what you notice.

Think and Grow: Modeling Real Life

This application allows students to show their understanding of subtracting all, 0, and 1 from a number.

- **Preview:** Have students discuss what they see in the picture. "Have you ever made a bracelet for yourself or someone else? What are some materials you can use to make a bracelet?"
- "You make 9 bracelets. You give all of your bracelets away. How can we show that in the picture?" Listen for crossing out each bracelet.
- **?** "How many bracelets do you have left? How can we write a subtraction sentence to show how many you have left?"
- **Note:** Before starting the next two problems give sufficient time for all students to draw 6 bracelets. If time allows, they can color the bracelets, otherwise suggest the bracelets be very simple!
- "These are the 6 bracelets your friend made. Your friend doesn't give any of the bracelets away. How can we write a subtraction sentence to show how many your friend has left?" Point to spot where the sentence is to be written.
- **?** "Your friend gives you one bracelet. How do we show this? How many does your friend have left?" Write the subtraction sentence.
- ⦿ Ask volunteers to share what they learned today about subtracting 0, 1, and all.

Closure

- Have students hold up four fingers. "Show me $4 - 0$ fingers." Pause "Show me $4 - 1$ fingers." Pause. "Show me $4 - 4$ fingers."
- Repeat, using a different number of fingers to start with.

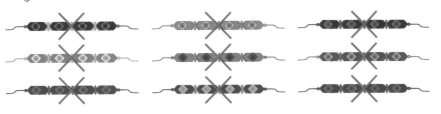

$$9 - 9 = 0$$

$$6 - 0 = 6$$

$$6 - 1 = 5$$

Directions:
- You make 9 bracelets. You give all of them away. Cross out the bracelets you give away. Then write a subtraction sentence to tell how many bracelets you have left.
- Your friend makes 6 bracelets. She does not give away any of her bracelets. Draw and color your friend's bracelets. Then write a subtraction sentence to tell how many bracelets she has left.
- Your friend gives you a bracelet. Write a subtraction sentence to tell how many bracelets she has left now.

346   three hundred forty-six

© Big Ideas Learning, LLC

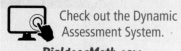
Connect and Extend Learning

Practice Notes

- Remind students that the number 0 looks like a circle. Ask them what's inside the circle. ("Nothing!") Tell students that this is an easy way to remember what the number 0 means.

Cross-Curricular Connections

Music

- Teach students to chant "Ten Little Monkeys Jumping on the Bed." Have students hold up fingers as they count down. You can also have them sing the chant, using the first two bars of the alphabet song:

  10 little monkeys, jumping on the bed
  1 fell off and bumped his head
  Mama called the doctor and the doctor said:
  "No more monkeys jumping on the bed!"

  9 little monkeys, jumping on the bed
  1 fell off and bumped his head
  Mama called the doctor and the doctor said:
  "No more monkeys jumping on the bed!"

  Continue counting down. When you reach 0, use the words:

  0 little monkeys jumping on the bed
  Nobody fell off and bumped his head
  Mama called the doctor and the doctor said:
  "Tell those monkeys it's time for bed!"

Learning Target: Find and explain subtraction patterns.

$$4 - 0 = 4$$ same number

$$4 - 4 = 0$$ none left

$$4 - 1 = 3$$ previous number when counting

Directions: Complete the subtraction sentence to tell how many dots are left. Tell what you notice.

1 previous number when counting

$$3 - 1 = 2$$

2 same number

$$3 - 0 = 3$$

3 none left

$$3 - 3 = 0$$

Directions: **1**–**3** Complete the subtraction sentence to tell how many dots are left. Tell what you notice.

© Big Ideas Learning, LLC

Connect and Extend Learning

Extend Student Learning
Interpersonal

- Prepare for the activity by printing out the Button Price Instructional Resource and cutting out the price boxes. Ask three students to serve as shopkeepers, and give each one a collection of buttons to sell. Distribute 5 pennies or counters to each of the other students.
- Have one of the shopkeepers sell their buttons for 0 cents each, one sell their buttons for 1 cent each, and one sell their buttons for 5 cents each.
- Divide the remaining students into three groups, and have each group line up in front of a different shopkeeper.
- Have the students in each group each buy one button from their shopkeeper.
- Ask students from each group to report how many cents they started with, how many cents they paid for their button, and how many cents they have left.

Lesson Resources	
Surface Level	**Deep Level**
Resources by Chapter • Extra Practice • Reteach Differentiating the Lesson Skills Review Handbook Skills Trainer	Resources by Chapter • Enrichment and Extension Graphic Organizers Dynamic Assessment System • Lesson Practice

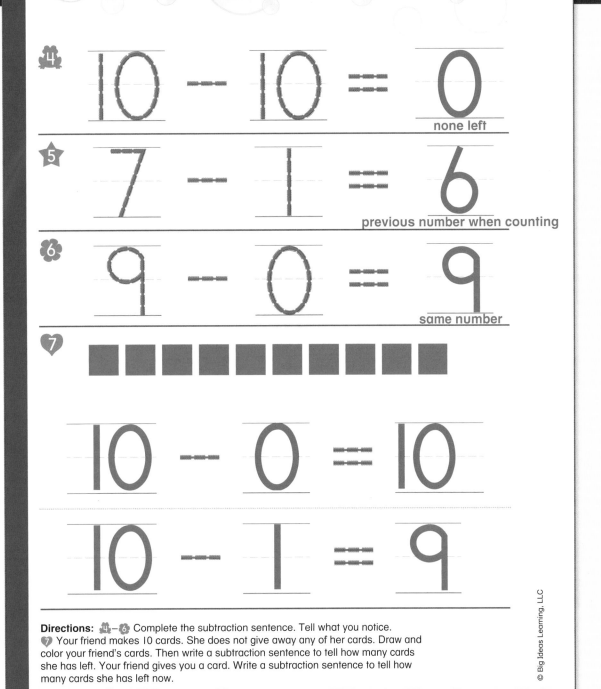

4 $10 - 10 = 0$

none left

5 $7 - 1 = 6$

previous number when counting

6 $9 - 0 = 9$

same number

7

$10 - 0 = 10$

$10 - 1 = 9$

Directions: **4–6** Complete the subtraction sentence. Tell what you notice.
7 Your friend makes 10 cards. She does not give away any of her cards. Draw and color your friend's cards. Then write a subtraction sentence to tell how many cards she has left. Your friend gives you a card. Write a subtraction sentence to tell how many cards she has left now.

348   three hundred forty-eight

7.5

Learning Target
Subtract within 5.

Success Criteria
- Show and tell how to subtract numbers within 5.
- Complete the subtraction sentence.

Warm-Up

Practice opportunities for the following are available in the Resources by Chapter or at *BigIdeasMath.com*.
- Daily skills
- Vocabulary
- Prerequisite skills

ELL Support

Point out that the goal for this lesson is to subtract fluently within a group of five. They may have heard the word fluently in the context of speaking a language. To speak fluently means to speak easily. To subtract fluently means to subtract quickly and easily.

Laurie's Notes

Preparing to Teach

This is the second section in kindergarten where the focus is on **fluency**. Mathematics literature refers to procedural fluency as *the skill in carrying out procedures flexibly, accurately, efficiently and appropriately*. Students have worked with two subtraction situations, *take from* and *take apart*, and have modeled and reasoned about subtraction. In this section you want to see evidence that students can accurately and efficiently subtract numbers within 5 and will know the difference without the use of counters or picture stories. The additional practice of this lesson will help students move towards fluency.

Materials
- two-color counters
- Five Frames*

*Found in the Instructional Resources

Dig In (Circle Time)

There is no new content presented today so it would be helpful to make an anchor chart of the many different ways to do subtraction. Include drawing a picture of the problem, using fingers to count, using a number path, using counters and five frames, and using knowledge of all the ways to make five (partner numbers). Ask, "Did anyone do it another way?" Include all answers that make sense in the list.

◉ Share the learning target and success criteria for the day. Explain that you want them to show all of the ways they know to subtract numbers. "Tell your partner different ways you can show how to subtract two numbers."

◉ Explain what it means to subtract within 5. Show students a collection of five counters or linking cubes. "Can you start with some of these counters, take some away, and tell how many are left? Can you tell how to take away a number and find how many are left?"

- Have manipulatives and whiteboards available for students to demonstrate their thinking.

- **Critique the Reasoning of Others:** When students share their thinking with classmates, ask other students to comment on what they have heard. "Do you agree with how [name] explained using your fingers to take away a number? Did their thinking make sense? Why?"

- Since all of their work today will be subtracting within 5, display and review earlier anchor charts that show partner numbers to 5.

? Teaching Prompt   ◉ Learning Target

Learning Target: Subtract within 5.

Explore and Grow

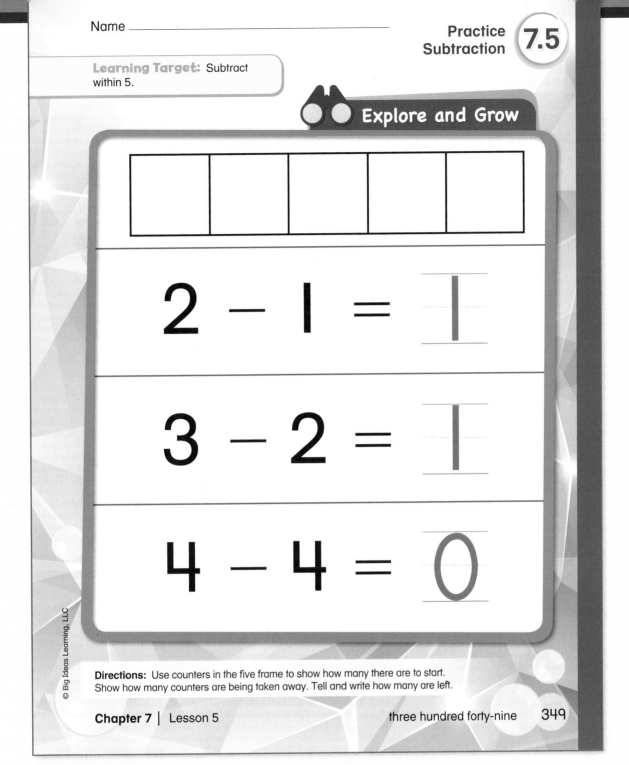

$$2 - 1 = 1$$

$$3 - 2 = 1$$

$$4 - 4 = 0$$

Directions: Use counters in the five frame to show how many there are to start. Show how many counters are being taken away. Tell and write how many are left.

Chapter 7 | Lesson 5

three hundred forty-nine   349

Explore and Grow

- Students have crossed out dots on a five frame to show subtraction. Since the five frame is used for all of the pictures, use counters and remove them to show subtraction.
- Have students explain the model to their partner. This gives them practice in explaining their thinking.
- "How did you complete the subtraction sentence? How do you know your answer is correct?"
- **Extension:** "Think of a subtraction sentence where there are 2 left."

ELL Support

Point out the hand pictured and explain that subtracting from a group of five can easily be modeled using the fingers on one hand. Have students read aloud chorally the example, "Five take away two is three." Model it using fingers. Have students work in pairs to practice verbal language. Have one student ask the other, "What is the answer to three take away one?" Then have them alternate roles for the other exercises.

Beginner students may state answers simply as numbers. **Intermediate** and **Advanced** students may answer with the subtraction sentences, such as, "Three take away one is two."

Think and Grow

Getting Started

- The example at the top shows the subtraction sentence, a number path, fingers, and counters. It can be used as a resource for students to refer back to as they work the problems on this page.
- Note that in the problems students only give the difference, meaning how many are left. They are no longer tracing or writing the entire subtraction sentence.

Teaching Notes

- **Model:** "Tell your partner how to show 5 − 2." Solicit ideas from volunteers. "So 5 − 2 is the same as what number?" Trace the 3.
- Observe as students are working on the three problems. Are they using models? Their fingers? Drawing a picture?
- When students finish, have them tell their partner how they found each answer.
- Share strategies as a class. Ask students to tell how they are finding the number left.
- **Supporting Learners:** Provide a five frame and counters as needed. Show the anchor chart for partner numbers to 5.
- **Extension:** Write the first problem 3 − 1 = 2 and the related problem 3 − 2 = 1. "What do you notice?" Do students recognize the partner numbers 1 and 2 when they write the two subtraction sentences?
- ⊙ Ask students to use their thumb signals to show how confident they feel about subtracting numbers within 5.

$$5 - 2 = \; ?$$

1 2 3 4 5	✋ − ✌ = 🖐
⬤ ⬤ ⬤ ✖ ✖	$5 - 2 = 3$

$$3 - 1 = 2$$

$$4 - 3 = 1$$

$$5 - 4 = 1$$

Directions: Complete the subtraction sentence. Tell how you found your answer. *Sample answer:* used counters

© Big Ideas Learning, LLC

Apply and Grow: Practice

SCAFFOLDING INSTRUCTION

Students are practicing their subtraction facts to five today. You could have small groups or learning centers specific to the supports and extensions needed by students. You might consider having students self-select where to work based upon their understanding of subtraction facts within 5. Explain that we each learn differently and at different rates. "What will be most helpful for your learning today?" See supports and extensions below.

EMERGING students are not fluent with their subtraction facts within 5. They need the support of models to find how many are left.

- **Exercises 1–4:** Have students say the subtraction sentence aloud. "I start with 2. I take away 2. I have 0 left." As they say the problem aloud they may use counters to model the problem.
- **Exercise 5:** Have students record how many are left for each problem. Trying to remember each result is challenging.

PROFICIENT students are efficient and accurate with their subtraction facts within 5.

- **Exercise 5:** Talk to your partner about the problem. How do you decide if the subtraction problem equals 3?

Additional Support

- Provide dot and number cards 0–5 so that students can model the problem and use the number cards to tell their thinking.

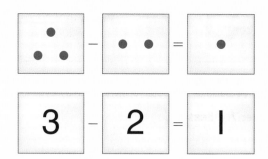

Extension: Adding Rigor

- Work with a partner. Write three subtraction problems that equal 2. ___ − ___ = 2

Meeting the needs of all learners.

Name _____

 $2 - 2 = 0$

 $5 - 0 = 5$

 $4 - 2 = 2$

 $5 - 3 = 2$

 ⑤ ⟨ 4 – 1 ⟩   2 – 1   ⟨ 3 – 0 ⟩

Directions: ①–④ Complete the subtraction sentence. Tell how you found your answer. ⑤ Circle all of the subtraction problems that equal 3.

© Big Ideas Learning, LLC

Think and Grow: Modeling Real Life

This application allows students to show and tell how to subtract a number from 5.

- **Preview:** "Have you played a video game before? What do you usually try to do in a video game? Do any of the games you've played have objects from outer space?" Have students share their experiences.
- In the first example there are 5 spaceships. "You capture some of the spaceships and they disappear." Students make a decision about how many to cross out which means they are captured and you take that many away from 5. "Now write a subtraction sentence to show how many spaceships are left."
- **?** "How do you know your subtraction sentence is correct? Tell your partner."
- The next problem is about aliens. Tell students the number of aliens they capture has to be different from the number of spaceships they captured.
- ⊙ Review the learning target. Students have done many subtraction problems today within 5. "Are you pretty good at knowing how to subtract within 5?"
- **Supporting Learners:** "How many spaceships do you see? You capture some." If students are confused about how many they should capture, suggest an amount for them. You capture 2 spaceships. Continue to chunk the problem for students.
- **Supporting Learners:** Have students use a five frame and counters to model the problem first before write the subtraction sentence.

Closure

- Use linking cubes to show a subtraction problem. For instance, hold a train with 5 cubes. Say, "I remove two. How many will be left?" Give students time to say their answer before you model with the cubes.
- Repeat using different numbers.

Sample answer:

5 - 2 = 3

Sample answer:

5 - 4 = 1

Directions: You are playing a video game.
- You have 5 spaceships. Some of them are captured. Cross out the spaceships that are captured. Then write a subtraction sentence to tell how many spaceships you have left.
- You need to capture 5 aliens to win. You capture some aliens. Cross out the aliens that you capture. Then write a subtraction sentence to tell how many aliens you still need to capture.

352   three hundred fifty-two

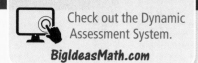
Connect and Extend Learning

Practice Notes

- Remind students of what they learned about the number 0:
  - When you take away every object in a group, 0 is left.
  - When you take away 0 from a group, you have the same number left that you started with.

Cross-Curricular Connections

Physical Education

- Bring a group of 5 students up to the front of the room. Tell them to stretch their left arms up, up, up towards the sky. Ask the class how many arms are reaching up to the sky. Then ask the class how many should fall back down. Pick a number from those suggested and call on students individually to put down their arms. Now ask the class how many arms are left still reaching up to the sky.

- Next, have the students in front of the room all put their arms down and stretch their right arms up, up, up towards the sky. Repeat the exercise with that arm.

- Have the students in front of the room go back to their places and bring up another group of students to the front of the room. Repeat the entire activity until all students have had a chance to be in the group at the front of the room.

- As you lead the students through the activity, make sure to sometimes choose 0 as the number of arms to lower, and sometimes choose the number of the whole group so that 0 remain reaching up.

Name _____

Learning Target: Subtract within 5.

$$5 - 1 = 4$$

| 1 | 2 | 3 | 4 | 5 |

Directions: Complete the subtraction sentence. Tell how you found your answer.

1.
$$5 - 5 = 0$$

2.
$$4 - 0 = 4$$

3.
$$5 - 2 = 3$$

Directions: 1–3 Complete the subtraction sentence. Tell how you found your answer.

Sample answer: **used counters**

Chapter 7 | Lesson 5

three hundred fifty-three **353**

Connect and Extend Learning

Extend Student Learning

Visual-Spatial

- Prepare for the activity by dividing decks of cards into 4 equal stacks by suit, each pile having the cards ace through 5 in that suit. (6 through 10 and face cards will not be used in this activity.)
- Divide students into groups of 4. Give each student in each group a stack of cards of a different suit. Be sure to explain that the ace card stands for the number 1.
- Have students choose 2 of their cards to create a subtraction sentence with a missing value.
- The group will look at each subtraction sentence and find the correct number of the missing value.

Lesson Resources	
Surface Level	**Deep Level**
Resources by Chapter • Extra Practice • Reteach Differentiating the Lesson Skills Review Handbook Skills Trainer	Resources by Chapter • Enrichment and Extension Graphic Organizers Dynamic Assessment System • Lesson Practice

4 $4 - 3 = 1$

Sample answer: used counters

5 $3 - 1 = 2$

Sample answer: used counters

6 $1 - 1$ $\boxed{4 - 2}$ $\boxed{5 - 3}$

7
Sample answer:

$5 - 2 = 3$

Directions: **4** and **5** Complete the subtraction sentence. Tell how you found your answer. **6** Circle all of the subtraction problems that equal 2. **7** You are playing a video game. You need to visit 5 moons. You visit some moons. Cross out the moons you visit. Then write a subtraction sentence to tell how many moons you have left to visit.

Learning Target

Use a group of 5 to write a subtraction sentence.

Success Criteria

- Use a ten frame to subtract 5.
- Subtract 5 and tell how many are left.
- Write a subtraction sentence.

Warm-Up

Practice opportunities for the following are available in the Resources by Chapter or at *BigIdeasMath.com.*

- Daily skills
- Vocabulary
- Prerequisite skills

ELL Support

Point out that by now students have learned to write addition sentences and subtraction sentences. Explain that the word sentence usually refers to information expressed in words, not symbols. They will learn about making sentences in Language Arts.

Laurie's Notes

Preparing to Teach

This section is connected to students' earlier work with the 5 + *n* pattern. We are still building number sense for the benchmark 5. Given a number between 6 and 10, we want students to be able to subtract 5 and know how many are left. There is no contextual setting for most of the problems in this section, rather the focus is on visual tools, fingers and ten frames. These tools help students easily see a group of 5 that can be subtracted.

Materials

- two-color counters
- Ten Frames*

*Found in the Instructional Resources

Dig In (Circle Time)

Fingers are again used as a model to help students subtract a group of 5 from a number. Students use their fingers to show a number between 5 and 10, using all of the fingers on one hand, and then some more. When you ask them to subtract 5 they put the hand with 5 fingers down.

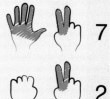

- Tell students you are going to ask them to use their fingers to show a number but you have a special rule: You must use all of the fingers on one hand, and then some more.
- "Show me the number 7." Check to see that students are showing 5 and 2 more. "Now show me how you take away 5." Observe to see if students know to put down the 5 fingers on one hand.
- ? "How many are left? Tell your partner how you found your answer.
- Have different students share how they found their answer. You want all students to recognize that the difference between 7 and 5 is how many you counted on from 5 to get 7. This hints at the relationship between addition and subtraction. (5 fingers plus 2 fingers is 7 fingers; 7 fingers take away 5 fingers is 2 fingers.)
- Write the subtraction sentence for this problem. 7 − 5 = 2
- Repeat this activity for start numbers of 6, 8, 9, or 10. You want students to see that when you count on from 5 to get to the start number, you have that same amount left when you take 5 away from that start number.
- ◉ Share the learning target and success criteria. Students have just demonstrated the second success criterion. "You used your fingers to show how to subtract a group of 5. Then you wrote a subtraction sentence to tell how many were left."

? Teaching Prompt   ◉ Learning Target

Learning Target: Use a group
of 5 to write a subtraction sentence.

Explore and Grow

Sample answer:

$$6 - 5 = 1$$

Directions: Color the counters to show how many there are in all. Cross out counters to take away 5. Complete the subtraction sentence.

© Big Ideas Learning, LLC

Chapter 7 | Lesson 6

three hundred fifty-five **355**

Explore and Grow

- Students cross out a group of 5 on the ten frame which is what they just did with their fingers. Although any 5 counters can be crossed out, the top row relates to the earlier relationship of the 5 + n pattern.
- "Look at the subtraction sentence. Tell your partner what it says and what you need to do." Listen for take away a group of 5.
- "How can we show subtract 5 with the counters?" cross out 5 If some students crossed out the top row and others did not, discuss as a class. "Let's see which method you like on the next problems we do.
- ⊙ "You used a ten frame to subtract a group of 5."

Laurie's Notes

Think and Grow
Getting Started

- The example at the top shows a ten frame with the top row of counters crossed out, and a subtraction sentence. The problem is just like the Explore and Grow page and should feel familiar to students.
- **Use Appropriate Tools Strategically:** Students may ask if any 5 counters can be crossed out when they subtract 5. The answer is yes. At a teachable moment have students look at the two models of 8 – 5. "We want to know how many are left when we subtract 5. Which model helps you see the answer more clearly? Explain."

Teaching Notes

- **Model:** "We want to take 5 away from 8. What number do we need to show in the ten frame?" 8 "How do we show taking 5 away?" cross out 5 counters "How many are left?" 3 "Does our subtraction sentence make sense?"
- ⊙ Tell your partner how you can use the ten frame to answer a subtraction sentence that says to subtract 5.
- Decide if students can work independently on the next two problems or if they need guided instruction. The answer may not be the same for all students.
- ❓ "How do you know how many are left?" Look at the ten frame to see how many counters are not crossed out.
- ❓ "How does the ten frame help you subtract a group of 5?" you can see how many are left
- When students finish have them compare their work with their partner. "Do they have the same work?"
- **Extension:** Ask students to think of a word problem to go with any of the subtraction sentences. You can give them counting bears or other small objects to act out their word problem.
- ⊙ "Can you use a ten frame to subtract 5? Explain how to write the addition sentence." Have students use their thumb signals to show how well they are doing with the learning target.

$$8 - 5 = 3$$

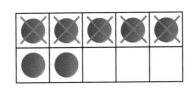

$$7 - 5 = 2$$

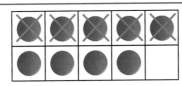

$$9 - 5 = 4$$

Directions: Cross out 5 counters to show how many to take away. Use the ten frame to complete the subtraction sentence.

356   three hundred fifty-six

Meeting the needs of
all learners.

Apply and Grow: Practice

SCAFFOLDING INSTRUCTION

Students are working with subtracting a group of 5 which can be thought of as the $n - 5$ pattern. Fingers, ten frames, linking cubes, and a rekenrek are all visual ways for students to see and develop an understanding of this pattern. All of the differences are 5 or less and they are represented by the counters on the bottom row of a ten frame as shown.

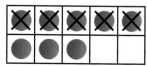

EMERGING students are not confident in their $5 + n$ pattern which means they don't see the difference when they answer $n - 5$. They may need support in writing a subtraction sentence when a model is given.

- **Exercise 1:** Have students say the subtraction sentence aloud. "I start with 5 and I want to take away 5." Do students recognize this as a *subtract all* problem?
- **Exercise 3:** Use a ten frame and counters to model. "How do you show 10?" Place 10 red counters. "What does the subtraction sentence tell you to do next?" subtract 5 "How can you show that with your counters?"

PROFICIENT students are able to use their number facts and $5 + n$ pattern to help them subtract a group of 5. They understand how to write the subtraction sentence modeled with a ten frame.

- **Exercises 1–3:** Note if students are completing the subtraction sentence without, or before, crossing out the counters.

Additional Support

- Provide a rekenrek for students to use as they complete the page. Represent the starting amount by sliding beads to the left. Five beads are red and the remainder white. The white beads represent the amount left when you subtract 5.

Extension: Adding Rigor

- Give pairs of students a set of number cards 6 to 10. One partner picks a card. Their partner uses their fingers to show the number using 5 fingers plus some more. Say, "___ subtract 5 equals ___."

Apply and Grow: Practice

1

$$5 - 5 = 0$$

2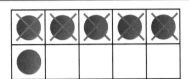

$$6 - 5 = 1$$

3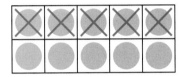

$$10 - 5 = 5$$

Directions: **1** and **2** Cross out 5 counters to show how many to take away. Use the ten frame to complete the subtraction sentence. **3** Draw 10 counters. Cross out 5 counters to show how many to take away. Use the ten frame to complete the subtraction sentence.

Chapter 7 | Lesson 6 three hundred fifty-seven **357**

© Big Ideas Learning, LLC

Ask students if they are familiar with bowling. Have them tell what they know about it. Explain that the objects pictured are called bowling pins and explain that players use balls to knock them down. Allow students time to complete the page. Then have students use their decks of number cards. Check for understanding by asking:

1. How many pins did you cross out in the top picture?
2. How many are left?
3. How many pins did you cross out in the bottom picture?
4. How many are left?

Check their subtraction sentences by having them write the sentence on an individual white board and hold it up.

Think and Grow: Modeling Real Life

This application allows students to show their understanding of subtracting in the context of bowling. No subtraction sentence is written for them to trace and complete, so they must also understand how to write a subtraction sentence to model a real-life problem.

- Preview: "Do you know what the game of bowling is? Have any of you ever gone bowling or watched people bowl?" If no one has a simple description of bowling, tell students the basic idea. You could even model it using paper cups and a ball.
- Teach this page by chunking out each of the steps.
- ? "How many pins do we start with? Let's count to be sure."
- ? "You knock down five pins on your first roll. How can we show this in the picture?" cross out 5 pins
- ? "How many pins are left? Explain." Listen for subtraction.
- Continue to chunk the problem, asking probing questions. You want students to do the thinking.
- ◉ Review the learning target. "Tell your partner how to use a group of 5 to write a subtraction sentence."
- Supporting Learners: Have students use a ten frame and counters to model the problem.

Closure

- Have partners take turns using their fingers to show a number more than 5. They need to use all of the fingers on one hand plus some more. Now take away 5 fingers. Say the subtraction sentence that matches their fingers.

Think and Grow: Modeling Real Life

Sample answer:

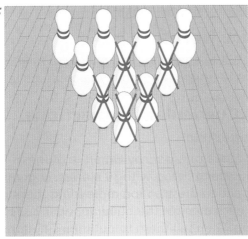 

$$10 - 5 = \boxed{5}$$

$$5 - 5 = 0$$

Directions: You have 2 rolls to knock down 10 bowling pins.

- On your first roll, you knock down 5 pins. Cross out the pins you knock down. Then write a subtraction sentence to match your picture. How many pins do you need to knock down on your second roll? Circle the answer.
- On your second roll, you knock down the pins that are left. Write a subtraction sentence to show how many pins you have left now.

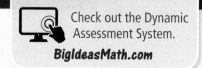
Connect and Extend Learning

Practice Notes

- Point out to students that when you take 5 away from any group that is 10 or less, the most you could be left with is 5.

Cross-Curricular Connections

Language Arts

- Read *Elevator Magic* by Stuart J. Murphy. Then have students draw a tall building with 10 stories. Use a whiteboard or overhead to draw an example for students to model. Have them label each story of the building, with 1 at the bottom and 10 at the top. Then tell them to put their finger on floor number 10. Say "Hop your finger down 5 times." Using the building on your whiteboard or overhead, show them how to hop down. Ask, "What floor are we on?" Repeat multiple times, starting on different floors.

Learning Target: Use a group of 5 to write a subtraction sentence.

$6 - 5 = 1$

Directions: Cross out 5 counters to show how many to take away. Use the ten frame to complete the subtraction sentence.

 1

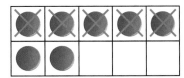

$5 - 5 = 0$

 2

$7 - 5 = 2$

Directions: **1** and **2** Cross out 5 counters to show how many to take away. Use the ten frame to complete the subtraction sentence.

Chapter 7 | Lesson 6

three hundred fifty-nine   **359**

Connect and Extend Learning

Extend Student Learning

Bodily-Kinesthetic

- Divide students into pairs. Have one student in each pair hold up all the fingers on one hand, and anywhere from 0 to 5 fingers on the other hand. Tell the other student to call out the total number of fingers being held up by the first student, by saying "_____ fingers!"
- Tell the students that they're about to take away 5, by lowering the hand with all 5 fingers being held up. Tell the students that when you say "take away 5", the student holding up fingers should put down the hand with 5 fingers held up and leave the other hand. Then the other student should call out, "_____ fingers left!"
- Call out to the students: "On your mark, get set, take away 5!"
- Have student switch roles and repeat the activity, then switch roles again and repeat the activity again. Do this a number of times.

Lesson Resources	
Surface Level	**Deep Level**
Resources by Chapter • Extra Practice • Reteach Differentiating the Lesson Skills Review Handbook Skills Trainer	Resources by Chapter • Enrichment and Extension Graphic Organizers Dynamic Assessment System • Lesson Practice

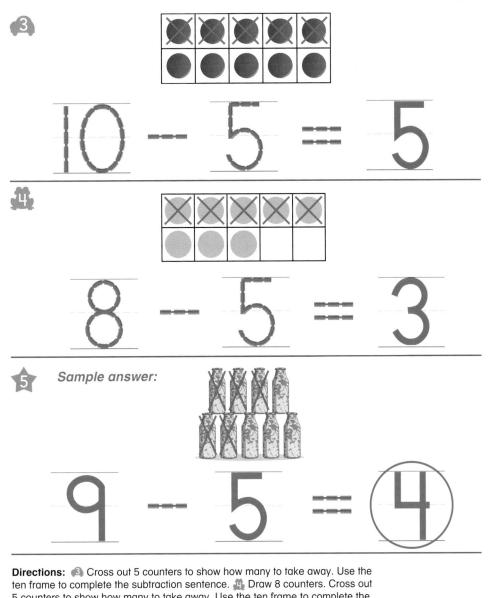

3 $10 - 5 = 5$

4 $8 - 5 = 3$

5 Sample answer:

$9 - 5 = \boxed{4}$

Directions: **3** Cross out 5 counters to show how many to take away. Use the ten frame to complete the subtraction sentence. **4** Draw 8 counters. Cross out 5 counters to show how many to take away. Use the ten frame to complete the subtraction sentence. **5** You have 2 throws to knock down 9 bottles. On your first throw, you knock down 5 bottles. Cross out the bottles you knock down. Then write a subtraction sentence to match your picture. How many more bottles do you need to knock down? Circle the answer.

7.7

Learning Target

Use related facts to add or subtract within 5.

Success Criteria

- Write addition and subtraction sentences to show related facts.
- Explain what is the same and different in these sentences.

Warm-Up

Practice opportunities for the following are available in the Resources by Chapter or at *BigIdeasMath.com.*

- Daily skills
- Vocabulary
- Prerequisite skills

ELL Support

Point out that the learning target for this lesson is to use related facts to add or subtract. They may have heard the word related in the context of talking about family members. To be related means to be interconnected. In this lesson they will see how math facts are related.

Laurie's Notes

Preparing to Teach

Students have a beginning understanding of subtraction and are able to write subtraction sentences. Some students may have already seen a connection between addition and subtraction as inverse operations. You now want all students to be able to think about a pair of partner numbers within 5 and be able to write the related addition and subtraction sentences for these numbers. There is an expectation of fluency for addition and subtraction within five.

Materials

- paper cups
- whiteboards and markers
- linking cubes

Dig In (Circle Time)

Use the cups to model related addition and subtraction facts within 5. Students record each pair of sentences on their whiteboard.

- Place 2 cups in the circle. "Plus 3 more." Add 3 cups to the circle. "How many in all?" Pause. "Write an addition sentence to answer the question." Students write $2 + 3 = 5$.

$$2 + 3 = 5$$
$$5 - 3 = 2$$

- Place 5 cups in the circle. "Take 3 away." Remove 3 cups from the circle. "How many are left?" Pause. "Write the subtraction sentence to answer the question." Students write $5 - 3 = 2$.
- Repeat this activity. Model $1 + 4 = 5$ and $5 - 4 = 1$.
- **Look for and Make Use of Structure:** Have students talk with their partner about the two sentences on their whiteboards. "What do you notice?"
- Students may not recall exactly the first pair of sentences, but the pair written on their whiteboards should remind them. Have students share their observations with the class.
- **Big Idea:** You can take an addition fact within 5 and write a related subtraction sentence.
- ⊙ Share the learning target and success criteria. Connect the activity they just did with the first success criterion. "How clear is your learning so far on this?" Frequent student self-assessment helps the learning become visible to students.

Learning Target: Use related facts to add or subtract within 5.

Explore and Grow

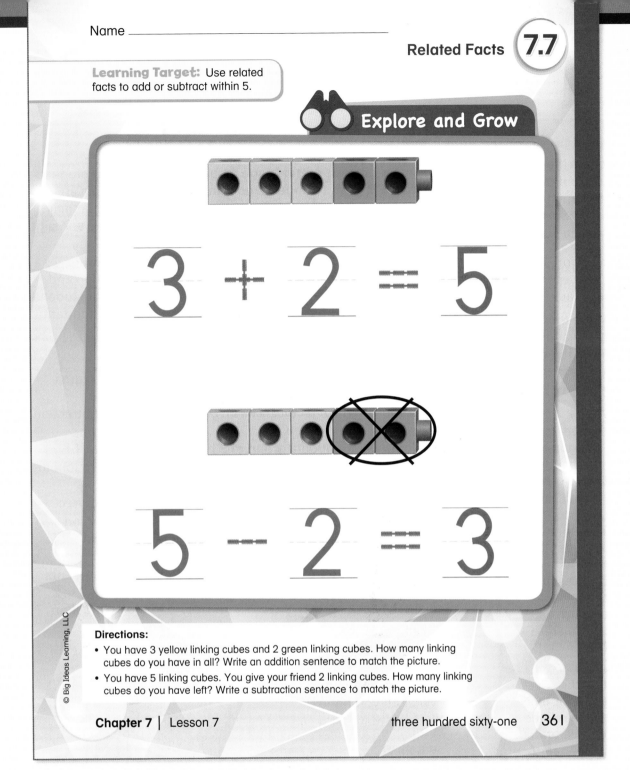

$$3 + 2 = 5$$

$$5 - 2 = 3$$

© Big Ideas Learning, LLC

Directions:
- You have 3 yellow linking cubes and 2 green linking cubes. How many linking cubes do you have in all? Write an addition sentence to match the picture.
- You have 5 linking cubes. You give your friend 2 linking cubes. How many linking cubes do you have left? Write a subtraction sentence to match the picture.

Chapter 7 | Lesson 7   three hundred sixty-one   36 l

Explore and Grow

- Model each problem with two colors of linking cubes. The work in circle time should help students complete this page.
- Show the model. "What addition sentence do you think of for this train?" Depending upon how you hold the linking cube train they may say 3 + 2 = 5 or 2 + 3 = 5. Discuss both addition sentences.
- Remove two cubes. "What subtraction sentence do you think of?" Mention the need to remove cubes. In the picture we can cross out cubes.

? **Turn and Talk:** "How are the two sentences related?"

Think and Grow

Getting Started

- The story pictures on this page must be interpreted by students in order for them to understand if the picture represents an addition or subtraction situation. You may need to guide their investigative skills to ensure the movement of the owls and pigs are understood.
- ⊚ A deeper level of learning has occurred when students are able to explain what is the same and different in addition and subtraction sentences for related facts. It is possible for students to correctly write the sentences without making this important connection. Listen for evidence of deeper learning.

Teaching Notes

- ❓ Model: "Tell your partner what you see in these two pictures. What is the same and what is different?" Give time for discussion. "Which picture tells an addition story? A subtraction story? How do you know?"
- Students will mention a group of 3 birds and a group of 1 bird. There are four birds in all. The one bird is either flying to join the three birds or is flying away from the three birds.
- Connect the story pictures to each sentence as students trace.
- ⊚ The context changes for the second set of pictures. Remind students they are looking for what is the same and different in the pictures.
- Circulate as students complete the two problems. Do students understand the related number facts $2 + 3 = 5$ and $5 - 3 = 2$ or are they seeing only the addition story and the subtraction story?
- ⊚ "Explain what is the same and different in the sentences you wrote."
- Extension: Ask students to think of a story problem to go with $1 + 4 = 5$. You can give them counting bears or other small objects to act out their story problem. "What is the related subtraction sentence? Can you think of a story problem for this sentence?"

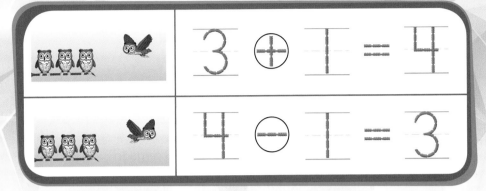

$$2 \;\oplus\; 3 \;=\; 5$$

$$5 \;\ominus\; 3 \;=\; 2$$

Directions: Tell whether the pictures show addition or subtraction. Then write addition and subtraction sentences to show the related facts.

Meeting the needs of
all learners.

Laurie's Notes

Apply and Grow: Practice

SCAFFOLDING INSTRUCTION

Students have written addition and subtraction sentences to represent a story picture or mathematical model. Knowing how to interpret the picture or model can be confusing to students. A picture of 3 dogs in a dog house with another dog outside does not suggest whether the one dog is joining the other three $(3 + 1 = 4)$ or the one dog is leaving the other three $(4 - 1 = 3)$. The context needs to be clear. Preview the page with students so the context is understood.

EMERGING students may be able to write an addition or subtraction sentence to represent a story picture if the context is understood as a joining or take away situation. They have not connected the inverse relationship of addition and subtraction.

- **Exercise 1:** Have students explain what the story pictures mean. Can they distinguish whether two groups are being joined or taken apart? Place counters on the picture to represent the bees. Have students manipulate the counters as they act out the story.
- **Exercises 2 and 3:** Ask students to explain what related facts are. Each of the sentences is correct, but only one pair of sentences involve related facts. If students are not at this level of deeper understanding, additional instruction is needed. See below.

PROFICIENT students understand that for a set of partner numbers, there is an addition and subtraction sentence that can be written using these numbers.

- **Exercise 1:** Have students explain what the story pictures mean.

Additional Support

- Give students 5 counters. Ask them to show partner numbers for 5 and explain why they are partner numbers. When they say the addition sentence $2 + 3 = 5$, emphasize the whole is 5. "What is the related subtraction sentence when the whole is 5, meaning how do we take apart 5 to show the original partner numbers?" $5 - 3 = 2$

Extension: Adding Rigor

- Pick partner numbers for any number, say 8. Write the related addition and subtraction sentences for the partner numbers. Example: $3 + 5 = 8$ and $8 - 5 = 3$

✓ Apply and Grow: Practice

1

$$5 \ominus 4 = 1$$

$$1 \oplus 4 = 5$$

2

$$\boxed{\begin{array}{l} 2 + 1 = 3 \\ 3 - 1 = 2 \end{array}} \quad \begin{array}{l} 5 + 3 = 8 \\ 5 - 3 = 2 \end{array}$$

Check students' work.

3

$$\begin{array}{l} 5 + 2 = 7 \\ 5 - 2 = 3 \end{array} \quad \boxed{\begin{array}{l} 3 + 1 = 4 \\ 4 - 1 = 3 \end{array}}$$

Check students' work.

Directions: **1** Tell whether the pictures show addition or subtraction. Then write addition and subtraction sentences to show the related facts. **2** and **3** Circle the addition and subtraction sentences that show related facts. Tell how you know.

Laurie's Notes

Think and Grow: Modeling Real Life

This application allows students to show their understanding of addition and subtraction sentences for related facts. There are three pairs of partner numbers for 5 (0 and 5, 1 and 4, and 2 and 3) so there are three different results you may expect on this page.

- **Preview:** "What are the animals on this page? Have you seen lizards in a zoo or in the woods? What color lizards have you seen?" Have students share their experiences.
- ? Read the first part of the directions. Students use two colors for the lizards.
- ? "What addition sentence can you write to represent the two colors of lizards? Tell your partner an addition story about your lizards."
- Have a few students share their stories with the class.
- **Extension:** Two students may use the same partner numbers but write different sentences: $2 + 3 = 5$ and $3 + 2 = 5$. Ask student to make observations about the two sentences, listening for a reference about the order of the partner numbers.
- "What subtraction sentence can you write to represent the two colors of lizards? Tell your partner a subtraction story about your lizards."
- ◉ "Today you used related facts to write addition and subtraction sentences. Where are you in your learning? Use your thumb signals."
- **Supporting Learners:** Have two students work together and use linking cubes to act out the problem.
- **Supporting Learners:** Group together the students who are having difficulty. Ask them about how they colored the lizards. "What are the [color] lizards doing? Can the [second color] lizards join them?"

Closure

- Show a number bond for the number 5. "Write addition and subtraction sentences for this number bond."

Think and Grow: Modeling Real Life

Sample answer:

$$4 + 1 = 5$$

Sample answer:

$$5 - 1 = 4$$

Directions:

• A zoo has 5 lizards. Some are green and some are brown. Color the lizards. Then write an addition sentence to match your picture.

• Write a subtraction sentence that shows the related fact. Tell a story to match your subtraction sentence. **Check students' work.**

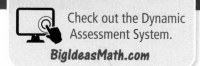
Connect and Extend Learning

Practice Notes

- Remind students that in an addition sentence, the first two numbers can be in any order. The third number, that represents the sum or whole, will be the same either way.
- Remind students that in a subtraction sentence, you can switch around the second and third number in the sentence and it will still be true.

Cross-Curricular Connections

Music

- Tell the students that they can make addition and subtraction sentences just by clapping.
- Tell students that you are going to clap, between 0–5 times. The class must listen to your claps and add the number of claps necessary to make 5 total claps. For example, if you clap 1 time, the class claps 4 times. Encourage students to clap in rhythm. Vary the speed of your claps and tell students to copy your speed.
- Next, call 1 student to the front of the class. Tell the class you are going to make a subtraction sentence. You clap 5 times. The student you called to help will clap between 0-5 times. The class must subtract the student's claps from your claps and then clap the answer. For example, you clap 5 times and the student helper claps 1 time. The class will clap 4 times ($5 - 1 = 4$). Again, encourage students to clap in rhythm.

Learning Target: Use related facts to add or subtract within 5.

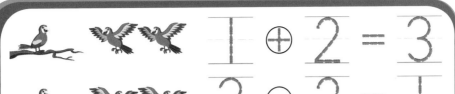

$$1 \oplus 2 = 3$$
$$3 \ominus 2 = 1$$

Directions: Tell whether the pictures show addition or subtraction. Then write addition and subtraction sentences to show the related facts.

❶

$$5 \ominus 1 = 4$$

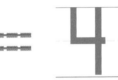

$$4 \oplus 1 = 5$$

Directions: ❶ Tell whether the pictures show addition or subtraction. Then write addition and subtraction sentences to show the related facts.

Chapter 7 | Lesson 7

three hundred sixty-five 365

Connect and Extend Learning

Extend Student Learning
Visual-Spatial

- Pick two different shapes and draw 1 or more of each on the board (for a total of no more than 5 shapes.)
- Ask the students to tell you what the four different addition and subtraction sentences are that can be made to describe the shapes on the board. Write the sentences on the board as the students call them out. For example, if you drew 2 circles and 3 squares, the four sentences would be as follows:

  $2 + 3 = 5$

  $3 + 2 = 5$

  $5 - 2 = 3$

  $5 - 3 = 2$
- Erase the shapes, draw a new set of two different shapes, and repeat the activity.

Lesson Resources	
Surface Level	**Deep Level**
Resources by Chapter	Resources by Chapter
• Extra Practice	• Enrichment and Extension
• Reteach	Graphic Organizers
Differentiating the Lesson	Dynamic Assessment System
Skills Review Handbook	• Lesson Practice
Skills Trainer	

2

$3 + 2 = 5$

$3 - 2 = 1$

$\boxed{\begin{array}{l} 1 + 3 = 4 \\ 4 - 3 = 1 \end{array}}$

Check students' work.

3

$\boxed{\begin{array}{l} 1 + 2 = 3 \\ 3 - 2 = 1 \end{array}}$

$6 + 2 = 8$

$6 - 2 = 4$

Check students' work.

 Sample answer:

B   B

B

R

R

$3 \oplus 2 = 5$

$5 \ominus 2 = 3$

Check students' work.

Directions: and **3** Circle the group of addition and subtraction sentences that shows related facts. Tell how you know. A tank at a pet store has 5 tree frogs. Some are blue and some are red. Color the frogs. Then write an addition sentence to match your picture. Write a subtraction sentence that shows the related fact. Tell a story to match your subtraction sentence.

366   three hundred sixty-six

© Big Ideas Learning, LLC

Performance Task

In this task, students demonstrate how to subtract numbers within 10 by representing two groups of objects, subtracting from a group to tell how many are left, and then writing corresponding subtraction sentences. In Exercise 1, students will draw nine bubbles that show more big bubbles than small bubbles. The subtraction sentence will depend on the number of big and small bubbles in the drawing. Use student responses to gauge their understanding about subtracting numbers within 10.

- Decide ahead of time whether students will be working independently, in pairs, or in groups.
- Pause between direction lines for students to complete each step.
- Have students share their work and thinking with others. Discuss as a class.

Exercise	Answers and Notes	Points
1	*Sample answer:* Draw six big bubbles and three small bubbles; $9 - 6 = 3$	3
2	*Sample answer:* Cross out four bubbles. Five bubbles are left; $9 - 4 = 5$	3
3	*Sample answer:* $5 - 5 = 0$	3
	Total	9

Performance Task 7

1–3. Sample answers are given.

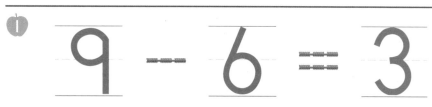

1 9 − 6 = 3

2 9 − 4 = 5

3 5 − 5 = 0

Directions: **1** You blow 9 bubbles in the air. There are more big bubbles than small bubbles. Draw the bubbles. Then write a subtraction sentence to tell how many small bubbles are in the air. **2** Some of the bubbles pop. Cross out the bubbles that pop. Then write a subtraction sentence to tell how many bubbles are left. **3** All of the remaining bubbles pop. Write a subtraction sentence to tell how many bubbles are left now.

Chapter 7 three hundred sixty-seven 367

Laurie's Notes

Losing Teeth

Materials

- 10 linking cubes
- 1 transparent spinner or 1 pencil and 1 paper clip
- Subtraction Recording Sheet*

*Found in the Instructional Resources

Losing Teeth reinforces the concept of subtracting numbers within 10.

- ❓ Have students look at the Student Edition page and the Subtraction Recording Sheet. "What do you see on these pages that have to do with math?" numbers, ten frame, minus sign, and equal sign This preview question helps students develop or strengthen number recognition as well as their vocabulary.
- Read the directions at the bottom of the page.
- Model how to use the spinners to place linking cubes on the ten frame and then take them off. Fill in a subtraction sentence on a Subtraction Recording Sheet.
- Have students work alone or with a partner to complete the activity.
- During game play, look for students' understanding of the minuend, subtrahend, and the difference. Note that students do not need to know these terms. Pose guiding questions to support students filling in the Subtraction Recording Sheet.
- When game play concludes, the discussion should focus on student reasoning about how students solved the subtraction sentences.
- ❓ **Use Appropriate Tools Strategically:** "As you played the game, how did you use the linking cubes to model subtraction?"
- **Supporting Learners:** Eliminate the use of spinners by providing students with numbers in the sentences on the Subtraction Recording Sheet. Provide two numbers, one as the minuend and the other as the subtrahend.

Closure

- ❓ "How did you remove your cubes from the ten frame?"

Losing Teeth

Directions: Spin the blue spinner. Put that many counters on the ten frame. Spin the red spinner. Take away that many counters from the ten frame. Tell how many counters are left. Complete the subtraction sentence on your Subtraction Recording Sheet. Repeat this process until you fill your sheet.

368   three hundred sixty-eight

Learning Target Correlation

Lesson	Learning Target	Exercises
7.1	Subtract a group of objects and tell how many are left.	1
7.2	Take from a group of objects and write a subtraction sentence.	2
7.3	Take apart a group of objects and write a subtraction sentence.	3, 4
7.4	Find and explain subtraction patterns.	5–7
7.5	Subtract within 5.	8–10
7.6	Use a group of 5 to write a subtraction sentence.	11
7.7	Use related facts to add or subtract within 5.	12

Chapter Practice 7

7.1 Understand Subtraction

1

7 __ take away 6 __ is 1 __ .

7.2 Subtraction: Take From

2

6 __ take away 3 __ is 3 __ .

6 __ − 3 __ = 3 __

© Big Ideas Learning, LLC

Directions: ① Complete the sentence to tell how many students there are in all, how many are leaving, and how many are left. ② Complete the sentence to tell how many lions there are in all, how many are leaving, and how many are left. Then complete the subtraction sentence to match.

Chapter 7   three hundred sixty-nine 369

Chapter Resources

Surface Level	Deep Level	Transfer Level
Resources by Chapter • Extra Practice • Reteach Differentiating the Lesson Skills Review Handbook Skills Trainer Game Library Math Musicals	Resources by Chapter • Enrichment and Extension Graphic Organizers Game Library Math Musicals	Dynamic Assessment System • Chapter Test Assessment Book • Chapter Tests A and B

3 and 4. Sample answers are given.

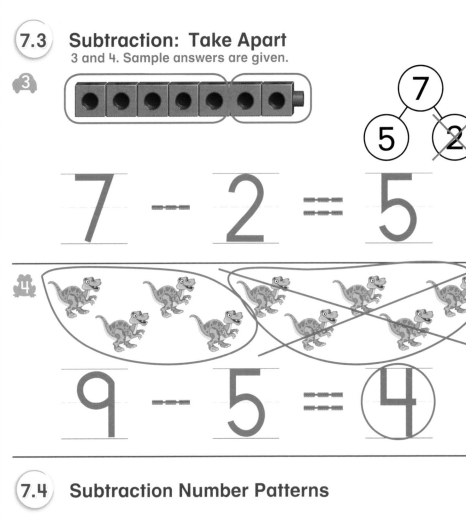

$7 - 2 = 5$

$9 - 5 = 4$

7.4 Subtraction Number Patterns

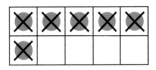 

$6 - 6 = 0$

none left

Directions: 3 Circle the linking cubes to show the parts in the number bond. Then write a subtraction sentence by taking one of the parts from the whole. Cross out the part on the number bond that you take away. 4 You have 9 toys. You want to give some to your friend. Put the toys into 2 groups. Circle the groups. Then cross out the group you give to your friend. Write a subtraction sentence to match your picture. Circle the number that shows how many toys you have left. 5 Complete the subtraction sentence to tell how many dots are left. Tell what you notice.

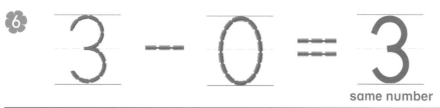

6   3 − 0 = 3

same number

7   8 − 1 = 7

previous number when counting

(7.5) Practice Subtraction

8   3 − 1 = 2

Sample answer: used counters

9   4 − 2 = 2

Sample answer: used counters

10

$$(4 - 0) \quad (5 - 1) \quad 2 - 2$$

Directions: 6 and 7 Complete the subtraction sentence. Tell what you notice. 8 and 9 Complete the subtraction sentence. Tell how you found your answer. 10 Circle all of the subtraction problems that equal 4.

© Big Ideas Learning, LLC

Chapter 7   three hundred seventy-one   371

(7.6) Use a Group of 5 to Subtract

$$9 - 5 = 4$$

(7.7) Related Facts

Sample answer:

$$2 \oplus 3 = 5$$

$$5 \ominus 3 = 2$$

Check students' work.

Directions: Cross out 5 counters to show how many to take away. Use the ten frame to complete the subtraction sentence. An aquarium has 5 starfish. Some are orange and some are purple. Color the starfish. Then write an addition sentence to match your picture. Write a subtraction sentence that shows the related fact. Tell a story to match your subtraction sentence.

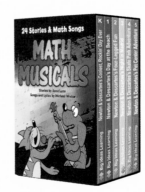

Math Musicals can be used with current topics, to review previous topics, or to preview upcoming topics.

Centers

Center 1: Losing Teeth

Materials per student: Student Edition page 368, Subtraction Recording Sheet*, transparent spinner or 1 pencil and 1 paper clip, 10 linking cubes

Have students complete the activity. See page T-368 for the directions.

Center 2: Skills Trainer

Materials: computers or devices with Internet access

Have students go to *BigIdeasMath.com* to access the Skills Trainer.

Center 3: Math Sentence Beads

Materials per student: piece of cardboard (approximately 12″ × 16″), elastic string, safety scissors, 40 beads

Prepare for the activity by writing ____ + ____ = ____ across the top of each piece of cardboard and ____ − ____ = ____ across the bottom. Then cut slits on each side of each equation and attach a string with 20 beads across the equation. For the activity, instruct students to move the beads along each of the elastic strings into the blanks to illustrate number sentences as they say them out loud.

Center 4: Addition Callout

Materials per pair: 2 sets of 5 playing cards; both sets include ace through 5

Organize students into pairs. Tell the students that for the purposes of the game aces are 1. Have each student take a set of cards and shuffle it. The game is played by each student in a pair drawing a card randomly from their stack at the teacher's signal. Students place their cards face up on the table, in between them (so that both students can see both cards). The first student to correctly say the sum of the two cards gets both cards added to their stack. The first student in a pair to acquire all the cards wins the game.

Center 5: Subtraction Callout

Materials per pair: 2 sets of 5 playing cards; one set of ace through 5, and one set of 6 through 10

Tell the students that for the purposes of the game aces are 1. Have each student take a set of cards and shuffle it. The game is played by each student in a pair drawing a card randomly from their stack at the teacher's signal. Students place their cards face up, in between them (so that both students can see both cards). The numbers on these cards represent the first two numbers in a subtraction sentence. The first student to correctly give the answer gets a point. The student in each pair with the most points at the end wins the game. Pairs should then switch stacks and repeat the activity.

*Found in the Instructional Resources

Chapter Assessment Guide

Chapter tests are available in the Assessment Book.
An alternative assessment option is listed below.

Visual-Spatial

Prepare for the assessment by assembling three groups of beads or counters, each group of a different color. Two of the groups should have 5 beads each and the third group should have 10 beads.

Call students over individually, and ask them to make 4 number sentences with the beads, using subtraction.

Task	Points
Making four correct number sentences	2 points per sentence; 8 points total

My Thoughts on the Chapter

What worked...

Teacher Tip

Not allowed to write in your teaching edition? Use sticky notes to record your thoughts.

What did not work...

What I would do differently...

Learning Target Correlation

Exercise	Lesson	Learning Target
1	5.2	Use number bonds to show the parts and the whole for numbers to 5.
2	1.1	Show and count the numbers 1 and 2.
3	5.1	Use partner numbers to show numbers to 5.
4	3.5	Show and count the number 8.
5	6.1	Add to a group of objects and tell how many.
6	7.4	Find and explain subtraction patterns.
7	7.2	Take from a group of objects and write a subtraction sentence.
8	4.2	Use counting to compare the numbers of objects in two groups.
9	6.8	Find partner numbers for 10 and write an addition sentence.
10	5.8	Use a group of five to put together and take apart numbers to 10.
11	2.2	Show and tell whether one group has a greater number of objects than another group.
12	7.5	Subtract within 5.

1
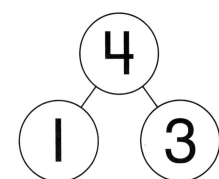

2

3

○ 0 and 5   ○ 4 and 1

● 2 and 2   ○ 2 and 3

Directions: Shade the circle next to the answer. ● Which group of animals matches the number bond? ● Which animal is shown 2 times? ● Which partner numbers do *not* make 5?

Chapter 7   three hundred seventy-three   373

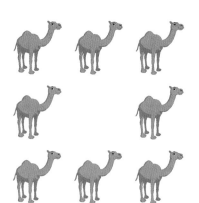 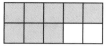 ○

 ●

 ○

 ○

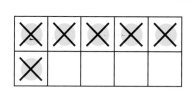

○ 5 and 4 is 9 in all.

○ 6 and 4 is 10 in all.

○ 5 and 3 is 8 in all.

● 6 and 3 is 9 in all.

✕	✕	✕	✕	✕
✕				

○ 6 − 0 = 6   ● 6 − 6 = 0   ○ 6 − 1 = 5

Directions: Shade the circle next to the answer. 🐸 Which ten frame shows the number of camels? ⭐ Which sentence tells how many students are in the group to start, how many join, and how many there are in all? ❀ Which subtraction sentence tells how many dots are left?

374   three hundred seventy-four

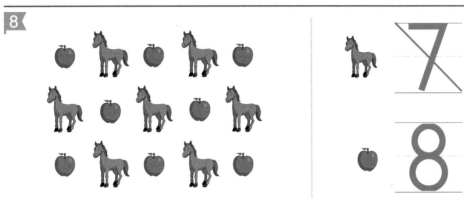

$$5 - 2 = 3$$

$$3 - 1 = 2$$

$$5 - 1 = 4$$

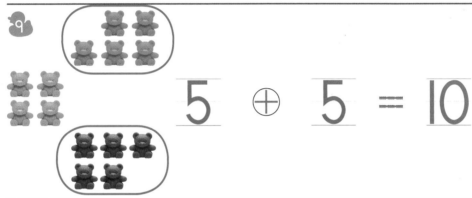

$$5 \oplus 5 = 10$$

Directions: ⑦ Match the subtraction sentences with the pictures that show how many there are in all, how many are leaving, and how many are left. ⑧ Count the objects in each group. Write each number. Draw a line through the number that is less than the other number. ⑨ Circle 2 groups of bear counters that make 10 bear counters in all. Then write an addition sentence.

Chapter 7   three hundred seventy-five   **375**

10 10–12. Sample answers are given.

B   B   R
B   B   R
B   R   R

5   4
   9

11

12

$$5 - 1 = 4$$

Directions: **10** Color 5 cars blue and the rest red. Then complete the number bond to match your picture. **11** Draw lines between the objects in each group. Circle the group that is greater in number than the other group. **12** You are playing a video game. You need to catch 5 pigs that escaped. You catch some of the pigs. Cross out the pigs you catch. Then write a subtraction sentence to tell how many pigs you have left to catch.

376   three hundred seventy-six

Appendix A

MATH MUSICALS

Sheet Music

Fish Crackers

WORDS AND MUSIC BY
MICHAEL WISKAR

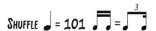

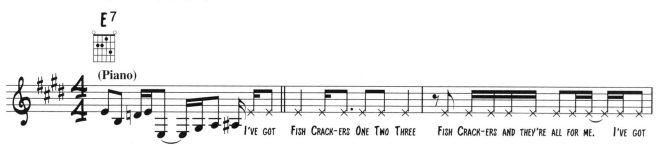

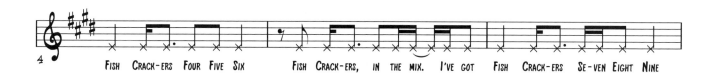

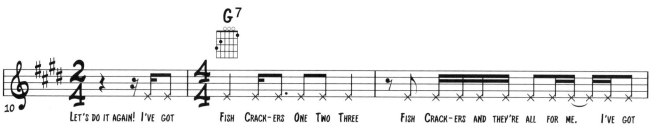

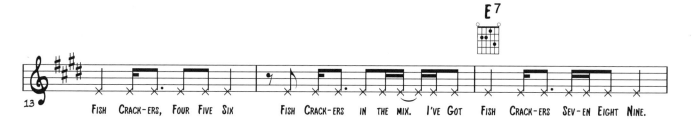

A2

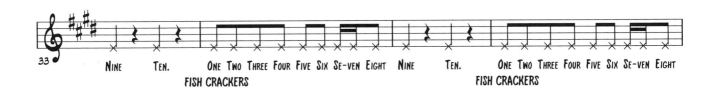

Cool Cats

Words and Music by
Michael Wiskar

A4

WORDS AND MUSIC BY
MICHAEL WISKAR

ROCKIN' DOGS AND COOL CATS

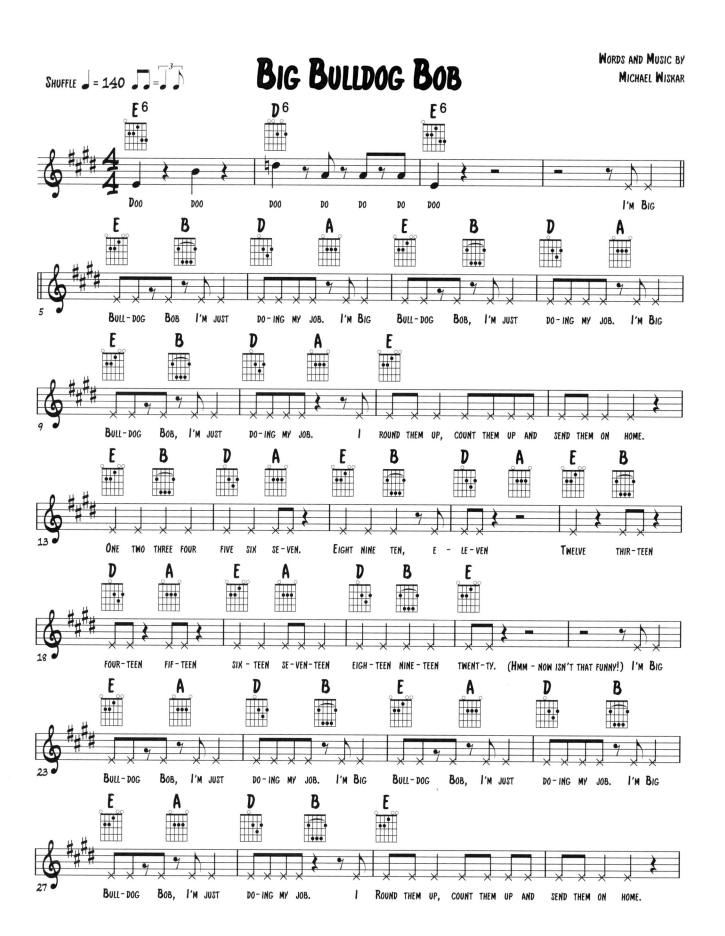

A6

A8

Best Friends
(I Get You and You Get Me)

Words and Music by
Michael Wiskar

A10

Glossary

A

above   [arriba, encima]

add   [sumar]

$$2 + 4 = 6$$

addition sentence
[enunciado suma]

$$2 + 3 = 5$$

B

balance scale   [balanza]

behind   [detrás]

below   [debajo]

beside   [al lado]

© Big Ideas Learning, LLC

capacity [capacidad]

category [categoría]

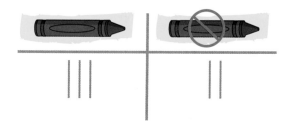

chart [gráfico]

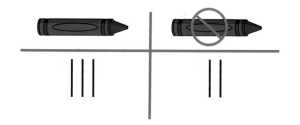

circle [círculo]

classify [clasificar]

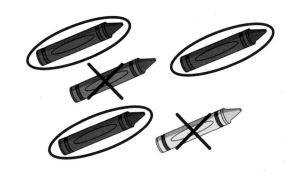

column [columna]

1	2	3	4	5	6	7	8	9	10
11	12	13	14	15	16	17	18	19	20
21	22	23	24	25	26	27	28	29	30
31	32	33	34	35	36	37	38	39	40
41	42	43	44	45	46	47	48	49	50
51	52	53	54	55	56	57	58	59	60
61	62	63	64	65	66	67	68	69	70
71	72	73	74	75	76	77	78	79	80
81	82	83	84	85	86	87	88	89	90
91	92	93	94	95	96	97	98	99	100

compare [comparar]

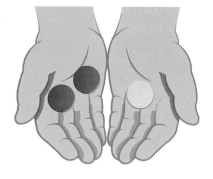

cone [cono]

count [contar]

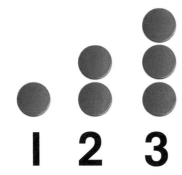

1 2 3

cube [cubo]

curve [curva]

curved surface [superficie curva]

cylinder [cilindro]

Glossary

D

decade number
[número de década]

1	2	3	4	5	6	7	8	9	10
11	12	13	14	15	16	17	18	19	20
21	22	23	24	25	26	27	28	29	30
31	32	33	34	35	36	37	38	39	40
41	42	43	44	45	46	47	48	49	50
51	52	53	54	55	56	57	58	59	60
61	62	63	64	65	66	67	68	69	70
71	72	73	74	75	76	77	78	79	80
81	82	83	84	85	86	87	88	89	90
91	92	93	94	95	96	97	98	99	100

E

eight [ocho]

8

A15

eighteen [dieciocho]

18

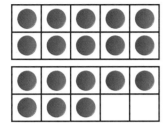

eleven [once]

11

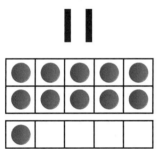

equal [igual]

3
3

equal sign [signo igual]

$$3 + 4 = 7$$

 F

fewer [menos]

fifteen [quince]

15

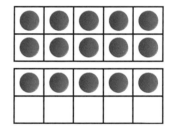

five [cinco]

5

five frame [cinco marco]

flat surface   [superficie plana]

four   [cuatro]

4

fourteen   [catorce]

14

greater than   [mas grande que]

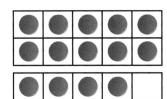

2

4

heavier   [más pesado]

height   [altura]

hexagon   [hexágono]

hundred chart [cientos de cartas]

1	2	3	4	5	6	7	8	9	10
11	12	13	14	15	16	17	18	19	20
21	22	23	24	25	26	27	28	29	30
31	32	33	34	35	36	37	38	39	40
41	42	43	44	45	46	47	48	49	50
51	52	53	54	55	56	57	58	59	60
61	62	63	64	65	66	67	68	69	70
71	72	73	74	75	76	77	78	79	80
81	82	83	84	85	86	87	88	89	90
91	92	93	94	95	96	97	98	99	100

I

in all [en todo]

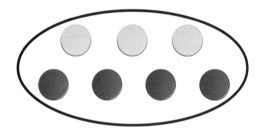

in front of [delante de]

 J

join [unirse]

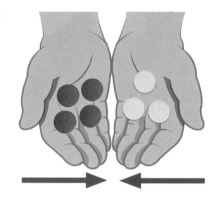

L

left [izquierda]

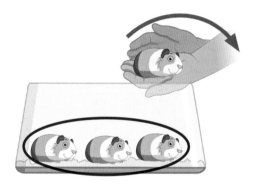

length [longitud]

A18

less than   [menos que]

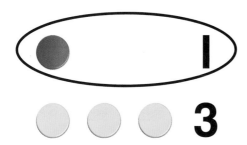

lighter   [más liviano]

longer   [más largo]

M

mark   [marca]

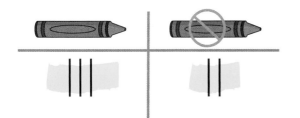

measurable attribute
[atributo mensurable]

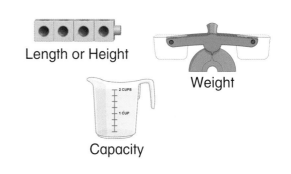

Length or Height

Weight

Capacity

minus sign   [signo menos]

$$3 - 2 = 1$$

more   [más]

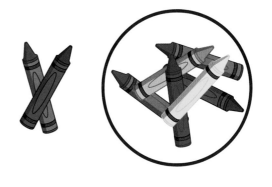

N

next to   [al lado de]

Glossary

nine   [nueve]

q

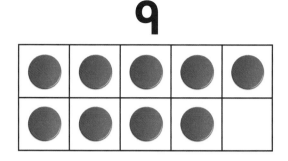

nineteen   [diecinueve]

19

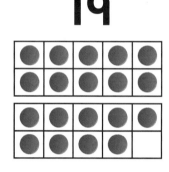

number   [número]

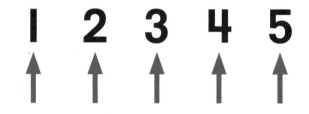

number bond   [número de bonos]

one   [uno]

I

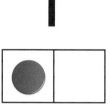

order   [ordenar]

part   [parte]

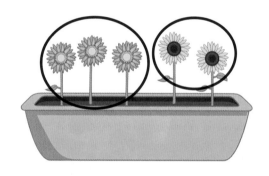

partner numbers
[números de socio]

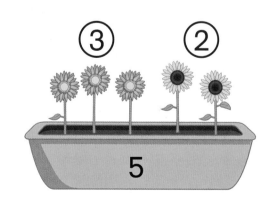

pattern [patrón]

$1 + 1 = 2$

$2 + 1 = 3$

$3 + 1 = 4$

plus sign [signo de más]

$$2 + 1 = 3$$

put together [juntar]

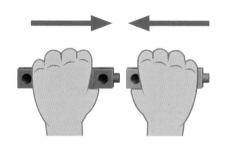

R

rectangle [rectángulo]

roll [rodar]

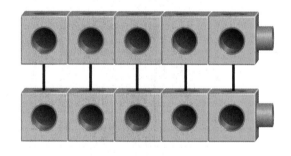

row [fila]

1	2	3	4	5	6	7	8	9	10
11	12	13	14	15	16	17	18	19	20
21	22	23	24	25	26	27	28	29	30
31	32	33	34	35	36	37	38	39	40
41	42	43	44	45	46	47	48	49	50
51	52	53	54	55	56	57	58	59	60
61	62	63	64	65	66	67	68	69	70
71	72	73	74	75	76	77	78	79	80
81	82	83	84	85	86	87	88	89	90
91	92	93	94	95	96	97	98	99	100

S

same as [igual que]

separate [separar]

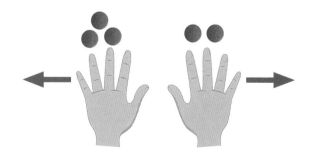

A21

seven [siete]

7

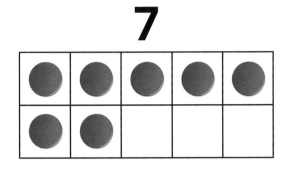

six [seis]

6

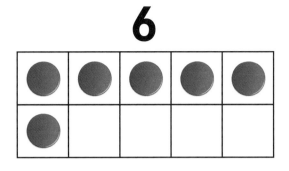

seventeen [diecisiete]

17

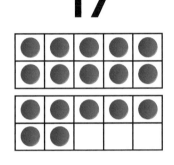

sixteen [dieciséis]

16

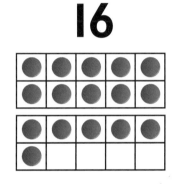

shorter [corta]

slide [deslizar]

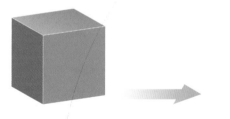

sort [ordenar]

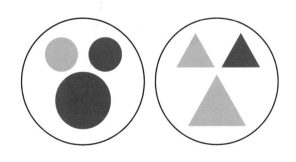

side [lado]

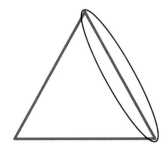

A22

sphere [esfera]

square [cuadrado]

stack [apilar]

subtract [restar]

$$3 - 1 = 2$$

subtraction sentence
[oración de resta]

$$4 - 1 = 3$$

 T

take apart [desmontar]

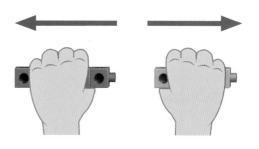

take away [quitar]

taller [más alto]

ten [diez]

10

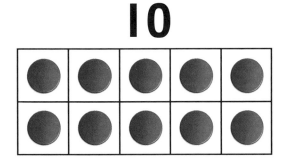

ten frame [diez marco]

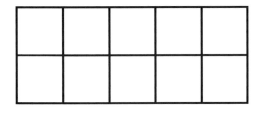

thirteen [trece]

13

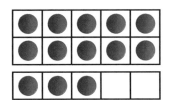

three [tres]

3

three-dimensional shape
[forma tridimensional]

triangle [triángulo]

twelve [doce]

12

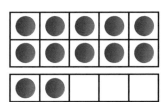

twenty [veinte]

20

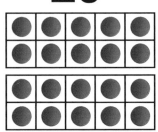

two [dos]

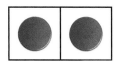

two-dimensional shape
[forma bidimensional]

 vertex [vértice]

vertices [vértices]

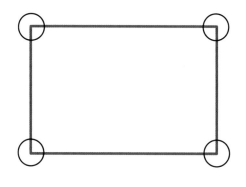

 W

weight [peso]

whole [todo]

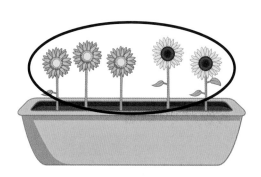

© Big Ideas Learning, LLC

A25

z

zero [cero]

Index

Index

© Big Ideas Learning, LLC

Index

Index

P

R

Index

Credits

Front matter

i enmyo/Shutterstock.com; **vii** Steve Debenport/E+/Getty Images; **xvii** FatCamera/E+/Getty Images Plus; **xxiii** Tom Fox-Davies; **xxix** monkeybusinessimages/iStock/Getty Images Plus; **xxxiii** Steve Debenport/E+/Getty Images

Chapter 1

1 BackyardProduction/iStock/Getty Images Plus, Liliya Drifan/iStock/Getty Images Plus, yotrak/iStock/Getty Images Plus, Tatomm/iStock/Getty Images Plus, kadmy/iStock/Getty Images Plus; **T-1D** Zeljko Bozic/iStock/Getty Images Plus; **T-25** colorcocktail/iStock/Getty Images Plus; **T-31** egal/iStock/Getty Images Plus; **T-37** *center* kali9/E+/Getty Images; *top right* bowdenimages/iStock/Getty Images Plus; *top left* asiseeit/E+/Getty Images Plus; *bottom right* asiseeit/E+/Getty Images; *bottom left* fstop123/E+/Getty Images; **T-38** Big Ideas Learning; **T-43** mariaflaya/iStock/Getty Images Plus; **T-49** Youst/DigitalVision Vectors/Getty Images

Chapter 2

57 Mikael Dubois/iStock/Getty Images Plus; **T-57D** Zeljko Bozic/iStock/Getty Images Plus; **T-75** ikuvshinov/iStock/Getty Images Plus

Chapter 3

95 PytyCzech/iStock/Getty Images Plus; **T-95D** Zeljko Bozic/iStock/Getty Images Plus; **T-107** andegro4ka/iStock/Getty Images Plus; **T-113** macrovector/iStock/Getty Images Plus; **T-119** Big Ideas Learning, LLC; **T-131** ryasick/E+/Getty Images, ronstik/iStock/Getty Images Plus; **T-312** jane/iStock/Getty Images Plus; **T-143** scanrail/iStock/Getty Images Plus, ET-ARTWORKS/DigitalVision Vectors/Getty Images, Korovin/iStock/Getty Images Plus

Chapter 4

169 hugocorzo/iStock/getty Images Plus; **T-169D** Zeljko Bozic/iStock/Getty Images Plus; **T-175** *left* 101dalmatians/E+/Getty Images; *right* bluebearry/iStock/Getty Images Plus; **201** m_pavlov/iStock/Getty Images Plus

Chapter 5

211 borchee/iStock/Getty Images Plus; **262** billnoll/iStock/Getty Images Pus; **T-219** Zeljko Bozic/iStock/Getty Images Plus; **T-223** IvancoVlad/iStock/Getty Images Plus; **T-249** Zeljko Bozic/iStock/Getty Images Plus; **T-254** TerraceStudio/Shutterstock.com

Chapter 6

267 inusuke/iStock/Getty Images Plus, richcarey/iStock/Getty Images Plus, dwphotos/iStock/Getty Images Plus; **T-267D** Zeljko Bozic/iStock/Getty Images Plus; **T-289** Zeljko Bozic/iStock/Getty Images Plus, **T-303** *from left to right* Toncsi/iStock/Getty Images Plus; Dr_Terwilliger/iStock/Getty Images Plus; smartstock/iStock/Getty Images Plus; kolesnikovserg/iStock/Getty Images Plus; Imo/E+/Getty Images

Chapter 7

323 rustamank/iStock/Getty Images Plus

Chapter 8

377 wnjay_wootthisak/iStock/Getty Images Plus; **T-383** Avalon_Studio/E+/Getty Images

Chapter 9

453 Big Ideas Learning

Chapter 10

497 Roman Pyshchyk /Shutterstock.com; **536** pixel_dreams/iStock/Getty Images Plus

Chapter 11

454 Paul Park/Moment Open/Getty Images

Chapter 12

595 Ian Lishman/Juice Images/Getty Images

Chapter 13

639 OlegDoroshin/Shutterstock.com

Cartoon Illustrations: MoreFrames Animation
Design Elements: oksanika/Shutterstock.com; icolourful/Shutterstock.com; Paul Lampard/123RF; FatCamera/E+/Getty Images; gradyreese/E+/Getty Images